HUMAN GENETICS

Concepts and Applications
third edition

Ricki Lewis

The University at Albany
CareNet Medical Group, Schenectady, New York

WCB McGraw-Hill

Boston, Massachusetts   Burr Ridge, Illinois   Dubuque, Iowa
Madison, Wisconsin   New York, New York   San Francisco, California
St. Louis, Missouri

WCB/McGraw-Hill

A Division of The **McGraw·Hill** *Companies*

HUMAN GENETICS: CONCEPTS AND APPLICATIONS, THIRD EDITION

This book is printed on acid-free paper.

2 3 4 5 6 7 8 9 0 VNH/VNH 9 3 2 1 0 9

ISBN 0–697–42296–8

Vice president and editorial director: *Kevin T. Kane*
Publisher: *James M. Smith*
Developmental editor: *Terrance Stanton*
Marketing manager: *Martin J. Lange*
Project manager: *Cathy Ford Smith*
Production supervisor: *Laura Fuller*
Designer: *K. Wayne Harms*
Photo research coordinator: *Lori Hancock*
Art editor: *Brenda A. Ernzen*
Supplement coordinator: *Audrey A. Reiter*
Compositor: *Shepherd, Inc.*
Typeface: *10/12 Minion*
Printer: *Von Hoffmann Press, Inc.*

Cover design: *Delgado Design*
DNA cover photo: *Uniphoto*
Diver cover photo: © */TSM/Ed Buck 1998*

The credits section for this book begins on page 411 and is considered an extension of the copyright page.

Library of Congress Cataloging-in-Publication Data

Lewis, Ricki.
    Human genetics : concepts and applications / Ricki Lewis. — 3rd ed.
      p.   cm.
    Includes bibliographical references and index.
    ISBN 0–697–42296-8
    1. Human genetics.   I. Title.
    [DNLM: 1. Anatomy. 2. Physiology. QS4 S159a 1998]
  QH431.L41855 1999
  599.93'5—dc21

                       98–18209
                       CIP

www.mhhe.com

dedicated to
Benjamin Lewis, a gentle
and great
man

brief contents

contents

Chapter 11

Cytogenetics 197

part four
Population Genetics 219

Chapter 12

When Gene Frequencies Stay Constant 219

Chapter 13

Changing Gene Frequencies 233

Chapter 14

Human Origins and Evolution 253

part five
Immunity and Cancer 271

Chapter 15

Genetics of Immunity 271

Chapter 16

Genetics of Cancer 293

part six
Genetic Technology   309

Chapter 17

Genetic Engineering   309

Chapter 18

Gene and Protein Therapy   325

Chapter 19

Agricultural and Environmental Biotechnology   341

Chapter 20

Reproductive Technologies   357

Chapter 21

The Human Genome Project   373

Answers to End-of-Chapter Questions   387

Glossary   401

Credits   411

Index   413

preface

I had expected that by the time I wrote the preface to *Human Genetics: Concepts and Applications,* third edition, I would enthusiastically trumpet all of the spectacular new discoveries and describe how they are impacting on our lives. Yet here I sit, befuddled. If we've learned anything about genetics over the past two years, it is that we don't know, or understand, nearly as much as we thought we did.

Consider:

- Testing for inherited breast cancer, and some other disorders, has proven to be much more complex than we expected. Studies on different population groups for inheritance of cancer-causing gene variants yield strikingly different results, making widespread genetic testing a long way off.

- Unraveling the complete genetic blueprints of the simplest species has revealed many genes whose functions we know nothing about. Imagine how little we know of our own genes!

- Many gene therapies, which made perfect sense theoretically, are disappointing in clinical reality.

- "Knocking out" genes in mice to create models of human disease often shows that genes once thought to be vital may not be so.

In the words of Alice, genetics is getting curiouser and curiouser. Added to the recognition of how much we still don't know is society's sometimes negative perception of the field. Information on cloning a mammal jumped to the media and political arena without much explanation and analysis from geneticists, who have been working on cloning for decades.

People refuse genetic tests for fear of discrimination by employers or insurers. The possibility of using genetic engineering to create powerful bioweapons lurks. And genetic determinism attempts to anchor all manner of behavioral traits strictly to DNA sequences, downplaying the role of the environment and what happens to us after those initial genetic instructions are set down.

Teaching and learning human genetics amidst these uncertainties and controversies is a daunting challenge. *Human Genetics: Concepts and Applications* confronts that challenge.

What's New in This Edition

Beyond the Single Gene In the early days of human genetic research, and to an extent today, matching gene to protein to disease was paramount. Identifying the abnormal salt channel behind cystic fibrosis, or the protein whose absence causes muscular dystrophy, were important discoveries, but we are learning that gene function often goes beyond a one gene-one protein explanation. And so the most important change in this edition is a subtle shift in emphasis, from considering the gene in isolation, to viewing the gene as an entity that interacts with other genes, and with environmental factors, to mold who and what we are.

In Real Life As in previous editions, true life stories bring the concepts of human genetics alive. New tales include

- Joan/John, who had his penis removed as an infant and fought for years the well-meaning efforts to raise him as a her.

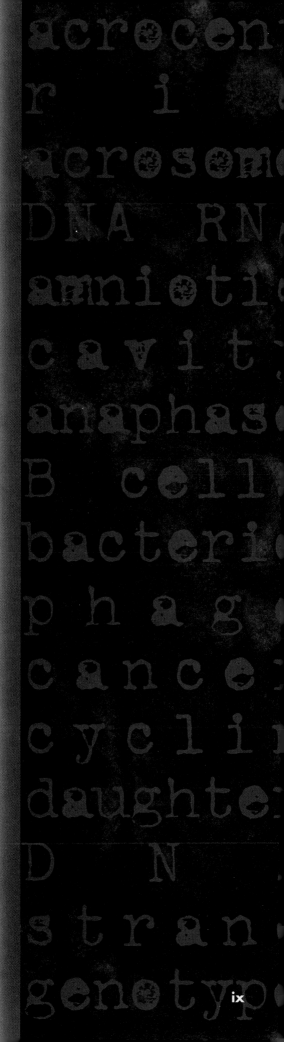

- "A Personal Look at Klinefelter Syndrome" by a young man who discovered that he had an extra chromosome when he tried to become a father.

- "Ashley's Message of Hope" comes from the parent of a child who died because she was missing a small part of a chromosome.

Technology Technology Timelines continue to show, at a glance, how methods to analyze genes and chromosomes, or treat diseases, have matured. A new timeline chronicles the ongoing effort to understand how Huntington disease develops.

Figures highlight technology, too. New figure 11.6 shows the evolution of the karyotype, from crude chromosome spreads done half a century ago, to today's spectacular chromosome paints. Ironically, figure 7.1 shows how some things *don't* change much, such as the continuously varying nature of complex traits. Other technologies updated in this edition include DNA-based forensics, human artificial chromosomes, cloning, umbilical cord stem cell technology, tissue engineering, and intracytoplasmic sperm injection. But the limits of technology are discussed as well. The first chapter addresses the ambiguity of genetic testing, and the final chapter probes genetic discrimination.

Summaries This third edition excels in encapsulating major concepts into summary figures and many new tables. Figure 13.7, for example, summarizes and compares, in one place, how nonrandom

Technology TIMELINE
Transplantation

1899	First allograft—a kidney from dog to dog.
1902	Pig kidney is attached to blood vessels of woman dying of kidney failure.
1905	First successful corneal transplant, from a boy who lost an eye in an accident to a man whose cornea is chemically damaged. Works because cornea cells lack antigens.
1940s	First kidney transplants on young people with end-stage kidney failure.
1950s	Blood typing predicts success of potential donor-recipient matches for organ transplants.
1960s	First effective immunosuppressant drugs revive interest in human allografts. Kidney xenografts between baboons and chimpanzees.
1967	First human heart transplant. Patient lives eighteen days.
1968	Uniform Anatomical Gift Act passes. Requires informed consent from next of kin before organs or tissues can be used for organ donation.
1970s	Transplants fall out of favor because they extend life only briefly and do not correct underlying disease, and because surgical complications and rejection reactions are common.
1980s	Improved immunosuppressant drugs, surgical techniques, and tissue matching, plus ability to strip antigens from donor tissue, reawaken interest in transplants.
1984	Doctors at Loma Linda University Medical Center transplant a baboon's heart into "Baby Fae," who was born with half a heart. She lives twenty days before rejecting the xenograft.
1992	Surgeons at the University of Pittsburgh Medical Center transplant a baboon's liver into a thirty-five-year-old man with hepatitis. The man lives for seventy-one days, dying of an unrelated cause.
1995	An AIDS patient receives bone marrow from an HIV-resistant baboon.
1997	Pig cell implants used to treat pancreatic failure and Parkinson disease.

Ashley's Message of Hope
reading 11.3

What is it like to have a child born with cri-du-chat syndrome? How does this affect the family and its future? What kinds of assistance can the medical community offer the family?

The birth of any child raises many questions. Will she have my eyes, her dad's smile? What will she want to be when she grows up? But the biggest question for every parent is "Will she be healthy?" If complications occur during birth or if the child is born with a genetic disorder, the questions become more profound and immediate. "How did this happen?" "Where do we go from here?" "Will this happen again?"

Our daughter, Ashley Elizabeth Naylor, was born August 12, 1988. We had a lot of mixed emotions the day of her birth, but mainly we felt fear and despair. The doctors suspected complications, which led to a cesarean section, but the exact problem was not known. Two weeks after her birth, chromosome analysis revealed cri-du-chat (cat cry) syndrome, also known as 5p⁻ syndrome because part of the short arm of one copy of chromosome 5 is missing. The prognosis was uncertain. This is a rare disorder, we were told, and little could be offered to help our daughter. The doctors used the words "profoundly retarded," which cut like a knife through our hearts and our hopes. It wasn't until a few years later that we realized how little the medical community actually knew about cri-du-chat syndrome and especially about our little girl!

Ashley defied all the standard medical labels, as well as her doctors' expectations. Her spirit and determination enabled her to walk with the aid of a walker and express herself using sign language and a communication device. With early intervention and education at United Services for the Handicapped, Ashley found the resources and additional encouragement she needed to succeed. In return, Ashley freely offered one of her best loved and sought after gifts—her hugs. Her bright eyes and glowing smile captured the hearts of everyone she met.

In May of 1992, Ashley's small body could no longer support the spirit that inspired so many. She passed away after a long battle with pneumonia. Her physical presence is gone, but her message remains: hope.

If you are a parent faced with similar profound questions after the birth of your child, do not assume one doctor has all the answers. Search for doctors who respect your child enough to talk to her, not just about her. Above all, find an agency or a school that can help you give your child a chance to succeed. Early education for your child and support for yourself are crucial.

If you are a student in a health field, become as knowledgeable as possible and stay current with the latest research, but most importantly, be sensitive to those

figure 1

Ashley Naylor brought great joy to her family and community during her short life.
Courtesy of Kathy Naylor.

who seek your help. Each word you speak is taken to heart. Information is important, but hope can make all the difference in a family's future.

—Kathy Naylor

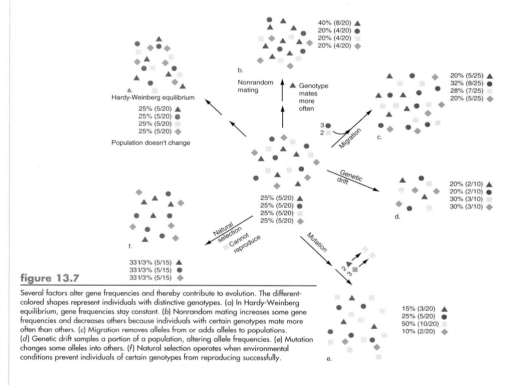

figure 13.7

Several factors alter gene frequencies and thereby contribute to evolution. The different-colored shapes represent individuals with distinctive genotypes. (a) In Hardy-Weinberg equilibrium, gene frequencies stay constant. (b) Nonrandom mating increases some gene frequencies and decreases others because individuals with certain genotypes mate more often than others. (c) Migration removes alleles from or adds alleles to populations. (d) Genetic drift samples a portion of a population, altering allele frequencies. (e) Mutation changes some alleles into others. (f) Natural selection operates when environmental conditions prevent individuals of certain genotypes from reproducing successfully.

New Summary Tables

Concepts/Applications Paradigm

Concept Chapter	Application Chapter
2 Cells	16 The Genetics of Cancer
	18 Gene and Protein Therapy
3 Human Development	20 Reproductive Technologies
6 Matters of Sex (linkage)	21 The Human Genome Project
8 DNA Structure & Replication	19 Agricultural & Environmental Biotechnology
9 Gene Function	12 When Gene Frequencies Stay Constant
10 Gene Mutation	13 Changing Gene Frequencies
11 Cytogenetics	14 Human Origins and Evolution
15 The Genetics of Immunity	17 Genetic Engineering

mating, mutation, migration, genetic drift, and natural selection change gene frequencies and alter Hardy-Weinberg equilibrium. In addition, all figures with chromosomes have been redone to emphasize clarity and consistency.

If It Isn't Broken— Don't Fix It!

The organization of concept chapters matched to application chapters continues in the third edition. Review and Applied Questions, Key Concepts, Chapter Outlines, and Suggested Readings remain as well, with appropriate updates.

Acknowledgments

This edition is dedicated to genetic counselors, who link families to researchers and physicians. Genetic counselors explain the science and technology, while comforting, educating, and providing perspective to patients and their loved ones. The scientific field of human genetics could not evolve into a medical specialty without them.

Many thanks to my wonderful family and pets, and to the terrific team at McGraw-Hill—Terry Stanton, Cathy Smith, Jim Smith, and Marty Lange. A special thanks to Toni Michaels, photo editor.

Supplementary Material

Instructor's Manual and Test Item File. A new Instructor's Manual/Test Item File, prepared by the author, is available to instructors and features detailed chapter outlines, answers to chapter questions, additional questions, and their answers. The Test Item File contains 20 to 30 objective multiple choice questions per chapter that can be used to generate exams. Many of the questions have been rewritten to increase rigor, and questions on new material have been added.

Microtest III. Microtest is a computerized classroom management service that includes a database of objective questions suitable for preparing exams and a grade-recording program. The software requires no programming experience and is available in DOS, Windows, and Macintosh formats.

Transparencies. A set of 50 transparencies is available free to adopters and consists of 50 illustrations from the text.

Case Study Workbook. This workbook was written by Ricki Lewis and is available to students and instructors for additional reading and problem solving (ISBN 22287).

Answer Key to the Case Study Workbook. This answer key contains the answers and solutions to the case studies covered in the Case Study Workbook.

Gene Game Software. This software program, written by William Sofer of the State University of New Jersey-Rutgers, is an easy to use, interactive Macintosh software game. It requires students to use critical thinking skills and apply the scientific method in cloning a fictitious fountain of youth gene. The Gene Game can be packaged with this text (ISBN 24893).

Explorations in Cell Biology and Genetics CD-ROM. This CD-ROM is an interactive multimedia program developed by George Johnson, of Washington University, and WCB. It calls on students to manipulate variables and examine how they impact the results as they explore genetics-related topics such as: Constructing a Genetic Map, Reading DNA, Exploring Meiosis: Down Syndrome, and more. The CD-ROM is compatible with both Windows and Macintosh systems (ISBN 29214).

Genetic Inheritance: Peas and *Drosophila* Software. This software program, developed by Mark Browning, Purdue University, allows the student to simulate hundreds of genetic crosses right at his/her computer to gain valuable practice in the quantitative aspects of genetics. Both the pea and *Drosophila* experiments investigate Mendel's laws of segregation and independent assortment, and how numbers of offspring affect test results. Once the student has mastered these concepts, he/she can be further challenged with the *Drosophila* experiments that explore the concepts of monohybrid, dihybrid, and trihybrid crosses, as well as the determination of linkage, map distances, and gene order on chromosomes. The software can also be packaged with the text (Macintosh ISBN 28861, Windows ISBN 35225).

Reviewers

I thank the reviewers of the first and second editions for their valuable observations and suggestions.

Reviewers for This Edition

Mary K. Bacon
Ferris State University
Sandra Bobick
Community College of Allegheny County
Virginia Carson
Chapman University
Frank C. Dukepoo
Northern Arizona University
Larry Eckroat
Pennsylvania State University at Erie
Miriam Golomb
University of Missouri–Columbia

George A. Hudock
Indiana University
Neil Jensen
Weber State College
Arthur L. Koch
Indiana University
Richard Landesman
University of Vermont
Mira Lessick
Rush University
Joshua Marvit
Penn State University
James J. McGivern
Gannon University
Denise McKenney
University of Texas of the Permian Basin
Wendell H. McKenzie
North Carolina State University
Michael E. Myszewski
Drake University
Donald J. Nash
Colorado State University
Michael James Patrick
Seton Hill College
Bernard Possidente
Skidmore College
Albert Robinson
SUNY at Potsdam
Peter Russel
Chaffey College
Polly Schulz
Portland Community College
Anthea Stavroulakis
Kingsborough Community College
Robert Wiggers
Stephen F. Austin State University
Virginia Wolfenberger
Texas Chiropractic College
Connie Zilles
West Valley College

Reviewers for First Edition

James A. Brenneman
University of Evansville
Mary Beth Curtis
Tulane University
Ann Marie DiLorenzo
Montclair State College
David Fromson
California State University–Fullerton
Michael A. Gates
Cleveland State University
Donald C. Giersch
Triton College
George A. Hudock
Indiana University–Bloomington
William J. Keppler
Florida International University
Jay R. Marston
Lane Community College
Mary Rengo Murnik
Ferris State University
Donald J. Nash
Colorado State University
David L. Parker
Northern Virginia Community College—Alexandria Campus
Peter A. Rosenbaum
SUNY–Oswego
Margaret R. Wallace
University of Florida
Roberta B. Williams
University of Nevada–Las Vegas
H. Glenn Wolfe
University of Kansas
Janet C. Woodward
St. Cloud State University

chapter one

Overview of Human Genetics

A Look Ahead

The year is 2003. A nurse draws blood from a pregnant woman for a routine prenatal exam. In the blood are a few immature red blood cells from the fetus. The nurse sends the blood sample to a laboratory, where a technologist, using an instrument that recognizes and separates out unusual cells, collects a few fetal cells.

An initial peek within the cells, at the **chromosomes** that carry **genes,** reveals the first piece of information—the individual will be a boy, shown when a fluorescent dye highlights a Y chromosome in each cell. A closer look at specific genes reveals much more (figure 1.1).

Happily, the future child will not have any of the more common inherited disorders. Despite the apparently healthy genetic background, some blood cells from the umbilical cord will be set aside at birth and deep-frozen. Should he one day require a bone marrow transplant to treat life-threatening anemia or cancer, his own cord blood cells will be infused into his body

where they will grow new bone marrow, tailor-made for his body.

Other results from the prenatal test indicate that the boy will be able to minimize effects of certain potentially unhealthy inherited characteristics. Tests to type the genes that predispose him to develop heart disease make it clear that a lifelong low-fat diet and regular exercise can extend his life. The same measures can help prevent or delay colon cancer, since he has inherited a pair of susceptibility genes. A computer evaluates how certain genes affect expression of other genes. Many inherited traits are not checked because they will not affect health. Hair and eye color and freckles will remain surprises.

This scenario takes place in the near future, but every one of the tests described is performed today. Other genetic screening tests, for fetuses as well as newborns, have been available for many years. Many new tests to detect genetic disease susceptibilities are being developed. They are raising questions for the health insurance industry on how to handle future illnesses.

Until recently, we didn't know the nature of most genes that cause disease.

However, a global scientific effort called the **human genome project** is rapidly adding more genes to the collection of those we can test for as it deciphers the complete genetic makeup, or **genome,** of humans.

Once a basic life science, human genetics is rapidly becoming a medical discipline. The human genome project is altering the way we view illness and is also revealing the many ways that people differ from each other.

Genetics in the News

Genetics is the study of inherited variation and traits. Genes are biochemical instructions that determine those inherited traits; they consist of sequences of building blocks of **deoxyribonucleic acid** (DNA). Genes strung together make up the larger chromosomes. Human cells have 23 pairs of chromosomes, which include two copies of each of about 70,000 genes.

A gene's sequence of DNA building blocks is like a language that instructs a cell to manufacture a particular protein.

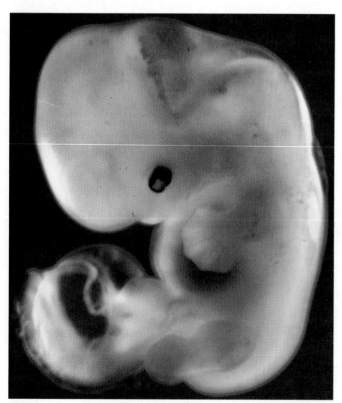

Fetus

Genetic tests
reveal

→ Sex

Baldness

Colon cancer
susceptibility

High risk of
substance
abuse

Alzheimer
disease

Future genetic
tests?

figure 1.1

Genetic tests of a fetus can reveal sex and many aspects of future health. Some traits, however, may be influenced by environmental factors or activities of other genes. Personality traits, for example, are very difficult to analyze.

An intermediate language, encoded in the building block sequence of **ribonucleic acid** (RNA), translates a gene's message into a protein's amino acid sequence. It is the protein that determines the trait.

A gene's DNA sequence can vary in many ways, just as the letters in a sentence can be rearranged to communicate a different message. Variants of a particular gene, different because they include changes in the DNA sequence, are called **alleles.** A change in a gene is a **mutation.** Most mutations we know of are associated with illness, but many are harmless, and some may even be helpful. A mutation, for example, makes a small percentage of the population resistant to HIV infection.

A generation ago, studying genetics meant examining patterns of trait transmission in fruit flies, bacteria, bread mold, corn, and other species whose physical characteristics or chromosomes are easy to study. A generation before that, biologists did not even know what type of chemical comprised the genetic material. While today's genetic researchers still use experimental organisms to unravel the details of how genes control traits, and even to serve as "models" of human disorders, the study of human genetics has grown explosively, touching our lives in a variety of ways. Following are some familiar applications of human genetics.

Establishing Identity

Comparing DNA sequences among individuals can establish, or rule out, that the DNA came from the same person, from blood relatives, or from unrelated people. Such DNA typing, or fingerprinting, has many applications.

In forensics, a DNA match for rare sequences between a tissue sample at a crime scene (blood, semen, skin, bone, or hair) and a blood sample from a suspect is strong evidence that the accused person was at the crime scene. In paternity cases, DNA-sequence matches can establish that a particular man fathered a particular child.

DNA evidence can solve historical mysteries. When anthropologists discovered remains of human infants at the site of a fourth century Roman bathhouse, they expected them to be female, evidence of infanticide in a society that valued males. But analysis of DNA sequences unique to the Y chromosome identified some males. This information, with other evidence, revealed

that the bathhouse was the workplace of prostitutes, who disposed of unwanted babies of either sex. DNA typing solves modern mysteries too. Forensic scientists use the technique to reassemble body parts of plane crash victims.

In 1995, the U.S. military began collecting and storing DNA samples from personnel, to identify future casualties. Some people objected, fearing use of their DNA information for other purposes. Two marines who refused to give blood were court-martialed, but the publicity from their objection led to passage of a law to limit the military's use of DNA samples to identifying casualties and criminals. Use of genetic information has emerged as a major issue in many areas.

Agriculture

Agriculture reflects a rich history of controlled breeding to select new combinations of traits in livestock, fruits, and vegetables. Manipulations of individual genes have added a precision not possible with traditional breeding plans, in which trait combinations passed to offspring can be unpredictable.

Genetic alterations can enhance characteristics or add new ones to agriculturally valuable organisms, even from different species. Cotton plants given certain bacterial genes, for example, produce a plastic-like chemical that causes them to produce ultra-warm cotton fibers. Cereal crops are made more nutritious by genetically boosting

their output of certain amino acids. Genetically altered trees can resist environmental stress and pests and produce more lignin, a chemical important in the pulp and paper industry. Some consumers, though, are wary of genetically altered crops, as figure 1.2 illustrates.

Crops and animals can also be genetically altered to produce biochemicals of use to humans as drugs, a technology called "pharming." A flock of such genetically-altered sheep, for example, produces the human protein clotting factor that people with hemophilia use.

Defining Race

The *American Heritage and Dictionary of the English Language* defines *race* as a "local geographic or global human population distinguished as a distinct group by genetically transmitted physical characteristics." Shared inherited characteristics, rather than acquired traits like dyed hair color, are used to define race because they indicate that a group of people descended from common ancestors and are therefore closely related by blood. When people tend to mate within their population, certain traits remain in that population, and the combination of traits comes to define a particular race.

Traditional race definitions, however, emphasize skin color, which is only one of thousands of inherited human traits. (Reading 1.1 describes a few of the odder ones.) Why not define race by hair texture,

figure 1.2

This cartoon, from *Time* magazine, illustrates the public's fear of genetic manipulation.
© Seymour Chwast, The Pushpin Group.

Do you have uncombable hair, misshapen toes or teeth, or a pigmented tongue tip? Are you unable to smell a squashed skunk, or do you sneeze repeatedly in bright sunlight? Do you lack teeth, eyebrows, eyelashes, nasal bones, thumbnails, or fingerprints? If so, your unusual trait may appear in a compendium called *Mendelian Inheritance in Man,* or "MIM" for short. A team at Johns Hopkins University led by reknowned geneticist Victor McKusick updates MIM daily. An online version is available at http://www3. ncbi.nlm.nih.gov/omim/. Entering a disease name retrieves a long list of information.

Most of the more than five thousand entries in MIM include family histories, clinical descriptions, the pattern of inheritance, and molecular information on the causative gene. Woven in amidst the medical terminology are the stories behind some fascinating inherited traits (figure 1).

Genes control whether hair is blond, brown, or black, has red highlights, and is straight, curly, or kinky. Widow's peaks, cowlicks, a whorl in the eyebrow, and white forelocks run in families; so do hairs with triangular cross sections. Some people have multicolored hairs, like cats; others have hair in odd places, such as on the elbows, nose tip, knuckles, palms, or soles. Teeth can be missing or extra, protuberant or fused, present at birth, shovel shaped, or "snowcapped." A person can have a grooved tongue, duckbill lips, flared ears, egg-shaped pupils, three rows of eyelashes, spotted nails, or "broad thumbs and great toes." Extra breasts are known in humans and guinea pigs, and one family's claim to genetic fame is a double nail on the littlest toe.

Unusual genetic variants can affect metabolism, producing either disease or harmless, yet noticeable, effects. Members

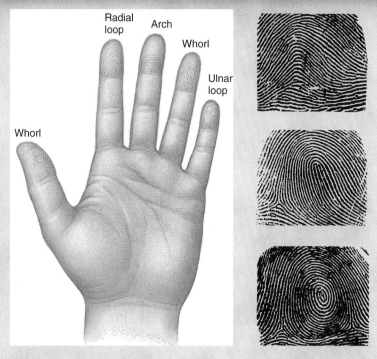

figure 1

Fingerprint patterns form characteristic arches, loops, and whorls. The actions of several genes determine the patterns, along with the fetus's fingertip movements at about 6 weeks of gestation, when these skin ridges are vulnerable to damage. This environmental effect is why identical twins, who have all the same genes, nevertheless have different fingerprints.

Source (for fingerprints only): Kent M. VanDeGraaff, *Human Anatomy,* 4th ed. Copyright © 1995 Times Mirror Higher Education Group, Dubuque, Iowa.

of some families experience "urinary excretion of odoriferous component of asparagus" or "urinary excretion of beet pigment," producing a strange odor or dark pink urine stream after consuming the offending vegetable. In blue diaper syndrome, an infant's urine turns blue on contact with air, thanks to an inherited inability to break down an amino acid.

One bizarre inherited illness is the jumping Frenchmen of Maine syndrome. This exaggerated startle reflex was first noted among French-Canadian lumberjacks from the Moosehead Lake area of Maine, whose ancestors were from the Beauce region of Quebec. Physicians first reported the condition at a medical conference in 1878. Geneticists videotaped the startle response in 1980, and the condition continues to appear in genetics journals. MIM gives a most vivid description:

If given a short, sudden, quick command, the affected person would respond with the

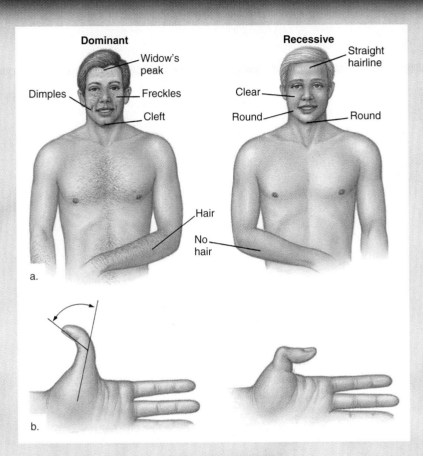

figure 2

Inheritance of some common traits: (*a*) freckles, dimples, hairy elbows, widow's peak, and a cleft chin; (*b*) the ability to bend the thumb backward or forward.

> appropriate action, often echoing the words of command . . . For example, if one of them was abruptly asked to strike another, he would do so without hesitation, even if it was his mother and he had an ax in his hand."

The jumping Frenchmen of Maine syndrome may be an extreme variant of the more common Tourette syndrome. Figure 2 illustrates some other genetic variants.

figure 1.3

Skin color is only one way that humans differ from each other. Race based on color is literally only skin deep. Golfer Tiger Woods, for example, objected to being called black, when he is actually part African American, Caucasian, Asian, and Native American.

ear-wiggling ability, or elevated blood pressure? The answer is simply that skin color differences are easy to see; an inherited inability to digest milk sugar is not nearly as obvious (figure 1.3).

Health Care

Inherited illness differs from other illnesses in two important ways. First, because of the laws of inheritance, a genetic condition recurs with a predictable probability—the subject of chapter 4. For example, if parents are each a carrier of a genetic disorder, then each of their children has a 1 in 4 chance of inheriting the disease. In contrast, the risk of passing an infectious disease to a family member depends upon physical contact.

The second key difference between inherited and other illnesses is that an inherited illness can be "diagnosed" before symptoms appear—even decades before. This is because the genes causing the problem are present in every cell from conception. Therefore, a test to diagnose an inherited condition can be done on any type of cell. Cystic fibrosis, for example, affects the respiratory passages, lungs, and pancreas, but a test for the responsible gene can be performed on blood or on cells from the inside of the cheek.

Identifying inherited illness long before it impairs health raises difficult issues. Elizabeth C. and Kris G., whose mother and sister died of inherited breast cancer, are pondering genetic testing for their own young daughters (figure 1.4). In 1989, Elizabeth and Kris were diagnosed with breast cancer; both underwent successful treatment. In 1994, Mary-Claire King and her colleagues at the University of California, Berkeley, discovered BRCA1—a gene that, when abnormal in a certain way, greatly increases the risk of developing breast and/or ovarian cancer.

The sisters participated in a research study and learned that an abnormal BRCA1 gene caused their cancers. Each of the sister's children faces a 1 in 2 chance of having inherited the faulty gene. Put another way, each child could have inherited either the abnormal or normal form of the gene from her mother. (Males can develop breast cancer, but this is rare because male hormones suppress action of the gene.)

When should Elizabeth and Kris have their daughters tested? Should they wait until the daughters are old enough to decide themselves?

Developing presymptomatic genetic tests for the 5 to 10 percent of cases of breast cancer that are inherited has been difficult for several reasons. Two-thirds of these cases are caused by mutations in two genes, BRCA1 and BRCA2. These genes are very large, and researchers do not yet know all of the mutations that cause cancer and those that do not. The type of mutation in Elizabeth and Kris is linked to an 86 percent risk of developing breast or ovarian cancer in families with several affected members. However, if this particular mutation occurs in a woman who does not have affected relatives, the risk might be only 50 percent. This means that other

figure 1.4

Elizabeth C. and Kris G. lost a mother and a sister to breast cancer. They, too, had the disorder, but were treated successfully. Should their young daughters be tested to see if they have inherited the breast cancer susceptibility gene that runs through the family? According to the laws of inheritance, each child has a 50 percent chance of having inherited the gene. If the mutant gene is inherited, the child would face an 80 to 90 percent risk of developing breast cancer or about a 44 percent chance of developing ovarian cancer. Researchers are developing ways to more precisely define risks in particular families, depending on the types of mutations and other gene variants and risk factors.

genes may affect the expression of BRCA1. Clearly, genetic testing for breast cancer, and probably other disorders, is not as simple as a "yes" or "no" answer.

Key Concepts

Genes are DNA sequences that instruct cells to produce particular proteins, which in turn determine traits. Chromosomes are strings of genes, and alternate forms of a gene are alleles. Mutations are changes in a gene's DNA sequence. Inherited disease recurs in families at a predictable rate and may be diagnosed before symptoms occur if the causative gene is known.

Levels of Genetic Investigation

The issues that testing for breast cancer genes pose illustrate the several levels at which we can consider human genetics. Genes are biochemicals, but they exert their effects at higher levels of biological organization, from the microscopic to the macroscopic (figure 1.5).

Molecules and Cells

The study of genes at the biochemical or cellular level is called **molecular genetics.** Normally, the BRCA1 gene instructs a cell to manufacture a type of protein, called a

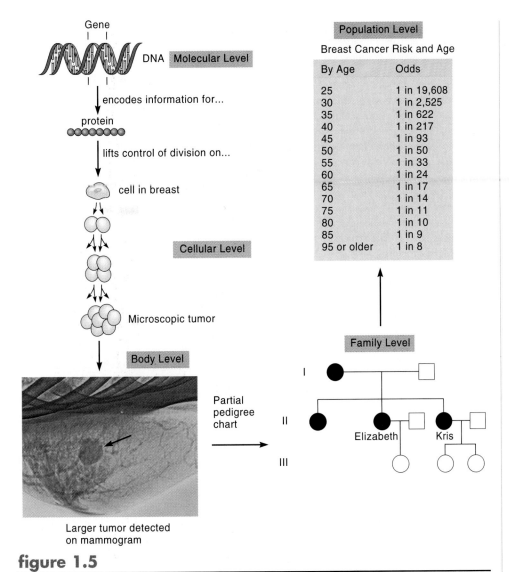

Population Level	
Breast Cancer Risk and Age	
By Age	Odds
25	1 in 19,608
30	1 in 2,525
35	1 in 622
40	1 in 217
45	1 in 93
50	1 in 50
55	1 in 33
60	1 in 24
65	1 in 17
70	1 in 14
75	1 in 11
80	1 in 10
85	1 in 9
95 or older	1 in 8

figure 1.5

Human genetics examines health and disease at the molecular, cellular, whole body, family, and population levels, as shown here for breast cancer caused by a mutation in the BRCA1 gene.

tumor suppressor, that limits the rate of cell division. When the BRCA1 gene mutates in a certain way, the tumor suppressor protein is absent or does not function adequately. In a single cell somewhere in a woman's breast, the constraints on cell division vanish, and the cell begins to proliferate. The cell divides when it should not, again and again. The errant cells become rounder, losing their distinctive characteristics as gland or lining cells, and the tiny collection of unusual, dividing cells grows into a tumor. When the growth consists of millions of cells, the woman may notice a lump or puckering in the skin of her breast, or a mammogram (an X ray of the breast)

may detect the small growth. A surgeon then excises the tumor, and if it is large or has spread, the woman may also receive chemotherapy or radiation treatments.

Because a gene and its effects are often separable, geneticists distinguish the gene responsible for a trait or illness from the actual expression of the trait or illness. The genes comprise the **genotype,** and the expression of these genes, the **phenotype.** The phenotype is usually detectable or even visible; the genotype is the instructions that produce the phenotype. For breast cancer, an abnormal BRCA1 gene constitutes the genotype; the tumor is the phenotype.

Individuals and Families

Tracing the recurrence patterns of traits within families, from generation to generation, is the province of **transmission genetics.** The field began with pea plant experiments that demonstrated basic laws of inheritance that apply to all complex organisms. The laws allow us to predict the patterns, called **modes of inheritance,** that genotypes and phenotypes follow as they recur in subsequent generations. The key to such predictions is the fact that each parent contributes one copy of each gene to an offspring.

Mode of inheritance depends upon two basic characteristics of an allele. First, an allele may be **dominant** or **recessive.** A dominant allele affects the phenotype when present in one copy. In contrast, a recessive allele must be present in two copies to be expressed. Whether an allele is dominant or recessive depends upon the biochemical nature of the particular trait. The cancer-predisposing mutant allele of BRCA1 is dominant. Hence, a person need have only one parent who has this allele to face a 1 in 2 chance of inheriting the predisposition.

The second way to describe mode of inheritance depends upon the type of chromosome a gene is part of. In human cells, the 46 chromosomes include two—the X and the Y—that contain genes that determine sex and are therefore called **sex chromosomes.** The other, non-sex-determining chromosomes are **autosomes.** A human male has 44 autosomes, one X and one Y chromosome; a female has 44 autosomes and two X chromosomes. Because of this difference in sex chromosome constitution, genes on the sex chromosomes follow different, **sex-linked,** patterns of inheritance in the two sexes.

Modes of inheritance for a particular trait depend on whether an allele is dominant or recessive and whether the gene that determines that trait is on a sex chromosome or an autosome. Therefore, a trait can be autosomal recessive, autosomal dominant, sex-linked recessive, or sex-linked dominant. Chapters 4, 5, and 6 discuss these patterns in detail.

Knowing the mode of inheritance of a gene is important in a practical sense because it can predict recurrence risk of a trait or illness in a particular person. While it might simply be fun to wonder whether a baby on the way will have one parent's hooked nose or the other's green eyes, it is important for families with a genetic disorder to understand the laws of inheritance in order to make reproductive decisions and prepare to care for affected family members.

Identifying and tracing modes of inheritance is the basis of a medical specialty called genetic counseling. Genetic counselors inform families of recurrence risks for specific genetic illnesses by applying the laws of inheritance to that family's health history. A major tool in genetic counseling is a chart, called a **pedigree,** that displays the blood relationships between family members and indicates which individuals have the trait or illness in question. Figure 1.5 shows a partial pedigree for Elizabeth C. and Kris G., the sisters who had breast cancer.

Populations

Breast cancer is a very common illness, affecting 1 in 9 women at some point in her life. However, the allele most associated with cancer is far more common in some populations than in others. The study of allele frequencies in populations is called **population genetics.**

A major reason why certain alleles are more common among certain people is that we tend to marry people like ourselves. BRCA1 breast cancer, for example, affects 1 in 800 women in the general U.S. population, but among Jewish women of eastern European descent—a population group called Ashkenazim—the figure climbs to 1 in 100! Throughout history, many societies isolated Jewish people by shunning them or forcing them to live in segregated ghettos. Over many generations, this led to a dozen or so inherited illnesses that are much more common among the Ashkenazim than other population groups.

Other populations tend to have higher incidences of certain inherited illnesses, due often to historical influences. These include the Amish, French-Canadians, Italians, and African Americans.

The Abnormal Explains the Normal

Much of the field of genetics examines disease. However, investigation of what has gone wrong to cause symptoms also reveals the body's normal functions. The value of studying *inherited* disease is that we can identify gene variants that harm health and the proteins they encode. This explains on a molecular level how the gene functions and what can go wrong.

Genetic studies of a group of disorders called epidermolysis bullosa (EB), for example, added to our knowledge of skin structure. In EB, the skin blisters from even slight touching. Several forms of the illness, with differing severities, result from abnormalities in different skin proteins. The simplex form of EB is mild. Blisters form, but they do not leave permanent scars. In this type of EB, a protein called keratin is abnormal in the cells of the epidermis, the outer skin layer (figure 1.6a). Dystrophic EB affects the lower skin layer, or dermis. Here, the protein collagen is the culprit.

The most severe form, junctional EB, disrupts the lining between the epidermis and dermis. Affected individuals usually die within the first weeks of life as they lose fluids through the torn skin and become infected. These children also have skinless patches where the layers rubbed off before birth. Genetic studies reveal that the skin literally comes apart because of an abnormal form of a protein called laminin. Laminin normally anchors the skin layers together, much as a staple seals two sheets of cardboard.

Geneticists learned many lessons from studying the genetics of EB: keratin is vital to the epidermis, collagen to the dermis, and laminin to the joining of the two skin layers. Researchers are using this knowledge to develop skin substitutes to treat severe burns.

The theme of the abnormal explaining the normal recurs throughout this book. Table 1.1 lists some common inherited illnesses. Discoveries of the genetic defects that cause these disorders have augmented our knowledge of normal lung, muscle, and blood functioning, respectively. However, for many traits, the terms *normal* and *abnormal* do not apply. Green eyes and kinky hair are variants, not abnormalities.

Identifying the protein defect behind a disorder reveals where to aim treatments. For example, a form of inherited immune deficiency arises because a protein called adenosine deaminase (ADA) is missing. Children with the disorder, called ADA deficiency, usually die from inability to fight off serious infections. Placing a normal copy of the ADA gene into certain white blood cells gradually repairs the problem, restoring immunity.

Knowing the gene and protein defect that cause an illness, however, doesn't always suggest a treatment. In Tay-Sachs disease, a fatty substance that normally insulates nerve cells and speeds transmission of nerve impulses builds up, eventually blocking nerve function (figure 1.7). An affected child slowly becomes deaf, blind, and unable to move, dying by three years of age. Even though we have known the nature of the abnormal gene and protein that cause Tay-Sachs disease for many years, we still do not know how to halt the disease process in the brain.

Identification of the disease-causing gene did provide other benefits, however. Fewer than ten babies with Tay-Sachs disease are born in the United States each year because tests identify couples in which each partner carries the gene that causes the disease. Because Tay-Sachs disease is always fatal, most of these couples choose not to bear biological children or

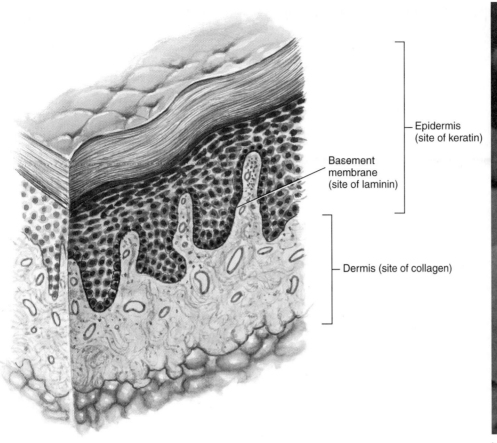

Epidermis
(site of keratin)

Basement
membrane
(site of laminin)

Dermis (site of collagen)

a.

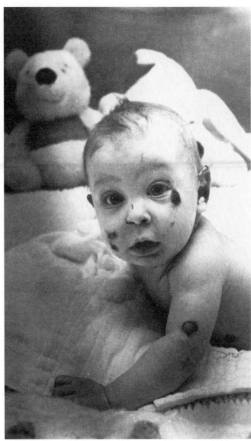

b.

figure 1.6

Studying the abnormal helps us understand the normal. (*a*) The different forms of epidermolysis bullosa (EB) reveal how important the proteins keratin, laminin, and collagen are to skin structure. (*b*) In EB, the skin blisters when anything touches it.

table 1.1

The Basis of Some Inherited Diseases

Disease	Signs and Symptoms	Underlying Defect
Cystic fibrosis	Buildup of mucus in respiratory tract; mucus-clogged pancreas; male infertility; lung infections; salty sweat	Misshaped channel in certain cells traps salt inside, thickening secretions outside.
Duchenne muscular dystrophy	Progressive muscle weakness	Lack of muscle protein dystrophin prevents muscle cells from withstanding contractions. Cells collapse.
Hemophilia	Poor blood clotting, easy bruising	Absence of a clotting factor allows unchecked bleeding.
Sickle cell disease	Too few red blood cells (anemia), bone and joint pain, frequent infection	Abnormal proteins in red blood cells link and bend cells into sickle shape, blocking local blood flow and causing joint pain. Bone marrow and spleen are stressed to produce more red cells. Too few red cells causes anemia; too few white cells impairs immunity.

figure 1.7

Parents of children who have Tay-Sachs disease usually do not suspect that something is wrong until the child loses skills accomplished by about six months of age and grows increasingly helpless. There is no treatment.

terminate pregnancies when a prenatal test reveals an affected fetus.

A more prevalent brain disorder for which we know several genetic causes but have been unable to halt symptom progression is Alzheimer disease. The resulting brain degeneration robs people of their memory and ability to reason. Knowing which genes are abnormal and how their protein products function in the brain will guide researchers in developing treatments. The beginning of Chapter 10 discusses genes that cause Alzheimer disease.

Key Concepts

In genetics, studying the abnormal helps explain normal body structure and function. Discovering the nature of the protein defect that underlies a disorder can lead to new treatments, but sometimes this information is not enough to help.

The Effects of Other Genes and the Environment

The environment modifies the expression of many inherited traits. An active lifestyle out in the sun, for example, can change skin color and trim body fat, both characteristics that are largely inherited. People with the same disease-causing alleles may not have precisely the same severity of symptoms because of the influences of other genes, and environmental factors such as nutrition, exercise habits, degree of stress, and access to health care. Even siblings with the same genetic illness may be affected to different degrees because of the influences of other genes. (Siblings have approximately 50 percent of the same alleles.)

The influences of other genes and the environment may explain why a small percentage of women who inherit the cancer-predisposing mutation in BRCA1 do *not* develop cancer. Are women with the cancer-predisposing BRCA1 allele who remain healthy lucky, having inherited another gene that counters the action of BRCA1, or does some difference in their lifestyle protect them? A major area of breast cancer research is identifying protective factors. Studies link lowered breast cancer risk to a low-fat diet, eating certain vegetables, exercising regularly, becoming pregnant early in adulthood, and breast-feeding. However, these are correlations only. Many investigations do not consider enough factors to confirm that any of these measures provide direct protection. For example, many such studies attempting to link environmental factors to breast cancer risk began before researchers discovered breast cancer genes. The women compared in the studies thus had highly varying inherited risks of developing breast cancer.

The Genetic Components of Common Disorders

Until recently, genetic diseases were thought to be very rare, since obviously inherited diseases, such as those listed in table 1.1, occur in a very small fraction of the population. These disorders—which number about 3,500—are caused by a single gene. However, many chronic diseases that affect huge

numbers of people, including heart disease and many cancers, are also rooted in our genes. They do not recur with as predictable a frequency as the rarer single-gene illnesses, because of environmental and other genetic influences. Chapter 7 addresses such conditions, called **multifactorial traits,** and table 1.2 lists some of them.

Mutant genes can cause disease susceptibilities by altering immune system function. Types of conditions that result from altered immunity include allergies, infections, and autoimmune disorders, in which the body harms itself. People can inherit high susceptibility to allergic asthma, resistance to an infection called schistosomiasis, and diabetes mellitus, in which the immune system attacks the pancreas.

Genes Affect Responses to the Environment

Why does a cup of coffee after dinner keep one person awake past midnight but not affect sleepiness in another? Why does an analgesic drug relieve headache in one person but not another? Why are only some of us substance abusers? Part of the answer to differing responses to what we take into our bodies may lie in genetics. **Ecogenetics** refers to gene-based differences in response to environmental factors.

The basis of ecogenetics may be enzymes (a type of protein) that detoxify certain chemicals. Such enzymes may have evolved because they help animals survive exposures to toxic plant chemicals. Today, because many drugs are derived from plant-based chemicals, variants of these enzymes dictate how quickly people clear certain drugs from their systems.

Drug-metabolizing enzymes were discovered in the 1940s, when physicians began using a drug called isoniazid to treat the lung infection tuberculosis (TB). The drug worked, but some patients suffered nerve damage. Researchers eventually found that certain people metabolize the drug rapidly, and they do not develop side effects. However, people who metabolize the drug slowly develop side effects because the drug is in their bodies longer.

Knowledge of ecogenetics might be helpful in some circumstances, but damaging in others. A smoker might want to know if he or she is among the 7 percent of the population who is genetically predisposed to develop lung cancer from prolonged cigarette smoking. However, people fear that information on inherited chemical sensitivities might restrict certain employment opportunities if employers gain access to the genetic information.

How Do Genes Mold Traits?

Some inherited traits are obvious—a patch of white hair in the same place on the scalp in a mother and son; a prominent nose; freckles or baldness. Others become clear with time, such as breast cancer striking several members of an extended family. Genes ultimately determine many of our physical characteristics and probably a good number of our emotional, psychological, and mental traits as well.

We rarely know precisely how a gene-encoded protein causes a particular trait. We can understand how an abnormally shaped protein builds up and bends red blood cells into a sickle shape, and how those sickled cells dam blood flow, causing excruciating pain. We can envision how lifting a brake on cell division results in the overgrowth that is cancer, or how a defective protein that normally anchors the two skin layers together fails, causing painful blistering and skinless areas. But how do genes determine the shape of an earlobe, athletic ability, or such hard-to-define characteristics as intelligence or personality?

The answers to some of these compelling questions, as well as a better understanding of the genetic bases of rare and common diseases, will come soon as researchers worldwide unravel our genetic blueprints. Genetic technology is almost certain to be a part of your future. This book will help you to understand more about how your body works, and about how you inherited traits from your parents and will pass them on to your children and grandchildren.

It is perhaps the most exciting time ever to be studying human genetics!

Key Concepts

Environmental factors and other genes influence the expression of individual genes. Single-gene disorders are rare, but some more common illnesses also have inherited components. Mutant genes that alter immunity can cause disease susceptibilities. Multifactorial traits result from the interactions of several genes and environmental influences. Ecogenetics considers inherited differences in response to drugs.

summary

1. A **gene** is a sequence of **DNA** building blocks in a **chromosome** that directs a cell to manufacture a particular protein. An **allele** is an alternate form of a gene. A **mutation** is a change in a gene. Humans have 23 pairs of chromosomes and about 70,000 genes. An adult passes one copy of each gene—or one allele (variant)—to an offspring.

2. Because of the laws of inheritance, a genetic condition affects family members at predictable frequencies, and if the causative gene is known, doctors may detect the condition before symptoms occur.

3. Genes produce effects at the molecular, cellular, body, family, and population levels. **Genotype** refers to the particular genes in an individual, and **phenotype** refers to gene expression.

4. **Transmission genetics** examines inheritance patterns between generations. An allele may be transmitted as a **recessive** or **dominant** trait on an **autosome** or **sex chromosome.** Mode of inheritance describes these two factors.

5. Genetic counselors inform families with inherited disease of recurrence risks, using **pedigrees** and their knowledge of the **mode of inheritance** for particular conditions.

6. **Population genetics** examines allele frequencies in large groups of people.

7. In genetics, studying the abnormal helps to explain normal body structure and function. Understanding the nature of the protein defect underlying a disorder can suggest treatment strategies.

8. Other genes and environmental influences can alter gene expression. People may inherit susceptibilities to conditions previously not thought to be genetic. Genes can alter immune function. Genes can control how quickly a person metabolizes a drug.

review questions

1. Distinguish between the terms in each of the following sets:

   a. dominant and recessive

   b. genotype and phenotype

   c. gene and chromosome

   d. autosome and sex chromosome

   e. DNA and RNA

2. How does DNA control inherited traits?

3. Cite three recent examples of genetics in the news.

4. What are two ways inherited illness differs from infection or injury?

5. What is mode of inheritance? Describe a circumstance when it might be important to know a particular gene's mode of inheritance.

6. Describe an illness at the molecular, cellular, body, family, and population levels. (You can use information presented later in the book.)

7. Does adding a permanent wave to hair, or wearing contact lenses that change the color of the eyes, change one's phenotype or genotype? Why?

8. What does a genetic counselor do?

9. How is it possible to predict whether a genetic disease will develop?

10. List three traits that are inherited but that the environment can alter.

11. Cite two ways that genes can alter environmental factors.

applied questions

1. Two brothers have sickle cell disease. One is hospitalized often for serious infections and joint pain, but the other is healthier. How is this possible?

2. If your parent had an inherited illness, would you want to be tested to see whether you inherited the causative gene? List the benefits and risks of acquiring such information.

3. A 54-year-old man and his 26-year-old son are each accused of committing a rape. Why would DNA printing be difficult in evaluating this case?

4. "Not everyone loves human genetics," said Charles Epstein, a noted geneticist, of the June 1993 day when he opened a package from the Unabomber, an antitechnology terrorist. The Unabomber's 1995 published "manifesto" evoked images of a future government that uses genetic technology to control reproduction and decide the traits of the next generation. The Unabomber was an extremist, but he is not alone in finding the field of human genetics frightening. What aspects of human genetics might disturb people?

5. Do you think fetuses or newborns should be screened for inherited disorders that will affect them later in life? Should they be screened for illnesses that currently have no treatment, such as Alzheimer disease?

6. Predictive genetic tests—those that presymptomatically diagnose inherited illness—will create a group of people dubbed "the healthy ill" that have a high probability of developing a particular illness. Do you think insurance companies and employers should have access to such information? Why or why not?

7. Allergies, autoimmune disorders, and infections are not typical inherited illnesses. How might genes, however, affect susceptibility to these types of conditions?

suggested readings

Colt, George Howe. April 1998. Were you born that way? *LIFE.* To what extent does genetics influence personality?

Diamond, Jared. November 1994. Race without color. *Discover.* We can define different races when we base the definition on different inherited characteristics.

Hamer, Dean, and Peter Copeland. 1998. *Living with Our Genes.* New York: Doubleday. Do genes determine who we are?

Lewis, Ricki. January 15, 1998. Genetic testing guidelines released. *Genetic Engineering News.* Protocols are being developed to prevent misuse of genetic test results.

Menotti-Raymond, Marilyn A., et al. April 24, 1997. Pet cat hair implicates murder suspect. *Nature,* vol. 386. DNA typing of Snowball the cat and white cat hairs on a murder victim nailed the perpetrator.

Smith, Christina King. February 15, 1996. Spectra biomedical sees future in personalized genetic profiling services. *Genetic Engineering News.* The scenario opening this chapter is speculative—but at least one company is making it reality.

The October 1997 issue of *Discover* magazine has several articles on genes and behavior.

The May 15, 1997 issue of *The New England Journal of Medicine* has several articles on inherited breast cancer.

chapter two

Cells

Molecular Medicine

The activities and abnormalities of **cells**—the fundamental units that make up the human body—underlie all inherited traits and illnesses. The continuing story of progress in treating cystic fibrosis (CF) illustrates how understanding events at the cellular or molecular level improves patients' lives and reveals how the body works.

Conquering Cystic Fibrosis

Early descriptions of CF mentioned the most seemingly benign symptom—salty sweat. Seventeenth-century Britons had a saying: "Woe to that child which when kissed on the forehead tastes salty. He is bewitched and soon must die." Physicians first described the condition in medical journals in 1938 as a defect in channels leading from certain glands, causing extremely thick mucus and resulting infections in the lungs; a clogged pancreas, preventing digestive juices from reaching the intestines; and salty sweat. Children with CF, with their slow growth and frequent infections, are sometimes first diagnosed simply as suffering from "failure to thrive."

In 1960, a CF patient rarely lived more than ten years. At that time, although they still did not know the gene or protein defect, physicians fought the symptoms with exercises, antibiotics, and digestive enzyme supplements. These approaches, still used today, treat the phenotype. Several new treatments, made possible by identifying the gene behind the disorder, attempt to correct the genotype.

One phenotypic treatment is postural drainage, a series of exercises usually performed twice a day to drain mucus from the lungs. A child lies across an adult's lap, or an older person lies on a bed, and a helper pounds the patient's chest and back to shake the mucus free in different parts of the lung.

Postural drainage, plus daily antibiotic drugs, can prevent some lung infections in CF patients. Still, many patients are hospitalized repeatedly for severe lung infections. This happens because the excess mucus creates an environment that encourages the growth of microorganisms that do not flourish in healthy lungs. CF patients also have digestive problems. To improve digestion and gain weight, the patient mixes a powder consisting of animal digestive juice extracts into a soft food such as applesauce and eats the mixture before each meal. This supplements the function of the mucus-clogged pancreas.

As physicians developed these measures, people with CF began living longer. However, it wasn't until researchers discovered the cause of cystic fibrosis at the cellular and molecular levels that they could develop more targeted therapies.

In 1989, geneticists at the University of Michigan at Ann Arbor and the Hospital for Sick Children in Toronto identified the CF gene. In most people with CF, the protein that this gene encodes—given the rather cumbersome name "cystic fibrosis transmembrane conductance regulator," or CFTR—lacks just one amino acid building block out of 1,480. Yet this small glitch is enough to alter the protein so that it cannot function.

The CFTR protein normally forms a channel in the **cell membranes** (outer layers) of cells that line the respiratory passages and certain glands such as the pancreas. The protein is manufactured deep inside the cell, then moves to the cell surface, where it functions as a channel, allowing chloride to leave the cell. Chloride joins sodium to form sodium chloride, or table salt. (Sodium enters and leaves cells through other channels.) In CF, the abnormal chloride channels stay inside the cells, unable to reach the surface. Chloride cannot move in and out of the cell as it normally would, and this indirectly blocks sodium transport, too. The result is a salty cellular interior that forces water into the cells, drying out the secretions that bathe them and leaving thick, sticky mucus. Figure 2.1 illustrates the progressive levels at which we can look at cystic fibrosis—gene, protein, and person.

Three drugs that became available in 1991 addressed CF at the cellular level by either allowing more sodium to enter lung-lining cells or enabling chloride to exit the cells. In 1992, a fourth drug was added—a natural protein that degrades the DNA that accumulates in infected lungs as white blood cells arrive as part of the inflammatory response. Several experimental gene therapies directly target the source of CF by introducing functional CFTR genes into affected cells in aerosol sprays.

Why Study Cells?

Recent advances in treating CF illustrate the value of understanding cell structures and functions. Our bodies include many variations on the cellular theme, with such specialized cell types as bone and blood, nerve and muscle. Cells interact, sending, receiving, and responding to information. They aggregate and may even move about the body. Cell numbers are critical to development, growth, and healing, processes that reflect the coordination of cell division and cell death.

We begin our look at cells by considering the chemicals that compose them.

Key Concepts

Cells are fundamental units of life. Inherited traits and illnesses arise from events at the cell and molecular levels. Cell specializations, interactions, and numbers are important factors in the human body's normal functioning.

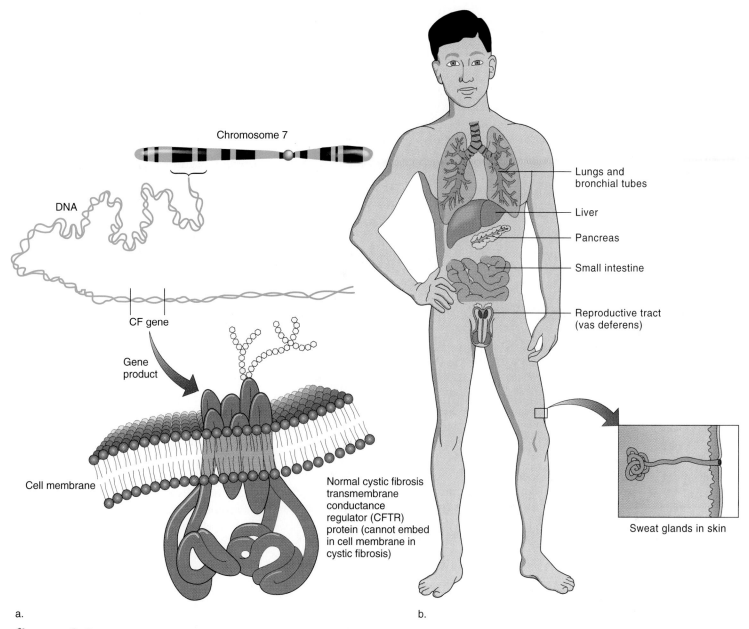

Chromosome 7

DNA

CF gene

Gene product

Cell membrane

Normal cystic fibrosis transmembrane conductance regulator (CFTR) protein (cannot embed in cell membrane in cystic fibrosis)

Lungs and bronchial tubes

Liver

Pancreas

Small intestine

Reproductive tract (vas deferens)

Sweat glands in skin

a.

b.

figure 2.1

From gene to protein to person. (*a*) The gene that encodes the CFTR protein, and causes cystic fibrosis when abnormal, resides on the seventh largest chromosome. The protein folds into a channel that regulates the flow of salt components into and out of cells lining the respiratory tract, pancreas, and possibly other organs. (*b*) In cystic fibrosis, this protein cannot embed in the cell membrane. Since the CFTR protein doesn't function, salt is trapped inside cells. This leaves behind very thick mucus in the lungs, pancreas, and intestines and produces a salty sweat.

a. Source: Data from M. C. Iannuzzi and F. S. Collins, "Reverse Genetics and Cystic Fibrosis," *American Journal of Respiratory Cellular and Molecular Biology* 2:309–316, 1990 American Lung Association.

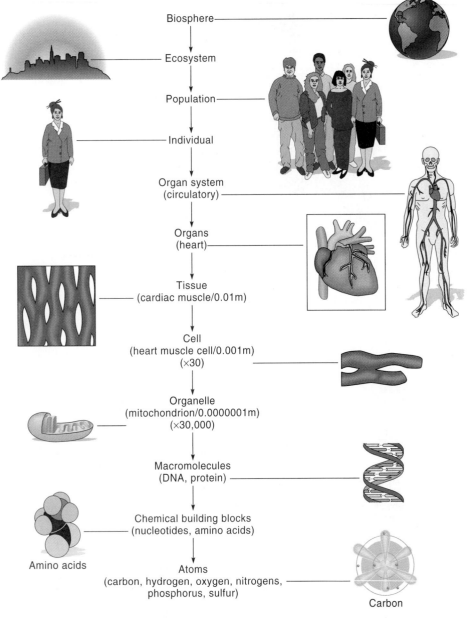

figure 2.2

Levels of biological organization.

large, and are therefore called **macromolecules.** The macromolecules that make up and fuel cells include **carbohydrates** (sugars and starches), **lipids** (fats and oils), **proteins,** and **nucleic acids.** Cells require vitamins and minerals in much smaller amounts, but they are also vital to health.

Carbohydrates provide energy. Lipids form the basis of several types of hormones, provide insulation, and serve as an energy reserve. Proteins have many diverse functions in the human body. They participate in blood clotting, nerve transmission, and muscle contraction and form the bulk of the body's connective tissue. **Enzymes** are proteins that are especially important because they speed, or catalyze, biochemical reactions so that they occur swiftly enough to sustain life. Several interesting proteins are mentioned later in this chapter.

Most important to the study of heredity are the nucleic acids deoxyribonucleic acid (DNA) and ribonucleic acid (RNA). DNA and RNA form a living language that converts information from past generations into specific collections of proteins that give a cell its individual characteristics.

Macromolecules interact and combine to form larger structures within cells. For example, the membranes that surround cells and compartmentalize their interiors consist of double layers (bilayers) of lipids embedded with carbohydrates and proteins. (Figure 2.12 depicts a cell membrane.)

The mysterious thing we call life is based on the not-so-mysterious chemical principles that govern all matter. Heredity is based on a highly organized subset of the chemical reactions of life. Reading 2.1 describes some drastic effects that result from abnormalities in the major types of biochemicals.

Cell Composition

Trillions of cells interact, forming tissues, organs, and organ systems that make up a human body (figure 2.2). All cells have certain features in common that allow them to perform the basic life functions of reproduction, growth, response to stimuli, and energy utilization. Body cells also have specialized features—a muscle cell, for example, is long and spindly and is filled with protein rods that enable it to contract, while a skin cell is flat and scaly, a nerve cell is very long and branching, and an adipose cell is little more than a blob of fat (figure 2.3).

The human body consists of about two hundred different cell types. These specializations are possible because different cells express different subsets of the complete set of genetic instructions all cells have (figure 2.4).

Cells are composed of chemicals. The chemicals of life (biochemicals) tend to be

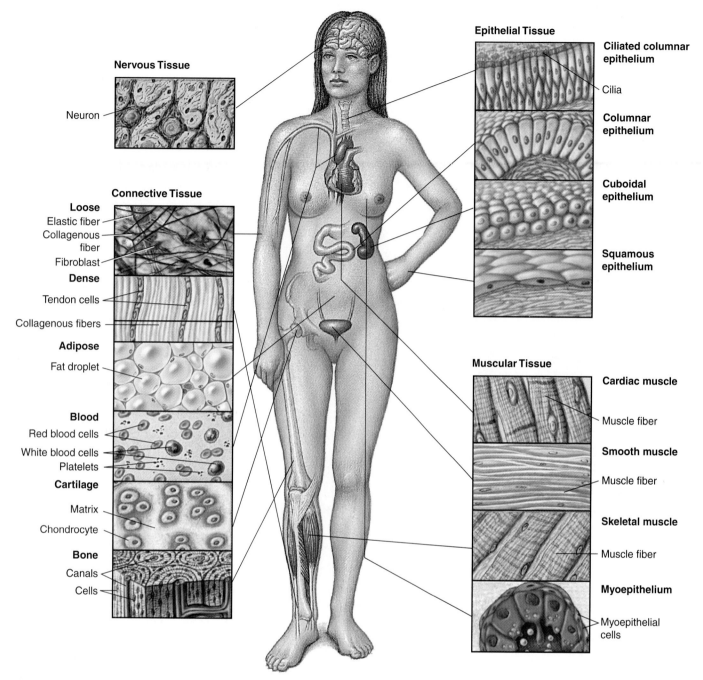

Nervous Tissue
Neuron

Connective Tissue
Loose
Elastic fiber
Collagenous fiber
Fibroblast
Dense
Tendon cells
Collagenous fibers
Adipose
Fat droplet
Blood
Red blood cells
White blood cells
Platelets
Cartilage
Matrix
Chondrocyte
Bone
Canals
Cells

Epithelial Tissue
Ciliated columnar epithelium
Cilia
Columnar epithelium
Cuboidal epithelium
Squamous epithelium

Muscular Tissue
Cardiac muscle
Muscle fiber
Smooth muscle
Muscle fiber
Skeletal muscle
Muscle fiber
Myoepithelium
Myoepithelial cells

figure 2.3

Human cell types. The organs in the human body consist of four basic tissue types: epithelial, or lining tissue; connective tissue, which provides form and support and includes loose and fibrous connective tissue, adipose (fat) tissue, blood, cartilage, and bone; nervous tissue; and muscular tissue. In an individual, these cell types all contain the same complete set of genetic instructions, but specialize by expressing certain subsets of genes.

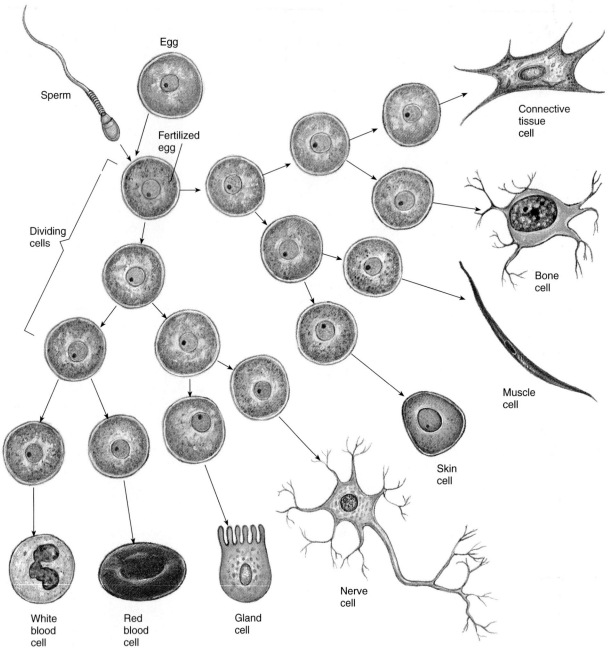

figure 2.4

The trillions of cells in an adult human derive from the original fertilized egg cell by cell division. As different genes turn off in different cells, the characteristics of specific cell types emerge. (Relative cell sizes are not to scale.)

Cell Complexity

Unicellular organisms, such as bacteria, consist of single cells. Multicellular organisms, such as humans, consist of many cells. Biologists recognize three types of cells based on complexity—**prokaryotes, archaea,** and **eukaryotes.** Human cells are eukaryotic and are characterized by membrane-bound structures called **organelles** ("little organs") that carry out specific functions. First we consider simpler cells.

Prokaryotic Cells

Prokaryotes include the bacteria and cyanobacteria, once known as blue-green algae. These cells are usually much smaller than ours (figure 2.5). A prokaryotic cell lacks a **nucleus,** the dark-staining, membrane-bound body in eukaryotic cells that encloses the DNA. Still, a prokaryote is organized and efficient enough to survive and flourish. Prokaryotes were the earliest cells to leave fossil evidence and are the most abundant organisms on earth today.

The chemicals of life must work together precisely to keep an organism functioning. Because so many biological functions involve proteins, and because proteins are the direct products of genes, inherited traits and illnesses can be understood at a biochemical level. These genetic disorders illustrate defects in the major macromolecules of life.

Carbohydrate

The new parents grew frustrated as they tried to feed their baby, who yowled and pulled up her chubby legs in pain a few hours after each formula feeding. Finally, a doctor identified the problem—the baby lacked the enzyme lactase, which enables the digestive system to break down milk sugar (lactose). Bacteria multiplied in the undigested lactose in the child's intestines, producing gas, cramps, and bloating. Switching to a soybean-based, lactose-free infant formula helped. The father, who often suffered from gas pains after eating dairy foods, had passed *lactose intolerance* to his daughter.

Lipid

A sudden sharp pain began in the man's arm and spread to his chest—the first sign of a heart attack. At age thirty-six, he was younger than most people who suffer heart attacks, but he had inherited a gene that halved the number of protein receptors for cholesterol on his liver cells. Because cholesterol could not enter the liver cells efficiently, it built up in his arteries, constricting blood flow in his heart and eventually causing a mild heart attack. A fatty diet had accelerated his inherited heart disease, *familial hypercholesterolemia*.

Protein

The first sign that the newborn was ill was also the most innocuous—his urine smelled like maple syrup. For the first few weeks, when babies normally sleep much of the time, it was hard to tell Tim was too sleepy. But he vomited so often that he hardly grew. A blood test revealed that Tim had inherited *maple syrup urine disease*. He could not digest three types of amino acids (protein building blocks), so these amino acids accumulated in his bloodstream. A diet very low in these amino acids has helped Tim, but this treatment is new and his future uncertain.

Nucleic Acids

From birth, Michael's wet diapers contained orange, sandlike particles, but otherwise he seemed healthy. By six months of age, though, the baby's urination was obviously painful. A physician also noted that his writhing movements were not normal attempts to crawl, but were involuntary.

When the doctor inspected the orange particles in Michael's diaper, she suspected *Lesch-Nyhan syndrome,* a disorder caused by extremely low levels of an enzyme called HPRT. A blood test confirmed the diagnosis. The near-absence of the enzyme meant that Michael's body could not recycle two of the four types of DNA building blocks, instead converting them into uric acid, which forms crystals in urine.

Other symptoms that lay in Michael's future were not as easy to understand—severe mental retardation and seizures. Most inexplicable would be the aggressive and self-destructive behavior that is a hallmark of Lesch-Nyhan syndrome. By age three or so, Michael would respond to stress by uncontrollably biting his fingers, lips, and shoulders. He would probably die before the age of thirty of kidney failure or infection.

Vitamins

Vitamins enable the body to use the carbohydrates, lipids, and proteins we eat. Julie inherited *biotinidase deficiency,* which greatly slows the rate at which her body can use the vitamin biotin.

If Julie hadn't been diagnosed in a state-sponsored newborn screening program and started on biotin supplements shortly after birth, her future would have been grave. By early childhood, she would have shown a variety of biotin-deficiency symptoms, including mental retardation, seizures, skin rash, and loss of hearing, vision, and hair. Her slow growth, caused by her body's inability to extract energy from nutrients, would have eventually proved lethal.

Minerals

Ingrid is in her thirties, but she lives in the geriatric ward of a state mental hospital, unable to talk or walk. Although her grin and drooling make her appear mentally deficient to some, Ingrid is alert and communicates by pointing to letters on a board. In 1980, she was a vivacious, normal high-school senior. Then symptoms of *Wilson disease* began to appear, as her weakened liver could no longer control the excess copper her digestive tract absorbed from food.

The initial symptoms of Ingrid's inherited copper poisoning were stomachaches, headaches, and an inflamed liver (hepatitis). By 1983, very odd changes began—slurred speech; loss of balance; a gravelly, low-pitched voice; and altered handwriting. Ingrid received many false diagnoses, including schizophrenia, multiple sclerosis, and Parkinson's disease, before a psychiatrist noted the greenish rings around her irises (caused by copper buildup) and diagnosed Wilson disease. Only then did Ingrid receive helpful treatment. A drug, penicillamine, enabled her to excrete the excess copper in her urine, which turned the color of bright new pennies. Although Ingrid's symptoms did not improve, the treatment halted the course of the illness. Without the drug, she would have soon died.

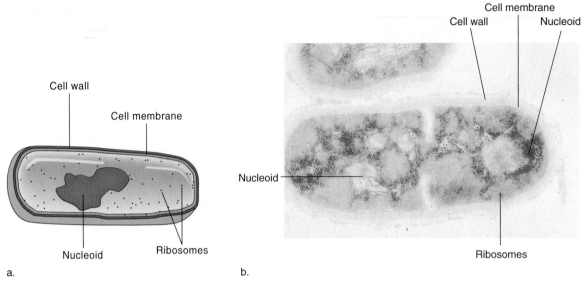

Cell wall

Cell membrane

Nucleoid

Ribosomes

a.

Cell membrane

Cell wall

Nucleoid

Nucleoid

Ribosomes

b.

figure 2.5

A prokaryotic cell. The single DNA molecule of a prokaryotic cell resides in a seemingly dense region of the cytoplasm called the nucleoid, but no true membrane-bound nucleus houses DNA, as in more complex cells. The prokaryotic cell contains many ribosomes, as well as fats, proteins, carbohydrates, and pigments. A cell membrane and, in many cases, a cell wall surround a prokaryotic cell. Part (a) is a schematic view of a bacterium, shown in (b).

Prokaryotes are used in genetic technology. Human genes inserted into prokaryotic cells instruct the cells to manufacture desired proteins. People with diabetes inject insulin synthesized in bacteria containing human insulin genes.

Rigid cell walls surround most prokaryotic cells—eukaryotic cells lack them. Many antibiotic drugs halt infection by interfering with a bacterium's ability to build its cell wall. Bacteria are classified by their shapes and staining properties of cell walls. Just inside the prokaryote's cell wall is a cell membrane. Some bacteria also have enzyme-studded internal membranes.

A prokaryote's genetic material is a single molecule of DNA associated with proteins unique to these cells. Both prokaryotic and eukaryotic cells contain **ribosomes,** spherical structures consisting of RNA and protein. Ribosomes provide a physical support for RNA action; in a ribosome, RNA that corresponds to a gene's DNA sequence links amino acids to build a protein. Because the DNA, RNA, and ribosomes in prokaryotic cells are in close contact with each other, protein synthesis in these simple organisms occurs more swiftly than in complex cells, where DNA and RNA are separated.

Archaeal Cells

In the late 1970s, biologists discovered a type of microorganism that had prokaryotic and eukaryotic features. Called *archaea* because they were at first thought to be the most ancient types of cells, these single-celled organisms, like prokaryotes, lack nuclei, but they do have outer coverings more complex than those of prokaryotes. On the other hand, certain molecules in archaea are unique—as different from their counterparts in prokaryotes as they are from the molecules in eukaryotes.

We knew nothing of the archaea for a long time because many of them live in very harsh environments (by human standards) that are difficult to simulate in a laboratory or to explore—for example, in hot springs and in thermal vents on the ocean floor. In fact, some archaean biochemicals are valuable in industry because they resist extremes of heat, acidity or basicity, or salinity. More recently, scientists have discovered archaea in less extreme habitats, such as the surface layers of oceans. In 1996, researchers sequenced the genome of an archeon. We still do not know much about the archaea, but their discovery has upset the long-held view that cells come in just two major forms, prokaryotic and eukaryotic.

Eukaryotic Cells

A eukaryotic cell usually has at least a thousand times the volume of a prokaryotic cell. How can a large cell remain sufficiently organized to carry out the biochemical reactions of life? Organelles subdivide a cell's functions by providing specialized compartments where certain biochemical reactions occur.

Saclike organelles sequester biochemicals that might harm other cellular contents. Some organelles are membranes studded with enzymes that catalyze reactions. On some membranes, different enzymes align in the sequence in which they participate in pathways of linked biochemical reactions. In general, organelles keep related biochemicals and structures close enough to function efficiently and eliminate the need for the entire cell to maintain a high concentration of a particular biochemical.

"Bags within a bag" describes the organization of a eukaryotic cell (figure 2.6), with the organelles comprising the "bags" in the larger "bag" (the cell). The most

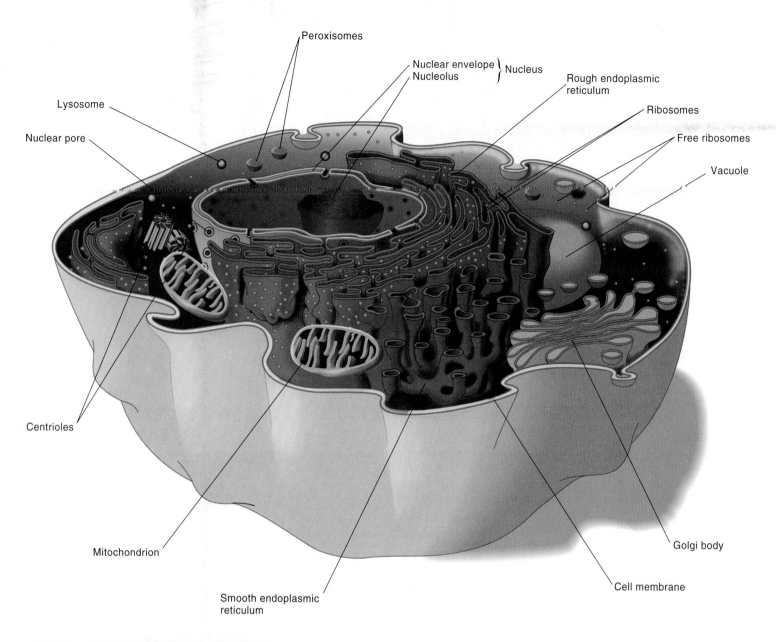

Peroxisomes

Nuclear envelope ⟩ Nucleus
Nucleolus

Rough endoplasmic
reticulum

Lysosome

Ribosomes

Free ribosomes

Nuclear pore

Vacuole

Centrioles

Mitochondrion

Smooth endoplasmic
reticulum

Golgi body

Cell membrane

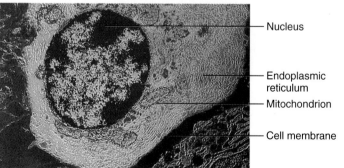

Nucleus

Endoplasmic
reticulum

Mitochondrion

Cell membrane

figure 2.6

A eukaryotic cell has many organelles. The nucleus houses genetic material. RNA carries genetic information into the cytoplasm, where free ribosomes and ribosomes on the rough ER translate the message into protein. The smooth ER and Golgi body participate in secretion, and mitochondria house the energy reactions and contain a small amount of DNA. Centrioles take part in cell division; lysosomes contain enzymes that degrade certain biochemicals; and peroxisomes contain enzymes with a variety of functions.

prominent organelle, the nucleus, is enclosed in a **nuclear envelope** and contains the chromosomes. Portals called nuclear pores are rings of proteins that allow certain biochemicals to exit or enter the nucleus. Within the nucleus, in a darkened area called the **nucleolus** ("little nucleus"), ribosomes form. The remainder of the cell consists of other organelles and the jellylike **cytoplasm.** The organelles (including the nucleus) and cytoplasm are the living parts of the cell. Nonliving cellular components include stored proteins, carbohydrates, and lipids, pigment molecules, and various other small chemicals.

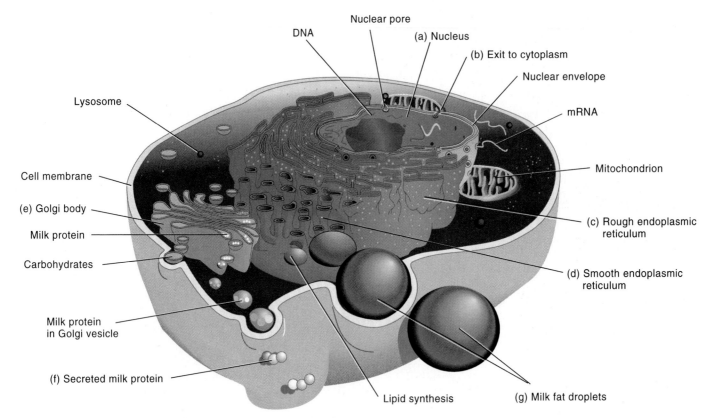

DNA
Nuclear pore
(a) Nucleus
(b) Exit to cytoplasm
Nuclear envelope
mRNA
Lysosome
Cell membrane
(e) Golgi body
Milk protein
Carbohydrates
Milk protein
in Golgi vesicle
(f) Secreted milk protein
Lipid synthesis
Mitochondrion
(c) Rough endoplasmic
reticulum
(d) Smooth endoplasmic
reticulum
(g) Milk fat droplets

figure 2.7

In milk secretion, organelles interact to synthesize, transport, store, and export biochemicals. Secretion begins in the nucleus (*a*), where messenger RNA molecules bearing genetic instructions for milk protein production exit to the cytoplasm (*b*). Most proteins are synthesized on membranes of the rough endoplasmic reticulum (*c*) using amino acids in the cytoplasm. Lipids are synthesized in the smooth ER (*d*), and sugars are synthesized, assembled, and stored in the Golgi body (*e*). An active mammary gland cell releases milk proteins from vesicles that bud off of the Golgi body (*f*). Fat droplets pick up a layer of lipid from the cell membrane as they exit the cell (*g*). A nursing baby receives a chemically complex secretion—milk.

Key Concepts

Prokaryotes include bacteria and cyanobacteria. These simpler cells lack nuclei, are bound by a cell wall and cell membrane, and may contain internal membranes. DNA, RNA, and ribosomes are in close association in prokaryotes, speeding protein synthesis. Archaea have characteristics of prokaryotes and eukaryotes as well as unique features. Many of them inhabit harsh environments. Eukaryotic cells have membrane-bound organelles.

Organelles

Organelles interact to coordinate basic life functions and sculpt the characteristics of specialized cell types. Several types of organelles may interact in a complex function such as secretion.

Secretion—The Eukaryotic Production Line

Secretion begins when the body sends a biochemical message to a cell to begin producing a substance, such as when hormones that a woman's body releases when an infant suckles signal a cell in her breast to begin producing milk (figure 2.7). In response, information in certain genes is copied into sequences of **messenger RNA** (mRNA), which then exit the nucleus. In the cytoplasm, the messenger RNAs, with the help of ribosomes and another type of RNA called **transfer RNA,** direct the manufacture of proteins.

Protein synthesis occurs on a maze of interconnected membranous tubules and sacs that winds from the nuclear envelope to the cell membrane. This membrane labyrinth is the **endoplasmic reticulum** (ER). The portion of the ER nearest the

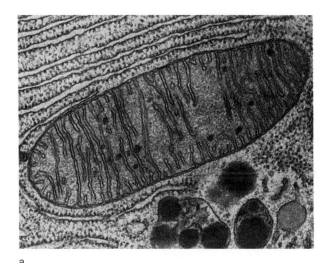

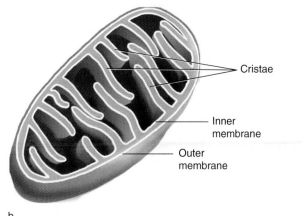

Cristae

Inner membrane

Outer membrane

a.

b.

figure 2.8

A mitochondrion consists of an outer membrane and a highly folded inner membrane. Within the inner folds are enzymes that catalyze biochemical reactions that extract energy from the bonds holding together nutrient molecules (×79,000).

nucleus, which is flattened and studded with ribosomes, is called the rough ER because it appears fuzzy when viewed under an electron microscope. Messenger RNA attaches to the ribosomes on the rough ER. Amino acids from the cytoplasm then are strung together, following the instructions in the mRNA's sequence, to form proteins that will either exit the cell or join membranes. Proteins are also synthesized on ribosomes not associated with the ER. These proteins remain in the cytoplasm.

The ER acts as a quality control center for the cell. Its chemical environment enables the protein the cell is manufacturing to fold into the three-dimensional shape necessary for its specific function. Misfolded proteins are pulled out of the ER and degraded, much as an obviously defective toy might be pulled from an assembly line at a toy factory and discarded.

As the rough ER winds out toward the cell membrane, the ribosomes become fewer, and the diameters of the tubules widen, forming a section called the smooth ER. Here, lipids are synthesized and added to the proteins arriving from the rough ER. The lipids and proteins travel until the tubules of the smooth ER eventually narrow and end, and then they exit in membrane-bound, saclike organelles called **vesicles** that pinch off from the tubular endings of the membrane.

A loaded vesicle takes its contents to the next stop in the secretory production line, the **Golgi body.** This processing center is a stack of flat, membrane-enclosed sacs where sugars are synthesized and linked to form starches or attach to proteins to form glycoproteins or to lipids to form glycolipids. Proteins finish folding in the Golgi body. The components of complex secretions, such as milk, are temporarily stored here. Droplets then bud off the Golgi body in vesicles that move outward to the cell membrane, fleetingly becoming part of the membrane until they are released (secreted) to the cell's exterior. Some substances, such as lipids, retain a layer of surrounding membrane when they leave the cell.

Energy Production—Mitochondria

The activities of secretion, as well as the many chemical reactions taking place in the cytoplasm, require continual energy. Organelles called **mitochondria** provide energy from the products of digestion—nutrients (figure 2.8). A mitochondrion has an outer membrane similar to those in the ER and Golgi body and an intricately folded inner membrane. The inner membrane's folds hold enzymes that catalyze the biochemical reactions that release energy from the chemical bonds of nutrient molecules.

The number of mitochondria in a cell varies greatly, from a few hundred to tens of thousands, depending upon the cell's activity level. A typical liver cell, for example, has about 1,700 mitochondria, but a muscle cell, with its very high energy requirement, has many more.

Mitochondria are especially interesting to geneticists because, like the nucleus, they contain genetic material. Another unusual characteristic of mitochondria is that they are inherited from the mother only, because mitochondria are in the middle regions of sperm cells but usually not in the head regions that enter eggs. A class of inherited diseases whose symptoms result from abnormal mitochondria are always passed from mother to offspring. These illnesses usually produce extreme muscle weakness, because muscle activity requires many mitochondria. Chapter 5 discusses mitochondrial inheritance. Evolutionary biologists study mitochondrial genes to trace the beginnings of humankind, discussed in chapter 14.

Packets of Enzymes—Lysosomes and Peroxisomes

Eukaryotic cells break down molecules and structures as well as produce them. Organelles called **lysosomes** are the cell's "garbage disposals"; they dismantle captured bacteria, worn-out organelles, fats, carbohydrates, and other debris. Lysosomes are abundant in liver cells, where their enzymes break down toxins.

A lysosome forms as a sac that buds off the ER or Golgi body (figure 2.9). In

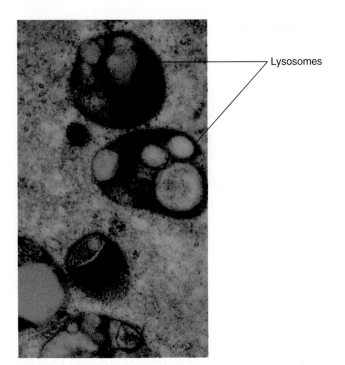

figure 2.9

Lyosomes are sacs containing about forty types of enzymes that require a very acidic environment to function (×14,137).

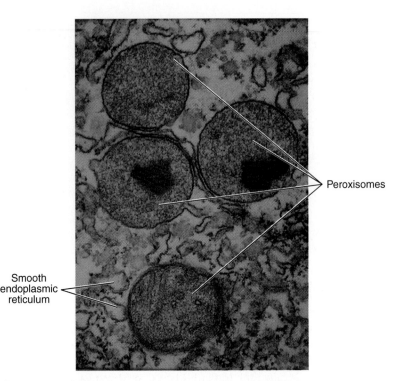

Lysosomes

Peroxisomes

Smooth endoplasmic reticulum

figure 2.10

Peroxisomes are abundant in liver cells, where they assist in detoxification.

human cells, each lysosome contains more than forty different types of enzymes, each degrading a specific biochemical. These enzymes can work only in a very acidic environment. The lysosome compartmentalizes a highly acidic region for the enzymes without exposing other cellular constituents to these harsh conditions. Vesicles ferry debris to the lysosomes. If lysosomes rupture and release their enzymes, the entire cell is digested from within and dies. Lysosomes may play a role in aging by destroying cells in this way.

Peroxisomes are sacs with outer membranes that are studded with several types of enzymes (figure 2.10). These enzymes perform a variety of functions, including breaking down certain lipids and rare biochemicals, synthesizing bile acids used in fat digestion, and detoxifying compounds that result from excess oxygen exposure. Peroxisomes are large and abundant in liver and kidney cells.

The correct enzyme balance in lysosomes and peroxisomes is crucial to health. Absence or malfunction of a single enzyme type leads to a disorder called an **inborn error of metabolism.** (Such a disorder can result from abnormalities in other enzymes, too.) In general, when an enzyme cannot function, the biochemical it would normally act upon accumulates. The nature of the accumulating substance determines specific symptoms. Table 2.1 describes peroxisomal disorders.

The nervous system degeneration of Tay-Sachs disease (figure 1.7) results from absence of a particular lysosomal enzyme which causes fatty material to build up on

table 2.1

Peroxisomal Disorders

Disorder	Defect
Infantile Refsums disease	Accumulation of very-long-chain fatty acids due to too few peroxisomes, in liver and skin cells. Symptoms include mental retardation, abnormal face, impaired vision and hearing, enlarged liver, weak bones.
Primary hyperoxaluria type I	A peroxisomal enzyme enters mitochondria instead of peroxisomes, where it cannot catalyze its reaction. Toxins accumulate.
X-linked adrenoleuko-dystrophy	Accumulation of very-long-chain fatty acids, which depletes fatty sheaths of brain cells. Symptoms include weakness, dizziness, low blood sugar, darkening skin, behavioral complications, loss of muscular control.
Zellweger syndrome	Peroxisomes are absent because their parts cannot be assembled. Only 35 of the 40 enzyme types can function free in the cytoplasm. Symptoms include abnormal face, hands, and feet; kidney cysts; malformed liver.

table 2.2

Structures and Functions of Organelles

Organelle	Structure	Function
Endoplasmic reticulum	Membrane network; rough ER has ribosomes, smooth ER does not	Site of protein synthesis and folding; lipid synthesis
Golgi body	Stacks of membrane-enclosed sacs	Sugars made and linked into starches, or joined to lipids or proteins; proteins finish folding; secretions stored
Lysosome	Sac containing digestive enzymes	Debris degraded, cell contents recycled
Mitochondrion	Two membranes; inner one enzyme-studded	Releases energy from nutrients
Nucleus	Porous sac containing DNA	Separates DNA from rest of cell
Peroxisome	Sac containing enzymes	Catalysis of several reactions
Ribosome	Two associated globular subunits of RNA and protein	Scaffold for protein synthesis
Vesicle	Membrane-bound sac	Temporarily stores or transports substances

nerve cells. Long before developmental skills wane, lysosomes swell.

The 1992 film *Lorenzo's Oil* recounted the true story of a child with a metabolic disorder caused by an absent peroxisomal enzyme. Six-year-old Lorenzo Odone had adrenoleukodystrophy (ALD). His peroxisomes lacked a normally abundant protein that transports an enzyme into the peroxisome, where it catalyzes a reaction that helps break down a certain type of lipid called a very-long-chain fatty acid. Without the enzyme transporter protein, the fatty acid builds up in cells of the brain and spinal cord. Early symptoms include low blood sugar, skin darkening, muscle weakness, and heartbeat irregularities. The patient eventually loses control over the limbs and usually dies within a few years. Ingesting a type of lipid in rapeseed oil— the oil in the film title—slows buildup of the very-long-chain fatty acids for a few years, but eventually impairs blood clotting and other vital functions. Ultimately, the illness progresses.

Table 2.2 summarizes the structures and functions of organelles. Reading 2.2, at the chapter's end, discusses infectious agents, such as viruses, that are simpler than cells and therefore not considered alive—but that nonetheless exert powerful effects on the human body.

Key Concepts

Organelles in eukaryotic cells compartmentalize biochemicals that interact or that require harsh or specific conditions. The nucleus contains DNA. In secretion, mRNA carries the information to synthesize a protein from DNA out of the nucleus. The mRNA then attaches to ribosomes in the rough ER, where proteins are synthesized and folded. Lipids join the secretion in the smooth ER and sugars at the Golgi body. The secretion then buds off in vesicles and exits the cell. Mitochondria consist of double membranes whose inner folds carry enzymes. These enzymes catalyze reactions that extract energy from nutrients. Lysosomes contain enzymes that degrade cellular debris, and peroxisomes house enzymes that detoxify certain substances, break down lipids, and synthesize bile acids.

The Cytoskeleton

A cell is more than a collection of organelles and chemicals in a sac. A cell's surface, which is part of the cell membrane, interacts with other cells. Just inside the cell membrane, rods of the protein actin, called **microfilaments,** and tubules of the protein tubulin, called **microtubules,** form an interior scaffolding, or **cytoskeleton** ("cell skeleton") (figure 2.11). The cell membrane and cytoskeleton form a structural framework—a cellular architecture—that distinguishes cell types from one another. Within human bodies, these distinctions help specialized cells assemble into tissues and organs. Between human bodies, these differences, especially at cell surfaces, form the basis of immunity, which is the body's ability to recognize its own cells as "self" and others as "nonself." Chapter 15 discusses genetic aspects of immunity.

Disruption of just one type of protein that normally functions in the cell membrane or cytoskeleton can be devastating. Recall how the inability of just one type of cell membrane protein to reach the cell's surface causes cystic fibrosis. Hereditary spherocytosis causes a greater disruption— it disturbs the interface between the cell membrane and the cytoskeleton. The muscular dystrophies shatter links between the cytoskeleton, cell membrane, and the mixture of proteins and glycoproteins outside the cell, called the **extracellular matrix.**

Hereditary Spherocytosis

The doughnut shape of red blood cells enables them to squeeze through the narrowest blood vessels on their 300-mile, 120-day journey in the circulation. Red blood cells derive much of their strength from rods of a protein called spectrin that form a meshwork beneath the cell membrane. Proteins called ankyrins attach the spectrin rods to the cell membrane (figure 2.12). Spectrin molecules are like steel girders, and ankyrins are like nuts and bolts. If either is absent, the structural support of the cell collapses.

This is precisely what happens in hereditary spherocytosis. Because the ankyrins are abnormal, parts of the red blood cell membrane disintegrate, causing the cell to balloon out. The bloated cells obstruct narrow blood vessels—especially in the spleen, the organ which normally disposes of aged red blood cells. Anemia develops as the spleen destroys red blood cells more rapidly than the bone marrow can replace them, producing great fatigue

figure 2.11

Hollow protein microtubules (made of tubulin) and solid protein rods (made of actin) form the cytoskeleton, the supportive framework of the cell.

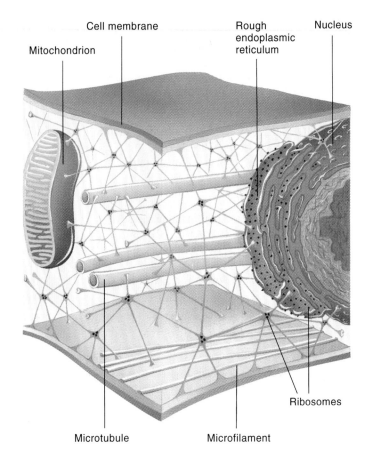

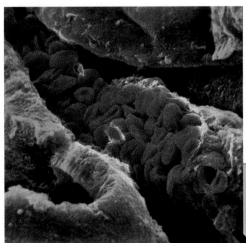

a.

figure 2.12

The red blood cell membrane. (*a*) The cytoskeleton that supports the cell membrane of a red blood cell enables it to withstand the great turbulent force of the circulation. (*b*) In the cell membrane, proteins called ankyrins bind molecules of spectrin from the cytoskeleton to the interior face. On its other end, ankyrin binds proteins that help ferry molecules across the cell membrane. In hereditary spherocytosis, abnormal ankyrin leads to collapse of the cell membrane—a problem for a cell whose function depends upon its shape.

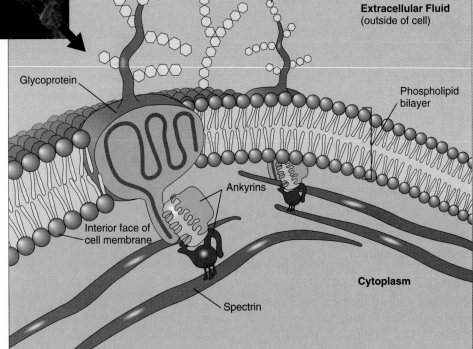

b.

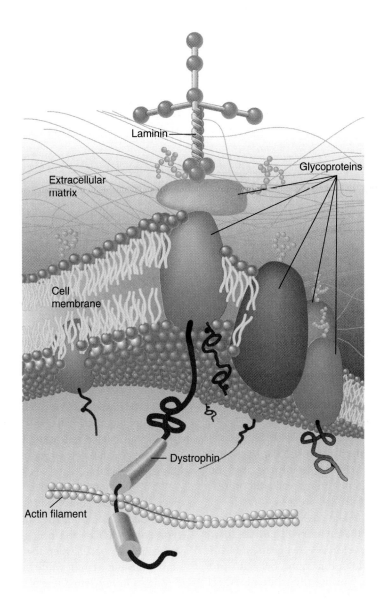

Laminin

Extracellular matrix

Glycoproteins

Cell membrane

Dystrophin

Actin filament

figure 2.13

Different types of muscular dystrophy are caused by defects in dystrophin or its associated glycoproteins in the cell membranes of skeletal and cardiac muscle cells.

Cell-Cell Interactions

Precisely coordinated biochemical steps orchestrate the cell-cell interactions that make multicellular life possible. Defects in cell communication and interaction cause some long-studied inherited illnesses. We look now at two broad types of interactions between cells.

Signal Transduction

Organelles, cell membranes, and cytoskeletons are dynamic structures that constantly communicate with each other and with the environment outside the cell. A key factor in this biological communication is the cell membrane, where a process called **signal transduction** takes place. In signal transduction, molecules on the cell membrane assess and transmit incoming messages to the cell's interior. Some signals must reach receptors for the cell to function normally; others, such as a signal to divide when cell division is not warranted, must be ignored. Because cascades of proteins carry out signal transduction, it is a genetically controlled process.

Signal transduction begins at a cell's surface, where protruding receptor molecules bind **first messenger** molecules (hormones and growth factors, discussed shortly) and, in doing so, contort. These movements cause the receptors to touch other receptors in the membrane, changing their shapes too. This action triggers changes in other molecules called **second messengers** inside the cell, which activate linked sequences of chemical reactions. The culmination of all this signaling is a particular cellular response, such as secretion, cell division, muscle contraction, or energy release (figure 2.14).

Defects in signal transduction underlie many inherited disorders. In neurofibromatosis type I (NF1), for example, tumors

and weakness. Removing the spleen can treat the condition. Researchers expect to find defective ankyrin behind hereditary problems in other cell types because of its critical location in the cell's architecture.

The Muscular Dystrophies

Muscle cells face even greater physical force than blood cells, because they are anchored in place. Most of a muscle cell consists of filaments of the proteins actin and myosin. A less abundant muscle protein, dystrophin, literally holds skeletal (voluntary) muscle cells together by linking actin in the cytoskeleton to a specific group of glycoproteins that are part of the cell membrane (figure 2.13). Some of these glycoproteins touch a cross-shaped protein called laminin on the outside of the cell. Laminin is anchored at its other end in the extracellular matrix. Missing or abnormal dystrophin or any of the glycoproteins causes a muscular dystrophy. These illnesses vary in severity and age of onset, but, in all cases, muscles weaken and degenerate. Eventually, fat and connective tissue replace the muscle.

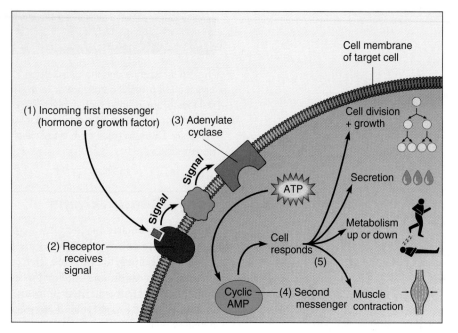

figure 2.14

First messengers (hormones and growth factors) dock at receptors on cell surfaces, triggering a chain of events that stimulates second messengers to signal a specific cellular response, such as cell division or secretion.

figure 2.15

Inability of signal transduction to keep out a message to divide lies behind neurofibromatosis type I (NF1), causing benign tumors of nervous tissue to grow beneath the skin, such as on this person's wrist.

(usually benign) grow in nervous tissue under the skin and in parts of the nervous system. At the cellular level, NF1 occurs when cells fail to block transmission of a growth factor signal that triggers cell division. Affected cells misinterpret the signal and divide when inappropriate. A tumor grows (figure 2.15).

The earliest known depiction of NF1 was a thirteenth-century illustration of a man covered with skin growths. A 1749 French magazine featured a girl covered with pigmented patches and tumors. In 1768, an English physician reported the case of a severely affected man whose father also had the condition. Cases accumulated, and in 1882, medical student Friedrich Daniel von Recklinghausen described what we now call NF1 or von Recklinghausen neurofibromatosis.

Cell Adhesion

Cells touch through adhesion, a precise sequence of interactions between proteins that join cells. Inflammation—the painful, red swelling at a site of injury or infection—illustrates cell adhesion. Inflammation occurs when white blood cells (leukocytes) move to the endangered body part, where they halt infection. **Cellular adhesion molecules,** or CAMs, help guide white blood cells to the injured area. Because CAMs are proteins, cell adhesion is a genetically controlled process.

Three types of CAMs act in sequence during the inflammatory response (figure 2.16). First, a selectin CAM coats the white blood cell's tiny projections. Selectins provide traction, slowing the white blood cell to a roll by binding to carbohydrates on the capillary (microscopic blood vessel) wall cells. Next, clotting blood, bacteria, or decaying tissue release a chemical attractant that signals the white blood cell to stop. The chemical attractant activates a CAM called an integrin, which latches onto the white blood cell, and another type of CAM called an adhesion receptor protein that extends from the capillary wall at the injury site. The adhesion receptor protein touches the cytoskeleton beneath the capillary lining cell membrane. The integrin and adhesion receptor protein then pull the white blood cell between the tilelike lining cells to the other side—the injury site.

What happens if the signals that direct white blood cells to injury sites fail? A young woman named Brooke Blanton knows the answer all too well. Her first symptom was teething sores that did not heal. These and other small wounds never accumulated pus (bacteria, cellular debris, and white blood cells), which is a sign the body is fighting infection. Doctors eventually diagnosed Brooke with a newly recognized disorder called leukocyte-adhesion deficiency. Her body lacks the CAMs that enable white blood cells to stick to blood vessel walls. As a result, her blood cells zip right past wounds. Brooke must avoid injury and infection, and she receives antiinfective treatments for even the slightest wound.

More common disorders may also reflect abnormal cell adhesion. Lack of cell adhesion eases the journey of cancer cells from one part of the body to another. Arthritis may occur when the wrong adhesion molecules rein in white blood cells, inflaming a joint where there is no injury.

Cell adhesion is critical to many other functions. CAMs guide cells surrounding an embryo to grow toward maternal cells and form the placenta, the supportive organ linking a pregnant woman to the fetus. Sequences of CAMs also help establish connections between nerve cells that underlie learning and memory.

Key Concepts

In signal transduction, cell surface receptors receive information from first messengers and pass them to second messengers, which then trigger a cellular response.

Cell adhesion molecules (CAMs) guide white blood cells to injury sites using a sequence of cell-protein interactions. CAMs are also important in prenatal development and nerve cell interactions.

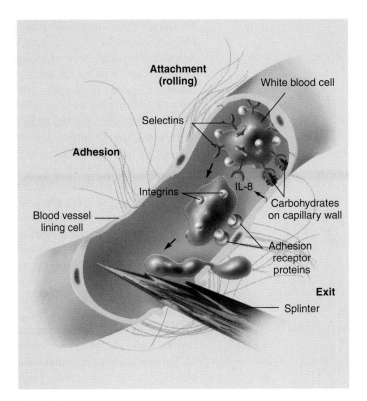

figure 2.16

Cell adhesion molecules (CAMs) assist cell movements. Three types of CAMs help guide white blood cells to an injured area. First, CAMs called selectins bind to and slow down a white blood cell approaching an injury site in a capillary. Next, chemical attractants attach the white blood cell to the capillary wall. Integrins squeeze through the capillary wall and grab the white blood cell, and with adhesion receptor proteins, pull the cell through the junctions in the capillary lining to the injured tissue. There, the white blood cell releases biochemicals that fight infection.

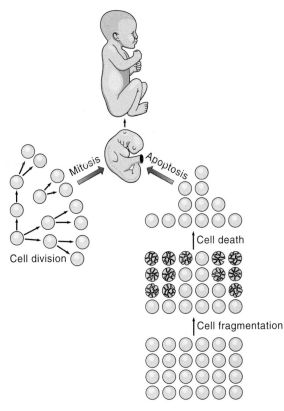

figure 2.17

Biological structures in animal bodies enlarge, allowing organisms to grow, as opposing processes regulate cell number. Cell numbers increase from mitosis and decrease from apoptosis.

Coordination of Cell Division and Cell Death

Two opposing processes—cell division and cell death—regulate cell number. A form of cell division, called **mitosis,** occurs in non-sex, or **somatic** cells (all cells but sperm and eggs). Mitosis increases cell number. A form of cell death, called **apoptosis,** normally removes certain cells during growth and development, decreasing cell number. In contrast is necrosis, which is abnormal tissue decay. Muscle degeneration in muscular dystrophy is necrosis, not apoptosis. Genes control both mitosis and apoptosis.

Mitosis and apoptosis maintain body form, especially the shapes of organs (figure 2.17). Both processes are vital in the embryo and fetus, the two major stages of prenatal (before birth) development. Certain tissues normally overgrow, and then extra cells die. This sculpting of living tissue occurs, for example, as the fingers and toes emerge from weblike precursor structures. Apoptosis also helps reduce nerve cell connections and helps establish the immune system in prenatal development.

After birth, mitosis and apoptosis protect the body. Mitosis fills in new skin to heal a scraped knee. Apoptosis removes skin cells damaged by the ultraviolet radiation in sunlight, causing them to peel and thus rids the body of cells that could turn cancerous. Overall, coordination of mitosis and apoptosis maintains a balance between growth and tissue loss. Cancer is one consequence of disruption in this balance; it occurs when mitosis is too frequent or when apoptosis is too infrequent. Chapter 16 addresses cancer in depth.

Key Concepts

Mitosis (cell division) and apoptosis (cell death) regulate cell number in growth and development. In the prenatal stages, coordination of these processes sculpts body form. After birth, mitosis and apoptosis protect. Disruption of either process can lead to cancer or other disorders.

The Cell Cycle

Many cell divisions transform a single fertilized egg into a many-trillion-celled person. A series of events called the **cell cycle** describes when a cell is dividing or not dividing.

Cell cycle rate varies in different tissues at different times. A cell lining the small intestine's inner wall may divide throughout life; a cell in the brain may

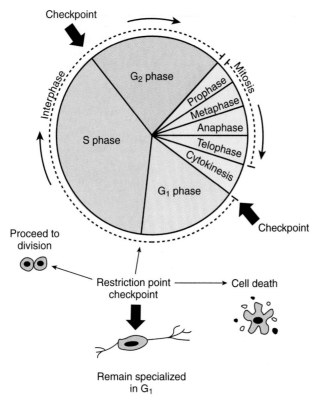

figure 2.18

The cell cycle is divided into interphase, when cellular components are replicated, and mitosis, when the cell splits in two, distributing its contents into two daughter cells. Interphase is divided into two gap phases (G₁ and G₂), when the cell duplicates specific molecules and structures, and a synthesis phase (S), when it replicates the genetic material. Mitosis can be described as consisting of stages—prophase, metaphase, anaphase, and telophase. Several checkpoints control the cell cycle. Of particular importance is the checkpoint called the restriction point, at the end of G₁. It determines a cell's fate—whether it will continue in the cell cycle and divide, stay in G₁ as a specialized cell, or die.

never divide; a cell in the deepest skin layer of a ninety-year-old may divide more if the person lives long enough. Frequent mitosis enables the embryo and fetus to grow rapidly. By birth, mitotic rate slows dramatically. Later, mitosis must maintain the numbers and positions of specialized cells in tissues and organs.

Regulation of mitosis is a daunting task. Nearly a tenth of an adult's cells are replaced every day, adding up to at least ten quadrillion mitoses in a lifetime. These divisions do not occur at random. Too little mitosis, and an injury may go unrepaired; too much, and an abnormal growth forms.

The cell cycle is a continual process, but we divide it into stages for ease of study. The two major stages are **interphase** (not dividing) and mitosis (dividing) (figure 2.18). In mitosis, a cell's chromosomes are replicated

and distributed into two daughter cells. This maintains the set of 23 chromosome pairs characteristic of a human somatic cell. Another form of cell division, meiosis, produces sperm or eggs. These cells contain half the usual amount of genetic material, or 23 single chromosomes. The next chapter discusses meiosis.

Interphase—The Cell Prepares

Interphase is a very active time. The cell not only continues the basic biochemical functions of life, but it also replicates its DNA and other subcellular structures that will be necessary to distribute into daughter cells.

Interphase is divided into two **gap (G) phases** and one **synthesis (S) phase.** During the first gap phase, (G₁), the cell synthesizes

proteins, lipids, and carbohydrates. It will utilize these molecules to surround the two new cells that form from the original one. G₁ is the period of the cell cycle that varies the most in duration among different cell types. Slow-growing cells, such as those in the liver, may remain in this phase for years, whereas the fast-growing cells in bone marrow speed through G₁ in 16 to 24 hours. Early embryonic cells may skip G₁ entirely.

The next period of interphase, **S phase,** is a time of great synthetic activity. The cell replicates its billions of DNA building blocks, chemical units called **nucleotides** that come in four varieties and that combine in sequences that encode genetic information. In most human cells, S phase takes 8 to 10 hours. Many proteins are also synthesized during this phase, including those that form the **spindle** structure that will pull the chromosomes apart. Microtubules form structures called **centrioles** that are located near the nucleus. Centriole microtubules are oriented at right angles to each other, forming paired oblong structures that organize other microtubules into the spindle.

In the second gap phase, **G₂,** the cell synthesizes more proteins. Membranes are assembled from the synthesized products of G₁ and stored as small, empty vesicles beneath the cell membrane. These vesicles will be used to enclose the two daughter cells. G₂ ends as replicated DNA winds more tightly around its associated proteins. The DNA is now so contracted that it binds stains, making the chromosomes visible when viewed under a microscope. Interphase has ended, and mitosis is imminent.

Mitosis—The Cell Divides

As mitosis begins, the chromosomes are in replicated form (figure 2.19). A replicated chromosome consists of two very long strands of identical chromosomal material, called **chromatids,** each consisting of an uninterrupted DNA molecule. The two chromatids of a replicated chromosome join at an area in each called a **centromere.** At a certain point during mitosis, the two centromeres part, allowing each chromatid pair to separate into two individual unreplicated chromosomes.

During interphase, the chromosomes are not yet condensed enough to be visible

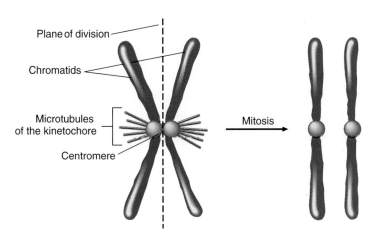

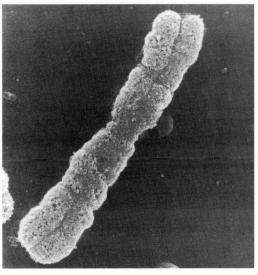

a. One replicated chromosome consisting of two chromatids

b. Two unreplicated chromosomes consisting of one chromatid each

c.

figure 2.19

Replicated and unreplicated chromosomes. (*a*) Chromosomes are replicated during S phase, before mitosis begins. The two genetically identical chromatids of a replicated chromosome join at the centromere, a region that appears as a constriction. (*b*) In anaphase centromeres part, and each chromosome now becomes a single chromatid. (*c*) A human chromosome in the midst of forming two chromatids from one. A longitudinal furrow extends from the chromosome tips inwards.

(figure 2.20*a*). During **prophase,** the first stage of mitosis, DNA coils tightly, shortening and thickening the chromosomes, rendering them visible when stained (figure 2.20*b*). This condensation allows chromosomes to separate more easily than if they were stretched out, tangled strands. Also during prophase, microtubules assemble to form the spindle. Microtubules are assembled as needed from tubulin building blocks in the cytoplasm, then they are disassembled after performing a function. Drugs used to treat cancer work by either preventing tubulin from assembling into microtubules or by preventing microtubules from falling apart into tubulin subunits. Either strategy halts division of the fastest-dividing cells, which includes cancer cells and certain normal cells.

Toward the end of prophase, the membrane surrounding the nucleus breaks down. The nucleolus is no longer visible.

Metaphase follows prophase (figure 2.20*c*). Chromosomes attach to the spindle at their centromeres and align along the center of the cell. When the centromeres part, each daughter cell will thus receive one chromatid from each replicated chromosome. Metaphase chromosomes are under great tension, but they appear motionless because they are pulled with equal force on both sides, like a tug-of-war rope pulled taut.

Next, during **anaphase,** the cell membrane indents at the center where the metaphase chromosomes line up (figure 2.20*d*). This pinching is the first sign that a band of microfilaments is forming inside the cell membrane. The centromeres part, which relieves the tension and releases one chromatid from each pair to move to opposite ends of the cell—like a tug-of-war rope breaking in the middle and the participants falling into two groups. As the chromatids separate, some spindle microtubules shorten and some lengthen. This moves the poles farther apart, stretching the dividing cell. During the very brief anaphase stage, a cell temporarily contains twice the normal number of chromosomes because each chromatid becomes an independently moving chromosome, but the cell itself has not yet physically divided in two.

In **telophase,** the final stage of mitosis, the cell looks like a dumbbell with a set of chromosomes at each end (figure 2.20*e*). The spindle falls apart, and nucleoli and the membranes around the nuclei reform at each end of the elongated cell. Division of the genetic material is now complete. Next, in cytokinesis, organelles and macromolecules distribute among the two daughter cells. The microfilament band contracts like a drawstring, separating the newly formed cells.

Key Concepts

During interphase, the cell synthesizes proteins, lipids, and carbohydrates during G_1; DNA and proteins during S phase; and still more proteins during G_2.

The cell cycle includes interphase and mitosis. During interphase, chromosomes replicate, and each consists of two chromatids attached at their centromeres. During mitosis, the cell divides.

Mitosis includes four stages. In prophase, replicated chromosomes condense. The spindle forms, and the nuclear membrane breaks down. During metaphase, chromosomes align down the center of the cell, held by the spindle. In anaphase, centromeres part, and one set of chromosomes is pulled to each end of the cell. In telophase, the cell pinches down the middle, and daughter cells separate.

figure 2.20

Mitosis in a human cell. (*a*) During interphase, chromosomes are not yet condensed, and hence not usually visible. (*b*) In prophase, chromosomes are condensed and visible when stained. The spindle assembles, centrioles appear at opposite poles of the cell, and the nuclear membrane breaks down. (*c*) In metaphase, chromosomes align along the plane of division of the spindle. (*d*) In anaphase, the centromeres part and the chromatids separate. (*e*) In telophase, the spindle disassembles and the nuclear membrane reforms. In a separate process, cytokinesis, the cytoplasm and other cellular structures distribute and pinch off into two daughter cells.

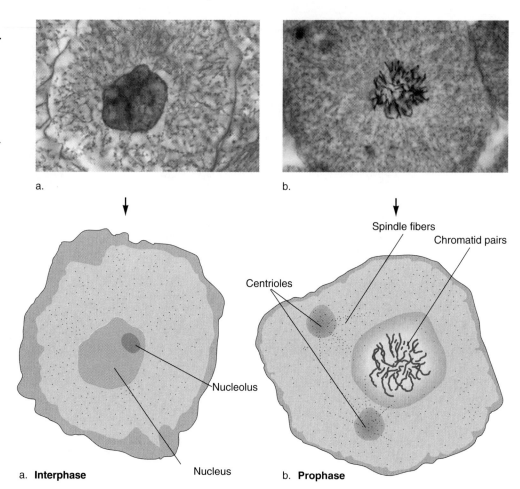

a.

b.

Spindle fibers

Chromatid pairs

Centrioles

Nucleolus

a. **Interphase**

Nucleus

b. **Prophase**

Control of the Cell Cycle

When and where a somatic cell divides is crucial to health; not surprisingly, then, the cell cycle is highly regulated. Built-in protein controls function as "checkpoints" that ensure that the proper sequence of events unfolds and that these events are paced in a way that coordinates activities within a tissue. For example, a cell cannot begin to divide until its DNA has replicated, yet it also must not replicate its DNA more than once before dividing. Checkpoints also ensure that the cell cycle pauses briefly so that most errors in the replicated DNA sequence may be repaired before they are perpetuated.

A Cellular Clock— Chromosome Ends

Mammalian cells grown (cultured) in a dish obey an internal "clock" that allows them to divide about 40 to 60 times. A connective tissue cell from a fetus, for example, divides in culture from 35 to 63 times—on average, about 50 times. However, a similar cell from an adult divides only 14 to 29 times. The number of divisions left declines with age.

How can a cell "know" how many divisions it has undergone and how many remain? The answer lies in chromosome tips, called **telomeres,** which function as a cellular clock that ticks down as pieces are lost from the very ends. Telomeres have hundreds to thousands of repeats of a specific 6-nucleotide DNA sequence. At each mitosis, the telomeres lose 50 to 200 of these nucleotides, gradually shortening the chromosome. After about 50 divisions, a critical amount of telomere DNA is lost, which signals mitosis to stop. The cell may remain alive but not divide again, or it may die. An enzyme called telomerase keeps chromosome tips long in sex cells, in cancer cells, and in a few types of normal cells that must supply many new cells, such as bone marrow cells. However, most cells do not produce telomerase and the chromosomes gradually shrink. Telomerase includes a 6-base RNA sequence that functions as a model, or template, used to add DNA nucleotides to telomeres.

Outside factors also affect a cell's mitotic clock. Crowding, which can slow or halt mitosis, is one influence. Normal cells growing in culture stop dividing when they form a one-cell-thick layer lining the container. If the layer tears, the cells that border the tear grow and divide to fill in the gap but stop dividing once it is filled. Perhaps a similar mechanism in the body limits its mitosis.

Chemical signals control the cell cycle from outside as well as from inside the cell.

Signals from Outside the Cell

Hormones and **growth factors** are biochemicals that influence mitotic rate. A hormone is a substance synthesized in a gland and transported in the bloodstream to another part of the body, where it exerts a specific effect. Hormones secreted in the brain, for example, signal the cells lining a

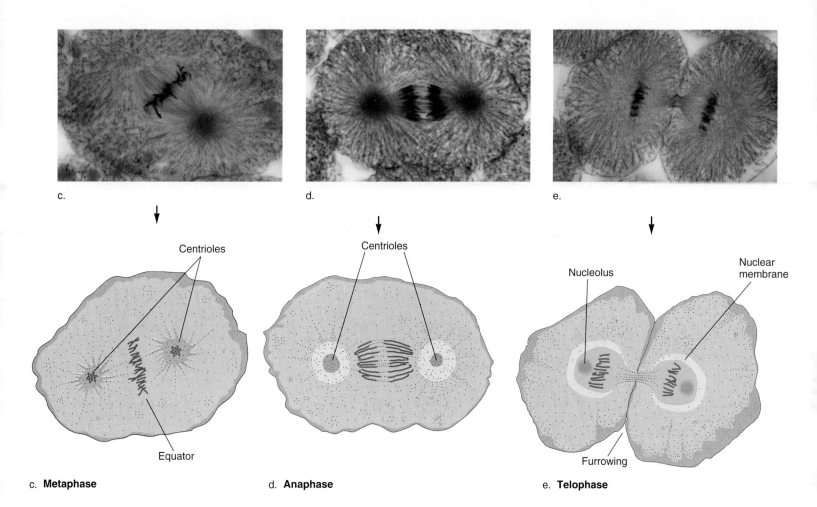

c.

d.

e.

Centrioles

Centrioles

Nucleolus

Nuclear
membrane

Equator

Furrowing

c. **Metaphase**

d. **Anaphase**

e. **Telophase**

woman's uterus to build up each month by mitosis in preparation for possible pregnancy. Growth factors act more locally. Epidermal growth factor, for example, stimulates new tissue to grow, by mitosis, beneath a scab.

Signals from Inside the Cell

Two types of proteins, cyclins and kinases, interact inside cells to activate the genes whose products carry out mitosis. Cyclins are synthesized and broken down at specific stages of the cell cycle, so their levels fluctuate. Cyclin levels rise during interphase as the cell approaches mitosis. When the level reaches a certain point, toward the end of interphase, each cyclin molecule binds to a kinase, an enzyme always present in the cell. Another type of enzyme activates the cyclin-kinase pairs, and they "turn on" the genes that trigger mitosis. As mitosis begins, the cell synthesizes enzymes that degrade cyclin. The cycle starts again as cyclin begins to build up during the next interphase.

Key Concepts

The cell cycle is tightly controlled. A cellular clock, driven by shrinking chromosome tips, limits a cell's number of divisions. Outside influences on the cell cycle include crowding, hormones, and growth factors. Within cells, cyclins and kinases interact to trigger mitosis.

Integrating Cell Function

Signal transduction, cell division, cell adhesion, and other cellular activities are interrelated. Because many types of proteins transmit messages from outside to inside cells, the varied symptoms of some inherited illnesses often reflect a breakdown in communication at the cellular level. Wiskott-Aldrich syndrome (WAS) illustrates how disruption of interacting cellular functions causes illness (figure 2.21).

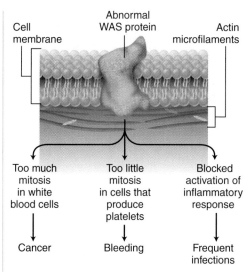

Cell
membrane

Abnormal
WAS protein

Actin
microfilaments

Too much
mitosis
in white
blood cells

Too little
mitosis
in cells that
produce
platelets

Blocked
activation of
inflammatory
response

Cancer

Bleeding

Frequent
infections

figure 2.21

In some genetic diseases, very different symptoms stem from a single defect at the cellular level. This is the case for Wiskott-Aldrich syndrome (WAS).

Simpler Than Cells

More complex than chemicals, yet not nearly as organized as cells, viruses and the even simpler prions straddle the boundary between the nonliving and the living. Although not technically alive, these entities can still have powerful effects on health.

Viruses

A virus is a nucleic acid (DNA or RNA) wrapped in a protein coat. A virus can reproduce only if it can access a host cell's energy resources and protein synthetic machinery.

A virus may have only a few genes, which encode multiprotein structures that function as modular units, like the panes of glass of a greenhouse. Ebola virus is an extremely simple, but deadly virus; HIV is complex in structure (figure 1). It is a slower killer.

Human chromosomes probably harbor viral DNA sequences that are vestiges of past infections. A DNA virus reproduces by inserting its DNA into the host cell's genetic material. An RNA virus must first copy its RNA into DNA. The enzyme reverse transcriptase copies RNA to DNA inside the host cell. The DNA representing the RNA virus then inserts into the host cell's chromosome. Because making DNA from RNA is the reverse of the usual DNA-into-RNA process in cells, RNA viruses are called retroviruses. HIV is a retrovirus.

Once viral DNA integrates into the host's DNA, it can either remain and replicate along with the host's DNA without causing harm, or it can take over the cell, eventually killing it. To do this, some of the virus's genes direct the host cell to replicate viral DNA and then use it to manufacture viral proteins at the expense of the cell's normal activities. The cell fills with viral DNA and protein, which assemble into new viruses. Soon, the cell bursts, releasing many new viruses into the body.

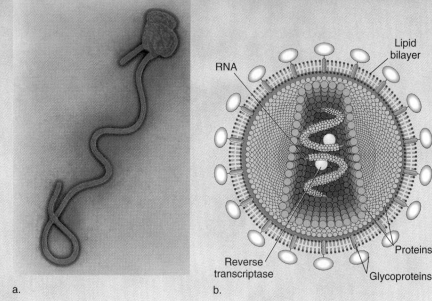

a.

b.

figure 1

(a) Ebola virus is a single strand of RNA and just seven proteins. People become infected by touching body fluids of those who have died of the infection. Symptoms progress rapidly, from headache and fever to vomiting of blood, to tearing apart of the internal organs. (b) The human immunodeficiency virus (HIV), which causes AIDS, consists of RNA surrounded by several protein layers. Once inside a human cell, the virus uses reverse transcriptase to synthesize a DNA copy of its RNA. The virus then inserts this copy into the host DNA.

Prions

Composed only of glycoproteins, prions (whose name derives from "protein infectious agent") are 1/100 to 1/1,000 the size of the smallest known virus. First described in 1966 as causing a sheep disease called scrapie, prions are an abnormal form of a glycoprotein found in the cells of many mammals that forms a gummy mass, causing different symptoms depend-

WAS is inherited on the X chromosome and therefore mostly affects males, who suffer impaired immunity, frequent infections, and white blood cell cancers. They also bleed easily because their too-few platelets are small and misshapen. The WAS gene normally encodes a protein called WASp, which lies just beneath the cell membrane in certain cells. WASp touches signaling pathway proteins above it in the membrane and contacts actin microfilaments where it dips into the cytoplasm below. When a growth factor binds to a cell surface receptor, it signals WASp to signal actin to assemble into the band structure that pulls the two cells apart as mitosis concludes. When biochemicals released in response to injury or infection signal a white blood cell, WASp stimulates actin to assemble into projections that enable the cell to migrate to the scene in an inflammatory response.

With WASp involved in so many activities, it isn't surprising that when it is abnormal, varied symptoms result. Mis-

a.

b.

figure 2

(a) Cows with bovine spongiform encephalopathy—"mad cow disease"—must be removed to stop the spread of infection (b) This child can no longer walk, stand, sit, or talk because of nervous system degeneration caused by kuru. Kuru is known only among the Fore people of eastern New Guinea. Before the 1980s, women and children became infected when preparing the brains of war dead, which were eaten. Today, the Fore people no longer practice cannibalism, and kuru has ceased.

ing on its location. The buildup usually occurs in the brain. Prions cause "mad cow disease" when animals are fed brain matter from infected cows or sheep (figure 2). Prions cause similar disorders in humans called Creutzfeldt-Jakob syndrome and kuru.

Abnormal prion protein arises from a abnormal mutant gene. Some families inherit prion-related disorders. However, abnormal prion protein can also be transmitted from one individual to another, passing the illness on in a noninherited, or acquired, fashion.

interpretation of growth signals may lead to too much mitosis, producing cancer, or too little mitosis, depleting platelets. Inability to transmit messages from sites of injury or infection cripples the inflammatory response. Revealing the underlying cause of this once-confusing inherited illness illustrates how much we can learn from cell biology.

Key Concepts

Inherited disorders that produce diverse symptoms can reflect disruption of the interaction between signal transduction, the cell membrane, the cytoskeleton, and other cellular structures and functions.

summary

1. **Cells** are the fundamental units of life and comprise the human body. Inherited illness can be understood at the cellular and molecular levels.

2. All human cells share certain features, but they are also specialized because they express different subsets of genes. Cells consist primarily of the **macromolecules carbohydrates, lipids, proteins,** and **nucleic acids.**

3. Cells are of three basic types: **prokaryotic, eukaryotic,** and **archaeal.** Prokaryotes are simple, containing **ribosomes, cell membranes,** and sometimes **cell walls.** The DNA, RNA, and protein in a prokaryotic cell are in close association because the cell lacks a nucleus. Prokaryotes include bacteria and cyanobacteria. Eukaryotes are larger and more complex than prokaryotes, with a variety of **organelle** types. Human cells are eukaryotic. The archaea have features of the other two types, plus some unique characteristics.

4. Organelles sequester related biochemical reactions, improving efficiency of life functions and protecting the cell. Along with organelles, the cell consists of **cytoplasm** and nonliving chemicals.

5. Organelles include the **nucleus,** ribosomes, **mitochondria, lysosomes,** and **peroxisomes.** The nucleus contains DNA and a **nucleolus,** which is a site of ribosome synthesis. Ribosomes provide scaffolds for protein synthesis; they exist free in the cytoplasm or complexed with the **rough ER.**

6. Organelles coordinate complex functions, including secretion, energy extraction, and enzyme activity. In secretion, the rough ER is the site of protein synthesis and folding, the **smooth ER** is the site of lipid synthesis, and the **Golgi body** packages secretion components into vesicles, which exit through the cell membrane. Enzymes in mitochondria extract energy from nutrients. Lysosomes contain enzymes that dismantle debris, and peroxisomes house enzymes that perform a variety of functions.

7. The **cytoskeleton** ("cell skeleton") is a protein framework consisting of hollow **microtubules,** which are made of tubulin, and solid **microfilaments,** which consist of actin. The cytoskeleton and the cell membrane distinguish different types of cells.

8. Cell-cell interactions include **signal transduction** and cell adhesion carried out by **cellular adhesion molecules.**

9. Coordination of cell division (**mitosis**) and cell death (**apoptosis**) maintains cell number, enabling numbers to increase during growth and development but preventing abnormal growth.

10. The **cell cycle** describes whether a cell is dividing (mitosis) or not (**interphase**). Interphase consists of G_1 **phase,** when the cell synthesizes proteins, lipids, and carbohydrates; **S phase,** when it replicates DNA; and G_2 **phase,** when it synthesizes more proteins.

11. Mitosis occurs in four stages: **prophase, metaphase, anaphase,** and **telophase.** In prophase, replicated chromosomes begin to condense, the **spindle** assembles, the nuclear membrane breaks down, and the nucleolus is no longer visible. In metaphase, the replicated chromosomes align along the center of the cell. In anaphase, the **centromeres** of replicated **chromatids** part, equally dividing the now unreplicated chromosomes among two forming daughter cells. In telophase, the new cells separate.

12. Internal and external factors control the cell cycle. **Telomere** size serves as a mitosis clock. Crowding, **hormones,** and **growth factors** signal cells from the outside; interactions of cyclins and kinases trigger mitosis from inside.

review questions

1. How can all of a person's cells contain exactly the same genetic material, yet appear to be as divergent as bone cells, nerve cells, muscle cells, and connective tissue cells?

2. Distinguish between
   a. a prokaryotic cell and a eukaryotic cell.
   b. interphase and mitosis.
   c. mitosis and apoptosis.
   d. rough ER and smooth ER.
   e. microtubules and microfilaments.
   f. a virus, a prion, and a cell.

3. What advantage does compartmentalization provide to a large and complex cell?

4. Why do many inherited conditions result from defective enzymes?

5. Describe the events that take place during secretion.

6. How are signal transduction and secretion similar?

7. Which organelle would be targeted to alter a genotype?

8. What functions do each of the following types of organelles perform?
   a. mitochondria
   b. lysosomes
   c. peroxisomes
   d. smooth ER
   e. rough ER
   f. Golgi body

9. Proteins are very diverse macromolecules. List five proteins discussed in the chapter and describe their functions in the cell or in the body.

10. What is the difference between apoptosis and necrosis?

11. How do hormones and growth factors function differently from cyclins and kinases?

12. How do chromosome tips control cell cycle rate?

13. Identify and describe the components of a virus. How does a virus differ structurally from a cell?

applied questions

1. How might abnormalities in each of the following contribute to cancer?

   a. cell adhesion

   b. signal transduction

   c. balance between mitosis and apoptosis

   d. cell cycle control

   e. telomerase activity

2. What abnormality at the cellular or molecular level lies behind each of the following disorders?

   a. cystic fibrosis

   b. adrenoleukodystrophy

   c. hereditary spherocytosis

   d. NF1

   e. leukocyte-adhesion deficiency

3. In the inherited condition glycogen cardiomyopathy, teens develop muscle weakness, including the heart muscle. Muscle cell samples contain huge lysosomes swollen with the carbohydrate glycogen. Describe the cause of the illness on a molecular level.

4. A woman gives birth to two children with the same extreme muscle weakness. The woman's sister also has a child with the condition, but the sisters have three brothers who each have several healthy, unaffected children. How might this condition be inherited?

5. Ann has inherited Sly disease. She is mentally retarded, has a heart defect, and will probably not live past her second birthday. Ann lacks an enzyme that normally breaks down glycolipid molecules called mucopolysaccharides. Which two organelles might be causing her illness? (Hint: One affects the phenotype, one the genotype.)

6. Explain how a single defect at the cellular and molecular levels causes the diverse symptoms of Wiskott-Aldrich syndrome.

7. Explain how different types of muscular dystrophy arise.

suggested readings

Armelagos, George J. January/February 1998. The viral superhighway. *The Sciences.* The ease of travel has spread new contagions.

Dubowitz, Victor. February 27, 1997. The muscular dystrophies—clarity or chaos? *The New England Journal of Medicine,* vol. 336. Muscular dystrophy is not a single disorder, which reflects the varied proteins important in muscle contraction.

Featherstone, Carol. January 3, 1997. The many faces of WAS protein. *Science,* vol. 275. A single protein defect causes several symptoms.

Friedman, K. J. et al. January 1998. Cystic fibrosis transmembrane regulator mutations among African Americans. *The American Journal of Human Genetics.* CF is rare among blacks, but recent discoveries will make genetic testing possible for this population.

Lewis, Ricki. February 6, 1995. Apoptosis activity: Cell death establishes itself as a lively research field. *The Scientist,* vol. 9. Cell death is a normal part of life.

Lewis, Ricki. February 19, 1996. Telomere findings may yield tips for treating cancer, geriatric disorders. *The Scientist,* vol. 10. Cancer cells ignore the telomere cell division clock.

Lewis, Ricki. September 1998. Telomere tales. *BioScience.* Understanding how telomeres serve as a cell division clock has diverse practical applications.

Palevitz, Barry, and Ricki Lewis. December 8, 1998. Show me the data: a Nobel lesson in the process of science. *The Scientist.* A comparison of the discovery of prions and an unpopular view of HIV.

Parolini, O., et al. January 29, 1998. X-linked Wiskott-Aldrich syndrome in a girl. *The New England Journal of Medicine,* vol. 338. Mutation and an unusual pattern of X inactivation led to expression of this sex-linked disorder in a girl.

Short, Nicholas. December 8, 1994. Cycles of growth and destruction. *Nature,* vol. 372. The cell cycle must be carefully controlled and coordinated to avoid disrupting the delicate relationship between cell division and cell death.

Thompson, Dick. September 28, 1992. The glue of life. *Time.* People lacking adhesion molecules live dangerously.

Travis, Gabriel H. March 1998. Mechanisms of cell death in the inherited retinal degenerations. *The American Journal of Human Genetics.* Apoptosis in the wrong place lies behind several forms of inherited blindness.

Valle, David, and Jutta Gartner. February 25, 1993. Penetrating the peroxisome. *Nature,* vol. 361. A missing or defective peroxisomal enzyme causes ALD—but it wasn't the one researchers suspected.

Welsh, Michael J. December 1995. Cystic fibrosis. *Scientific American.* The varied symptoms of this common inherited illness all stem from a defect at the cellular level.

chapter three

Human Development

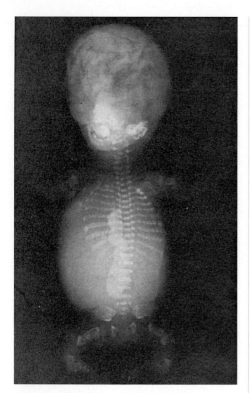

figure 3.1

Osteogenesis imperfecta breaks bones. Numerous skeletal injuries are already present at birth in some infants who have inherited osteogenesis imperfecta. This fetus has broken leg bones.

Genes Operate Throughout Life

The young mother was distraught when she brought her ten-month-old son to the emergency room. His arm had begun dangling at an abnormal angle after he had hauled himself up to a standing position for the first time. Two months earlier, the child had inexplicably broken two fingers, also following normal activity. Concerned, the child's pediatrician consulted the medical records for the boy's older sister and found that she, too, had suffered an unusually large number of broken bones. He would have to question the parents very carefully and run some tests before confronting them about child abuse.

The reason for the children's broken bones turned out to be not because of the parents' behavior, but because of their genes. The children's unusually fragile bones might even have broken before birth (figure 3.1). Both children had inherited a rare form of osteogenesis imperfecta from their healthy parents, who were carriers. As a result, the children lacked a type of collagen, which is a protein that is part of bone.

Genes orchestrate our physiology throughout life, and inherited disorders therefore affect people of all ages. Some genetic conditions, such as Duchenne muscular dystrophy and cystic fibrosis, appear in early childhood, whereas others, such as Huntington disease and Alzheimer disease, do not affect health for many years. No matter when inherited disease symptoms begin, the genes that cause them are present from conception.

The Reproductive System

The formation of a new individual begins with the **sperm** and the ovum (more precisely called an **oocyte**). Sperm and oocytes provide a mechanism for starting a new life and mix genetic contributions from past generations. As a result, each new individual has a unique combination of traits.

Sperm and oocytes are produced in the reproductive system. The reproductive systems of the human male and female are similarly organized. Each system has paired structures, called **gonads,** in which the sperm and oocytes are manufactured; a network of tubules to transport these cells; and hormones and glandular secretions that control the process.

The Male

Sperm cells are manufactured within a 125-meter-long network of **seminiferous tubules,** which are packed into paired, oval organs called **testes** (sometimes called testicles) (figure 3.2). The testes are the male gonads. They lie outside the abdomen within a sac called the scrotum. Their location outside the abdominal cavity allows the testes to maintain a lower temperature than the rest of the body; this lower temperature is necessary for the sperm cells to develop properly. Leading from each testis is a tightly coiled tube, the **epididymis,** in which sperm cells mature and are stored; each epididymis continues into another tube, the **vas deferens.** Each vas deferens bends behind the bladder to join the **urethra,** the tube that carries both sperm and urine out through the **penis.**

Along the sperm's path, three glands produce secretions. The vasa deferentia pass through the prostate gland, which produces a thin, milky, alkaline fluid that activates the sperm to swim. Opening into the vas deferens is a duct from the **seminal vesicles,** which secrete fructose, the sugar sperm require for energy, plus hormonelike prostaglandins, which may stimulate contractions in the female reproductive tract that help sperm and ovum meet. The **bulbourethral glands,** each about the size of a pea, join the urethra where it passes through the body wall. They secrete an alkaline mucus that coats the urethra before sperm are released. All of these secretions combine to form the **seminal fluid** in which the sperm cells travel.

During sexual arousal, the penis becomes erect so that it can penetrate and deposit sperm in the female reproductive tract. At the peak of sexual stimulation, a pleasurable sensation called **orgasm** occurs, accompanied by rhythmic muscular contractions that eject the sperm from each vas deferens through the urethra and out the penis. The discharge of sperm from the penis is called ejaculation. One human ejaculation typically delivers about 100 million sperm cells.

The Female

The female sex cells develop within paired organs in the abdomen called **ovaries** (figure 3.3). The ovaries are the female gonads. Within each ovary of a newborn female are about a million immature oocytes. An individual oocyte is surrounded by nourishing **follicle cells.** Each ovary houses oocytes in different stages of development. After puberty, once a month, one ovary releases the most mature oocyte. Beating cilia sweep the mature oocyte into the fingerlike projections of one of two **fallopian tubes.** The tube carries the oocyte into a muscular saclike organ, the **uterus,** or womb.

The lower end of the uterus narrows to form the **cervix,** which opens into the tube-like **vagina** that exits from the body. The vaginal opening is protected on the outside by two pairs of fleshy folds. At the upper

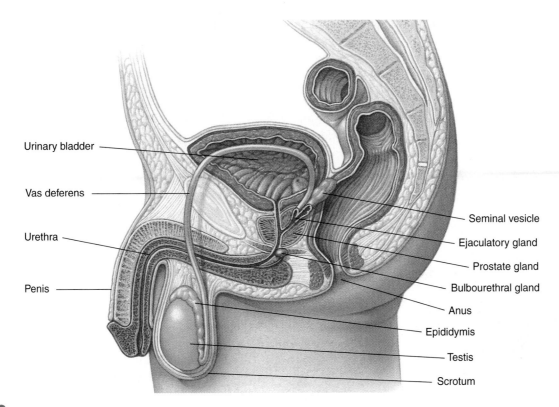

Urinary bladder

Vas deferens

Urethra

Penis

Seminal vesicle

Ejaculatory gland

Prostate gland

Bulbourethral gland

Anus

Epididymis

Testis

Scrotum

figure 3.2

The human male reproductive system. Sperm cells are manufactured within the seminiferous tubules, which tightly wind within the testes, which descend into the scrotum. Sperm mature and are stored in the epididymis and exit through the vas deferens. The paired vasa deferentia join in the urethra, through which seminal fluids exit the body. The prostate gland, seminal vesicles, and bulbourethral glands add secretions to the sperm cells to form seminal fluid.

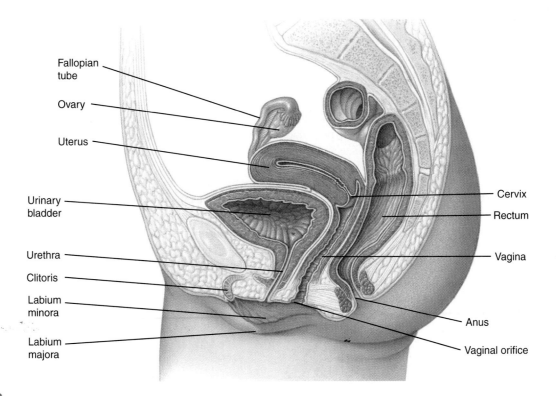

Fallopian tube

Ovary

Uterus

Urinary bladder

Urethra

Clitoris

Labium minora

Labium majora

Cervix

Rectum

Vagina

Anus

Vaginal orifice

figure 3.3

The human female reproductive system. Immature egg cells are packed into the paired ovaries. Once a month after puberty, one oocyte is released from an ovary and is drawn into a nearby fallopian tube. If a sperm fertilizes the oocyte in the fallopian tube, the fertilized ovum continues into the uterus, where for nine months it develops into a new individual. If the oocyte is not fertilized, it is expelled, along with the built-up uterine lining, from the body.

juncture of both pairs is a 2-centimeter-long structure called the **clitoris,** which is anatomically similar to the penis. Rubbing the clitoris triggers female orgasm. Hormones control the cycle of oocyte maturation and the preparation of the uterus to nurture a fertilized ovum.

Key Concepts

Reproductive systems have paired gonads that house reproductive cells, tubes for transporting these cells, and glands. Sperm develop in the seminiferous tubules, mature and collect in each epididymis, enter the vasa deferentia, and join the urethra in the penis. The prostate gland adds an alkaline fluid, seminal vesicles add fructose and prostaglandins, and bulbourethral glands secrete mucus.

In the female, ovaries contain oocytes. Each month, one oocyte is released from an ovary and is captured by the fingerlike projections of a fallopian tube, which leads to the uterus. If the oocyte is fertilized, it nestles into the uterine lining and develops. Otherwise, it exits the body during the menstrual flow. Hormones control the cycle of oocyte development.

Meiosis

The sperm and oocyte are **gametes,** which are also called sex cells. Unlike other cells in the human body, gametes contain just 23 different chromosomes—half the usual amount of genetic material. Somatic (nonsex) cells contain 23 pairs or 46 chromosomes. Gametes are **haploid** ($1n$), which means that they have only one of each type of chromosome. Somatic cells are **diploid** ($2n$), signifying their double chromosomal load.

Halving the number of chromosomes during gamete formation makes sense. If the sperm and oocyte each contained 46 chromosomes, then when they joined, the fertilized ovum would contain twice the normal number of chromosomes, or 92. Such a genetically overloaded cell usually does not support normal development. About one in a million newborns has three or four sets of chromosomes, but they have problems in all organ systems and live only a few days.

Gametes form from special cells, called germ-line cells, in a type of cell division called **meiosis** that halves the chromosome number. A further process, maturation, sculpts the distinctive characteristics of sperm and oocyte, which are completely different in appearance. The organelle-packed oocyte has 90,000 times the volume of the streamlined, top-heavy sperm.

Stages of Meiosis

Meiosis entails two divisions of the genetic material. The first division is called **reduction division** (or meiosis I) because it reduces the number of chromosomes from 46 to 23. The second division, called the **equational division** (or meiosis II) is like mitosis, producing four cells from the two cells formed in the first division (figure 3.4).

As in mitosis, meiosis occurs after an interphase period when DNA is replicated (table 3.1). The cell in which meiosis begins has **homologous pairs** of chromosomes, or homologs for short. Homologs look alike and carry the genes for the same traits in the same sequence. One homolog comes from the person's mother, and one from the father. When meiosis begins, the DNA of each homolog replicates, forming two chromatids joined at two centromeres. The chromosomes are not yet condensed enough to be visible under a microscope.

After interphase, prophase I (so called because it is the prophase of meiosis I) begins as replicated chromosomes condense and become visible (figure 3.5a). A spindle forms. Toward the middle of prophase I, the homologs line up next to one another, gene by gene, in a phenomenon called **synapsis.** A mixture of RNA and protein holds the chromosome pairs together.

Toward the end of prophase I, the synapsed chromosomes separate but remain attached at a few points along their lengths. At this time, the homologs exchange parts in a process called **crossing over** (figures 3.5b, 3.6). After crossing over, each homolog contains genes from each parent. (Prior to this, all of the genes on a homolog were derived from one parent.) New gene combinations arise from crossing over when the parents carry different forms of the same gene, called **alleles.**

To understand how crossing over mixes trait combinations, consider a simplified example. Suppose that homologs carry genes for hair color, eye color, and finger length. One of the chromosomes carries alleles for blond hair, blue eyes, and short fingers. Its homolog carries alleles for black hair, brown eyes, and long fingers. After crossing over, one of the chromosomes might bear alleles for blond hair, brown eyes, and long fingers, and the other bears alleles for black hair, blue eyes, and short fingers. The daughter cells that result from meiosis will carry a mix of the parent cell traits.

Meiosis continues in metaphase I, when the homologs align down the center of the cell (figure 3.5c). Each member of a homolog pair attaches to a spindle fiber at opposite poles (figure 3.5d). The pattern in which the chromosomes align during metaphase I is important in generating genetic diversity. For each homolog pair, the pole the maternally- or paternally-derived member goes to is random. The situation is analogous to the number of different ways that 23 boys and 23 girls could line up in

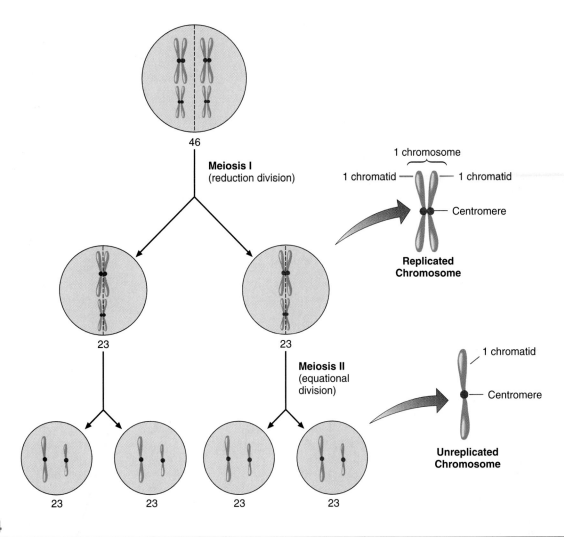

figure 3.4

Meiosis is a special form of cell division that sets aside haploid gametes. In humans, the first meiotic division reduces the number of chromosomes to 23, all in the replicated form. In the second meiotic division, each cell from the first division undergoes a mitosis-like division. The result of the two divisions of meiosis is four haploid cells. (The illustration depicts only two chromosomes.)

table 3.1

Comparison of Mitosis and Meiosis

Mitosis	Meiosis
One division	Two divisions
Two daughter cells per cycle	Four daughter cells per cycle
Daughter cells genetically identical	Daughter cells genetically different
Chromosome number of daughter cells same as that of parent cell (2n)	Chromosome number of daughter cells half that of parent cell (1n)
Occurs in somatic cells	Occurs in germ-line cells
Occurs throughout life cycle	In humans, completes after sexual maturity
Used for growth, repair, and asexual reproduction	Used for sexual reproduction, in which new gene combinations arise

boy-girl pairs. The greater the number of chromosomes, the greater the genetic diversity generated.

For two pairs of homologs, four (2^2) different metaphase configurations are possible (figure 3.7). For three pairs of homologs, eight (2^3) configurations can occur. Our 23 chromosome pairs can therefore line up in 8,388,608 (2^{23}) different ways. This random arrangement of the members of homolog pairs in metaphase is called **independent assortment.** It accounts for a basic law of inheritance discussed in the next chapter.

Homologs separate in anaphase I (figure 3.5d) and finish moving to opposite

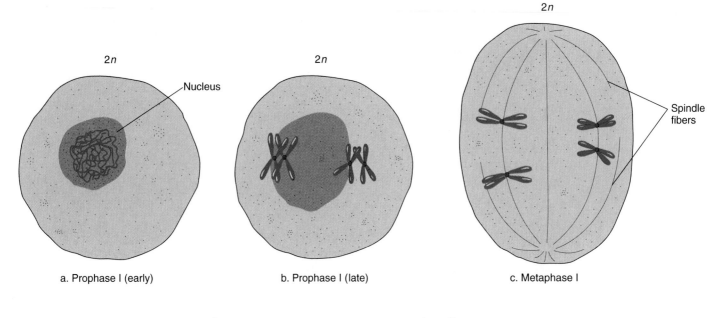

a. Prophase I (early)

b. Prophase I (late)

c. Metaphase I

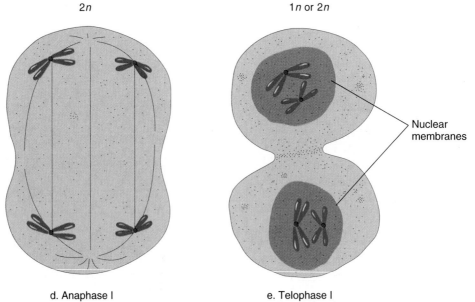

d. Anaphase I

e. Telophase I

figure 3.5

Meiosis I. (*a*) In early prophase I, replicated chromosomes condense and become visible as a tangle within the nucleus. (*b*) By late prophase I, the pairs align and homologs cross over. (*c*) In metaphase I, spindle fibers align the homologs. (*d*) In anaphase I, the homologs move to opposite poles. (*e*) In telophase I, the genetic material is partitioned into two daughter nuclei, each containing only one homolog from each pair.

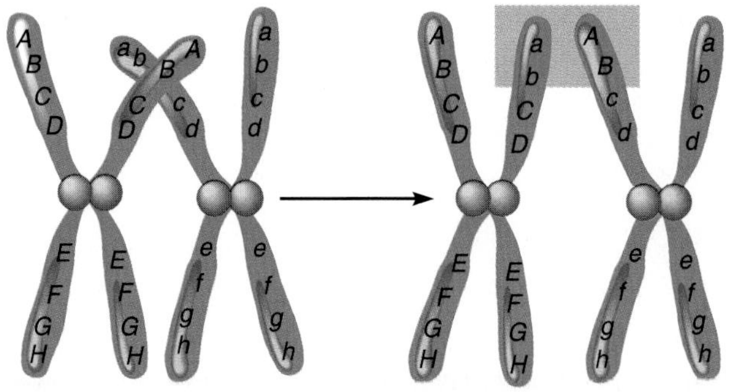

figure 3.6

Crossing over recombines genes. The capital and lowercase forms of the same letter represent different forms (alleles) of the same gene.

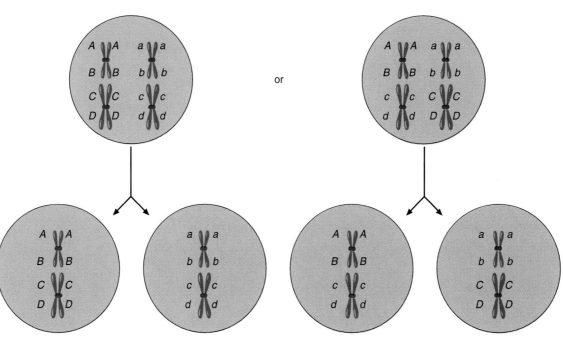

or

figure 3.7

Independent assortment. The pattern in which homologs align during metaphase I determines the combination of maternally and paternally derived chromosomes in the daughter cells. This illustration traces two chromosome pairs, distinguished by size, with different alleles of the same gene indicated by capital and lowercase forms of the same letter. Two pairs of chromosomes can align in two different ways to produce four different possibilities in the daughter cells. The potential variability meiosis generates skyrockets when all 23 chromosome pairs and the effects of crossing over are considered.

poles in telophase I (figure 3.5e). During a second interphase, chromosomes unfold into very thin threads. Proteins are manufactured, but the genetic material is not replicated a second time. It is the single DNA replication, followed by the double division of meiosis, that halves the chromosome number.

Prophase II marks the start of the second meiotic division. The chromosomes are again condensed and visible (figure 3.8a). In metaphase II (figure 3.8b), the replicated chromosomes align down the center of the cell. In anaphase II (figure 3.8c), the centromeres part and the chromatids move to opposite poles. In telophase II (figure 3.8d), nuclear envelopes form around the four nuclei, which then separate into individual cells (figure 3.8e). The net result of meiosis is four haploid cells, each carrying a new assortment of genes and chromosomes.

Meiosis and Genetic Variability

Meiosis generates astounding genetic variety. Any one of a person's more than 8 million possible combinations of chromosomes can combine with any one of the more than 8 million combinations of his or her partner, raising potential variability to more than 70 trillion ($8,388,608^2$) genetically unique individuals! Crossing over contributes even more genetic variability.

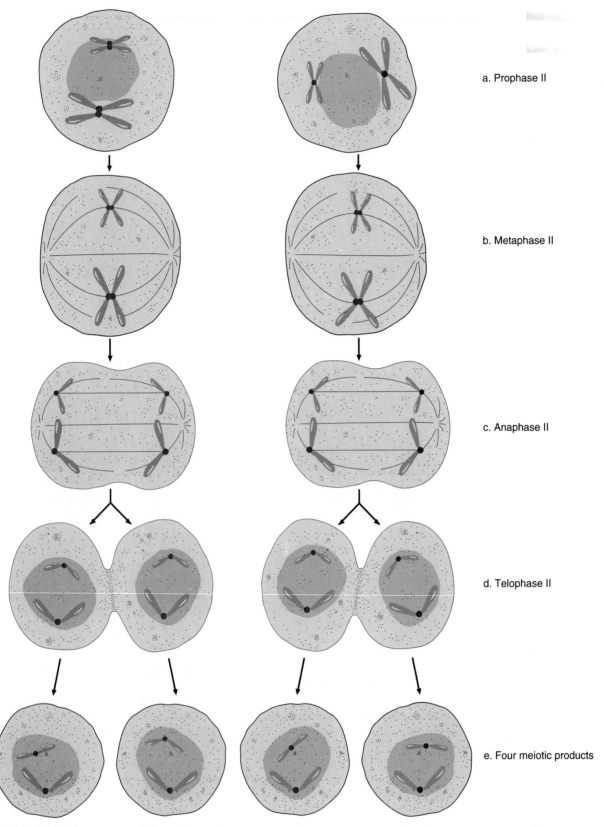

a. Prophase II

b. Metaphase II

c. Anaphase II

d. Telophase II

e. Four meiotic products

figure 3.8

Meiosis II. The second meiotic division is very similar to mitosis. (*a*) In prophase II, chromosomes are visible. (*b*) In metaphase II, the spindle aligns the chromosomes. (*c*) In anaphase II, centromeres part, and each chromatid pair divides into two chromosomes, which are pulled toward opposite poles. (*d*) In telophase II, the two separated sets of chromosomes are enclosed in separate nuclei and then are partitioned into two daughter cells. (*e*) The net yield from the entire process of meiosis: four haploid daughter cells.

Gamete Maturation

Meiosis occurs in both sexes, but the sperm looks nothing like the oocyte. Although each type of gamete has a haploid set of chromosomes, different distributions of other cell components create the differences between them.

Sperm Development

Spermatogenesis, the specialization of sperm cells, begins with a **spermatogonium,** a diploid cell. A spermatogonium divides, yielding two daughter cells: one daughter cell continues to specialize into a mature sperm, and the other remains unspecialized as a stem cell that retains the capacity to divide.

Bridges of cytoplasm join several spermatogonia, and their daughter cells continue meiosis together. As they mature, these spermatogonia accumulate cytoplasm and replicate their DNA, becoming **primary spermatocytes.**

During reduction division (meiosis I), each primary spermatocyte divides, forming two equal-sized haploid cells called **secondary spermatocytes** (figure 3.9). In meiosis II, each secondary spermatocyte divides to yield two equal-sized **spermatids.** Each spermatid then specializes, developing the characteristic sperm tail, or

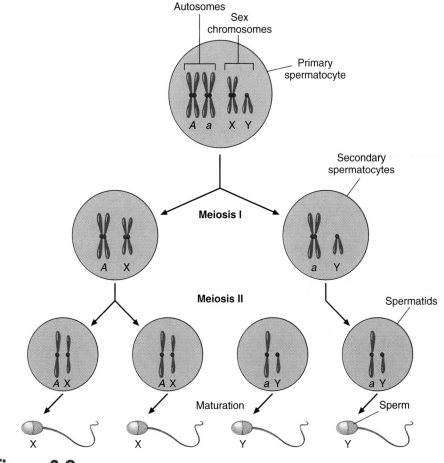

figure 3.9

Sperm formation. Human primary spermatocytes have the diploid number of 23 chromosome pairs. The large pair of chromosomes represents a pair of autosomes, and the small pair represents the sex chromosomes. A human cell contains 22 pairs of autosomes.

flagellum. The base of the tail has many mitochondria and ATP molecules that form an energy system that propels sperm inside the female reproductive tract. After spermatid formation, some of the cytoplasm connecting the cells falls away, leaving mature, tadpole-shaped **spermatozoa,** or sperm (figures 3.10 and 3.11). A sperm, which is a mere 0.0023 inch long, must travel about 7 inches to reach an oocyte.

Each sperm cell consists of a tail, body or midpiece, and head region. A small protrusion on the front end, the **acrosome,** contains enzymes that help the cell penetrate the oocyte. Within the bulbous sperm head, DNA is wrapped around proteins. The sperm's DNA at this time is genetically inactive. A male manufactures trillions of sperm in his lifetime. Only a very few will near an oocyte.

Meiosis in the male has some built-in protections against sperm causing birth defects. Spermatogonia exposed to toxins tend to be so damaged that they never mature into sperm. More mature sperm cells exposed to toxins are often so damaged that they cannot swim. However, seminal fluid can carry some drugs. These can affect a fetus by harming the uterus or by entering the woman's circulation and passing to the **placenta,** the organ connecting pregnant woman to fetus. Cocaine can affect a fetus by attaching to thousands of binding sites on sperm without harming the cells or impeding their movements. Therefore, sperm can ferry cocaine to an oocyte, potentially affecting the embryo that may develop. The antianxiety drug diazepam (Valium) has been shown in one study to damage chromosomes of developing sperm.

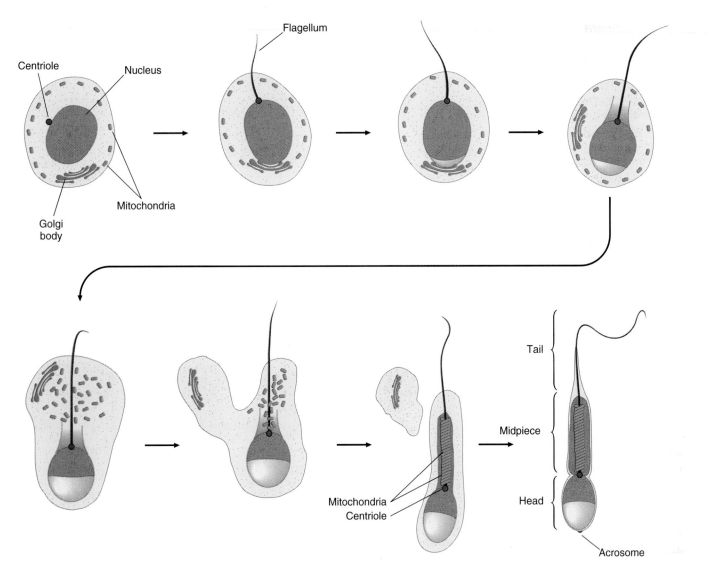

figure 3.10

From spermatogonium to spermatozoon. The head of the mature sperm consists mostly of the cell's nucleus. The tail elongates as excess cytoplasm is stripped away. Mitochondria provide energy.

The acrosome contains enzymes that penetrate the protective layers around the oocyte.

figure 3.11

Human sperm. (a) Scanning electron micrograph of human sperm cells. (b) When human sperm were first seen in the microscope, they were thought to be infectious microbes. This 1694 illustration presents another popular idea about the role of sperm—some people thought they carried a preformed human, called a homunculus.

a.

b.

Ovum Development

Meiosis in the female, called **oogenesis** (egg making), begins, as does spermatogenesis, with a diploid cell. This cell is called an **oogonium.** Unlike the male cells, oogonia are not attached to each other, but they are surrounded by a layer of follicle cells. Each oogonium grows, accumulates cytoplasm and replicates its DNA, becoming a **primary oocyte.** The ensuing meiotic division in oogenesis, unlike that in spermatogenesis, produces cells of different sizes.

In meiosis I, the primary oocyte divides into two cells: a small cell with very little cytoplasm, called a **polar body,** and a much larger cell called a **secondary oocyte** (figure 3.12). Each cell is haploid. In meiosis II, the tiny polar body may divide to yield two polar bodies of equal size, or it may simply decompose. The secondary oocyte, however, divides unequally in meiosis II to produce another small polar body and the mature egg cell, or **ovum,** which contains a large amount of cytoplasm. In short, most of the cytoplasm among the four meiotic products concentrates in only one of them, the ovum. The woman's body absorbs the polar bodies, and they normally play no further role in development. However, genetic tests on polar bodies can reveal whether or not an oocyte contains a particular disease-causing gene (figure 3.13).

At birth, a female's million or so oocytes arrest in prophase I. By puberty, 400,000 remain. After puberty, meiosis I continues in one or several oocytes each month, but halts again at metaphase II. In response to specific hormonal cues each month, one secondary oocyte is released from an ovary; this is **ovulation.** If a sperm penetrates the oocyte membrane, then female meiosis completes, and a **fertilized ovum** forms. Female meiosis only finishes if fertilization occurs. If the secondary oocyte is not fertilized, it degenerates and leaves the body in the menstrual flow.

A female ovulates about 400 oocytes between puberty and menopause. A sperm cell is likely to enter only a few of these oocytes. Only 1 in 3 of the oocytes that do meet and merge with a sperm cell will continue to grow, divide, and specialize to eventually form a new human life.

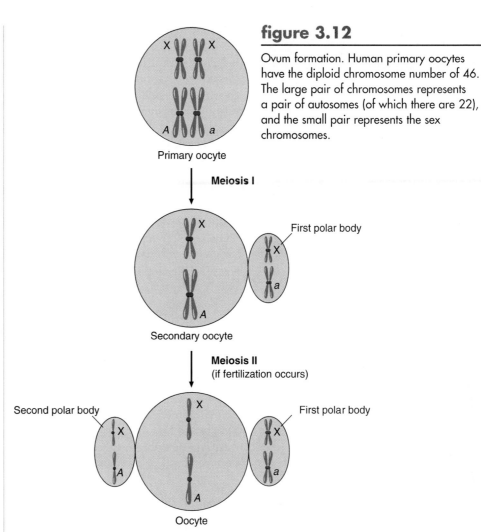

figure 3.12

Ovum formation. Human primary oocytes have the diploid chromosome number of 46. The large pair of chromosomes represents a pair of autosomes (of which there are 22), and the small pair represents the sex chromosomes.

Primary oocyte

Meiosis I

First polar body

Secondary oocyte

Meiosis II
(if fertilization occurs)

Second polar body

First polar body

Oocyte

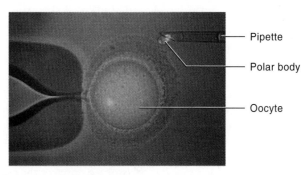

Pipette

Polar body

Oocyte

figure 3.13

The fact that an oocyte shares a woman's divided genetic material with a much smaller polar body is the basis for a new technique to select oocytes that do not contain a specific disease-causing allele. If a woman is known to be a carrier of a genetic disorder and the polar body contains a disease-causing allele, the fact that the oocyte has received the wild type version of the gene is inferred. Polar body biopsy is possible because the polar body remains attached to the oocyte. Small pipettes are used to do the manipulations.

Spermatogonia divide mitotically, yielding one stem cell and one cell that accumulates cytoplasm and becomes a primary spermatocyte. In meiosis I, each spermatogonium halves its genetic material to form two secondary spermatocytes. In meiosis II, each secondary spermatocyte divides, yielding two equal-sized spermatids attached by bridges of cytoplasm.

Maturing spermatids separate and shed some cytoplasm. A mature sperm has a tail, body, and head, with an enzyme-containing acrosome on the tip.

An oogonium accumulates cytoplasm and replicates its chromosomes, becoming a primary oocyte. In meiosis I, the primary oocyte divides, forming a small polar body and a large, haploid secondary oocyte. In meiosis II, the secondary oocyte divides, yielding another small polar body and a mature ovum. Oocytes arrest at prophase I until puberty, when one or several oocytes continues meiosis during ovulation. Meiosis completes at fertilization.

Prenatal Development

Fertilization

Hundreds of millions of sperm cells are deposited in the vagina during sexual intercourse. A sperm cell can survive in the woman's body for up to 6 days, but it can only fertilize the oocyte in the 12 to 24 hours after ovulation.

The woman's body helps sperm reach an oocyte. A process called **capacitation** in the woman's body chemically activates sperm. The oocyte also secretes a chemical that attracts sperm. Sperm are also assisted by contractions of the female's muscles, by their tails moving, and by upwardly moving mucus propelled by waving, hairlike fringes on cells of the female reproductive tract. Still, only 200 or so sperm near the oocyte.

When a sperm contacts the ring of follicle cells guarding a secondary oocyte, its tip (the acrosome) bursts, releasing enzymes that bore through a protective layer of glycoprotein called the **zona pellucida.** Fertilization, or conception, begins when the outer membranes of the sperm and secondary oocyte meet (figure 3.14). The encounter is dramatic. A wave of electricity spreads physical and chemical changes across the entire oocyte surface—changes that keep other sperm out. If more than one sperm entered an oocyte, the resulting cell would have too much genetic material to develop normally. However, when two sperm fertilize two oocytes, fraternal twins result.

Within 12 hours of the sperm's penetration, the nuclear membrane of the ovum disappears, and the two sets of chromosomes, called **pronuclei,** approach one another. Fertilization completes when the two genetic packages meet, forming the genetic instructions for a new individual. Reading 3.1 describes cloning, another way to begin development of a new organism.

The fertilized ovum is called a **zygote.** For the first two weeks of prenatal development, the structure is called a **preimplantation embryo,** or preembryo for short.

Cleavage and Implantation

About a day after fertilization, the zygote divides mitotically, beginning a period of rapid cell division called **cleavage** (figures 3.15 and 3.16). The resulting early cells are called **blastomeres.** When they have divided to form a solid ball of 16 or more cells, the preembryo is called a **morula** (Latin for "mulberry," which it resembles).

During cleavage, organelles and molecules from the secondary oocyte's cytoplasm still control cellular activity, but some of the preembryo's genes begin to function. The ball of cells hollows out, and its center fills with fluid as it becomes a **blastocyst.** Some of the cells form a clump called the **inner cell mass.** These cells will eventually form the embryo.

A week after conception, the blastocyst begins to nestle into the rich lining of the woman's uterus. This event, called implantation, takes about a week. As it starts, the outermost cells of the preembryo, called the **trophoblast,** secrete **human chorionic gonadotropin** (hCG), a hormone which prevents menstruation. HCG detected in a woman's urine or blood indicates pregnancy.

The Embryo Forms

During the second week of prenatal development, a space, the **amniotic cavity,** forms between the inner cell mass and the outer cells anchored to the uterine lining. The inner cell mass then flattens into a two-layered disc. The layer nearest the amniotic cavity is the **ectoderm** (Greek for "outside skin"). The inner layer, closer to the blastocyst cavity, is the **endoderm** (Greek for "inside skin"). Shortly after, a third layer forms in the middle, called the **mesoderm** ("middle skin"). This three-layered structure is the **gastrula,** and the cell layers are called **primary germ layers** (figure 3.17). The forming individual is now considered an **embryo.** In an embryo, the cells are no longer all the same.

When germ layers form, cell fates are determined. The position of a cell in relation to other cells in the embryo triggers the expression of some genes but not others. For example, an ectoderm cell destined to become part of the outer skin would not express its muscle protein genes even though they are present but would use the gene for keratin, an abundant skin protein.

Supportive Structures

During the embryo period—weeks 3 through 8 of pregnancy—organs develop and structures form that support and protect the embryo. These include chorionic villi, the placenta, the yolk sac, the allantois, the umbilical cord, and the amniotic sac.

By the third week after conception, fingerlike projections called **chorionic villi** extend from the area of the embryonic disc close to the uterine wall. They dip into pools of the pregnant woman's blood. The blood systems of the pregnant woman and the embryo are separate, but nutrients and oxygen diffuse across the chorionic villi from the woman's circulation to the embryo, and wastes leave the embryo's circulation and enter her circulation, to be excreted.

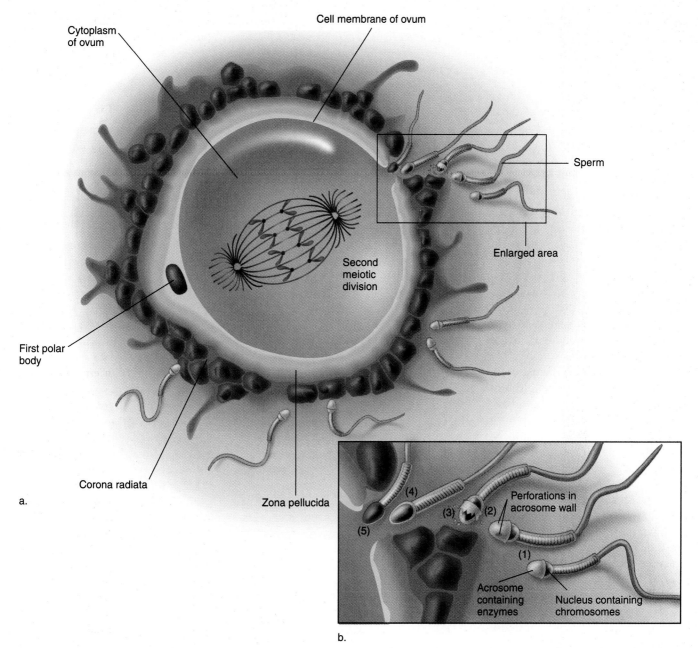

Cytoplasm
of ovum

Cell membrane of ovum

Sperm

Enlarged area

Second
meiotic
division

First polar
body

Corona radiata

a.

Zona pellucida

(4)

(3)

(2)

(5)

Perforations in
acrosome wall

(1)

Acrosome
containing
enzymes

Nucleus containing
chromosomes

b.

figure 3.14

At the moment of fertilization (*a*), the sperm's acrosome bursts (*b*), spilling forth enzymes that help the sperm's nucleus enter the oocyte.

By 10 weeks, the placenta is fully formed. This structure will connect woman to fetus for the rest of the pregnancy. The placenta secretes hormones that maintain pregnancy and alter the woman's metabolism to shuttle nutrients to the fetus.

Other structures nurture the developing embryo. The **yolk sac** manufactures blood cells, as does the **allantois,** a membrane surrounding the embryo that gives rise to the umbilical blood vessels. The umbilical cord forms around these vessels and attaches to the center of the placenta. Toward the end of the embryonic period, the yolk sac shrinks, and the amniotic sac swells with fluid that cushions the embryo and maintains a constant temperature and pressure. The amniotic fluid, which contains fetal urine and cells, comes from the pregnant woman's blood.

Two of the supportive structures that develop during pregnancy are the basis of prenatal tests, discussed in detail in chapter 11. In **amniocentesis,** a sample of amniotic fluid is taken after the fifteenth week of pregnancy, and fetal cells in the fluid are examined for biochemical and chromosome anomalies. **Chorionic villus sampling** examines chromosomes from cells snipped off the chorionic villi at 10 weeks.

When in February 1997, Scottish researchers announced that they had cloned a sheep, the news made headlines everywhere. (Clones are genetically identical individuals.) "Dolly" was conceived when a nucleus from a mammary gland cell of a six-year-old sheep was placed into an oocyte from another type of sheep whose nucleus had been removed. The cytoplasm of the oocyte then turned on all the genes in the nucleus required to restart development.

Dolly didn't surprise biologists as much as she did the rest of the world—researchers had cloned amphibians back in the 1960s, and cloning has been part of agricultural practice for more than a decade. But these earlier cloned animals had been generated using nuclei from cells of an embryo. Cloning from an adult cell is more challenging, because many of its genes are shut off to sculpt the characteristics of a specialized, or differentiated, cell.

The Scottish researchers succeeded in cloning from an adult cell where others had failed because of a variation on the cloning "recipe"—they "starved" the donor cells, depriving them of nutrients so that temporarily they left the cell cycle and were neither dividing nor preparing to divide. Because the chromosomes were not replicating, there was less chance of chromosomal abnormalities occurring, which had botched many past cloning attempts. Also, the "Dolly" experiment may have worked because the donor mammary gland cell might not have been specialized and therefore was easier to coax into a new beginning. The mammary gland contains many cells that can change gene expression as the gland transforms from an inactive structure to an actively secreting milk machine.

The experiment that let to Dolly was not simple—she was one of 277 attempts

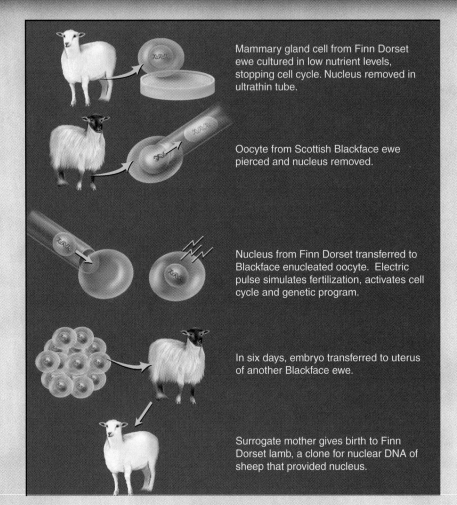

Mammary gland cell from Finn Dorset ewe cultured in low nutrient levels, stopping cell cycle. Nucleus removed in ultrathin tube.

Oocyte from Scottish Blackface ewe pierced and nucleus removed.

Nucleus from Finn Dorset transferred to Blackface enucleated oocyte. Electric pulse simulates fertilization, activates cell cycle and genetic program.

In six days, embryo transferred to uterus of another Blackface ewe.

Surrogate mother gives birth to Finn Dorset lamb, a clone for nuclear DNA of sheep that provided nucleus.

figure 1

The steps of cloning.

(figure 1). Despite the difficulty of cloning, and the fact that we do not even know if it is possible in humans, many countries have banned the procedure in humans. Yet, discussions continue on possible applications in other areas.

Agriculture and Pharming

On the surface, it appears that cloning could produce farm animals with desired combinations of characteristics much faster than would be possible using conventional controlled breeding. However, because true clones would be of the same sex, the difficult cloning technique would have to be performed repeatedly—which would be too costly for animals that supply milk and meat and are thus required in very large numbers.

The expense and difficulty of cloning would be justified, however, in a field called "transgenic pharming." A transgenic animal is one that has a particular gene of interest stitched into the DNA of each of its cells, along with controls that enable the animal to secrete the gene's protein product in milk. Just a few of these special animals can be very valuable to us. A flock of transgenic Scottish sheep, for example, secrete enough of a human clotting factor in their milk to treat many people who have hemophilia. Creating a single transgenic animal costs from $1 million to $2 million. Cloning could rapidly make a few extra copies—and produce much more drug.

Cloning farm animals is problematical though. In the late 1980s, a company called Granada Genetics formed to clone cattle from nuclei of cells of 32-celled embryos. Of each ball of cells used to generate 32 individuals, usually only 2 or 3 survived long enough to be born, and then a third of those died shortly after birth. The problem, still not understood, was that the newborns were very large and needed a great deal of care to survive. Granada went out of business. A far simpler technique that several companies and researchers use to clone organisms is embryo splitting. Digestive enzymes are applied to a 32-cell embryo, which separates the cells, and 32 individual animals are then gestated in surrogate mothers.

Model Organisms

Transgenic organisms are also important as models of human genetic disease. Many researchers work with transgenic mice given human disease-causing genes, such as those that cause Alzheimer disease, obesity, rickets, cartilage disorders, cystic fibrosis, Duchenne muscular dystrophy, and Huntington disease. Cloning would enable researchers to make more copies of important transgenic model organisms.

Cloning could also generate genetically identical rhesus monkeys for use as models of human diseases. Shortly after Dolly's debut, the press erroneously compared an experiment on rhesus monkeys at the Oregon Regional Primate Research Center to the nuclear transfer procedure that led to Dolly. The researchers had fused cells from two 8-celled embryos with enucleated, unfertilized oocytes. The two animals that were born derived from the two embryos—it was obvious that they were not clones because they were of opposite sex! In addition, they were cloned from early embryos, not from adult cells, as was Dolly.

Conserving Endangered Species

Many "frozen" zoos already exist—deep-frozen sperm, oocytes, or embryos of endangered species. Nuclei from frozen cells could be transferred to enucleated oocytes from the endangered or a related species, then gestated in a surrogate of a related species. For now, though, embryo splitting is easier to do than nuclear transfer.

Basic Research

Dolly and other cloned animals may answer important biological questions about aging. Did Dolly begin aging when the experiment took place, or was she, as a single cell, already six years old? Did her chromosomes suddenly regrow their telomeres when the nucleus was placed in an oocyte's cytoplasm? How did that cytoplasm turn on quiescent genes?

Cloning could also answer questions about cancer. A cancer cell loses its specialized characteristics because of changes in gene expression and in regulation of the cell cycle. Similar changes occurred in the first cell that became Dolly, as it dedifferentiated and began development anew. This process could provide clues to how cancer begins.

Not an Exact Clone

Dolly isn't an exact genetic replica of the sheep that donated the nucleus. She differs in at least three ways:

Mitochondrial DNA Mitochondria contain a small number of genes that encode a few proteins as well as nonprotein-encoding RNA molecules. A fertilized egg has only mitochondria from the oocyte, because none enter from the sperm. Dolly's nuclear genes may be from the nucleus donor, but her mitochondrial genes are from the oocyte donor's cytoplasm—and those two sheep were of different breeds.

X Inactivation Chapter 6 discusses a phenomenon in female mammals called X inactivation. At a species-specific time in early prenatal development, one X chromosome is shut off in each cell of a female mammal. Whether the turned-off X is the one from the mother or the father occurs at random in each cell. Therefore, all female mammals are mosaics of gene expression for genes on the X chromosome. The pattern of X inactivation of Dolly would most likely not be like that of the sheep that donated the nucleus.

The Environment Human identical twins are more alike than clones are because they have the same mitochondrial DNA. Yet identical twins are hardly the same in every aspect of their existence because experiences and other aspects of the environment, such as nutrition, stresses, and exposure to infectious diseases, mold who we are.

figure 3.15

Cleavage divisions lead to formation of a mulberrylike structure, the morula, which then hollows out to form the blastocyst. The outer cell layer is the trophoblast, and the clump of cells on one side of the interior is the inner cell mass.

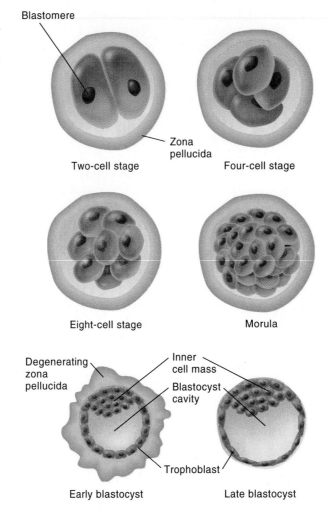

Blastomere

Zona pellucida

Two-cell stage

Four-cell stage

Eight-cell stage

Morula

Degenerating zona pellucida

Inner cell mass

Blastocyst cavity

Trophoblast

Early blastocyst

Late blastocyst

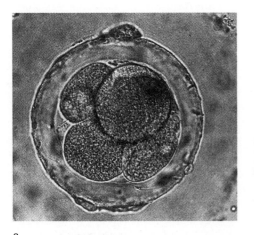
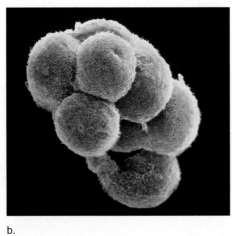

a.　　　　　b.　　　　　c.

figure 3.16

Electron micrographs of a prenatal human at the (*a*) 4-cell stage, (*b*) 16-cell stage, and (*c*) morula stage.

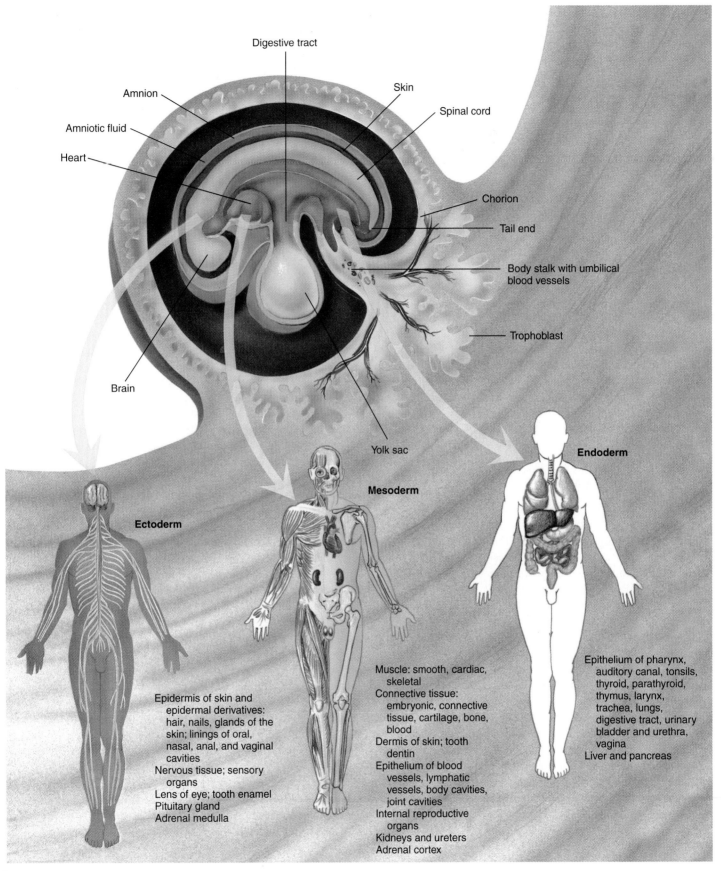

Digestive tract

Amnion

Amniotic fluid

Heart

Skin

Spinal cord

Chorion

Tail end

Body stalk with umbilical blood vessels

Trophoblast

Brain

Yolk sac

Ectoderm

Epidermis of skin and
    epidermal derivatives:
    hair, nails, glands of the
    skin; linings of oral,
    nasal, anal, and vaginal
    cavities
Nervous tissue; sensory
    organs
Lens of eye; tooth enamel
Pituitary gland
Adrenal medulla

Mesoderm

Muscle: smooth, cardiac,
    skeletal
Connective tissue:
    embryonic, connective
    tissue, cartilage, bone,
    blood
Dermis of skin; tooth
    dentin
Epithelium of blood
    vessels, lymphatic
    vessels, body cavities,
    joint cavities
Internal reproductive
    organs
Kidneys and ureters
Adrenal cortex

Endoderm

Epithelium of pharynx,
    auditory canal, tonsils,
    thyroid, parathyroid,
    thymus, larynx,
    trachea, lungs,
    digestive tract, urinary
    bladder and urethra,
    vagina
Liver and pancreas

figure 3.17

These organ systems arise from each of the primary germ layers laid down in the early embryo.

Because the villi cells and the embryo's cells come from the same fertilized ovum, an abnormal chromosome detected in villi cells should be present in the embryo.

Umbilical cords are a valuable medical tool because they contain stem cells that can divide to give rise to any type of blood cell. Cord blood can replace and repopulate depleted or damaged bone marrow in several disorders. In Fanconi anemia, for example, children lack stem cells in bone marrow and must have frequent blood transfusions. The first successful cord blood transplant to cure Fanconi anemia was done in 1988. The approach can also be used to treat some forms of leukemia and is used in gene therapy to correct certain enzyme deficiencies. Cord blood transplants are better than bone marrow transplants because they do not hurt the donor, they are more likely to be accepted by the recipient, and they are less likely to cause graft versus host disease, in which the transplant attacks the recipient's tissues. New parents are now asked to donate their newborn's cord blood to banks that store the cells for future use within the family or for donation.

The Embryo Develops

As the days and weeks proceed, different rates of cell division in different parts of the embryo fold the forming tissues into intricate patterns. In a process called **embryonic induction,** the specialization of one group of cells causes adjacent groups of cells to specialize. Gradually, these changes mold the three primary germ layers into organs and organ systems. **Organogenesis** describes the transformation of the simple three layers of the embryo into distinct organs. During the weeks of organogenesis, the developing embryo is particularly sensitive to environmental influences such as chemicals and viruses.

During the third week of prenatal development, a band called the **primitive streak** appears along the back of the embryo. It gradually elongates to form an axis that other structures organize around as they develop. The primitive streak eventually gives rise to connective tissue precursor cells and the **notochord,** a structure that

forms the basic framework of the skeleton. The notochord induces overlying ectoderm to specialize into a hollow **neural tube,** which develops into the brain and spinal cord (central nervous system).

Many nations designate day 14 of prenatal development and primitive streak formation as the point beyond which they ban research on the developing human as unethical. The reason is that the primitive streak is the first sign of a nervous system, and this is also the time at which implantation completes.

Formation of the neural tube, called neurulation, is a key event in early development because it marks the beginning of organ formation. Shortly after neurulation begins, a reddish bulge containing the heart appears. It begins to beat around day 18. Soon the central nervous system starts to form.

The fourth week of embryonic existence is one of spectacularly rapid growth and differentiation. Arms and legs begin to extend from small buds on the torso. Blood cells begin to form and to fill primitive blood vessels. Immature lungs and kidneys appear.

If the neural tube does not close normally at about day 28, a deformity called a neural tube defect results, leaving open an area of the spine so that parts of the brain or spinal cord protrude (Reading 14.2). If this happens, a fetal liver biochemical called alpha fetoprotein leaks at an abnormally rapid rate into the pregnant woman's circulation. If a maternal blood test at the fifteenth week of pregnancy detects high levels of alpha fetoprotein, the fetus may have a neural tube defect, though further testing is necessary to make a diagnosis.

By the fifth and sixth weeks, the embryo's head appears to be far too large for the rest of its body (figure 3.18). Limbs end in platelike structures with tiny ridges, which undergo apoptosis to mold fingers and toes. The eyes are open, but they do not yet have lids or irises. By the seventh and eighth weeks, a skeleton composed of cartilage appears. The embryo is now about the length and weight of a paper clip. At eight weeks of gestation, the prenatal human has rudiments of all of the structures that will be present at birth. It is now a **fetus.**

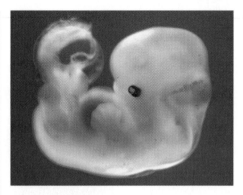

figure 3.18

A human embryo at 6 weeks. Nearly all organs are present in rudimentary form.

The Fetus

The body proportions of a fetus gradually approach those of a newborn. Initially, the ears lie low, and the eyes are widely spaced. Bone begins to replace the softer cartilage. As nerves and muscles coordinate, the fetus moves.

Sex is determined at conception, when a sperm bearing an X or Y chromosome meets an oocyte, which always carries an X chromosome. An individual with two X chromosomes is a female, and one with an X and a Y is a male. A gene on the Y chromosome, called **SRY** (for "sex-determining region of the Y"), determines maleness. Differences between the sexes do not appear until week 6, after the SRY gene is activated in males. Male hormones then stimulate male reproductive organs and glands to differentiate from existing, indifferent structures. In a female, the indifferent structures of the early embryo develop as female organs and glands. Sexuality is discussed further in chapter 6.

By week 12, the fetus sucks its thumb, kicks, makes fists and faces, and has the beginnings of baby teeth. It breathes amniotic fluid in and out, and urinates and defecates into it. The first trimester (three months) of pregnancy is over.

By the fourth month, the fetus has hair, eyebrows, lashes, nipples, and nails. An ultrasound scan or X ray of a 17-week fetus that has inherited osteogenesis imperfecta, described at the opening of the chapter, might already show such effects of the disease as an abnormally shaped skull and rib cage, rib bones that are thin at the ends, and shortened and misshapen limb bones. Ultrasound scanning bounces sound waves off of the fetus, creating an image.

By 18 weeks, the vocal cords have formed, but the fetus makes no sounds because it doesn't breathe air. By the end of the fifth month, the fetus curls into the classic head-to-knees position. It weighs about a pound. Figure 3.19 shows the upper part of a fetus at this stage. During the sixth month, the skin appears wrinkled because there isn't much fat beneath it. The skin turns pink as capillaries fill with blood. By the end of the second trimester, the woman feels distinct kicks and jabs and may even detect a fetal hiccup. The fetus is now about 9 inches long.

In the final trimester, fetal brain cells rapidly form networks as organs elaborate and grow. A layer of fat forms beneath the skin. The digestive and respiratory systems mature last, which is why infants born prematurely often have difficulty digesting milk and breathing. Approximately 266 days after a single sperm burrowed its way into an oocyte, a baby is ready to be born.

The birth of a live, healthy baby is against the odds, if we consider human development from the beginning. Of every 100 secondary oocytes that are exposed to sperm, 84 are fertilized. Of these 84, 69 implant in the uterus, 42 survive 1 week or longer, 37 survive 6 weeks or longer, and only 31 are born alive. Of those fertilized ova that do not survive, about half have chromosomal abnormalities that are too severe to maintain the activities of life. Chapter 11 looks at specific chromosome anomalies, and chapter 20 discusses infertility.

Fetal tissues may be useful medically because they have unique healing properties. Because they are not yet completely specialized, fetal tissues implanted into an adult may not evoke an immune response, as transplanted adult tissues often do. Furthermore, many fetal cells—such as those in neural tissues—have a capacity to divide that has ceased in their adult counterparts. For these reasons, fetal tissue may be useful to replace tissue in neurodegenerative disorders such as Parkinson disease and Alzheimer disease, as well as to fill in damaged tissue in injured spinal cords. However, such use of fetal tissue is highly controversial because it cannot come from naturally aborted material, which often has abnormal chromosomes.

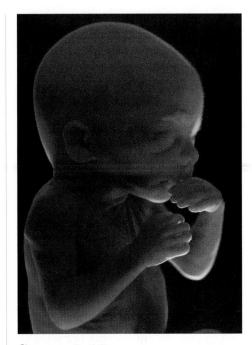

figure 3.19

A fetus at 20 weeks.

Birth Defects

When genetic abnormalities or toxic exposures affect an embryo, developmental errors occur, resulting in birth defects. Although development can derail in many ways, about 97 percent of newborns are apparently healthy.

The Critical Period

The specific nature of a birth defect usually depends on which structures are developing when the damage occurs. The time when genetic abnormalities, toxic substances, or viruses can alter a specific structure is its **critical period** (figure 3.20). Some body parts, such as fingers and toes, are sensitive for short periods of time. In contrast, brain development is sensitive throughout prenatal development, and connections between nerve cells change throughout life. Because of the brain's continuous critical period, many birth defect syndromes include mental retardation.

About two-thirds of all birth defects arise from a disruption during the embryonic period. More subtle defects that become noticeable only after infancy, such

---

Key Concepts

Following sexual intercourse, sperm are capacitated and drawn to the secondary oocyte. Acrosomal enzymes assist penetration of the oocyte, and chemical and electrical changes in the oocyte's surface block additional sperm entry. The two sets of chromosomes meet, forming a zygote. Cleavage cell divisions form a morula and then a blastocyst. The outer layer of cells invades and implants in the uterine lining. The inner cell mass develops into the embryo and its membranes. Certain blastocyst cells secrete hCG, and germ layers form in the second week. Cells in a specific germ layer later become part of particular organ systems, due to differential gene expression.

During week 3, chorionic villi extend toward the maternal circulation, and the placenta begins to form. Nutrients and oxygen enter the embryo, and wastes pass from the embryo into the maternal circulation. The yolk sac and allantois manufacture blood cells, the umbilical cord forms, and the amniotic sac expands with fluid. Amniocentesis and chorionic villus sampling check fetal chromosomes early in development. Umbilical cord blood is useful in transplants.

During week 3, the primitive streak appears, followed rapidly by the central nervous system, heart, notochord, neural tube, limbs, digits, facial features, and other organ rudiments. By week 8, all of the organs that will be present in the newborn have begun to develop.

During the fetal period, structures grow, specialize, and begin to interact. Bone replaces cartilage in the skeleton, body growth catches up with the head, and sex organs become more distinct. In the final trimester, the fetus moves and grows rapidly, and fat fills out the skin.

as learning disabilities, are often caused by disruptions during the fetal period. A disruption in the first trimester might cause mental retardation; in the seventh month of pregnancy, however, it might cause difficulty in learning to read.

Some birth defects can be attributed to an abnormal gene that acts at a specific point in prenatal development. In a rare inherited condition called phocomelia (seal limbs), for example, an abnormal gene halts limb development from the third to fifth week of the embryonic period, causing the infant to be born with "flippers" in place of arms and legs. Geneticists can predict the chances that a genetically caused birth defect will recur in a family.

Many birth defects, however, are caused by toxic substances the pregnant woman is exposed to. These environmentally caused problems cannot be passed on to future generations and will not recur unless the exposure occurs again. Chemicals or other agents that cause birth defects are called **teratogens** (Greek for "monster-causing"). While it is best to avoid teratogens while pregnant, some women may need to remain on a potentially teratogenic drug to maintain their own health. Table 3.2 lists some familiar drugs that are teratogens.

Teratogens

Thalidomide

The idea that the placenta protects the embryo and fetus from harmful substances was tragically disproven between 1957 and 1961, when ten thousand children were born in Europe with what seemed, at first, to be phocomelia. Because doctors realized that this genetic disorder is very rare, they began to look for another cause. They soon discovered that the mothers had all taken a mild tranquilizer, thalidomide, early in pregnancy, during the time an embryo's limbs form. The "thalidomide babies" were born with incomplete or missing legs and arms.

The United States was spared from the thalidomide disaster because an astute government physician noted the drug's adverse effects on laboratory monkeys. Still, several "thalidomide babies" were born in South America in 1994, where pregnant women were given the drug without warnings. In

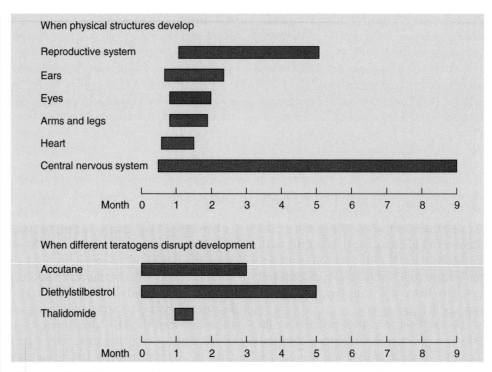

figure 3.20

The nature of a birth defect resulting from drug exposure depends upon which structures are developing at the time of exposure. The time of sensitivity during development for a particular structure is called the critical period. (Accutane is an acne medication. Diethylstilbestrol [DES] was used in the 1950s to prevent miscarriage.)

table 3.2
Teratogenic Drugs

Drug	Medical Use	Risk to Fetus
Alkylating agents	Cancer chemotherapy	Growth retardation
Aminopterin, methotrexate	Cancer chemotherapy	Skeletal and brain malformations
Coumadin derivatives	Seizure disorders	Tiny nose Hearing loss Bone defects Blindness
Diphenylhydantoin (Dilantin)	Seizures	Cleft lip, palate Heart defects Small head
Diethylstilbestrol (DES)	Repeat miscarriage	Vaginal cancer, vaginal adenosis Small penis
Isotretinoin (Accutane)	Severe acne	Cleft palate Heart defects Abnormal thymus Eye defects Brain malformation
Lithium	Manic depression	Heart and blood vessel defects
Penicillamine	Rheumatoid arthritis	Connective tissue abnormalities
Progesterone in birth control pills	Contraception	Heart and blood vessel defects Masculinization of female structures
Pseudoephedrine	Nasal decongestant	Stomach defects
Tetracycline	Antibiotic	Stained teeth
Thalidomide	Morning sickness	Limb defects

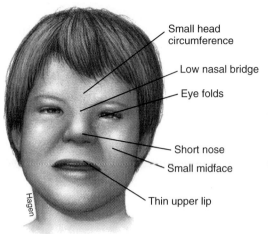

- Small head circumference
- Low nasal bridge
- Eye folds
- Short nose
- Small midface
- Thin upper lip

a.

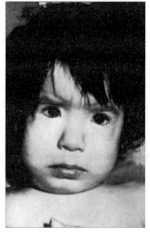

b.

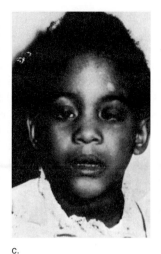

c.

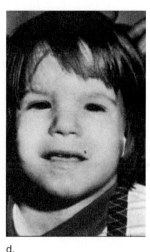

d.

figure 3.21

Fetal alcohol syndrome. Some children whose mothers drank alcohol during pregnancy have characteristic flat faces (a) that are strikingly similar in children of different races (b, c, and d). Pregnant women with alcoholism have a 30 to 45 percent chance of having a child who is affected to some degree by prenatal exposure to alcohol. Two mixed drinks per day seems to be the level at which damage occurs, but experiments on cells growing in culture suggest that even lower intakes can impair cellular function—in particular, cell adhesion.

spite of its teratogenic effects, thalidomide is still a valuable drug—it is used to treat leprosy and AIDS-related illnesses.

Cocaine

Cocaine is very dangerous to the unborn. It can cause spontaneous abortion by inducing a stroke in the fetus, and cocaine-exposed infants who do survive are more distracted and unable to concentrate on their surroundings than normal infants. Other health and behavioral problems arise as these children grow. A problem in evaluating prenatal effects of cocaine is that affected children are often exposed to other substances and situations that could also account for their symptoms.

Cigarettes

Chemicals in cigarette smoke stress a fetus. Carbon monoxide crosses the placenta and prevents the fetus's hemoglobin molecules from adequately binding oxygen. Other chemicals in smoke prevent nutrients from reaching the fetus. Studies comparing the placentas of smokers and nonsmokers show that smoke-exposed placentas lack important growth factors, causing poor growth before and after birth. Cigarette smoking during pregnancy is linked to spontaneous abortion, stillbirth, prematurity, and low birth weight.

Alcohol

A pregnant woman who has just one or two drinks a day, or perhaps a large amount at a single crucial time in prenatal development, risks fetal alcohol syndrome in her unborn child. Because tissue culture experiments show that even small amounts of alcohol can harm nerve cells, and because each woman metabolizes alcohol slightly differently, doctors advise that it is best to entirely avoid alcohol when pregnant or when trying to become pregnant.

A child with fetal alcohol syndrome (FAS) has a characteristic small head, misshapen eyes, and a flat face and nose (figure 3.21). He or she grows slowly before and after birth. Intellectual impairment ranges from minor learning disabilities to mental retardation.

The effects of FAS continue beyond childhood. Teens and young adults with the syndrome are short and have small heads. More than 80 percent of them retain facial characteristics of a young child with FAS, including abnormal lips, misaligned or malformed teeth, and a wide space between the upper lip and the nose. These facial traits make people with FAS look similar, but not abnormal.

The long-term mental effects of prenatal alcohol exposure are more severe than the physical vestiges. Many adults with FAS function at early grade-school level. They often lack social and communication skills and find it difficult to understand the consequences of actions, form friendships, take initiative, and interpret social cues. Aristotle noticed problems in children of alcoholic mothers more than twenty-three centuries ago. In the United States today, fetal alcohol syndrome is the third most common cause of mental retardation in newborns. From 1 to 3 of every 1,000 infants has the syndrome—that's more than 40,000 affected children born each year.

Nutrients

Certain nutrients ingested in large amounts, particularly vitamins, act as drugs in the human body. The acne medicine isotretinoin (Accutane) is a vitamin A derivative that causes spontaneous abortions and defects of the heart, nervous system, and face. The tragic effects of this drug were first noted exactly nine months after dermatologists began prescribing it to young women in the early 1980s. Today, the drug package bears prominent warnings, and doctors never prescribe it for pregnant women. A vitamin A-based drug used to treat psoriasis, as well as excesses of vitamin A itself, also cause birth defects. Some forms of vitamin A are stored in body fat for up to three years.

Vitamin C can also harm a fetus when the pregnant woman takes too much of it. The fetus becomes accustomed to the large amounts the woman takes, and after birth, receives much less, causing symptoms of vitamin C deficiency (scurvy). The baby bruises easily and is prone to infection.

Malnutrition in a pregnant woman also threatens the fetus. A woman must consume extra calories while she is pregnant or breastfeeding. Obstetrical records of pregnant women before, during, and after World War II link inadequate nutrition in early pregnancy to an increase in the incidence of spontaneous abortion. The aborted fetuses had very little brain tissue. Poor nutrition later in pregnancy affects the development of the placenta, which can cause low birth weight, short stature, tooth decay, delayed sexual development, learning disabilities, and possibly mental retardation.

Occupational Hazards

Some women (and men) encounter teratogens in the workplace. Researchers note increased rates of spontaneous abortion and children born with birth defects among women who work with textile dyes, lead, certain photographic chemicals, semiconductor materials, mercury, and cadmium. We do not know much about the role the male plays in transmitting environmentally caused birth defects. Men whose jobs expose them to sustained heat, such as smelter workers, glass manufacturers, and bakers, may produce sperm that can fertilize an oocyte and possibly cause spontaneous abortion or a birth defect. A virus or a toxic chemical carried in semen may also cause a birth defect.

Infection

Viruses are small enough to cross the placenta and reach a fetus. Some viruses that cause very mild symptoms in an adult, such as chicken pox, may be devastating to a fetus. Men can transmit infections to an embryo or fetus during sexual intercourse. Following are descriptions of how certain viral infections affect a developing offspring.

HIV HIV can reach a fetus through the placenta or infect a newborn via blood contact during birth. Fifteen to 30 percent of infants born to HIV positive women are HIV positive themselves. The risk of transmission can be significantly cut if the woman takes certain drugs used to treat AIDS while pregnant. All fetuses of HIV infected women are at higher risk for low birth weight, prematurity, and stillbirth if the woman's health is failing.

Researchers are currently following several dozen children who had HIV at birth and during early childhood but are now free of it. Their survival—tentatively attributed to a combination of a weakened viral strain and a strong immune system—may hold clues that will enable us to eventually conquer AIDS.

Rubella Australian physicians first noted the teratogenic effects of the rubella virus that causes German measles in 1941. In the United States, public attention did not focus on rubella until the early 1960s, when an epidemic of the usually mild illness caused 20,000 birth defects and 30,000 stillbirths. Women who contract the virus during the first trimester of pregnancy run a high risk of bearing children with cataracts, deafness, and heart defects. Rubella's effects on fetuses exposed during the second or third trimesters of pregnancy include learning disabilities, speech and hearing problems, and juvenile-onset diabetes.

The incidence of these problems, collectively called "congenital rubella syndrome" has dropped markedly thanks to widespread vaccination. However, it resurfaces in populations where people are not vaccinated. A resurgence of the syndrome in 1991, for example, was largely attributed to a cluster of Amish women in rural Pennsylvania who had not been vaccinated. In that isolated group, 14 of every 1,000 newborns had rubella exposure; the incidence in the general U.S. population is 0.006 per 1,000!

Herpes Herpes simplex virus can be very harmful to a fetus and newborn because the immune system is not yet completely functional. Forty percent of babies exposed to active vaginal herpes lesions become infected, and half of these infants die from it. Of those infants who are infected but survive, 25 percent sustain severe nervous system damage, and another 25 percent have widespread skin sores. A woman with a history of the infection can have her vaginal secretions checked periodically during pregnancy for evidence of an outbreak. If she has sores at the time of delivery, a Caesarian section (surgical delivery) can protect the child.

Hepatitis Pregnant women are now routinely checked for hepatitis B infection, which causes liver inflammation, fatigue, and other symptoms in adults. Each year in the United States, 22,000 infants are infected with this virus during birth. Although these babies do not have symptoms, they are at high risk for developing serious liver problems as adults. A vaccine given to the newborns of infected women can help prevent future complications.

Key Concepts

The critical period is the time during prenatal development when a structure is sensitive to damage caused by a faulty gene or environmental insult. Most birth defects develop during the embryonic period and are more severe than problems that arise later in pregnancy. Teratogens are agents that cause birth defects and include drugs, cigarettes, certain nutrients, malnutrition, occupational hazards, and infections.

Maturation and Aging

Cells die, and form from mitosis, throughout prenatal existence and long after, until death of the individual. Because genes control cell division and death, maturation and aging are, to an extent, genetically regulated.

The life spans of cells are reflected in the waxing and waning of biological structures and functions as they peak and then decline at characteristic rates. Although some structures and functions peak very early—such as the number of brain cells or hearing acuity, which do so in childhood—age thirty seems to be a developmental turning point after which several functions begin to decline. Some researchers estimate that after this age, the human body becomes functionally less efficient by about 0.8 percent each year.

In the fourth decade of life, certain adult-onset inherited conditions may produce their first symptoms. In polycystic kidney disease, for example, cysts that may have been present in the kidneys in one's twenties begin causing bloody urine, high blood pressure, and abdominal pain in the

Unlocking the Secrets of Alzheimer Disease

reading 3.2

When the five living American presidents gathered at the funeral of former President Richard M. Nixon in 1993, Bill Clinton, George Bush, Jimmy Carter, and Gerald Ford sensed that something was wrong with their compatriot Ronald Reagan. The former president was forgetful, answered inappropriately, and, said Gerald Ford, seemed "hollowed out." Reagan's memory continued to fade in and out, and six months later he penned a moving letter to the public confirming a diagnosis of Alzheimer disease (AD). He joined millions of other Americans with the illness.

German neurologist Alois Alzheimer first identified the condition in 1907 as affecting those in their forties and fifties, and it became known as "presenile dementia." So common are the memory loss and inability to reason of Alzheimer disease—affecting 5 percent of U.S. citizens over age 65 and 25 percent of those over 85—that for a long time physicians regarded these symptoms as normal aging. Today, Alzheimer disease is considered a disorder. It strikes 4 million Americans annually.

Alzheimer disease begins gradually. Mental function declines steadily for three to ten years after the first symptoms appear. Confused and forgetful, Alzheimer patients often wander away from family and friends. Finally, the patient cannot perform basic functions such as speaking or eating and must be cared for in a hospital or nursing home. Death is often due to infection.

On autopsy, the brains of Alzheimer patients contain gummy plaques of a protein called beta-amyloid in learning and memory centers (figure 1). Alzheimer brains also contain structures called neurofibrillary tangles, which consist of a protein called tau. Tau binds to and disrupts microtubules in nerve cell branches, destroying the shape of the cell.

From 5 to 10 percent of Alzheimer cases are inherited. These cases have an early onset, producing first symptoms in the forties and fifties. Three genes are known to cause Alzheimer disease. The amyloid precursor protein gene encodes beta-amyloid, and genes called presenilins 1 and 2 control amyloid production.

Another gene implicated in Alzheimer disease encodes a form of a protein called apolipoprotein E (APO-E), which seems to increase the risk of developing the disorder. In studies of families with two or more affected members, the APO-E variant was unusually common among those with Alzheimer disease. Apolipoproteins help the body process cholesterol, but their role in the brain is not understood. Individuals who inherit one or two copies of the APO-E variant have up to a 30 percent chance of developing Alzheimer disease, compared to 9 percent for the general population.

Early or even presymptomatic diagnosis of an illness lacking treatment may seem to be of dubious value. However, early knowledge may enable families to plan better for caring for their ill relatives. It may also help physicians distinguish early Alzheimer disease from other disorders. Finally, the ability to identify Alzheimer disease early may enable researchers to test new treatments as the disease starts, when they may be more helpful in slowing or preventing symptoms.

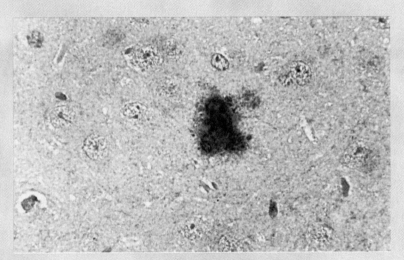

figure 1

The dark area in this slice of brain from a transgenic mouse is a beta-amyloid deposit, produced under instructions from a human gene present in each of the mouse's cells. This mouse model may provide a means to test new treatments for Alzheimer disease before human clinical trials.

thirties. Similarly, hundreds of benign polyps, symptomatic of familial polyposis of the colon (discussed in chapter 16), may coat the inside of the large intestine of a twenty-year-old, but they do not cause bloody stools until the third decade, when some of them may already be cancerous. The joint destruction of osteoarthritis may begin in one's thirties but is not painful until ten or twenty years later. The personality changes, unsteady gait, and diminishing mental facilities of Huntington disease begin near age forty. Reading 3.2 describes Alzheimer disease, which begins in adulthood and can be inherited.

figure 3.22

The Luciano brothers inherited progeria and appear much older than their years.

Accelerated Aging Disorders

Genes control aging both passively (as structures break down) and actively (by initiating new activities). A class of inherited diseases that accelerate the aging timetable vividly illustrates the role of genes in aging.

The most severe aging disorders are the **progerias.** In Hutchinson-Gilford syndrome (figure 3.22), one form of progeria, a child appears normal at birth but slows in growth by the first birthday. Within just a few years, the child ages with shocking rapidity, acquiring wrinkles, baldness, and the prominent facial features characteristic of advanced age. The body ages on the inside as well, as arteries clog with fatty deposits. The child usually dies of a heart attack or a stroke by age twelve, although some patients live into their twenties. Only a few dozen cases of this syndrome have ever been reported.

An adult form of progeria called Werner syndrome becomes apparent before age twenty, causing death from diseases associated with aging before age fifty. People with Werner syndrome develop, as young adults, atherosclerosis, diabetes mellitus, hair graying and loss, osteoporosis, cataracts, and wrinkled skin. Curiously, they do not develop Alzheimer disease or hypertension.

In 1996, researchers discovered the gene that causes Werner syndrome. It encodes a helicase, which is an enzyme necessary for DNA to replicate to repair errors in its sequence. The compromised DNA repair explains the early onset of several conditions.

Not surprisingly, the cells of progeria patients show aging-related changes. Recall that normal cells growing in culture divide about 50 times before dying. Cells from progeria patients die in culture after only 10 to 30 divisions. Understanding how and why progeria cells race through the aging process may help us to understand genetic control of normal aging.

Is Longevity Inherited?

Aging reflects genetic activity plus a lifetime of environmental influences. Families with many very aged members have a fortuitous collection of genes plus shared environmental influences, such as good nutrition, excellent health care, devoted relatives, and other advantages. An interesting hypothesis proposes that we inherit longevity from our mother, and her mother, and her mother, and so on. This is because certain mitochondrial genes protect against free radical damage, and only females transmit mitochondrial genes.

It is difficult to tease apart inborn from environmental influences on life span. One approach compares adopted individuals to both biological and adoptive parents. In one study, Danish adoptees with one biological parent who died of natural causes before age fifty were more than twice as likely to die before age fifty themselves as were adoptees whose biological parents lived beyond this age. This suggests an inherited component to longevity. Interestingly, adoptees whose natural parents died early due to infection were more than five times as likely to also die early of infection, perhaps because of inherited immune system deficiencies. Age at death of the adoptive parents had no influence on that of the adopted individuals. Chapter 7 explores the "nature versus nurture" phenomenon more closely.

Our increased understanding of gene function, plus identification of the environmental factors that promote long life, will give us many opportunities to intervene—not only to extend life, but to make it healthier, from meiosis all the way through the last golden years.

Key Concepts

Aging occurs throughout the human lifetime as cells die. Aging usually becomes more apparent after age thirty. Adult onset genetic disorders may appear in one's forties.

Genes control aging both passively and actively. Progerias, inherited rapid-aging disorders, may help us understand genetic control of aging, while adoption studies reveal the effects of genes versus environmental influences. Families with many aged members can probably thank their genes as well as the environment.

summary

1. Genes exert effects throughout the human life cycle, from **meiosis** through aging.

2. The cells that combine to form a new human are produced in the male and female reproductive systems. These systems include paired **gonads** in which sperm and **oocytes** are manufactured, networks of tubes, and glands. Male **gametes** (**spermatozoa**) originate in **seminiferous tubules** within the paired **testes.** They then pass through a series of tubes, including the **epididymis** and **vasa deferentia,** where they mature before exiting the body through the **urethra** during sexual intercourse. The prostate gland, the **seminal vesicles,** and the **bulbourethral glands** add secretions to the sperm. Female gametes (oocytes) originate in the **ovaries.** Each month after puberty, one ovary releases an oocyte into a **fallopian tube.** The oocyte then moves to the **uterus.**

3. Meiosis is a form of cell division that halves the chromosome number in sex cells, maintaining the chromosome number of a species from generation to generation. This constancy results from two cell divisions with only one round of DNA replication. Meiosis ensures genetic variability by partitioning different combinations of genes into gametes as a result of **crossing over** and **independent assortment.**

4. Maturation completes gamete manufacture. **Spermatogenesis** begins with **spermatogonia,** which accumulate cytoplasm and replicate their DNA to become **primary spermatocytes.** After **reduction division** (meiosis I), the cells become haploid **secondary spermatocytes.**

In the **equational division** of meiosis II, the secondary spermatocytes divide to each yield two **spermatids,** which then differentiate.

5. In **oogenesis,** some oogonia grow and replicate their DNA, becoming **primary oocytes.** In meiosis I, the primary oocyte divides to yield one large **secondary oocyte** and a much smaller **polar body.** In meiosis II, the secondary oocyte divides to yield the large **ovum** and another small polar body. Female meiosis completes at fertilization.

6. In the female reproductive tract, sperm are **capacitated** and drawn chemically and physically towards a secondary oocyte. One sperm burrows through the oocyte's protective layers with **acrosomal** enzymes. Fertilization occurs when the sperm and oocyte's **pronuclei** fuse, forming the **zygote.** Electrochemical changes in the egg surface block further sperm entry. In one day, cleavage begins and a 16-celled **morula** forms. Between days 3 and 6, the morula arrives at the uterus and hollows, forming a **blastocyst** made up of individual **blastomeres.** The **trophoblast** layer and **inner cell mass** form. Around day 6 or 7, the blastocyst implants and trophoblast cells secrete **hCG,** which prevents menstruation.

7. During the second week, the **amniotic cavity** forms as the inner cell mass flattens. **Ectoderm** and **endoderm** form, and then **mesoderm** appears, establishing the **primary germ layers.** Cells in each particular germ layer begin to develop into specific organ systems. During the third week, the **placenta, yolk sac, allantois,** and

umbilical cord begin to form as the amniotic cavity swells with fluid. Organs form throughout the embryonic period. Structures gradually appear, including the **primitive streak,** the **notochord** and **neural tube,** arm and leg buds, the heart, facial features, and the skeleton.

8. The **fetal period** begins in the third month. Organ rudiments laid down in the embryonic period grow and specialize. The developing organism moves and reacts, and gradually, body proportions resemble those of a baby. In the last trimester, the brain develops rapidly, and fat is deposited beneath the skin. The digestive and respiratory systems mature last.

9. Birth defects can result from a malfunctioning gene or an environmental intervention. Environmentally caused birth defects are not transmitted to future generations.

10. The time when a structure is sensitive to damage from an abnormal gene or environmental intervention is its **critical period.**

11. A substance that causes birth defects is a **teratogen.** Alcohol, chemicals in cigarette smoke, and certain drugs and infections are teratogens.

12. Aging is an ongoing process. Many genetic disorders first produce symptoms in mid-adulthood. In passive aging, structures break down, perhaps due to faulty DNA repair. In active aging, genes program cell death. Inherited and environmental factors influence longevity. Genes for long life may come through the maternal line.

review questions

1. How many sets of human chromosomes are present in each of the following cell types?

   a. an oogonium

   b. a primary spermatocyte

   c. a spermatid

   d. a cell from either sex during anaphase of meiosis I

   e. a cell from either sex during anaphase of meiosis II

   f. a secondary oocyte

   g. a polar body derived from a primary oocyte

2. List the structures and functions of the male and female reproductive systems.

3. A dog has 39 pairs of chromosomes. Considering only independent assortment, how many genetically different puppies are possible when two dogs mate? Is this number an underestimate or overestimate of the actual total? Why?

4. How does meiosis differ from mitosis?

5. What do oogenesis and spermatogenesis have in common, and how do they differ?

6. How does gamete maturation differ in the male and female?

7. Describe the events of fertilization.

8. Exposure to teratogens tends to produce more severe health effects in an embryo than in a fetus. Why?

9. List four teratogens, and explain how they disrupt prenatal development.

10. Cite two pieces of evidence that genes control aging.

applied questions

1. Using your knowledge of human prenatal development, at what stage do you think it is ethical to ban experimentation? Cite reasons for your answer. (The options of banning the research altogether, or of allowing research at any stage, are as valid an option as pinpointing a particular stage.)

2. If a pregnant woman is to have an abortion and agrees to donate the fetus's tissues, should the man who impregnated her be informed of her intention? Should he have a role in the decision? Cite a reason for your answer.

3. Some Vietnam War veterans who were exposed to the herbicide Agent Orange claim that their children—born years after the exposure—have birth defects caused by a contaminant in Agent Orange called dioxin. What types of cells in these men must the chemical have affected in order to cause birth defects years later?

4. In about 1 in 200 pregnancies, a sperm fertilizes a polar body instead of an oocyte. A mass of tissue that is not an embryo develops. Why can't a polar body support development of an embryo, whereas an oocyte, which is genetically identical to it, can?

5. Suppose that in a polar body biopsy, the polar body is found to carry a disease-causing allele. The woman then knows that the particular oocyte associated with that polar body has the normal allele. How does she know this?

6. Should a woman be held legally responsible if she drinks alcohol, smokes, or abuses drugs during pregnancy and it harms her child? Should liability apply to all substances that can harm a fetus, or only to those that are illegal?

7. A genetic counselor sees two patients concerned about their pregnancies. The first is a woman who took an antibiotic known to cause birth defects during the sixth week of pregnancy, when she had an infection and did not know that she was pregnant. The second woman is concerned because a previous child died of an inherited illness. How would the information the counselor provides differ for these two patients?

8. What difficulties might be encountered in studying the inheritance of longevity?

suggested readings

Goldberg, Jeff. July 1995. Fetal attraction. *Discover.* Fetal tissue may be useful for transplants.

Hayflick, Leonard. 1994. *How and why we age.* New York: Ballantine. Biological aspects of aging, written by a master.

Holcomb, L., et al. January 1998. Accelerated Alzheimer-type phenotype in transgenic mice carrying both mutant amyloid precursor protein and presenilin 1 transgenes. *Nature Medicine,* vol. 4. Mice given two different Alzheimer genes have extreme illness.

Kassiner, J. P., and N. A. Rosenthal. March 26, 1998. Should human cloning research be off limits? *The New England Journal of Medicine,* vol. 338. Nuclear transplantation has many potential applications. Will society allow them to be developed?

Lewis, Ricki. September 29, 1997. Embryonic stem cells debut amid little media attention. *The Scientist.* Specially cultured primordial germ cells from human embryos may yield tissues for transplant.

Lewis, Ricki. October 1997. One sheep, one hopeful step. *The World and I.* A look at applications of cloning technology.

Pennisi, Elizabeth. April 12, 1996. Premature aging gene discovered. *Science,* vol. 272. The gene that, when mutant, causes a rapid-aging disorder, encodes an enzyme DNA requires to replicate.

Simpson, J. L. December 7, 1995. Pregnancy and the timing of intercourse. *The New England Journal of Medicine,* vol. 333. Attempts to time intercourse to influence the sex of a child usually do not work.

Stearns, Tim. January 1, 1995. The form and the substance. *Nature Medicine,* vol. 1. Aristotle said that the sperm provides form and the egg substance to a new organism.

Strain, L., et al. January 15, 1998. A true hermaphroditic chimera resulting from embryo amalgamation after in vitro fertilization. *The New England Journal of Medicine,* vol. 338. How a child arose who has both male and female chromosome constitutions.

Thompson, Clare. May 12, 1995. Umbilical cords: Turning garbage into clinical gold. *Science,* vol. 268. Stem cells that give rise to blood cells, and that are thus of great medical value, are present in umbilical cord blood.

van Bockxmeer, Frank M. January 1994. ApoE and ACE genes: Impact on human longevity. *Nature Genetics,* vol. 6. Geneticists are searching for genes that confer longevity.

chapter four

Mendel's Laws

Thoughts About Genetics Through History— and Before

Inherited similarities can be startling, such as the physical likeness between John Lennon and son Julian and in their distinctive singing voices (figure 4.1).

Although growing up in a musical environment can shape a talent, heredity plays a role, too. Interest in heredity must be as old as humankind itself, as people throughout time have wondered at their similarities—and fought over their differences (figure 4.2).

Farmers in Mexico used genetics six thousand years ago when they carefully set aside seed from the hardiest plants of a wild grass each season and used it to start the next season's crop. In this way, over many plant generations, domesticated corn was bred. Four thousand years earlier, other farmers domesticated wheat. The Old Testament reveals a remarkable comprehension of heredity: A boy whose mother's sister had a son who bled to death upon circumcision was exempt from the ritual. This was an ancient recognition of the transmission of hemophilia through a female carrier, to be discussed in chapter 6.

In the nineteenth century, the idea that different parts of the body control trait transmission became popular. Later, scientists gave genes a number of colorful names, including "pangens," "idioblasts," "bioblasts," "plastidules," "nuclein," "plasomes," "stirps," "gemmules," or just "characters." But an investigator who used the term "elementen" made the most lasting impression on what would become, a quarter century after his death in 1884, the science of genetics. His name was Gregor Mendel.

As a child in what was once Czechoslovakia near the Polish border, Mendel learned farming from his family and tended fruit trees for the lord of a manor. Surviving extreme poverty, he was university-educated in science and teaching. At the age of twenty-one, Mendel entered the Augustinian monastery at Brno. There, he learned about plant breeding from the abbot, a man dedicated to scientific research, who built a greenhouse for plant breeding experiments.

a.

b.

figure 4.1

Heredity is apparent in appearances and talents, as singers and songwriters John (*a*) and Julian (*b*) Lennon illustrate.

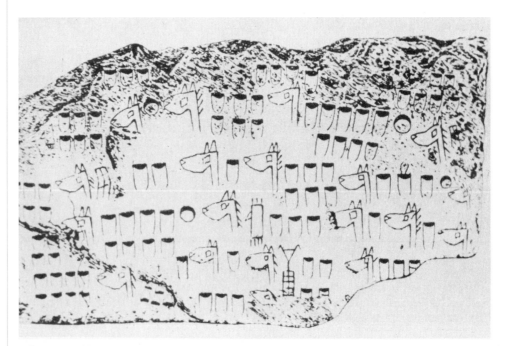

figure 4.2

Ancient cultures recognized inheritance patterns. A horse breeder in Asia 4,000 years ago etched a record of his animals' physical characteristics in stone.

Mendel was active in local plant and animal breeding programs. His nine years of carefully setting up crosses of pea plants enabled him to generalize about the mechanism of heredity.

Although peas had been popular with plant breeders since the 1820s, Mendel was the first to envision how ratios of offspring classes revealed transmission of distinct "elementen," or characters, although he still did not know how such information might be passed on in a physical sense. This chapter considers Mendel's two basic laws of inheritance: segregation and independent assortment. Mendel derived them from experiments with peas, but they apply to any diploid species, including humans.

Following the Inheritance of One Gene—Segregation

Mendel worked with many pea plant variants, but he was especially interested in seven easily distinguishable characteristics, each of which had two obviously different expressions (figure 4.3). He noted that short plants bred to other short plants were "true-breeding," consistently yielding seeds that gave rise only to more short plants. In contrast, tall plants were not always true-breeding. Some tall plants, when crossed with a short plant or another tall plant, produced only tall plants in the next generation. This suggested that tallness always masked shortness. But when certain other tall plants were crossed with each other, about one-quarter of the plants in the next generation were short (figure 4.4). Of the remaining three-quarters of the plants, one-third proved (by further crosses to short plants) to be "true-breeding tall," always producing tall offspring, but the other two-thirds produced some short plants in the next generation.

Mendel suggested that gametes distribute "characters" that control these traits, because these cells physically link generations. The characters would separate from each other as gametes form. When gametes join at fertilization, the characters would then group into new combinations. Mendel reasoned that if each character (for example, tall versus short) was packaged into a separate gamete, and if opposite-sex gametes combine at random, then the pea plant crosses would produce the ratios of traits he observed. Mendel's idea that pairs of characters separate during gamete formation would later be called the **law of segregation.**

In 1865, Mendel presented his experimental results to a local natural history

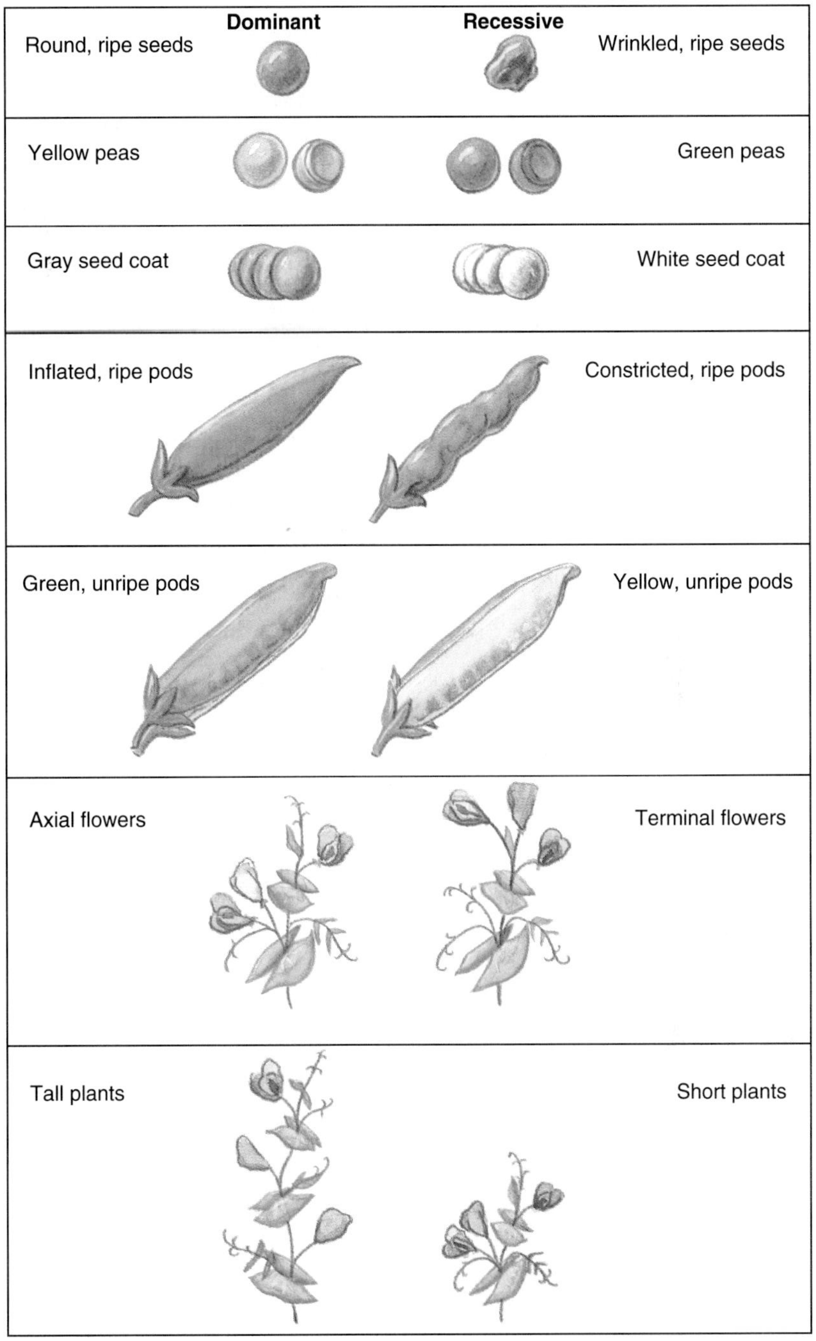

figure 4.3

Gregor Mendel studied transmission of seven traits in peas. Each trait had two easily distinguished expressions. Seeds were round or wrinkled; peas yellow or green; seed coats gray or white; ripe pods inflated or constricted; unripe pods green or yellow; flowers axial (arising sideways from stems) or terminal (arising only from the top of the plant); and plants either tall (6 to 7 inches) or short (3/4 to 1 1/2 inch).

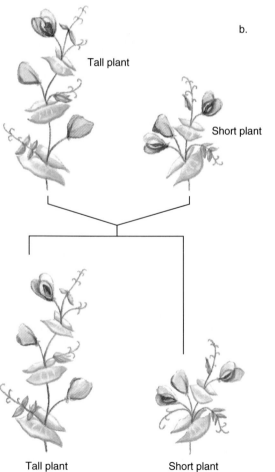

Short plants

Short plants

a.

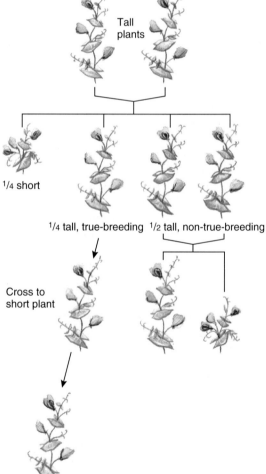

Tall plant

Short plant

Tall plants

b.

Tall plant

Short plant

Tall plant

Short plant

c.

figure 4.4

Mendel crossed short and tall pea plants. (*a*) When Mendel crossed short pea plants to short pea plants, all of the progeny were short. (*b*) Certain tall plants crossed to short plants produced all tall plants. (*c*) Other tall plants crossed to short plants produced some tall plants and some short plants. (*d*) When the tall plants that did not breed true were crossed to each other, one-quarter of the plants in the next generation were short, and three-quarters were tall. Of these tall plants, one-third were true-breeding, and the other two-thirds were not true-breeding. Genotypes are indicated in parentheses.

Tall plants

1/4 short

1/4 tall, true-breeding 1/2 tall, non-true-breeding

Cross to short plant

d.

society, receiving an enthusiastic but limited response. Few people realized that he was demonstrating broad principles applicable far beyond peas. A year later, he published "Experiments with Plant Hybrids" in the natural history society's journal. Again, few noticed the work to the point of attempting to repeat it, the usual response to an important scientific discovery.

Mendel sent the report to a well-known Swiss botanist who dismissed the work as too rational and not mystical enough to be important. Undaunted, Mendel published more findings in 1869, again to little notice. Frustrated, he eventually turned his energies to monastery administration.

In 1900, botanists Hugo deVries of Holland, Carl Correns of Germany, and Erich von Tschermak of Austria read Mendel's 1866 paper. They realized that his observations, hypotheses, and conclusions explained data they had gathered on crosses in other plant species. From 1900 to 1906, researchers repeated and confirmed Mendel's ratios in many species. His ideas were to become even more widely accepted in the years to follow, as the role chromosomes play in heredity unraveled.

In the early 1900s, several researchers noted that chromosomes behave much like Mendel's characters. Paired characters and paired chromosomes both separate and are contributed—one from each parent—to offspring. Mendel's characters and chromosomes are inherited in random combinations. Chromosomes provided a physical basis for what Mendel described but could not actually see. In 1909, Wilhelm Johannsen renamed Mendel's "elementen," or characters, "genes" (Greek for "give birth to"). Soon after, English biologist William Bateson coined the term "genetics" for the study of genes.

For the next few years, the gene remained a black box; many biologists accepted its existence, but few suggested anything about its physical nature. In 1917, Thomas Hunt Morgan, head of a large genetics laboratory at Columbia University, published "The Theory of the Gene," which reiterated Mendel's findings but also extended them to embrace information on chromosome structure and function. In the 1940s, attention turned to discovering the gene's chemical basis (chapter 8). Although scientists discovered the chemistry in 1953, we are still learning the details of how genes control each other. Compared to many other life sciences, the field of genetics is young.

Terms Used to Describe Single Genes

Mendel's observation of two different expressions of an inherited trait—for example, short and tall—reflects the fact that a gene can exist in many alternate forms, or **alleles.** An individual having two identical alleles for a gene is **homozygous** for that gene. An individual with two different alleles is **heterozygous.**

The genes that Mendel worked with each had two alleles—that is, two obvious expressions. However, a gene may have many alleles, or variants, because a change may occur in any of the hundreds or thousands of DNA bases that make up a gene. Since Mendel knew nothing of DNA and its informational nature, he could detect gene variants only if the phenotype was altered—if a plant produced yellow or green peas, for example.

Mendel noted that for some genes, one variant could mask the expression of another. The allele that masks the effect of the other is **completely dominant,** and the masked allele is **recessive.** When Mendel crossed a true-breeding tall plant to a short plant, the tall allele was completely dominant to the short allele, and the plants of the next generation were all tall (figure 4.4).

Whether a trait is dominant or recessive depends upon the particular nature of the phenotype. Often, on a biochemical level, the heterozygote is actually intermediate, or a mix between the homozygous dominant and homozygous recessive, even though at the whole-person level, the heterozygote and homozygous dominant genotypes are indistinguishable. This is the case in Tay-Sachs disease and several other inborn errors of metabolism. The heterozygote (with one dominant and one recessive allele) actually produces half the normal amount of the enzyme that the gene encodes, but this amount is apparently sufficient for normal function so that the person remains as healthy as a person with two dominant alleles. Only a person with two recessive alleles has the disease.

Recessive disorders tend to be more severe, and produce symptoms at much earlier ages, than dominant disorders. This is because disease-causing recessive alleles can remain, even flourish, in populations because heterozygotes carry them without becoming ill. In contrast, if a dominant mutation arises that causes severe illness early in life, people who have the allele are too ill or do not live long enough to reproduce, and the allele eventually vanishes from the population. Dominant disorders whose symptoms do not appear until adulthood, or that do not drastically disrupt health, remain in a population because people with them are able to reproduce.

When a gene has two alleles, it is common to symbolize the dominant one with a capital letter, and the recessive one with the corresponding lowercase letter. If both alleles are recessive, the individual is homozygous recessive, and this is symbolized by two lowercase letters, such as tt for short plants. An individual with two dominant alleles is homozygous dominant, written with two capital letters, such as TT for tall pea plants. An individual with the other possible allele combination is heterozygous. This individual has one dominant and one recessive allele, such as non-true-breeding tall, or Tt, pea plants.

An organism's appearance does not always reveal its alleles—that is, phenotype does not always reflect genotype. For example, a pea plant may have a tall phenotype but be either genotype TT (homozygous dominant) or Tt heterozygous. A phenotype is **wild type** if it is the most common expression of a particular gene in a population. Wild type often means normal. An allele that mutates from wild type is termed mutant. Mutant means variant, but not necessarily harmful.

In analyzing genetic crosses, the first generation is called the parental generation, or P_1; the second generation is the first filial generation, or F_1; the next generation is the second filial generation, or F_2, and so on. In your family, your grandparents might be considered the P_1 generation, your parents the F_1 generation, and you and your siblings the F_2 generation. Table 4.1 summarizes terms used to describe transmission of genes.

table 4.1
A Glossary of Genetic Terms

Term	Definition
Allele	An alternate form of a gene
Dihybrid	An individual who is heterozygous for two particular genes
Dominant	An allele that masks the expression of another allele
F_1	The first filial generation; offspring
F_2	The second filial generation; offspring of offspring
Genotype	The allele combination in an individual
Heterozygous	Possessing different alleles of a gene
Homozygous	Possessing identical alleles of a gene
Independent assortment	Mendel's second law; a gene on one chromosome does not influence the inheritance of a gene on a different (nonhomologous) chromosome because meiosis packages chromosomes randomly into gametes
Monohybrid	An individual heterozygous for a particular gene
Mutant	A phenotype or allele resulting from a change (mutation) in a gene
Mutation	A change in a gene
P_1	The parental generation
Phenotype	The observable expression of an allele combination
Recessive	An allele whose expression is masked by another allele
Segregation	Mendel's first law; alleles of a gene separate into equal numbers of gametes
Sex-linked	A gene located on the X chromosome or a trait that results from the activity of a gene on the X chromosome
Wild type	The most common phenotype or allele for a gene in a population.

Mendel's Laws and Meiosis

The patterns of trait transmission Mendel observed for a single gene reflect the events of meiosis. When a gamete is produced, the two copies of a particular gene separate, as the homologs that carry them do. In a pea plant of genotype *Tt*, for example, gametes carrying either *T* or *t* form in equal numbers in anaphase of meiosis I. When gametes meet to start the next generation, they combine at random; that is, a *t*-bearing oocyte has as great a chance of combining with a *t*-bearing sperm as with a *T*-bearing sperm. Equal gamete formation and random combinations of gametes underlie Mendel's first law. Figure 4.5 shows the role genes and chromosomes play in segregation.

Mendel crossed short pea plants (*tt*) with true-breeding tall plants (*TT*) (figure 4.4*b*). The resulting seeds grew into F_1 plants that all had the same phenotype: tall (genotype *Tt*). In another experiment, he crossed *Tt* plants with each other (figure 4.4*d*) in what is called a **monohybrid cross,** because one (mono) trait is being

followed by crossing two heterozygous (hybrid) individuals. There are three possible outcomes of such a cross: *TT, tt,* and *Tt*. A *TT* individual results from a *T* sperm fertilizing a *T* oocyte; a *tt* plant results from a *t* oocyte meeting a *t* sperm; and a *Tt* individual results from either a *t* oocyte fertilized by a *T* sperm, or a *T* oocyte fertilized by a *t* sperm.

Because there are twice as many ways to produce a heterozygote than there are to produce either homozygote, the **genotypic ratio** expected of a monohybrid cross is 1 *TT*:2 *Tt*:1 *tt*. Since *Tt* plants as well as *TT* plants are tall, the corresponding **phenotypic ratio** is three tall plants to one short plant, a 3:1 ratio. The numbers of different types of pea plants that Mendel observed when he crossed *Tt* plants to other *Tt* plants closely approximate the theoretical 3-tall-to-1-short phenotypic ratio—787 tall plants and 277 short plants in the next generation.

Mendel distinguished the two genotypes resulting in tall progeny—*TT* and *Tt*—with more crosses. He bred tall plants whose genotype he did not know to *tt*

plants. If a tall plant crossed to a *tt* plant produced both tall and short progeny, then the original tall plant was genotype *Tt*. But if it produced only tall plants, then it must be *TT*. The technique of crossing an individual of unknown genotype to a homozygous recessive individual is called a **test cross.** It is based on the fact that the homozygous recessive is the only genotype that is revealed by the phenotype—that is, a short plant can only be genotype *tt*. The homozygous recessive serves as a "known" that an individual of unknown genotype can be crossed with.

A Punnett square is a chart used to track the contributions of each parent and the resulting genotypes and phenotypes in offspring (figure 4.6). It diagrams how alleles can combine in a cross between two particular individuals. The different types of alleles the female contributes are listed along the top of the square; the male's alleles are listed on the left-hand side. Each compartment within the square contains the genotypes that result when gametes containing the corresponding alleles join.

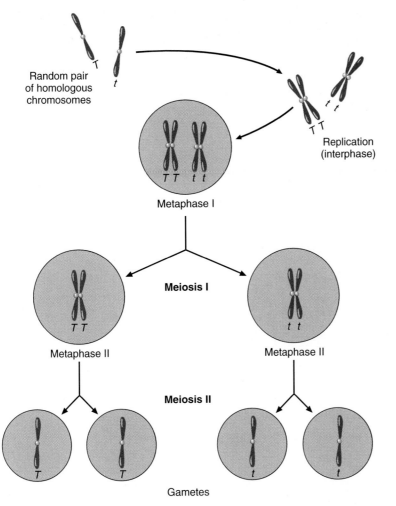

Random pair
of homologous
chromosomes

Replication
(interphase)

Metaphase I

Meiosis I

Metaphase II

Metaphase II

Meiosis II

Gametes

figure 4.5

Mendel's first law—gene segregation. During meiosis, homologous pairs of chromosomes (and the genes that comprise them) separate from one another and are packaged into separate gametes. At fertilization, gametes combine at random to form the individuals of a new generation.

Female gametes

	T	t
T	TT	Tt
t	Tt	tt

Male gametes

a. Genotypic ratio: 3 tall:1 short
    Phenotypic ratio: 1 *TT*:2 *Tt*:1 *tt*

Female gametes

	T	T
t	Tt	Tt
t	Tt	Tt

Male gametes

b. Genotypic ratio: all *Tt*
    Phenotypic ratio: all tall

Female gametes

	T	t
t	Tt	tt
t	Tt	tt

Male gametes

c. Genotypic ratio: 1 *Tt*:1 *tt*
    Phenotypic ratio: 1 tall:1 short

figure 4.6

Punnett squares are helpful in following the transmission of traits. The Punnett square in (*a*) describes Mendel's monohybrid cross of two tall pea plants. In the progeny, tall plants outnumber short plants 3:1. The genotypic ratio is 1 *TT*:2 *Tt*:1 *tt*. The square in (*b*) shows a cross of two homozygotes, and (*c*) shows a cross of a heterozygote with a homozygous recessive.

From observing crosses in which two tall pea plants produced short offspring, and other crosses, Mendel deduced that "characters" for height segregate during meiosis, then combine at random with those from the opposite gamete at fertilization. A homozygote has two identical alleles, and a heterozygote has two different alleles. The allele expressed in a heterozygote is dominant; the allele not expressed is recessive. Dominance or recessiveness reflects the nature of the phenotype.

The most common phenotype is the wild type, and an allele that changes from wild type is mutant. A monohybrid cross yields a genotypic ratio of 1:2:1 and a phenotypic ratio of 3:1.

A test cross uses a homozygous recessive individual to reveal an unknown genotype. Punnett squares help calculate expected genotypic and phenotypic ratios among progeny.

Single Mendelian Traits in Humans

In humans, disorders or traits that a single gene specifies are said to be **Mendelian traits.** Even the most prevalent Mendelian disorders, such as cystic fibrosis and Duchenne muscular dystrophy, are very rare, usually affecting 1 in 10,000 or fewer births. About 2,500 Mendelian disorders are known, and some 2,500 other conditions are suspected to be Mendelian, based on their recurrence patterns in large families. Figure 4.7 shows a common Mendelian inherited trait, albinism.

Modes of Inheritance

The patterns in which Mendelian traits appear in families, termed **modes of inheritance,** designate whether the gene is carried on an autosome (nonsex chromosome) or on the X chromosome. (Very few genes are on the Y chromosome.) It also reveals whether the associated phenotype is recessive or dominant. Hence, modes of inheritance include **autosomal recessive, autosomal dominant,** X-linked

Student James Poush saw Mendel's laws in action when he explored his own family for a science fair project. His work was the first full report on an autosomal dominant condition called distal symphalangism (figures 1 and 2).

James had never thought that his stiff fingers and toes with their tiny nails were odd. Others in his family had them, too. But when he studied genetics, he realized that his quirk might be a Mendelian trait. After much detective work, James identified 27 affected individuals among 156 relatives, and he went on to analyze a second family with the disorder.

James concluded that the trait is autosomal dominant. Of 63 relatives with an affected parent, 27 (43 percent) expressed the phenotype, close to the 50 percent expected of autosomal dominant inheritance. The figure is lower, James reasons, because of underreporting and a few cases where a person inherited the dominant gene but didn't express the phenotype (a phenomenon discussed in the next chapter).

The dominant allele responsible for distal symphalangism affects people to different degrees; people have different digits affected, and to different extents. Some relatives did not realize they had inherited the variation until James pointed it out to them!

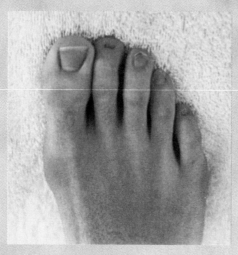

figure 1

Rudimentary nails, shown here on the second and fifth toes, are characteristic of distal symphalangism.

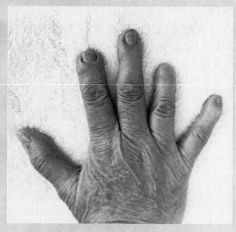

figure 2

Another symptom of distal symphalangism is brachydactyly, or short fingers.

figure 4.7

Albinism can result from a monohybrid cross in a variety of organisms. A heterozygote has one allele that directs the synthesis of an enzyme required to manufacture the skin pigment melanin and one allele that cannot make the enzyme. Each child of two carriers has a 1 in 4 chance of inheriting the two deficient alleles and being unable to manufacture melanin.

recessive, and X-linked dominant. This chapter considers the first two modes of inheritance; chapter 6 discusses traits transmitted on the X chromosome.

In autosomal dominant inheritance, the trait can appear in either sex because the gene is carried on an autosome. Since it is dominant, if a child has the trait, at least one parent must also have it. Autosomal dominant traits do not skip generations. If no offspring inherit the trait in one generation, its transmission stops because the offspring have only the recessive form of the gene. Reading 4.1 tells of a high-school student who identified a previously unknown autosomal dominant trait in his family—weird toes.

In autosomal recessive inheritance, two carrier (heterozygous) parents who do not have the trait typically are surprised to

"The Sun Is a Monster"

reading 4.2

Three-year-old Katie Maher says that the sun is a monster. For her, because of an autosomal recessive disorder, sunlight can be extremely dangerous.

Caren and Dan Maher had no reason to suspect that their youngest child would have a serious inherited medical condition; after all, their other three children were healthy. But one day when Katie was about a month old, her parents put her under a tree in the backyard to enjoy the warm spring weather. Almost immediately, Katie broke out everywhere in spots. As the little girl shrieked in pain, the spots turned to blisters, and later to scabs. Some of them might one day become skin cancers (figure 1).

At first the Mahers thought the skin reaction was an isolated incident, perhaps an allergic reaction to something in their yard. But it happened every time Katie encountered sunlight. Even a shaft of light entering through a window and falling on the little girl could cause painful blisters to form instantaneously.

Eventually, Katie was diagnosed with *xeroderma pigmentosum*, a disruption of her DNA's ability to repair damage caused by ultraviolet radiation in sunlight. Because this ability to repair normally helps prevent skin cancer, Katie is highly susceptible. She is one of only about 250 people in the world with the condition. Xeroderma pigmentosum is inherited as an autosomal recessive trait—that is, each of Katie's parents is a carrier. The parents were unaware of any other affected relatives because never before had two mutant copies of the gene been passed to the same individual.

Today, Katie lives a shaded, indoor existence, which her parents hope will enable her to live long and without pain. She is liberally smeared with sunblock up to eight times a day to protect against accidental sun exposures. To go to a doctor, she bundles up at night and travels in a car with blocked windows. These measures may prevent her from developing skin cancer, which affects more than half of all children with xeroderma pigmentosum by the time they enter their teens.

Like many families with a chronically ill member, the Mahers have adapted their way of life to make Katie's easier. The children play in the yard with Katie at night, and the jungle gym is in the garage, where the windows are covered and low-ultraviolet incandescent light bulbs are used, to allow occasional daytime play. Caren and Dan have started a special camp where children with the disorder can turn night into day so that they, like other children, can enjoy the outdoors.

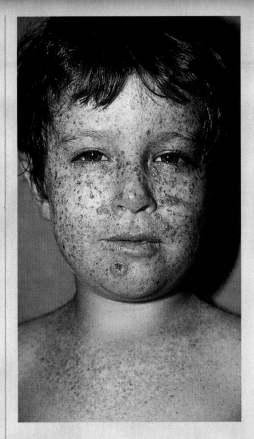

figure 1

The marks on this child's face are a result of sun exposure. He is highly sensitive because he has inherited xeroderma pigmentosum. The large lesion on his chin is a skin cancer.

give birth to a child who does. (This happened to the family discussed in Reading 4.2.) Either sex can be affected because the gene controlling the trait is on an autosome, but only individuals who inherit a recessive allele from each parent exhibit the trait because the dominant variant would mask it. Figure 4.8 depicts this situation for two people who are carriers for the autosomal recessive illness cystic fibrosis. Each of their children has a 25 percent risk (1 in 4) of having two wild type (*CC*) alleles, a 50 percent (1 in 2) chance of being a carrier (*Cc*), and a 25 percent risk of having CF (genotype *cc*). Note that this is the classic 1:2:1 genotypic ratio of a monohybrid cross.

Sometimes a rare autosomal recessive illness occurs in families in which the parents are blood relatives who each inherited the same rare allele from a common ancestor. In *Mendelian Inheritance in Man*, a compendium of all human inherited traits, very rare illnesses are often reported in families that share the same bloodlines, a situation called **consanguinity.**

The ratios predicted from Mendel's law apply to each newly conceived child (or pea plant or other diploid organism), just as tossing a coin has a 50 percent chance of coming up heads with each throw, no matter how many heads have already been thrown. Many people believe that if they have had one child with a recessive disorder, the next three are guaranteed to be healthy. Can you see why this is not correct?

The nature of the phenotype should be considered when evaluating transmission

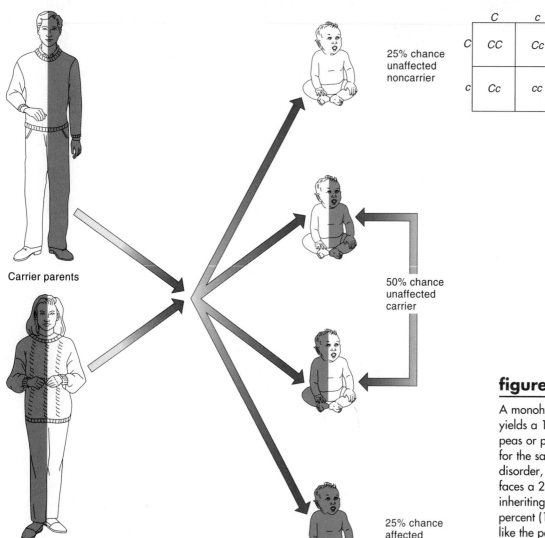

	C	c
C	CC	Cc
c	Cc	cc

25% chance
unaffected
noncarrier

50% chance
unaffected
carrier

25% chance
affected

Carrier parents

figure 4.8

A monohybrid cross (two heterozygotes) yields a 1:2:1 genotypic ratio, whether in peas or people. When parents are carriers for the same autosomal recessive trait or disorder, such as cystic fibrosis, each child faces a 25 percent (1 in 4) chance of inheriting two wild type alleles (*CC*); a 50 percent (1 in 2) chance of being a carrier, like the parents (*Cc*); and a 25 percent chance of inheriting two disease-causing recessive alleles (*cc*).

of Mendelian traits. For example, each adult sibling of a person who is a known carrier of Tay-Sachs disease has a two-thirds chance of being a carrier. The probability is two-thirds, and not one-half, because there are only three genotypic possibilities for an adult—homozygous for the wild type allele, or a carrier who inherits the mutant allele from either the mother or father. A homozygous recessive individual for Tay-Sachs disease would never have survived childhood. We will return to this concept in the next chapter.

Geneticists who study human traits and illnesses hardly set up crosses as Mendel did, but they can pool information from families whose members have the same trait or illness, based on symptoms,

biochemical tests, or genetic tests. Consider a simplified example of 50 couples where both partners are carriers of sickle cell disease. If 100 children are born, about 25 of them would be expected to have sickle cell disease. Of the remaining 75, theoretically 50 would be carriers like their parents, and the remaining 25 would have two nonmutant or wild type alleles.

Pedigree Analysis

Families are the primary tool of the human geneticist, and the bigger the family, the better. The more children in a generation, the easier it is to discern modes of inheritance. Family relationships and phenotypes are displayed in a standard chart called a

pedigree. A human pedigree serves the same purpose as one for purebred dogs or cats or thoroughbred horses—it helps keep track of relationships and traits.

A pedigree is built of shapes connected by lines. Vertical lines represent generations; horizontal lines that connect shapes at their centers depict parents; shapes connected by vertical lines joined horizontally above them represent siblings. Squares indicate males; circles, females; and diamonds, individuals of unknown sex. Figure 4.9 shows these and other commonly used pedigree symbols. Colored shapes indicate individuals who express the trait under study, and half-filled shapes represent known carriers.

The earliest pedigrees were genealogical, indicating family relationships but not

Symbols

○, □ = Normal female, male

●, ■ = Female, male who expresses trait

◑, ◧ = Female, male who carries an allele for the trait but does not express it (carrier)

⊘, ⊠ = Dead female, male

◇ = Sex unspecified

⊘, ⊠ (SB) = Stillbirth

(P) [P] ⟨P⟩ = Pregnancy

△ = Spontaneous abortion (miscarriage)

△ = Terminated pregnancy (shade if abnormal)

Lines

| = Generation

— = Parents

┊ = Adoption

⊓ = Siblings

△ (twins) = Identical twins

⋀ = Fraternal twins

═ = Parents closely related (by blood)

—//— = Former relationship

↗ = Person who prompted pedigree analysis (proband)

Numbers

Roman numerals = generations

Arabic numerals = individuals

figure 4.9

Symbols representing individuals are connected to form pedigree charts, which display inheritance patterns of particular traits.

traits. Figure 4.10 shows such a pedigree for a highly inbred part of the ancient Egyptian royal family. The term *pedigree* arose in the fifteenth century, from the French "pie de grue," which means "crane's foot." Pedigrees at that time, typically depicting large families, consisted of parents linked by curved lines to their offspring. The overall diagram often resembled a bird's foot.

An extensive family tree of several European royal families that indicates which members had the bleeding disorder hemophilia is believed to be one of the first pedigrees to trace an inherited disorder (figure 6.7a). The mutant gene probably originated in Queen Victoria of England in the nineteenth century. In 1845, a genealogist named Pliny Earle constructed a pedigree of a family with color blindness, using musical notation—half notes for unaffected females, quarter notes for color-blind females, and filled-in and squared-off notes to represent the many color-blind males. In the early twentieth century, pedigrees took on a

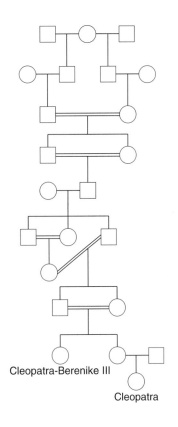

Cleopatra-Berenike III

Cleopatra

figure 4.10

This pedigree of Egypt's Ptolemy dynasty shows only genealogy, not traits. It appears almost ladderlike because of the extensive inbreeding. From 323 B.C. to Cleopatra's death in 30 B.C., the family experienced five brother-sister pairings, plus an uncle-niece relationship. Cleopatra married her brother, Ptolemy XIII, when he was ten years old! These marriage patterns were an attempt to preserve the royal blood.

Source: Cherwell Scientific Publishing, Inc., Palo Alto, CA.

negative note when eugenicists used the diagrams to attempt to declare such traits as criminality, feeblemindedness, and promiscuity the consequence of faulty genes.

Today, pedigrees are important both for helping families identify the risk of transmitting an inherited illness and as starting points for gene searches. In some instances, however, genealogy remains an important motivation for developing pedigrees. Groups of people who have kept meticulous family records can be invaluable in helping researchers follow the inheritance of particular genes. In the United States, the Mormons and the Amish have been particularly helpful and useful in genetic studies.

Very large pedigrees are helpful in gene hunts because they provide researchers with knowledge of many individuals with a particular disorder. The researchers can then search these peoples' DNA to identify a particular sequence they have all inherited but that is not found in healthy family members. Discovery of the gene that causes Huntington disease, for example, took researchers to a remote village in Venezuela and an enormous family whose pedigree looked more like wallpaper than a family tree. The gene was eventually traced to a sailor believed to have introduced the mutant gene in the nineteenth century.

A person familiar with Mendel's laws can often tell a mode of inheritance just by looking carefully at a pedigree. Consider an autosomal recessive trait, which can affect both sexes and can (but doesn't necessarily) skip generations. Figure 4.11 is a pedigree for albinism. If a condition is known to be inherited as an autosomal recessive trait, carrier status can be inferred for individuals who have affected (homozygous recessive) children. In figure 4.11, since individuals III-1 and III-3 are affected, individuals II-2 and II-3 (both parents) must be carriers.

An autosomal dominant trait does not skip generations and can affect both sexes. Transmission stops whenever an individual does not inherit the causative gene. A typical pedigree for an autosomal dominant trait has some squares and circles filled in

to indicate affected individuals in each generation (figure 4.12).

Two other modes of inheritance, involving the sex chromosomes X and Y, are discussed in chapter 6. These, too, can be traced with pedigrees. However, sometimes a pedigree may fit more than one mode of inheritance. Figure 4.13 illustrates such an inconclusive pedigree for alopecia, a form of hair loss. The same pedigree can indicate autosomal recessive or autosomal dominant inheritance. Further family information or biochemical tests to detect carriers can sometimes clarify an ambiguous situation.

Often genetic counselors are asked to predict the probability, or risk of recurrence, of a condition in a particular individual. This requires thinking through Mendel's laws for more than one generation. Pedigrees and Punnett squares can be helpful in doing these calculations. Consider the family depicted in figure 4.14.

Michael Stewart has sickle cell disease, a condition inherited as an autosomal recessive trait. This means that his unaffected parents, Kate and Brad, must each

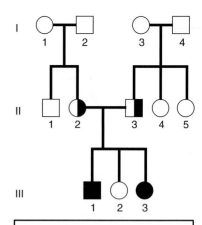

In words:
"One couple has a son and daughter with normal pigmentation. Another couple has one son and two daughters with normal pigmentation. The daughter from the first couple has three children with the son of the second couple. Their son and one daughter have albinism; their other daughter has normal pigmentation."

figure 4.11

A pedigree for an autosomal recessive trait, albinism. Note the carrier parents of affected children.

figure 4.12

A pedigree for an autosomal dominant trait. Familial hypertrophic cardiomyopathy appears in every generation in this family.

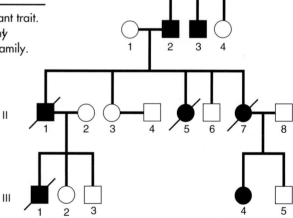

"When individual III-1 died suddenly of heart failure while playing basketball at age 19, his family and doctors were perplexed; he had seemed healthy. But the family history and microscopic examination of his heart tissue revealed familial hypertrophic cardiomyopathy, an inherited overgrowth of heart muscle. The boy's father had died young of heart failure too, as had two of the father's sisters. The 19-year-old's two cousins, whose mother had died of the condition, had tests for the mutant gene. One of them, a girl, inherited the gene. Restricting her exercise to swimming may extend her life. The 19-year-old's paternal grandfather and a paternal great-uncle also had the disorder."

Alopecia as an autosomal recessive trait

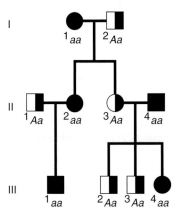

If A = normal hair
   a = alopecia

Alopecia as an autosomal dominant trait

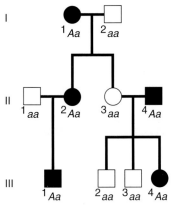

If a = normal hair
   A = alopecia

figure 4.13

An inherited trait that does not impair health enough to prevent reproduction can result in an inconclusive pedigree, because an affected individual may have one causative dominant allele, or two causative recessive alleles, depending on the mode of inheritance. This is the case for alopecia, in which some hair on the head falls out, grows back, and falls out again. Alopecia can be inherited as an autosomal recessive trait (the pedigree on the left) or an autosomal dominant trait (the pedigree on the right).

be heterozygotes (carriers). Michael's sister Ellen, also healthy, is expecting her first child. Ellen's husband, Tim, has no family history of sickle cell disease. Ellen wants to know the risk that her child will inherit the mutant allele from her.

Ellen's request is really asking two questions. First, what is the risk that she herself is a carrier? Because Ellen is actually the product of a monohybrid cross, and we know that she is not homozygous recessive, then she has a 2 in 3 chance of being a carrier, as the Punnett square indicates.

If Ellen is a carrier, then the next question is, what is the chance that she will pass the mutant allele to an offspring? That chance is 1 in 2, because she has two copies of the gene, and according to Mendel's first law, only one goes into each gamete.

To calculate the overall risk to Ellen's child, we can multiply the probabilities—that is, the chance that Ellen is a carrier multiplied by the chance that if she is, she will pass the mutant allele on. This is an application of the **product rule,** which states

that the chance that two independent events will both occur equals the product of the chance either event will occur on its own. (We will return to the product rule soon.) If we assume Tim is not a carrier, Ellen's chance of giving birth to a child who carries the mutant allele is therefore 2/3 times 1/2, which equals 2/6, or 1/3. Ellen thus has a 1 in 3 chance of producing a child who is a carrier for sickle cell disease.

Pedigrees can be difficult to construct and interpret for several reasons. People sometimes hesitate to supply information because they are embarrassed by symptoms affecting behavior or mental stability. Tracing family relationships can be complicated by adoption, children born out of wedlock, blended families, and assisted reproductive technologies, such as surrogate mothers and artificial insemination by donor (chapter 20). Moreover, many people cannot trace their families back more than three or four generations, which may not provide sufficient evidence to reveal mode of inheritance.

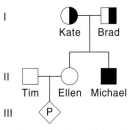

a. Ellen's brother Michael has sickle cell disease.

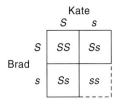

b. Probability that Ellen is a carrier: $^2/_3$

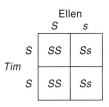

c. If Ellen is a carrier, chance that fetus is a carrier: $^1/_2$

Total probability = $^2/_3 \times ^1/_2 = ^1/_3$

figure 4.14

Making predictions. Ellen's brother Michael has sickle cell disease, as depicted in pedigree (a). Ellen wonders what the chance is that her fetus has inherited the sickle cell allele from her. First, she must calculate the chance that she is a carrier. The Punnett square in (b) shows that this risk is 2 in 3. (She must be genotype SS or Ss but cannot be ss because she does not have the disease.) The risk to the fetus, assuming Ellen's husband Tim is not a carrier, is half her risk of being a carrier, or 1 in 3 (c).

Evolving Technology

The pedigree is perhaps the most classic genetic tool. It is still a powerful way to see, at a glance, how a trait passes from generation to generation. However, with today's increasingly molecular-oriented view of

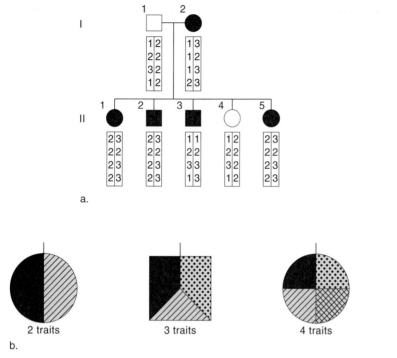

a.

2 traits

3 traits

4 traits

b.

figure 4.15

Pedigrees evolve. (*a*) The numbers in bars beneath pedigree symbols enable researchers to track specific chromosomes. (*b*) Pedigree symbols can be divided into two, three, or even four segments to depict more than one trait.

genetics, geneticists have refined pedigrees to provide even more information.

Much genetic research today focuses on DNA sequences near or part of the gene of interest. Molecular information is often included as numbers in bars beneath modern pedigree symbols (figure 4.15*a*). This allows investigators to track transmission of particular chromosomes as well as of phenotypes.

When pedigrees grow too large to easily manipulate, researchers use computer programs and mathematical expressions to follow alleles, an approach called segregation analysis. These sophisticated tools can distinguish modes of inheritance, number of genes being considered, and even certain environmental influences. The pedigree symbols—squares and circles—are sometimes subdivided to hold more information (figure 4.15*b*).

Another type of information added to pedigrees is carrier status for an autosomal recessive condition. Biochemical tests can reveal, for example, if a person is a carrier for Tay-Sachs disease, sickle cell disease, or cystic fibrosis. Such tests are very valuable for people whose siblings have affected children. Once genes are discovered and researchers are able to distinguish wild type from disease-causing mutant sequences, carrier tests can be developed. Many carrier tests will be introduced over the next few years as the human genome project adds to our knowledge of human genes.

Following the Inheritance of Two Genes— Independent Assortment

The law of segregation follows the inheritance of two alleles for a single gene. In a second set of experiments, Mendel examined the inheritance of two different traits, each attributable to a gene with two different alleles. Specifically, Mendel looked at seed shape, which was either round or wrinkled (determined by the *R* gene), and seed color, which was either yellow or green (determined by the *Y* gene). When he crossed plants with round, yellow seeds to plants with wrinkled, green seeds, all the progeny had round, yellow seeds. Therefore, round was completely dominant to wrinkled, and yellow was completely dominant to green.

Next, Mendel took F₁ plants (genotype *RrYy*) and crossed them to each other in a **dihybrid cross,** so named because two individuals heterozygous for two genes are crossed. He found four types of seeds in the F₂ generation: round, yellow (315 plants); round, green (108 plants); wrinkled, yellow (101) plants; and wrinkled, green (32 plants). This is an approximate ratio of 9:3:3:1 (figure 4.16).

Mendel then took each plant from the F₂ generation and crossed it to wrinkled, green (*rryy*) plants. These test crosses established whether each F₂ plant was true-breeding for both genes (*RRYY* or *rryy*), true-breeding for one but heterozygous for the other (*RRYy, RrYY, rrYy,* or *Rryy*), or heterozygous for both genes (*RrYy*). Based upon the results of the dihybrid cross, Mendel concluded that a gene for one trait does not influence transmission of a gene for another trait. This is Mendel's second law, the law of **independent assortment.** It is true only for genes on different chromosomes. The seed shape and seed color genes that Mendel worked with fit this criterion.

With the idea of independent assortment, Mendel had again inferred a principle of inheritance that has its physical basis in meiosis. Independent assortment occurs because chromosomes from each parent combine in a random fashion (figure 4.17). In Mendel's dihybrid cross, each parent produces equal numbers of gametes of four different types: *RY, Ry, rY,* and *ry.* (Note that each of these combinations has one gene for each trait.) A Punnett square for this cross (figure 4.18) shows that the four types of seeds—round, green (*RRYY, RrYY, RRYy,* and *RrYy*); round, yellow (*RRyy, Rryy*); wrinkled, green (*rrYY, rrYy*); and wrinkled,

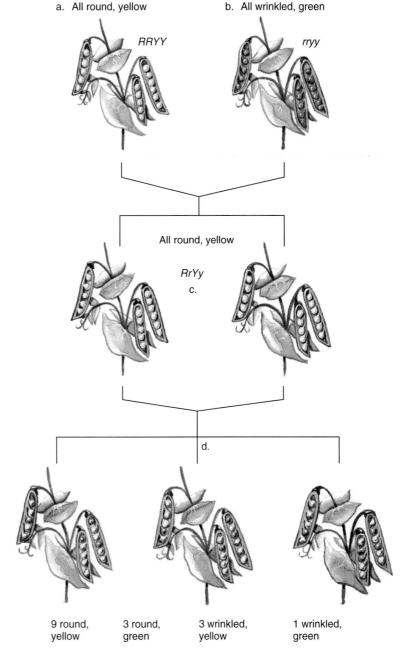

a. All round, yellow — *RRYY*
b. All wrinkled, green — *rryy*
All round, yellow — *RrYy* — c.
d.

9 round, yellow
3 round, green
3 wrinkled, yellow
1 wrinkled, green

figure 4.16

Mendel's crosses involving two genes. To study the inheritance pattern of two genes, Mendel crossed (*a*) a true-breeding plant with round, yellow seeds (*RRYY*) to (*b*) a plant with wrinkled, green seeds (*rryy*). The peas of the F₁ generation were all round and yellow (*RrYy*) (*c*). When the F₁ dihybrid pea plants were crossed to each other (*d*), the F₂ seeds were round, yellow (*RrYy, RRYy, RrYY, RRYY*); round, green (*Rryy* and *RRyy*); wrinkled, yellow (*rrYY* and *rrYy*); and wrinkled, green (*rryy*) in a 9:3:3:1 ratio. (Individual peas are counted as progeny in the F₂ generation, not the entire parent plant.)

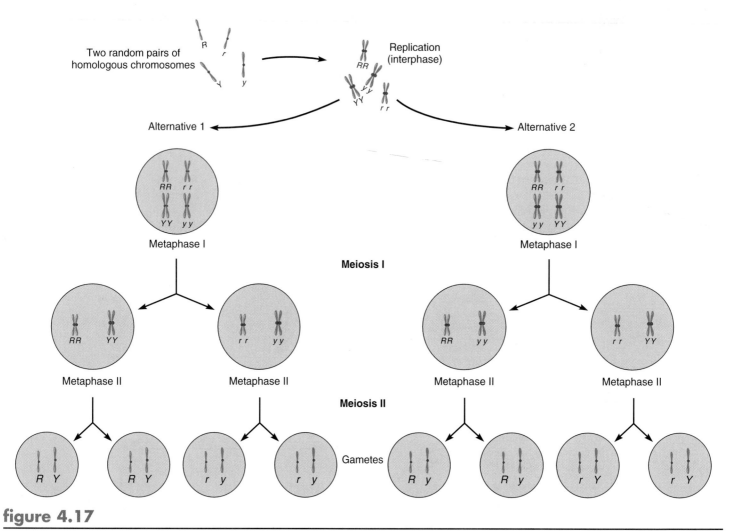

figure 4.17

The independent assortment of genes carried on different chromosomes results from the random alignment of chromosome pairs during metaphase of meiosis I. An individual of genotype *RrYy,* for example, manufactures four types of gametes, containing the dominant alleles of both genes (*RY*), the recessive alleles of both genes (*ry*), and a dominant allele of one with a recessive allele of the other (*Ry* and *rY*). The allele combination depends upon which chromosomes are packaged together into the same gamete—and this happens at random.

yellow (*rryy*)—are present in the ratio 9:3:3:1, just as Mendel found.

Using Probability to Analyze More than Two Genes

A Punnett square for three genes has 64 boxes; for four genes, 256 boxes. An easier way to predict genotypes and phenotypes is to use the mathematical laws of probability Punnett squares are based on. Probability predicts the likelihood of an event.

The product rule can be used to predict the chance of obtaining a wrinkled, green

(*rryy*) plant from dihybrid (*RrYy*) parents. Consider the dihybrid one gene at a time. A Punnett square for *Rr* crossed to *Rr* (figure 4.19) shows that the probability of *Rr* plants producing *rr* progeny is 25 percent, or 1/4. Similarly, the chance of two *Yy* plants producing a *yy* individual is 1/4. The chance of dihybrid parents (*RrYy*) producing homozygous recessive (*rryy*) offspring is therefore 1/4 multiplied by 1/4, or 1/16.

Now consult the 16-box Punnett square for Mendel's dihybrid cross again (figure 4.18). Only 1 of the 16 boxes is *rryy,* just as the product rule predicted. Figure 4.20 uses probability to predict the

chance that a woman with two unusual genetic traits and a man with a third odd trait will conceive a child who has all three traits.

Gregor Mendel, some say, was lucky. He just happened to have picked traits located on different chromosomes, making it possible for him to elegantly demonstrate independent assortment. The genes he worked with in pea plants had two very clear expressions—green or yellow, wrinkled or smooth, short or tall. But tracing inheritance of traits isn't always so clearcut. The next chapter focuses on exceptions and extensions to Mendel's laws.

Key Concepts

Mendel's second law, the law of independent assortment, considers genes transmitted on different chromosomes. In a dihybrid cross of heterozygotes for seed color and shape, Mendel produced a phenotypic ratio of 9:3:3:1. He concluded that a gene on one chromosome does not influence the transmission of a gene on another chromosome. Meiotic events explain segregation and independent assortment. Punnett squares and probability can be used to follow independent assortment.

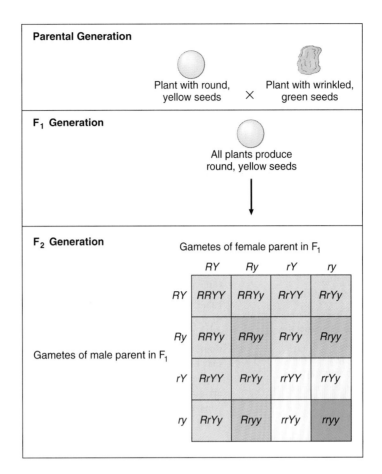

figure 4.18

A Punnett square can be used to represent the random combinations of gametes dihybrid individuals produce.

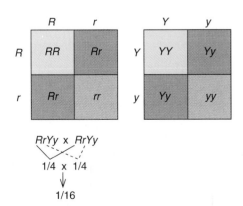

figure 4.19

The product rule.

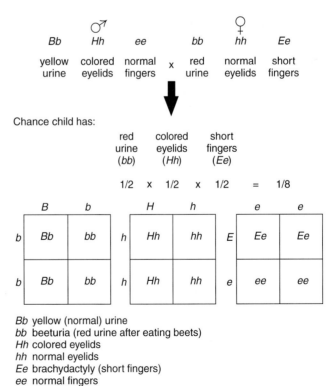

figure 4.20

Using probability to track three traits. A man with normal urine, colored eyelids, and normal fingers wants to have children with a woman who has red urine after she eats beets, normal eyelids, and short fingers. The chance that a child of theirs will have red urine after eating beets, colored eyelids, and short fingers is 1/8.

summary

1. Gregor Mendel described the two basic laws of inheritance—**segregation** and **independent assortment**—based on the results of pea plant crosses. The laws derive from actions of chromosomes during meiosis, although Mendel did not know this. The laws apply anew to each offspring.

2. The law of segregation states that alleles of a gene are distributed into separate gametes during meiosis. Mendel demonstrated this using short and tall pea plants.

3. A diploid individual with two identical alleles of a gene is **homozygous.** A **heterozygote** has two different alleles. A gene may have many alleles.

4. A **completely dominant** allele masks the expression of a recessive allele. An individual may be homozygous dominant, homozygous **recessive,** or heterozygous. Recessive disorders tend to be more severe, and cause symptoms earlier, than dominant disorders.

5. The wild type phenotype is the most common in a population. A change in DNA, or a mutation, may cause a variant phenotype.

6. In a **monohybrid cross,** two individuals heterozygous for a single trait breed and yield a **genotypic ratio** of 1 homozygous recessive : 2 heterozygotes : 1 homozygous dominant.

7. A **test cross** reveals an unknown genotype by mating an individual to a homozygous recessive, whose genotype is obvious.

8. A **Punnett square** is a chart used to follow transmission of alleles.

9. Inheritance of an **autosomal recessive** trait may affect either males or females and may skip generations. In **autosomal dominant** inheritance, males and females may be affected, and generations are not skipped. Autosomal recessive conditions are more likely to occur in families with **consanguinity.**

10. A **pedigree** is a chart that depicts family relationships and patterns of inheritance for particular traits. Modern pedigrees may include molecular information.

11. The chance that two independent genetic events will both occur is equal to the product of the probabilities that each event will occur on its own. This principle, called the **product rule,** is useful in calculating the risk of inheriting a certain genotype over two generations and in following inheritance of two genes on different chromosomes.

12. Mendel's second law, the law of independent assortment, follows transmission of two or more genes on different chromosomes. It states that a random assortment of maternally and paternally derived chromosomes in meiosis results in gametes that have different combinations of these genes.

review questions

1. How does meiosis explain Mendel's laws of segregation and independent assortment?

2. How was Mendel able to derive the two laws of inheritance without knowing about chromosomes?

3. Distinguish between
   a. autosomal recessive and autosomal dominant inheritance.
   b. Mendel's first and second laws.

   c. a homozygote and a heterozygote.
   d. a monohybrid and a dihybrid cross.

4. Why would Mendel's results for the dihybrid cross have been different if the genes for the traits he followed were located on the same chromosome?

5. Why are extremely rare autosomal recessive traits or disorders more likely to

appear in families in which blood relatives have children together?

6. How does the pedigree of the ancient Egyptian royal family in figure 4.10 differ from a pedigree a genetic counselor might use today?

applied questions

1. Draw a pedigree depicting the Maher family, discussed in Reading 4.2. What is the probability that any of Katie's three siblings is a carrier (heterozygote) of xeroderma pigmentosum?

2. Round bumps on the knuckles, called knuckle pads, are inherited as an autosomal dominant trait in several well-studied large families. It is apparently a common trait, because Renaissance artists included them in many paintings and sculptures. The following pedigree

traces the trait through three generations of a modern family:

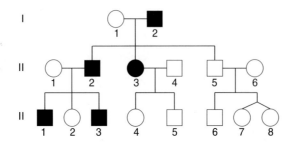

a. Does this pedigree conclusively demonstrate autosomal dominant inheritance? That is, is autosomal recessive inheritance also possible?

b. If the trait is autosomal recessive in this family, which individuals must be carriers (heterozygotes)?

c. If the trait is autosomal dominant, what is the probability that individual III-6 can pass it on to his children?

3. Ataxia telangiectasia (AT) is an autosomal recessive condition. Homozygous recessive individuals are extremely sensitive to radiation damage, have impaired immunity, and are at high risk for developing certain cancers. Heterozygotes have higher-than-normal sensitivity to radiation. How is this possible, if the wild type gene is completely dominant?

4. Oguchi disease is an autosomal recessive form of night blindness. Normally, the eyes take from 10 to 30 minutes to adapt to darkness. In Oguchi disease, adaptation takes hours. To the right is a pedigree of an affected family. Why might this rare trait appear in the fifth generation?

5. Craniometaphyseal dysplasia is an overgrowth of facial bones that is autosomal dominant. It produces broad faces with large jaws and hearing loss and facial tics if too-large bones press on certain nerves. In the Perez family, two of the three daughters, and one of the two sons, have the condition. Their mother and maternal grandfather are also affected. Draw a pedigree for this family.

6. The Jackson Laboratory in Bar Harbor, Maine, has supplied genetically identical mice to researchers for decades. These mice are obtained by repeatedly crossing siblings, to generate strains that are homozygous for all genes. Cloning, however, would generate individuals that are identical, but may be

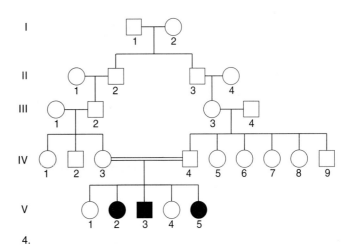

4.

heterozygous for some genes (see Reading 3.1). Why would the Jackson lab mice, when bred, yield offspring genetically identical to themselves, but cloned mice would not (assuming you could generate male and female cloned mice, which would require two sets of experiments)?

7. Achondroplasia is a common form of hereditary dwarfism that causes very short limbs, stubby hands, and an enlarged head. Below are four pedigrees depicting families with this specific type of dwarfism: What is the most likely mode of inheritance? Cite a reason for your answer.

8. Henri de Toulouse-Lautrec (1864–1901) was a French artist who had a form of

dwarfism called pycnodysostosis. His grandmothers were sisters, and his parents were first cousins.

a. Draw the portion of his pedigree indicating these relationships.

b. In Toulouse-Lautrec's generation, 4 of the 16 children, of both sexes, had the family dwarfism. It had not appeared in earlier generations. What does this information reveal about the probable mode of inheritance?

c. Toulouse-Lautrec's mother's sister married and had his cousins with his father's brother. How does this fact complicate drawing a pedigree? (Try it!)

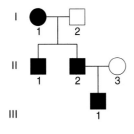 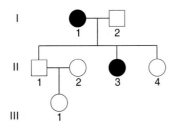 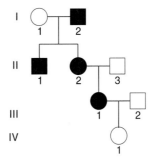 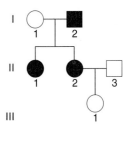

7.

9. Hereditary fructose intolerance is a liver enzyme deficiency inherited as an autosomal recessive trait. The affected individual cannot digest fruit sugar (fructose). When an infant begins to eat fruits, the undigested sugar causes vomiting, liver impairment, and difficulty gaining weight. However, people learn by trial-and-error which foods make them ill, and most gradually adopt a diet that enables them to maintain a healthy weight and avoid symptoms. To the right

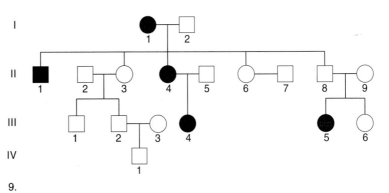

9.

is a pedigree tracing fructose intolerance in the Wolf family:

a. Even though autosomal recessive conditions typically skip generations, this one doesn't. Why not?

b. Who in the pedigree must be carriers (heterozygotes)?

c. If individual II-2 is not a carrier of fructose intolerance, what is the risk that individual III-1 is a carrier?

10. A couple has a child with an autosomal recessive form of glycogen storage disease, a deficiency of a lysosomal enzyme. An enlarged liver and heart and weak muscles cause the baby to die from heart and lung failure at 20 months. Now the woman is pregnant again. Her doctor offers her and her husband genetic counseling, but they decline, claiming familiarity with the laws of inheritance—since they have already had an affected child, they reason, the next three will be healthy. Why is their reasoning incorrect?

11. Caleb has a double row of eyelashes, which he inherited from his mother as a dominant trait. His maternal grandfather is the only other relative to have the trait. Veronica, a woman with normal eyelashes, falls madly in love with Caleb, and they marry. Their first child, Polly, has normal eyelashes. Now Veronica is pregnant again and hopes they will have a child who has double eyelashes. What chance does a child of Veronica and Caleb have of inheriting double eyelashes? Draw a pedigree of this family.

12. A man and woman want to have children, but each is a known carrier of Tay-Sachs disease. To avoid conceiving a child who will inherit this fatal disorder, the woman is artificially inseminated with sperm from a man who does not carry the Tay-Sachs gene. How is this procedure (discussed in chapter 20) a solution to the couple's problem?

13. The child in figure 4.20, who has red urine after eating beets, colored eyelids, and short fingers, is of genotype $bbHhEe$. If he has children with a woman who is a trihybrid for each of these genes, what are the genotypic and phenotypic ratios for their offspring?

14. In the pedigree below, individual III-1 died at age two of Tay-Sachs disease. The two people in the F_1 generation must therefore be carriers. What is the probability that each individual in the P_1 generation is a carrier?

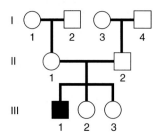

15. Chands syndrome is an autosomal recessive condition characterized by very curly hair, underdeveloped nails, and abnormally shaped eyelids. In the following pedigree, which individuals must be carriers?

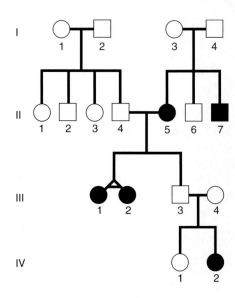

suggested readings

Bennett, Robin L., et al. March 1995. Recommendations for standardized human pedigree nomenclature. *The American Journal of Human Genetics,* vol. 56. Everything you need to know to draw a pedigree.

Derr, Mark. March 1996. The making of a marathon mutt. *Natural History.* Breeders of champion sled dogs consider Mendel's laws.

Elmer-Dewitt, Philip. October 5, 1992. Catching a bad gene in the tiniest of embryos. *Time.* Screening preimplantation embryos for autosomal recessive, disease-causing alleles validates Mendel's first law.

Frey, Julia B. June 1995. What dwarfed Toulouse-Lautrec? *Nature Genetics,* vol. 10. The famous French artist's family had an extremely complex, inbred pedigree.

Lewis, Ricki. December 1994. The evolution of a classic genetic tool. *BioScience,* vol. 44. Classical pedigrees embrace molecular information.

chapter five

Extensions and Exceptions to Mendel's Laws

A Family With Tourette Syndrome

The Simmons family knew that Anthony had some kind of medical problem. When he was seven years old, he began exhibiting facial tics, frequent blinking, and head jerking. Other habits weren't as obvious— repeatedly tapping objects, clearing his throat, and grimacing for no apparent reason. Because Anthony's father, Ralph, and Ralph's mother, May, also frequently grimaced, cleared their throats, and tapped things, everyone thought that Anthony was just imitating their quirks. But Anthony's sister Erica, a year older than he, didn't pick up these family habits, nor did older brother Tim.

Tim, however, had behavior problems at school. He would often shout foul language in class, and when the teacher reprimanded him, he'd just repeat her words. Sometimes if he got angry, he'd throw his books down and make a noise that sounded like a dog barking. Anthony's cousin Charles had similar problems at school, cursing and mimicking; the family attributed this to his spending time with Tim. Neither Anthony's other cousins, nor Charles's mother Eva, had these habits.

The Simmons' were surprised to learn that several family members have Tourette syndrome, a disorder that disrupts the distribution of a chemical in the brain. This chemical deficiency causes all of the symptoms seen in the family—not just Anthony's. The blinking, tics, grimaces, tapping, barking, and uncontrollable utterances are all characteristic of the syndrome. Before the media brought Tourette syndrome to public attention in the 1970s, and still today to some extent, affected individuals suffered greatly when onlookers interpreted their behavior as intentional.

Tourette syndrome can be inherited as an autosomal dominant trait, but, because it causes so many different symptoms, the inheritance pattern is often not obvious in a pedigree. Relatives can have different subsets of symptoms, the same symptoms to different degrees, or even inherit the causative gene but not show symptoms at all, yet pass it to children who do show symptoms. This was the case for Eva and her son Charles (figure 5.1). Tourette syndrome

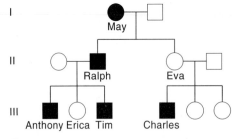

figure 5.1

A not-so-obvious Mendelian trait—Tourette syndrome. The Simmons family at first thought that Anthony was the only one with a medical problem. A genetic counselor carefully examined the family history, asking questions about everyone's quirks and behaviors, then drew a pedigree. She referred the family to a neurologist, who diagnosed Tourette syndrome in Ralph, May, Tim, and Charles. Tourette syndrome is sometimes inherited, usually as an autosomal dominant trait. Eva inherited the gene, but does not show symptoms. However, she passed the gene to Charles, who is affected.

illustrates how transmission of inherited traits is not always as straightforward as they were in Mendel's peas.

When Gene Expression Appears to Alter Mendelian Ratios

Mendel's crosses yielded offspring that were easily distinguished from each other. A pea is either yellow or green, round or wrinkled; a plant is either tall or short. For some characteristics, though, offspring classes do not occur in the proportions predicted by working out Punnett squares or probabilities. In other cases, transmission patterns of a visible trait are not consistent with the mode of inheritance, as was the case for Tourette syndrome in the Simmons family. In these instances, Mendel's laws operate, and the underlying genotypic ratios remain unchanged, but either the nature of the phenotype or influences from other genes or the environment alter phenotypic ratios. Following are several circumstances that appear to contradict Mendel's laws—although the laws actually still apply.

Lethal Allele Combinations

Genes begin to function soon after fertilization. Some allele combinations cause such severe problems in an embryo or fetus that development ceases, usually before the eighth week of gestation. Such an individual is never born and never seen as a phenotypic class of offspring. An allele that causes such early death is termed a **lethal allele.**

In humans, lethal alleles can cause spontaneous abortion (miscarriage). When a man and woman each carry a recessive lethal allele for the same gene, each pregnancy has a 25 percent chance of spontaneously aborting—this represents the homozygous recessive class. Alleles are sometimes also considered lethal if they cause death before a person is old enough to reproduce.

Sometimes a double dose of a dominant allele is lethal. This is the case for Mexican hairless dogs. Inheriting one dominant allele confers the coveted hairlessness trait, but inheriting two dominant alleles is lethal to the unlucky embryo. Breeders cross hairless to hairy ("powderpuff") dogs, rather than hairless to hairless, to avoid losing the lethal homozygous dominant class—a quarter of the pups, as figure 5.2 indicates.

Multiple Alleles

A person has two alleles for any autosomal gene (one allele on each homolog), but a gene can exist in more than two allelic forms because a gene can mutate in many ways. Different allele combinations can produce variations in phenotype. This is the case for congenital adrenal hyperplasia (CAH), an inborn error of metabolism in which an enzyme deficiency causes male sex hormones to build up. Four forms of the illness are known, each caused by a different combination of alleles:

1. In the salt-losing form of CAH, shock or death occurs in infancy because the kidneys cannot conserve sodium.

2. In the simple virilizing form, high levels of male sex hormones cause females to be born with very large clitorises, but normal female internal

Alleles
h = hair (wild type)
H = hairless (mutant)

Genotypes
HH
Hh
hh

Phenotypes
lethal
Mexican hairless
hairy

Cross 1

Mexican hairless   ×   Mexican hairless
Hh Hh

	H	h
H	HH	Hh
h	Hh	hh

$1/4$ die as embryos (HH)
Of survivors:
$2/3$ = Mexican hairless (Hh)
$1/3$ = hairy (hh)

1 : 2 : 1
hh Hh HH
hairy   Mexican   dead
      hairless

Cross 2

hairy   ×   Mexican hairless
hh Hh

	H	h
h	Hh	hh
h	Hh	hh

All survive:
$1/2$ = Mexican hairless
$1/2$ = hairy

1 : 1
hh Hh
hairy   Mexican
     hairless

b.

figure 5.2

Lethal alleles. (*a*) This Mexican hairless dog has inherited a dominant allele that makes the animal hairless. Inheriting two such dominant alleles is lethal during embryonic development. (*b*) Breeders cross Mexican hairless dogs to hairy ("powderpuff") dogs to avoid dead embryos and stillbirths that represent the *HH* genotypic class.

reproductive structures. Sometimes these genetic girls are mistaken for phenotypic boys. In both sexes, sexual maturity is early, with enlarged penises and clitorises, and bone growth is too rapid and ends too soon, causing short stature.

3. In the late onset variety of CAH, masculinization occurs in late childhood or during puberty, producing hirsutism (hairiness). Affected females have dark facial hair.

4. In the least severe or cryptic form of CAH, enzyme levels are not abnormal enough to cause symptoms.

Different Dominance Relationships

Recall that in complete dominance, one allele is expressed, while the other isn't. Alternatively, some genes show **incomplete dominance,** in which the heterozygous phenotype is intermediate between that of either homozygote. In familial hypercholesterolemia (FH), for example, a person with two disease-causing alleles completely lacks receptors on liver cells that take up cholesterol from the bloodstream. A person with one disease-causing allele has half the normal number of cholesterol receptors. Someone with two wild type alleles has the normal number of receptors. The phenotypes parallel the number of receptors—those with two mutant alleles die as children of heart attacks, those with one mutant allele may die in young adulthood, and those with two wild type alleles do not develop this inherited form of heart disease.

A classic example of incomplete dominance is the snapdragon plant. A red-flowered plant of genotype *RR* crossed to a white-flowered *rr* plant can give rise to a *Rr* plant—which has pink flowers. This intermediate color is presumably due to an intermediate amount of pigment.

Different alleles that are both expressed in a heterozygote are **codominant.** Two alleles of the I gene, which determines ABO blood type, are codominant. People of blood type A have a molecule called antigen *A* on the surfaces of their red blood cells. Blood type B corresponds to red blood cells with antigen *B*. A person with type AB has red blood cells with both the *A* and *B* antigens, and the red cells of a person with type O blood have neither antigen.

The *I* gene encodes the enzymes that place the *A* and *B* antigens on red blood cell surfaces. The three alleles are I^A, I^B, and *i*. People with type A blood may be either genotype $I^A I^A$ or $I^A i$; type B corresponds to $I^B I^B$ or $I^B i$; type AB to $I^A I^B$; and type O to *ii*. Even though the I^A and I^B alleles are codominant, they segregate between generations (figure 5.3). ABO blood types are discussed further in chapter 13.

Epistasis—When One Gene Masks Expression of Another

Mendel's laws can appear to not operate when one gene masks the effect of a different gene, a phenomenon called **epistasis.** (Do not confuse this with dominance relationships between alleles of the same gene.) The Bombay phenotype, for example, is a result of two interacting genes: the *I* and *H* genes. The relationship of these two genes affects the expression of the ABO blood type.

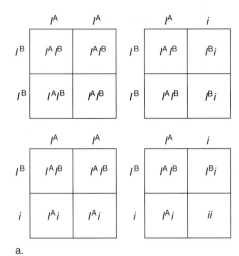

a.

figure 5.3

(a) The I^A and I^B alleles of the I gene are codominant, but they follow Mendel's law of segregation. These Punnett squares follow the genotypes of four ways of crossing a person with type A blood with a person with type B blood. Is it possible for parents with type A and type B blood to have a child who is type O? (b) ABO blood types are based on antigens on red blood cell surfaces.

The product of the H allele is an enzyme that inserts a sugar molecule onto a particular glycoprotein on the red blood cell surface. The recessive allele h produces an inactive form of the enzyme that cannot insert the sugar. The A and B antigens attach to the sugar molecule that the H gene controls. As long as at least one H allele is present, the ABO genotype dictates the ABO blood type. However, in a person with genotype hh, the A and B antigens cannot adhere to the red blood cell, and they fall away. The person has blood type O based on phenotype (a blood test), but may have any ABO genotype (figure 5.4).

Penetrance and Expressivity

The same allele combination can produce different degrees of a phenotype in different individuals, even siblings, because of influences such as nutrition, toxic exposures, other illnesses, and other genes. Most disease-causing allele combinations are **completely penetrant,** which means that everyone who inherits the combination has some symptoms. A genotype is **incompletely penetrant** if some individuals

Blood Group	Antigens on Red Blood Cells
A	
B	
AB	
O	

b.

do not express the phenotype, or have no symptoms. Polydactyly, having extra fingers or toes, is incompletely penetrant (figure 5.5). Some people who inherit the dominant allele have more than five digits on a hand or foot, yet others who are known to have the allele (because they have an affected parent and child) have the normal number of fingers and toes. The penetrance of a gene is described numerically. If 80 of 100 people who have inherited the dominant polydactyly allele have extra digits, the allele is 80 percent penetrant.

A phenotype is **variably expressive** if the symptoms vary in intensity in different people. One person with polydactyly might have an extra digit on both hands and a foot; another might have two extra digits on both hands and both feet; a third person might have just one extra fingertip on a finger. Penetrance refers to the all-or-none expression of a genotype; expressivity refers to the severity of the expression.

Pleiotropy—One Gene, Many Effects

A Mendelian disorder with many symptoms is termed **pleiotropic.** Such conditions can be difficult to trace through families because people with different subsets of symptoms may look as though they have different disorders (as occurred in the Simmons family, described as the chapter opened).

Pleiotropy occurs when a single protein affects different parts of the body or participates in more than one type of biochemical reaction. This is the case for Marfan syndrome, an autosomal dominant defect in an elastic connective tissue protein called fibrillin. The protein is abundant in the lens of the eye, in the aorta (the largest artery in the body, leading from the heart), and in the bones of the limbs, fingers, and ribs. Once researchers knew this, the Marfan syndrome symptoms of lens dislocation, long limbs, spindly fingers, and a caved-in chest made sense. The most serious symptom is a life-threatening weakening in the aorta wall, sometimes causing the vessel to suddenly burst. However, if the weakening is detected early, a synthetic graft can be inserted to replace the weakened section of artery wall.

Another autosomal dominant, pleiotropic disease, porphyria, had interesting effects on the royal families of Europe. King George III ruled England during the American Revolution (figure 5.6). At age fifty, he first experienced abdominal pain and constipation, followed by weak limbs, fever, a fast pulse, hoarseness, and dark red urine. Next, nervous system symptoms began, including insomnia, headaches, visual problems, restlessness, delirium, convulsions, and stupor. His confused and racing thoughts, combined with his ripping off his

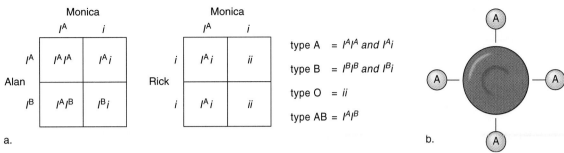

type A = $I^A I^A$ and $I^A i$

type B = $I^B I^B$ and $I^B i$

type O = ii

type AB = $I^A I^B$

b.

figure 5.4

(a) Gene masking at "General Hospital." Monica has just had a baby. Is the father Alan or Rick? Monica's blood type is A, Alan's is AB, and Rick's is O. The child's blood type is O. Considering only the ABO blood type, it looks as if Rick is the father. Whether Monica's genotype is $I^A i$ or $I^A I^A$, she cannot have a type O child with Alan, whose genotype is $I^A I^B$. If Monica's genotype is $I^A i$, she could have a type O child with Rick, whose genotype is ii.

But nosy nurse Amy, who has just learned about the Bombay phenotype, suggests that the baby have a blood test to see if he manufactures the H protein and that the adults look into their family histories to see if any other relatives' blood types are incompatible with their parents' blood types. Sure enough, the baby is of genotype hh, and Alan's family has several ABO blood type incompatibilities. Monica and Alan are Hh, but Rick is HH. The baby has a type O phenotype, but his ABO genotype can be either $I^A I^A$, $I^A i$, $I^B i$, or $I^A I^B$. What he cannot be is Rick's son.

(b) The effect of an hh genotype. A and B antigens, dictated by the I genotype, cannot bind and are therefore not expressed.

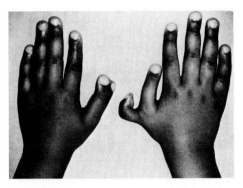

figure 5.5

The dominant allele that causes polydactyly is incompletely penetrant and variably expressive. Some people who inherit the allele have the normal number of fingers and toes. Those in whom the allele is penetrant express the phenotype to differing degrees.

figure 5.6

King George III suffered from the autosomal dominant disorder porphyria—and so did several other family members. Because of pleiotropy, the family's varied illnesses and quirks appeared to be different, unrelated disorders.

wig and running about naked while at the peak of a fever, convinced court observers that the king was mad. Just as Parliament was debating his ability to rule, he mysteriously recovered.

But George's plight was far from over. He relapsed thirteen years later, then again three years after that. Always the symptoms appeared in the same order, beginning with abdominal pain, fever, and weakness and progressing to nervous system symptoms. Finally, an attack in 1811 placed George in a prolonged stupor, and

the Prince of Wales dethroned him. George III lived for several more years, experiencing further episodes.

In George III's time, doctors were permitted to do very little to the royal body, and they simply made their diagnoses based on what the king told them. Twentieth-century researchers found that an inborn error of metabolism, porphyria, caused George's red urine. Because of the absence of an enzyme, part of the blood pigment hemoglobin called a porphyrin ring is routed into the urine instead of

being broken down and metabolized by cells. Porphyrin builds up and attacks the nervous system, causing many of the symptoms. Examination of physician's reports on George's relatives—easy to obtain for a royal family—showed that several of them had symptoms of porphyria as well. Before the realization that porphyria is pleiotropic, the royal disorder appeared to be several different illnesses.

Porphyria is rare, and people with it are often misdiagnosed as having a seizure disorder. Unfortunately, some seizure medications, as well as certain anesthetics, worsen porphyria's symptoms.

Phenocopies—When It's Not in the Genes

An environmentally caused trait that appears to be inherited is called a **phenocopy**. Such a trait can either resemble a Mendelian disorder's symptoms or mimic inheritance by occurring in certain relatives. The limb birth defect caused by the drug thalidomide, discussed in chapter 3, is a phenocopy of the inherited illness phocomelia. An infection can also appear to be a Mendelian disorder. Children who have AIDS may contract the infection from HIV positive parents. But these children acquire AIDS by viral infection, not by inheriting a gene.

table 5.1

Factors That Alter Mendelian Phenotypic Ratios

Phenomenon	Effect on Phenotype	Example
Lethal alleles	A phenotypic class dies very early in development	Spontaneous abortion
Multiple alleles	Produces many variants of a phenotype	Congenital adrenal hyperplasia
Incomplete dominance	A heterozygote's phenotype is intermediate between those of two homozygotes	Snapdragon flower color
Codominance	A heterozygote's phenotype is distinct from and not intermediate between those of the two homozygotes	ABO blood types
Epistasis	One gene masks another's phenotype	Bombay phenotype
Penetrance	Some individuals inheriting a particular genotype do not have the associated phenotype	Polydactyly
Expressivity	A genotype is associated with a phenotype of varying intensity	Polydactyly
Pleiotropy	The phenotype includes many symptoms, with different subsets in different individuals	Porphyria
Phenocopy	An environmentally caused condition whose symptoms and recurrence in a family make it appear to be inherited	Infection
Genetic heterogeneity	Different genotypes associated with same phenotype. Carriers of different genes would not have offspring at a high risk of inheriting phenotype	Hearing impairment

Genetic Heterogeneity—More than One Way to Inherit a Trait

Different genes can produce phenotypes that are clinically indistinguishable. **Genetic heterogeneity** is at work when a phenotype can be caused by more than one gene at a time. Genetic heterogeneity can make it appear that Mendel's laws are not operating. For example, 132 forms of deafness are transmitted as autosomal recessive traits. If a man who is heterozygous for a deafness gene on one chromosome has a child with a woman who is heterozygous for a deafness gene on a different chromosome, then that child faces only the general population risk of inheriting either form of deafness. He or she *doesn't* face the 25 percent risk that Mendel's law predicts for a monohybrid cross because the parents are heterozygous for *different* genes. Cleft palate and albinism are other traits exhibiting genetic heterogeneity—that is, different genes can cause them.

Genetic heterogeneity can occur when genes encode different enzymes that participate in the same biochemical pathway. For example, eleven biochemical reactions lead to blood clot formation. Clotting disorders may result from abnormalities in genes specifying any of these enzymes, leading to several types of bleeding disorders.

Table 5.1 summarizes phenomena that appear to alter Mendelian inheritance.

Key Concepts

A number of factors can appear to disrupt Mendelian ratios. A lethal allele combination is not seen as a progeny class. Different allele combinations may produce different phenotypes. In incomplete dominance, the heterozygote phenotype is intermediate between those of the homozygotes, and in codominance, two different alleles are each expressed. In epistasis, one gene masks expression of another. Finally, genotypes vary in penetrance (percent of individuals affected) and expressivity (intensity of symptoms) of the phenotype.

A gene with more than one expression is pleiotropic. A trait caused by the environment but resembling a known genetic trait or occurring in certain family members is a phenocopy. Genetic heterogeneity occurs when different genes cause the same phenotype.

When Mendel's Laws Do Not Apply

Gregor Mendel derived the two laws of inheritance working with traits that genes located on different chromosomes in the nucleus confer. When genes do not conform to these conditions, however, the associated traits may not appear in Mendelian ratios. The remainder of this chapter considers three types of gene transmission that do not fulfill the requirements for Mendelian inheritance.

Maternal Inheritance and Mitochondrial Genes

The genes that Mendel studied were part of chromosomes in pea plant cell nuclei. The basis of the law of segregation is that both parents contribute these genes equally to offspring. This is not the case for genes in mitochondria, the organelles that house the biochemical reactions that provide cellular energy.

Inheritance patterns and mutation rates for mitochondrial genes differ form those for nuclear genes, for a number of reasons (table 5.2). First, mitochondrial genes are maternally inherited, which means that they are passed only from an individual's mother. This is because sperm do not contribute mitochondria when they fertilize an oocyte. Maternal inheritance produces distinctive pedigrees. A woman passes a mitochondrial trait to all her children, while an affected male cannot pass the trait to any of his children, as the pedigree in figure 5.7 illustrates.

table 5.2

Features of Mitochondrial DNA

No crossing over

No DNA repair

Maternal inheritance

Many copies per mitochondrion and per cell

High exposure to oxygen free radicals

No histones

No introns

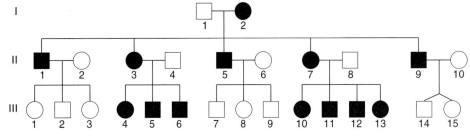

figure 5.7

This pedigree shows the distinctive transmission pattern of a mitochondrial gene mutation. Mothers pass the gene to all offspring. Fathers do not transmit mitochondrial genes, because sperm do not contribute mitochondria to fertilized ova.

Mitochondrial DNA is DNA, but its functioning differs in key ways. For example, this DNA does not cross over. Mitochondrial DNA also mutates faster than nuclear DNA for two reasons. One, it lacks DNA repair enzymes. Secondly, the mitochondrion is the site of the energy reactions that produce oxygen free radicals that damage DNA. Also, mitochondrial DNA is not wrapped in histone proteins, as nuclear DNA is, nor are genes interrupted by sequences called introns that do not encode protein (histones and introns are discussed in the next unit). Finally, inheritance of mitochondrial genes differs from inheritance of nuclear genes simply because a cell has one nucleus but many mitochondria—and each mitochondrion harbors several copies of its "chromosome" (figure 5.8).

The mitochondrial DNA, sometimes called our "twenty-fifth chromosome," consists of 16,569 nucleotide bases that include 37 genes as well as apparently noncoding sequences. Of the 37 genes, 22 encode tRNA molecules; 2 encode rRNA molecules; and 13 encode proteins that function in cellular respiration, the biochemical reactions that use energy from digested nutrients to produce ATP, the biological energy molecule.

Because the two main functions of mitochondrial DNA are protein synthesis and energy production, diseases resulting from mutations affect these two vital and general processes. These disorders tend to affect tissue with many mitochondria, such as skeletal (voluntary) muscle. It isn't surprising that a major symptom is often profound fatigue. A class of inherited illnesses called mitochondrial myopathies,

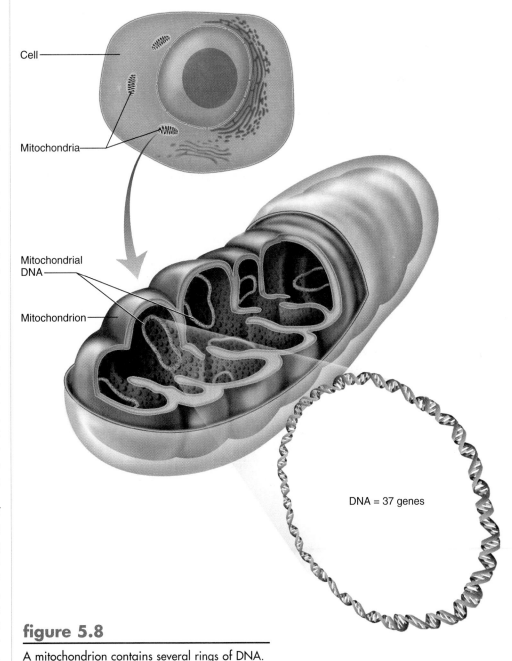

figure 5.8

A mitochondrion contains several rings of DNA.

for example, produces weak and flaccid muscles and intolerance to exercise. The abnormally shaped mitochondria appear red and ragged when stained and viewed under a microscope.

A defect in an energy-related gene, however, can produce symptoms other than fatigue. This is the case for the first maternally inherited illness to be noted, Leber's hereditary optic neuropathy (LHON). This visual problem was described in 1871 and its maternal transmission noted, but it was not associated with a mitochondrial mutation that impairs electron transport in the energy reactions until 1988. Symptoms of LHON usually begin in early adulthood with a loss of central vision. Eyesight worsens and color vision vanishes, as the central portion of the optic nerve degenerates.

A mutation in a mitochondrial gene encoding a tRNA or rRNA can be devastating because it affects protein synthesis, a process with widespread importance. Consider what happened to Linda Schneider, a once active and articulate dental hygienist and travel agent. In her forties, Linda gradually began to slow down at work. She heard a buzzing in her ears and developed difficulty in talking and walking. Then her memory would fade in and out, she would become lost easily in familiar places, and her conversation would not make sense. Her condition worsened, and she developed diabetes, seizures, and pneumonia and became deaf and demented. After many false diagnoses, which included stroke, Alzheimer disease, and a prior disorder, she was finally found to have a mitochondrial illness called MELAS. This stands for "mitochondrial encephalopathy lactic acidosis syndrome." Linda died. Her son and daughter will likely develop the condition because of the pattern of transmission of a mitochondrial mutation.

The fact that a cell contains many mitochondria makes possible a condition called **heteroplasmy,** in which a particular mutation may be present in some mitochondria, but not others—within the same cell (figure 5.9). At each cell division, the mitochondria distribute at random into daughter cells. Because of the laws of probability, after time, cells tend to acquire mitochondria of the same type (mutant or

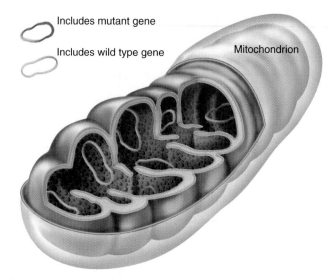

figure 5.9

In heteroplasmy, mitochondrial "chromosomes" can have different alleles.

not). But a person might have cells with predominantly mutation-bearing mitochondria, and other cells whose mitochondria have the wild type allele.

Heteroplasmy has several consequences for the inheritance of mitochondrial phenotypes. Expressivity may vary widely among siblings, depending upon how many mutation-bearing mitochondria were in the oocyte that became each brother or sister. Severity of symptoms among siblings also is influenced by which tissues have cells whose mitochondria bear the mutation. This is the case for a family with Leigh syndrome, which affects the enzyme that directly produces ATP. Two boys died of the severe form of the disorder because the brain regions that control movement rapidly degenerated. Another child was blind and had central nervous system degeneration. Several relatives, however, suffer only mild impairment of their peripheral vision. The more severely affected family members had more brain cells that received the mutation-bearing mitochondria.

The most severe mitochondrial illnesses are heteroplasmic. This is because homoplasmy—all mitochondria bearing the mutant gene—too severely impairs protein synthesis or energy production for development to proceed. Often, heteroplasmic, severe mitochondrial disorders do not produce symptoms until adulthood

because it takes many cell divisions, and therefore time, for a cell to receive enough mitochondria bearing mutant genes for harm to occur. LHON usually occurs in adulthood for this reason.

Mitochondrial diseases are rare—as far as we know. But mitochondrial DNA may play an important role in normal aging. This is suggested by the fact that the symptoms of mitochondrial illnesses tend to be the same as those seen in aging-related disorders, such as fatigue and degenerative changes. Perhaps accumulation of free radicals and of mutations that occur in mitochondrial DNA over a lifetime are part of normal aging. Individuals with mutations in mitochondrial DNA might experience these changes early, as disease symptoms.

Interest in mitochondrial DNA extends beyond the medical. Comparing mitochondrial DNA is a powerful forensic tool used to establish paternity, link accused criminals to crimes, and identify war dead. Mitochondrial DNA comparisons confirmed that the body in Jesse James's grave is truly he and solved the mystery of the Romanov family in Russia, which is detailed in Reading 8.1. Mitochondrial DNA analysis also reveals relationships among our immediate ancestors, as explained in chapter 14. It was critical, for example, in confirming that our species probably did not interbreed with the Neanderthals.

An Exception to Segregation— Uniparental Disomy

According to the law of segregation, parents contribute equally, gene by gene, to offspring. However, occasionally an offspring inherits two copies of a gene (or genes) from one parent, yet none from the other. This is called **uniparental disomy,** which literally means "two bodies from one parent." Uniparental disomy is a true exception to Mendel's first law in that one parent contributes two genes.

Uniparental disomy is a recent discovery. In 1988, Arthur Beaudet of the Baylor College of Medicine saw a very unusual cystic fibrosis patient. Beaudet was comparing CF alleles in the patient and her parents. Oddly, only the mother was a CF carrier— the father had two wild type alleles. Didn't both parents have to carry CF for a child to inherit the disorder? Plus, neither of the patient's seventh largest chromosomes, the home of the CF gene, matched her father's—both came from her mother (figure 5.10). How did this happen?

Apparently, in the patient's mother, an error in the separation of chromatids for each chromosome 7 in meiosis II led to formation of an oocyte bearing two identical chromosome 7s, instead of one. (This is a phenomenon called nondisjunction that is discussed further in chapter 11.) The unlucky patient had inherited two copies of her mother's CF-bearing chromosome 7 and none from her father. In effect, inheriting two of the same chromosome from one parent shatters the protection offered by combining genetic material, which is the defining characteristic of sexual reproduction.

The woman with CF had the pair of chromosomes inherited from her mother in all of her cells, indicating that her condition was present from conception. Uniparental disomy can also occur in somatic tissue, affecting only part of a person's body. This happens in Beckwith-Wiedemann syndrome, which causes kidney and adrenal tumors, an enlarged tongue, and other symptoms. These tumor cells can carry two copies of a gene inherited from one parent, while the person's other cells are heterozygous for the same gene. Several childhood cancers are also associated with uniparental disomy.

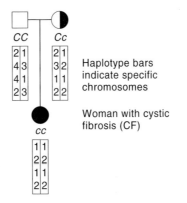

figure 5.10

Uniparental disomy doubles one parent's genetic contribution. According to the law of segregation, a child with cystic fibrosis (CF) cannot be born to a person who is homozygous dominant for the wild type allele. But it can happen. One way is for the wild type allele to mutate in the gamete that develops into the affected individual. But examinations of DNA sequences on the chromosome that includes the CFTR gene show mutation did not occur here. The numbers on the bars enable researchers to trace the parental origins of particular chromosomes. Instead, the woman with CF inherited two copies of her mother's chromosome 7, and neither of her father's. Unfortunately, it was the chromosome with the disease-causing allele that she inherited in a double dose.

Uniparental disomy may explain two syndromes associated with a particular region of the fifteenth largest chromosome. The disorders may actually be different expressions of the same gene, depending upon which parent transmits it. A phenotype that is different depending upon the sex of the parent who passes it on is subject to **genomic imprinting.** Uniparental disomy is one way that genomic imprinting can occur. Chapter 6 discusses another mechanism for differential gene expression depending upon the sex of the parent.

Two disorders that exhibit genomic imprinting caused by uniparental disomy are Prader-Willi syndrome and Angelman syndrome. These extremely rare disorders, which both cause mental retardation, are sometimes associated with missing genetic material on chromosome 15. A child with Prader-Willi syndrome (figure 5.11) is obese, has small hands and feet, eats

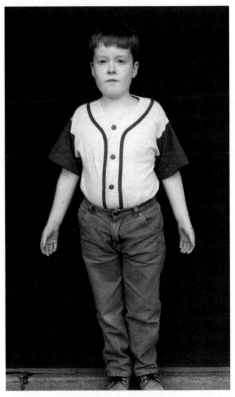

a.

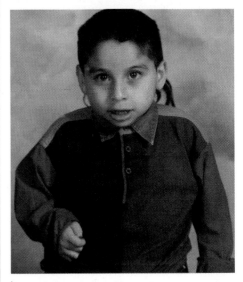

b.

figure 5.11

Two syndromes resulting from missing genetic material in the same chromosomal region. (a) Tyler has Prader-Willi syndrome. Note his small hands and feet. (b) Angelman syndrome also causes mental retardation, but the other symptoms differ from those of Prader-Willi syndrome. Note the distinctive features of this child's face, described originally as a "happy puppet."

uncontrollably, and does not develop signs of puberty. Angelman syndrome was first described in 1967 as "happy puppet syndrome" because of the affected child's appearance. He or she has an extended tongue, poor muscle coordination that gives a "floppy" appearance, a large jaw, laughs uncontrollably and excessively, and has peculiar convulsions in which the arms flap.

In 1989, researchers studied the chromosome region affected in Prader-Willi syndrome in several children. Surprisingly, in 40 percent of the cases, the regions on each homolog matched the mothers' chromosomes. Yet the chromosomes lacked the corresponding DNA from the father, which should have been there, according to the law of segregation. (In the other 60 percent of cases, a piece of missing DNA in one gene allowed only one parent's gene to be expressed.)

For Angelman syndrome, the situation was reversed. Children have a double dose of their father's DNA for the same chromosomal region implicated in Prader-Willi syndrome, with no maternal contribution. Could Prader-Willi and Angelman syndromes be different gender-directed manifestations of the same genetic variant? It seems so. Perhaps we will learn more as the story of this intriguing exception to Mendel's laws continues to unfold.

Linkage

Mendel's pea traits, although he did not know it, were conferred by genes on different chromosomes. When genes are on the same chromosome, they cannot separate during meiosis. Instead, they are packaged into the same gametes (figure 3.8). **Linkage** refers to the transmission of genes on the same chromosome. Linked genes do not assort independently and do not result in the predicted Mendelian ratios for crosses tracking two or more genes.

The unexpected ratios indicating linkage were first observed by William Bateson and R. C. Punnett in the early 1900s, again in pea plants. Bateson and Punnett crossed true-breeding plants with purple flowers and long pollen grains (genotype *PPLL*) to true-breeding plants with red flowers and round pollen grains (genotype *ppll*). The F_1 plants, of genotype *PpLl*, were then crossed

table 5.3

Observed and Expected Phenotypes for a Dihybrid Cross for Flower Color and Shape of Pollen Grain

Phenotype/ Genotype (P = purple flowers, p = red flowers) (L = long grain, l = round grain)	Number of Observed Plants	Number of Expected Plants (from 9:3:3:1 ratio)
Purple, long (*P_L_*)	284	215
Purple, round (*P_ll*)	21	71
Red, long (*ppL_*)	21	71
Red, round (*ppll*)	55	24
	381	381

among each other. Though Mendel's laws would predict a 9:3:3:1 ratio for an independently assorting, dihybrid cross, the F_2 generation did not demonstrate this ratio (table 5.3).

Bateson and Punnett noticed that two types of F_2 peas—those with the parental phenotypes *P_L_* and *ppll*—were more abundant than predicted, yet the other two progeny classes—*ppL_* and *P_ll*—were less common. The more prevalent parental allele combinations, Bateson and Punnett hypothesized, could reflect genes that are transmitted on the same chromosome and that therefore do not separate during meiosis (figure 5.12a). The two less common offspring classes could also be explained by a meiotic event—crossing over. Recall that this is an exchange between homologs that mixes up maternal and paternal gene combinations without disturbing the sequence of genes on the chromosome (figure 5.12b).

Progeny that exhibit this mixing of maternal and paternal alleles on a single chromosome are **recombinant.** *Parental* and *recombinant* are relative terms. Had the parents in Bateson and Punnett's crosses been of genotypes *ppL_* and *P_ll*, then *P_L_* and *ppll* would be recombinant rather than parental classes.

Two other terms are used to describe the arrangement of linked genes in heterozygotes. Consider a pea plant with genotype *PpLl*. These alleles can occur on the chromosomes in either of two ways. If the two dominant alleles are on one chromosome and the

two recessive alleles are transmitted on the other, the genes are in "coupling." In the opposite configuration, the genes are in "repulsion" (figure 5.13). This distinction is important; alleles in coupling tend to be transmitted together because they reside on the same homolog. However, alleles on different homologs separate at meiosis and are not transmitted together.

Researchers often symbolize groups of known alleles or DNA sequences linked on a certain chromosome in a notation called a **haplotype.** The bars in figure 5.10 are haplotypes. Haplotypes are sometimes depicted beneath pedigree symbols so that researchers can follow the inheritance of specific chromosomes as well as phenotypes.

If a specific haplotype appears only in family members with a particular inherited illness, and not in healthy individuals older than the age at which symptoms typically appear, detecting the telltale chromosome in younger people can provide a presymptomatic diagnosis of the family's disorder. Detecting a gene or DNA sequence linked to a disease-causing gene, and using it to predict the disease-causing gene's presence, is called genetic marker technology. It is discussed further in chapter 20.

Linkage Maps

As Bateson and Punnett were learning about linkage from pea crosses, geneticist Thomas Hunt Morgan and his coworkers

figure 5.12

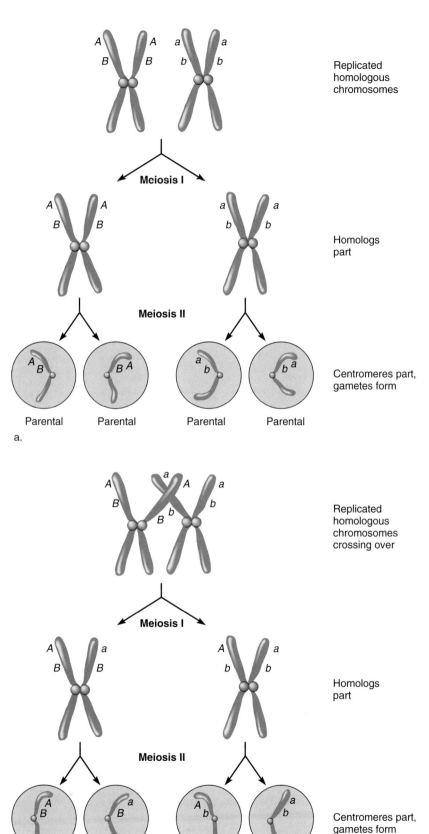

a.

b.

Inheritance of linked genes. (*a*) Genes that are linked closely to one another on the same chromosome are usually inherited together when that chromosome is packaged into a gamete. (*b*) Linkage between two genes can be interrupted if the chromosome they are located on crosses over with its homolog at a point between the two genes. Such crossing over packages recombinant arrangements of the genes into gametes.

at Columbia University were observing the results of crosses in the fruit fly *Drosophila melanogaster*. Morgan and his colleagues, like Bateson and Punnett, were comparing progeny class sizes to assess whether various combinations of two traits were linked. As data accumulated, the researchers realized that the pairs of traits were falling into four groups. Within each group, crossed dihybrids did not produce offspring according to the proportions Mendel's second law predicts. Not coincidentally, the number of these linkage groups—four—is exactly the number of chromosome pairs in the organism. The traits fell into four groups based on progeny class proportions because the genes controlling traits inherited together travel on the same chromosome.

Morgan wondered why the size of the recombinant classes varied depending upon which genes were studied. Might the differences reflect the physical relationship of the genes on the chromosome? Exploration of this idea fell to an undergraduate, Alfred Sturtevant. In 1911, Sturtevant developed a theory and technique that would profoundly affect the fledgling genetics of his day and the medical genetics of today. He proposed that, the farther apart two genes are on a chromosome, the more likely they are to engage in a crossover simply because there is more physical distance between the two genes.

The correlation between crossover frequency and the distance between genes is used to construct **linkage maps,** which are diagrams showing the order of genes on chromosomes and the relative distances between them. The frequency with which a crossover occurs between any two linked genes is inferred from the proportion of offspring that are recombinant. Genes at different ends of the same chromosome often cross over, generating a large recombinant class. But a crossover would rarely separate genes lying very close on the chromosome.

How Geneticists Develop Linkage Maps

As the twentieth century progressed, genes were rapidly mapped on all four chromosomes of the fruit fly, and along the human X chromosome. Mapping genes on the X chromosome was easier than doing so on the autosomes, because in human males, with their single X chromosome, recessive alleles on the X are expressed, a point we will return to in the next chapter.

By 1950, genetic researchers began to contemplate the daunting task of mapping genes on the 22 human autosomes. To start, a gene must be matched to its chromosome. Gene mapping began with the association of a particular chromosome abnormality with a physical trait. Matching phenotypes to chromosomal variants, a field called **cytogenetics,** is the subject of chapter 13.

In 1968, researchers were able to assign the first human autosomal gene to a chromosome. R. P. Donohue was observing chromosomes in his own white blood cells when he noticed a dark area consistently located near the centromere of one member of his largest chromosome pair (chromosome 1). He then examined chromosomes from several family members for the constriction, noting also whether each family member had a blood type called Duffy. (Blood types are inherited and refer to the patterns of proteins on red blood cell surfaces.) Donohue found that the Duffy blood type was linked to the chromosome variant. That is, he could predict a relative's Duffy blood type by whether or not the chromosome had the telltale dark area.

Finding a chromosomal abnormality and using it to detect linkage to another gene is a valuable but rarely found clue. More often, researchers must rely on the same sorts of experiments as Sturtevant conducted on his flies—calculating percent recombination (crossovers) between two genes. However, because humans do not have hundreds of offspring, as fruit flies do, obtaining sufficient data to estab-

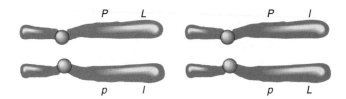

a. Coupling   b. Repulsion

P = Purple flowers
p = Red flowers
L = Long pollen grains
l = Round pollen grains

figure 5.13

Coupling and repulsion. A dihybrid for linked genes may carry those genes in coupling (both recessive or both dominant on the same homolog) (a) or in repulsion (one recessive and one dominant allele on the same homolog) (b). The significance of this distinction is that genes on the same homolog are transmitted together when gametes form.

Parent 1			Parent 2	
$\dfrac{r\ e}{r\ e}$			$\dfrac{R\ E}{r\ e}$	
Rh^-, no anemia			Rh^+, anemia	
			frequency	phenotype
parental F$_1$ genotypes		$\dfrac{r\ e}{r\ e}$	48%	Rh^-, no anemia
		$\dfrac{R\ E}{r\ e}$	48%	Rh^+, anemia
recombinant F$_1$ genotypes		$\dfrac{R\ e}{r\ e}$	2%	Rh^+, no anemia
		$\dfrac{r\ E}{r\ e}$	2%	Rh^-, anemia

figure 5.14

If we know the allele configurations of the parental generation, we can calculate the parental and recombinant class frequencies by pooling family data.

lish linkage relationships requires observing traits in many families and pooling the information.

Linkage and recombination can be observed directly in humans with an approach called **sperm typing.** In this technique, researchers use DNA probes to detect specific alleles of two linked genes in sperm cells. Because sperm are haploid, any of these alleles detected in a sperm cell must be present on the same homolog. If the allele configuration (coupling or repulsion) in the man's somatic cells is known, the researcher can calculate a recombination frequency by determining

the fraction of sperm cells that carry the alleles in a different configuration. Since sperm are plentiful in even a single ejaculate, they provide an enormous sample. Conceptually, sperm typing is thus the human equivalent of observing X-linked traits in hundreds of fruit flies.

As an idealized example of determining the degree of linkage by percent recombination, consider the traits of Rh blood type (*RR* and *Rr* give the more common Rh positive type; *rr* designates the Rh negative type) and a form of anemia called elliptocytosis (in which a dominant allele *E* causes the anemia) (figure 5.14). (Rh blood type is

Following Linked Genes: Blood Type and Nail-Patella Syndrome   reading 5.1

Greg and Susan met at a party and began talking because they each had oddly shaped finger and toenails as well as peculiar kneecaps. They fell in love, and when they eventually wed and thought about having children, they wondered if their offspring would inherit the unusual nails and kneecaps. To their surprise, a geneticist friend told them she could make predictions about their children if she knew their ABO blood types, using data obtained from many families that indicate how closely linked the two genes are.

Greg and Susan each had inherited nail-patella syndrome, a dominant trait whose gene resides on chromosome 9, a short distance—10 recombination map units—from the I gene that determines ABO blood type. Greg was type A, and Susan type B. The young couple was curious to find out what their chances were of having a child with nail-patella syndrome as well as the rare blood type AB. To tell them, the geneticist needed to determine the allele configurations for these two genes in Greg and Susan. She did so by questioning them about their parents.

Greg's mother also had peculiar nails and kneecaps, and she had type A blood. His father had normal nails and type O blood. Therefore, Greg must have inherited the dominant nail-patella syndrome allele (N) and the I^A allele from his mother, on the same homolog. Because his father had

normal nails and type O blood, Greg's other chromosome 9 must carry the alleles n and i.

Susan's mother had odd nails and type O blood, and so Susan inherited N and i on the same chromosome. Because her father had normal nails and type B blood, her homolog bears n and I^B.

What are the chances that Greg and Susan's child will have normal nails and the most common blood type, O? The only way

this genotype can arise is if a ni sperm (which occurs with a frequency of 45 percent, based on pooled data) fertilizes a ni oocyte (which occurs 5 percent of the time). The result—according to the product rule—is a 2.25 percent chance of producing a child with the $nnii$ genotype. This is also the same chance a child has of being born with nail-patella syndrome along with the rare blood type AB. Can you use the information in figure 1 to determine how this might happen?

	Greg		Susan
Phenotype	nail-patella syndrome, type A blood		nail-patella syndrome, type B blood
Genotype	NnI^A __		NnI^B __
Allele configuration	$N \parallel n$ $I^A \parallel i$		$N \parallel n$ $i \parallel I^B$
Gametes:	sperm	frequency	oocytes
Parental	$N\ I^A$	45%	$N\ i$
	$n\ i$	45%	$n\ I^B$
Recombinants	$N\ i$	5%	$N\ I^B$
	$n\ I^A$	5%	$n\ i$

figure 1

Greg inherited the N and I^A alleles from his mother, and that is why the alleles are on the same chromosome. His n and i alleles must therefore be on the homolog. Susan inherited alleles N and i from her mother, and n and I^B from her father. Population-based probabilities are used to calculate the likelihood of phenotypes in the offspring of this couple.

actually determined by several closely linked genes, but we will consider it to be a single gene here for simplicity.)

Suppose that in 100 one-child families, one parent is Rh negative with no anemia (*rree*), and the other parent is Rh positive with anemia (*RrEe*). Of the 100 offspring, 96 have parental genotypes, and 4 individuals are recombinants for these two genes. Percent recombination is therefore 4 percent, and the two linked genes are said to be 4 **map units** apart.

A map begins to emerge when percent recombination is known between all possible pairs of three linked genes. Consider genes x, y, and z. If the percent recombination between x and y is 10, between x and z is 4, and between z and y is 6, then the order of the genes on the chromosome is x-z-y (figure 5.15). Knowing the percent recombination between linked genes is useful in filling in genetic maps and also in predicting phenotypes of offspring (Reading 5.1).

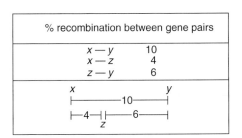

figure 5.15

If we know the percent recombination between all possible pairs of three genes, then we can determine their relative positions.

table 5.4

Mechanisms of Non-Mendelian Inheritance

Situation	Why Inheritance Pattern is not Mendelian
Mitochondrial genes	Each cell has many copies of mitochondrial genes, which are transmitted only by females
Uniparental disomy	One parent transmits two alleles of a gene, and the other parent transmits none
Linkage	Genes on the same homolog are packaged into the same gamete, unless separated by crossing over, and therefore do not assort independently

If geneticists had to rely on blood types and visible traits to explore the human genome, we wouldn't know much more today than we did twenty years ago. We do not need observable clues—either cytogenetic abnormalities or phenotypes—to track gene transmission, although they certainly help. Using the tools and techniques of molecular biology (chapter 21), we can detect, directly or by inference, a particular DNA sequence's presence and location among the chromosomes. In addition to "filling in the blanks" of the human genome, identifying genes and their locations provides diagnostic tests for disease.

Each October, the journal *Science* publishes updates of human chromosome maps. The first landmarks on these maps came from linkage and cytogenetic studies. Molecular geneticists mapping the human genome today are filling in the gaps between discoveries made since the dawn of the science of genetics. The maps are becoming very crowded as the human genome project nears completion.

Table 5.4 summarizes non-Mendelian inheritance.

Key Concepts

Mitochondrial genes are maternally inherited and tend to mutate rapidly. A cell contains many mitochondria, which have multiple copies of the mitochondrial genome. Mitochondrial genes encode RNAs that function generally in protein synthesis, or proteins that are part of energy metabolism. In heteroplasmy, cells contain mitochondria that have different alleles of a particular gene.

In uniparental disomy, an offspring receives two genes from one parent and none from the other. This may occur in gametes, fertilized ova, or somatic tissue. Uniparental disomy may cause genomic imprinting.

Genes on the same chromosome are linked, and they are inherited in different patterns than the unlinked genes Mendel studied. Crosses involving linked genes produce a large parental class and a small recombinant class (caused by crossing over). The farther apart two genes are on a chromosome, the more likely they are to cross over. Linkage maps are based on the relationship between crossover frequency and distance between genes on the same chromosome.

Cytogenetics correlates a phenotype to a chromosomal aberration. Linkage maps reflect the percent recombination between linked genes.

summary

1. In some crosses, the proportions of phenotypes Mendel's laws predict are not observed. Homozygosity for **lethal recessive alleles** stops development before birth, eliminating an offspring class. A gene can have multiple alleles because its sequence can be altered in many ways. Different types of dominance relationships between alleles may affect the ratios of offspring classes. Heterozygotes of **incompletely dominant** alleles have phenotypes intermediate between those associated with the two homozygotes. **Codominant** alleles are both expressed. In **epistasis,** one gene masks the effect of another.

2. An **incompletely penetrant** genotype is not expressed in all individuals who inherit it. Phenotypes that vary in intensity among individuals are **variably expressive.**

Pleiotropic genes have several expressions. A **phenocopy** appears to be inherited but is environmental. In **genetic heterogeneity,** two or more genes specify the same phenotype.

3. Only females transmit mitochondrial genes; males can inherit such a trait but cannot pass it on. Mitochondrial genes do not cross over, do not have DNA repair, and lack introns and histones. The 37 mitochondrial genes encode tRNA, rRNA, or proteins involved in energy reactions. Many mitochondrial disorders are **heteroplasmic,** with mitochondria in a cell harboring different alleles.

4. In **uniparental disomy** a double dose of genetic material is inherited from one parent, with no corresponding contribution from the other.

5. Genes on the same chromosome are **linked** and, unlike genes that independently assort, result in a large number of parental genotypes and a small number of **recombinant** genotypes. **Linkage maps** are developed from studies of linked genes. Researchers can examine a group of known DNA sequences linked on a chromosome (a **haplotype**) to follow the inheritance of certain chromosomes. Knowing whether linked alleles of two genes are in coupling or repulsion, and using crossover frequencies determined by pooling data, one can predict the probabilities of certain genotypes appearing in progeny. Genetic linkage maps are based on the likelihood of a crossover occurring between two linked genes, which is directly proportional to the distance between them.

review questions

1. Explain how each of the following phenomena can disrupt Mendelian phenotypic ratios.

    a. lethal alleles

    b. multiple alleles

    c. incomplete dominance

    d. codominance

    e. epistasis

    f. incomplete penetrance

    g. variable expressivity

    h. pleiotropy

    i. a phenocopy

    j. genetic heterogeneity

2. How does the relationship between dominant and recessive alleles differ from epistasis?

3. Why can transmission of an autosomal dominant trait with incomplete penetrance look like autosomal recessive inheritance?

4. Why does inheritance of ABO blood type exhibit both complete dominance and codominance?

5. Distal symphalangism, as Reading 4.1 describes, is variably expressive and incompletely penetrant. What does this mean?

6. What three phenomena listed in question 1 do the Simmons family from the chapter opening illustrate?

7. Describe why each of the following phenomena are exceptions to Mendel's laws.

    a. inheritance of mitochondrial DNA

    b. uniparental disomy

    c. linkage

8. What is the physical basis of the epistasis that causes the Bombay phenotype?

9. Make up a family that is incompletely penetrant and variably expressive for polydactyly. Draw a pedigree and describe each individual's phenotype.

10. How does a pedigree for a maternally inherited trait differ from one for an autosomal dominant trait?

11. How did using haplotypes help in the discovery of uniparental disomy?

12. How do Prader-Willi and Angelman syndromes differ in phenotype and genotype?

13. On what phenomenon are linkage maps based?

14. How is the concept of linkage useful in

    a. mapping relative positions of genes on chromosomes?

    b. providing diagnostic tests for inherited illness?

15. If researchers could study pairs of human genes as easily as they can study pairs of genes in fruit flies, how many linkage groups would they detect?

16. A Martian creature called a gazook has 17 chromosome pairs. On the largest chromosome are genes for three traits—round or square eyeballs (R or r); a hairy or smooth tail (H or h); and nine or eleven toes (T or t). Round eyeballs, hairy tail, and nine toes are dominant to square eyeballs, smooth tail, and eleven toes. A trihybrid male has offspring with a female who has square eyeballs, a smooth tail, and eleven toes on each of her three feet. She gives birth to 100 little gazooks, who have the following phenotypes:

40 have round eyeballs, a hairy tail, and nine toes

40 have square eyeballs, a smooth tail, and eleven toes

6 have round eyeballs, a hairy tail, and eleven toes

6 have square eyeballs, a smooth tail, and nine toes

4 have round eyeballs, a smooth tail, and eleven toes

4 have square eyeballs, a hairy tail, and nine toes

    a. Draw the allele configurations of the parents.

    b. Identify the parental and recombinant progeny classes.

    c. What is the crossover frequency between the R and T genes?

applied questions

1. For each of the diseases described in situations *a* through *k*, indicate which of the following phenomena (A–I) is at work. A disorder may result from more than one of these causes.

    A. lethal alleles

    B. multiple alleles

    C. epistasis

    D. incomplete penetrance

    E. variable expressivity

    F. pleiotropy

    G. a phenocopy

    H. genetic heterogeneity

    I. genomic imprinting

    a. Incontinentia pigmenti is a condition caused by a dominant allele transmitted on the X chromosome. Affected individuals within a family have different combinations of paralysis, missing or unusually shaped teeth, mental retardation, seizures, detached retinas, skin rash, bald spots, bleeding into the eye, and very light skin color.

    b. A woman has a severe case of neurofibromatosis type I. She has numerous brown spots on her skin and several large tumors beneath her skin. A gene test shows that her son has inherited the disease-causing autosomal dominant allele, but he has no symptoms.

    c. In 10 percent of cases of Huntington disease, symptoms begin in childhood, rather than the usual average age of thirty-eight. In 90 percent of these early-onset cases, the father has passed on the causative gene.

    d. A man and woman have six children. They also had two stillbirths—fetuses that died shortly before birth.

    e. Most children with cystic fibrosis have frequent lung infections and digestive difficulties. Some people have mild cases, with onset of minor respiratory problems in adulthood. Some men have cystic fibrosis, but their only symptom is infertility.

f. In Labrador retrievers, the *B* allele confers black coat color and the *b* allele brown coat color. The *E* gene controls expression of the *B* gene. If a dog inherits the *E* allele, the coat is golden no matter what the *B* genotype is. A dog of genotype *ee* expresses the *B* (black) phenotype.

g. Two parents are heterozygous for genes that cause albinism (lack of pigment), but each gene specifies a different enzyme in the biochemical pathway that leads to skin pigment synthesis. Their children thus do not face a 25 percent risk of having albinism.

h. Alagille syndrome, in its most severe form, prevents formation of ducts in the gallbladder, causing liver damage. Affected children also usually have heart murmurs, unusual faces, a line in the eye, and butterfly-shaped vertebrae. Such children often have one seemingly healthy parent who, when examined, proves to also have a heart murmur, unusual face, and butterfly vertebrae.

i. Two young children in a family have terribly decayed teeth. Their parents think it is genetic, but the true cause is a babysitter who puts them to sleep with juice bottles.

j. A woman develops dark patches on her face. Her family physician suspects that she may have alkaptonuria, an inherited deficiency of the enzyme homogentisic acid oxidase that produces symptoms of darkened skin, a stiff spine, darkened ear tips, and urine that turns black when it contacts the air. However, a dermatologist the woman is referred to discovers that she has been using a facial cream containing hydroquinone, which is known to cause dark skin patches in dark-skinned people.

k. An apparently healthy, twenty-four-year-old basketball player dies suddenly during a game when her aorta, the largest artery, ruptures. A younger brother is nearsighted and has long and thin fingers, and an older sister is extremely tall with long arms and legs. An examination reveals that the older sister, too, has a weakened aorta. All of these siblings have Marfan syndrome, although they are affected to different degrees.

2. If many family studies for a particular autosomal recessive condition reveal fewer affected individuals than Mendel's law predicts, the explanation may be either incomplete penetrance or lethal alleles. How might you use haplotypes to determine which of these two possibilities is the causative factor?

3. A man who has type O blood has a child with a woman who has type A blood. The woman's mother has AB blood, and her father, type O. What is the probability that the child has each of the following blood types?

   a. type O   c. type B

   b. type A   d. type AB

4. Two people who are heterozygous for familial hypercholesterolemia decide to have children, but they are concerned that a child might inherit the severe form of the illness. What is the probability that this will happen?

5. A young woman taking a genetics class learns about ABO blood types. She knows that she is type O but also knows that one of her parents is type AB and the other is type B. Adultery or adoption are not possible, so the woman wonders how her blood type could have arisen. Suggest how type AB and A parents could produce a child whose blood type is O.

6. Enzymes are used in blood banks to remove the *A* and *B* antigens from blood types A and B. This makes the blood type O.

   a. Does this alter the phenotype or the genotype?

   b. Removing the *A* and *B* antigens from red blood cells is a phenocopy of what genetic phenomenon?

suggested readings

Bendall, Kate et al. December 1997. Variable levels of a heteroplasmic point mutation in individual hair roots. *The American Journal of Human Genetics,* vol. 61. A cell contains many mitochondria, and a mitochondrion contains many copies of its genome.

Brody, Jane. March 1, 1995. Living with the mysteries of Tourette syndrome. *The New York Times.* Many people are unaware that the strange symptoms of Tourette syndrome reflect a genetic disorder.

Davies, Kevin. June 1994. The evolution of genetic maps. *Nature Genetics,* vol. 7. What began as an intellectual exercise is now a vital tool in medical genetics.

Feil, Robert, and Gavin Kelsey. December 1997. Genomic imprinting: a chromatin connection. *The American Journal of Human Genetics,* vol. 61. Mice are used to study how gene expression reflects the parental source of a particular allele.

Feinberg, Andrew P. June 1993. Genomic imprinting and gene activation in cancer. *Nature Genetics,* vol. 4. Some childhood cancers may be caused by uniparental disomy.

Marion, Robert. August 1995. The girl who mewed. *Discover.* Pleiotropy causes an array of symptoms and is thus very difficult to diagnose.

Sapienza, Carmen. 1995. Genome imprinting: an overview, *Developmental Genetics,* vol. 17. A brief and clear explanation of genomic imprinting.

Suarez, Brian K., and Carol L. Hampe. March 1994. Linkage and association. *The American Journal of Human Genetics,* vol. 54. A short history of linkage analysis.

Wallace, Douglas C. August 1997. Mitochondrial DNA in aging and disease. *Scientific American.* Mitochondrial genes do not follow Mendel's laws.

The April 1998 issue of *The American Journal of Human Genetics* has several articles on mitochondrial genetics.

chapter six

Matters of Sex

The Different Levels of Sexual Identity

At age 14, "Joan" told her physician that she had an intense desire to commit suicide, stemming from a conviction that she was really a he. Joan was right—she had been born a male.

When he was eight months old, the child named "John" at birth had minor surgery to correct an abnormality of his foreskin. By accident, the surgeons damaged the child's penis, badly enough to suggest to the parents that they alter the tissue to resemble female genitalia, and advised them to raise the child as a girl. The case was deemed a success in medical journals—but the victim disagrees.

John recalls feeling male from his earliest memories. He detested wearing dresses, played with "boy's" toys, and, as an adolescent, had an odd voice and mannerisms. He even attempted to urinate while standing, without knowing exactly why. Even though he/she was given estrogen supplements to make her appear more feminine, she knew she was male. So insistent was Joan/John that, at age 16, she had her breasts removed, a penis constructed, and began taking male hormones. Soon after, his father told him about the surgical accident during infancy. John eventually married a woman, adopted her children, and is today happy.

The true story of Joan/John illustrates the different levels at which we can consider sex and gender. Whether an individual is male or female is determined at conception, when he or she inherits an X and a Y chromosome, or two X chromosomes, with all of the genes normally on these chromosomes. Another level of sexual identity comes from the control that hormones exert over the development of reproductive structures. Finally, both biological factors and social cues influence sexual feelings, the sense of whether we are male or female. John/Joan as a child may have had a female exterior because he lacked a penis, but he had a male interior, mixed up hormonal cues, and intensely accurate feelings.

Table 6.1 summarizes the sequential layers of sexual identity.

Sexual Development

In humans, the sexes look alike until the sixth week of prenatal development. All embryos contain two-sided, unspecialized gonads (organs that will become either testes or ovaries) and two sets of tubes (figure 6.1). The potential female structures are called **Müllerian ducts,** and the potential male structures are called **Wolffian ducts.** At the sixth week, one of two events occurs: cascades of hormone action steer development along a male route, or in the absence of this hormonal exposure, development continues along a female pathway. The stage is set for this first divergence at conception.

Sex Chromosomes

In humans, the sexes have equal numbers of autosomes, but males have one X chromosome and one Y chromosome, and females have two X chromosomes. The sex with two different sex chromosomes is called the **heterogametic sex,** and the other, with two of the same sex chromosomes, is the **homogametic sex.** In mammals, the male is the heterogametic sex, but this is not true for other types of organisms, such as birds.

The human X chromosome has more than 1,000 genes. We know the Y chromosome is much smaller than the X chromosome, but we do not yet know how many genes it contains. In 1992, researchers at the Whitehead Institute for Biomedical Research in Cambridge, Massachusetts, mapped the Y chromosome (figure 6.2). They overlapped Y chromosomes missing small sections to establish gene order. Unlike the other chromosomes, the Y chromosome had no linkage map to provide preliminary information. This is because the Y chromosome does not have a homolog, and therefore its genes do not cross over. However, a quarter of the genes on the Y chromosome correspond to genes on the X chromosome. This is called the **pseudoautosomal region,** and here crossovers can occur between corresponding genes on the X and Y chromosomes. As researchers fill in the specific genes on the Y chromosome, we will learn about traits that are distinctly male and perhaps about how sex evolved.

In 1990, researchers discovered a gene on the Y chromosome (before it was mapped) that determines maleness, ending a long and exciting search. Scientists have known the Y chromosome was associated with being male since 1959. For many years, researchers sought the portion of the Y chromosome that dictates maleness. In 1982, Whitehead Institute researchers found an intriguing clue in some unusual people—men who have two X chromosomes (XX male syndrome) and women who have one X and one Y chromosome (XY female syndrome). This was just the reverse of the normal situation.

A close look at the composition of these people's sex chromosomes revealed that the XX males actually had a small piece of a Y chromosome, and the XY females lacked a small part of the Y chromosome. The part of the Y chromosome present in the XX males was the same part that was missing in the XY females. It was only a tiny part of the Y chromosome, about half a percent of the total structure. Yet somewhere within this stretch of 300,000 DNA bases was a gene that determined maleness. Which was it?

table 6.1
Sexual Identity

Level	Events	Timing
Chromosomal/ genetic	XY = male XX = female	Fertilization
Gonadal sex	Undifferentiated structure becomes testis or ovary	Begins in 7th prenatal week
Phenotypic sex	Development of external and internal reproductive structures continues as male or female in response to hormones	After 7th prenatal week
Gender identity	Strong feelings of being male or female develop	From childhood, possibly earlier

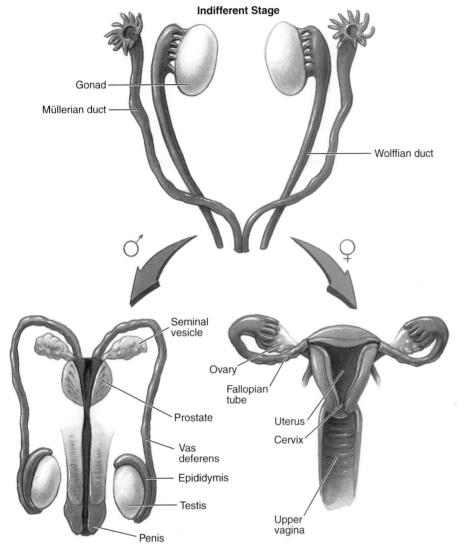

Indifferent Stage

Gonad

Müllerian duct

Wolffian duct

♂ ♀

Seminal vesicle

Ovary

Fallopian tube

Prostate

Uterus

Cervix

Vas deferens

Epididymis

Testis

Upper vagina

Penis

figure 6.1

Until 6 weeks of development, all embryos have the same "indifferent" sexual structures. If male hormones are synthesized after week 6, a male develops. If not, a female develops.

figure 6.2

The X and Y chromosomes in the human. Geneticists mapped the Y chromosome with the help of 96 men who have two X chromosomes and a tiny fragment of the Y chromosome. The Y chromosome harbors only a few genes, some of which are also found on the X chromosome. The SRY gene, at the tip of the short arm of the Y chromosome, sets into motion the cascade of gene activity that directs development of a male. Without the SRY gene, a female develops.

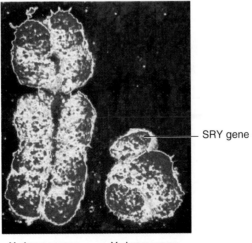

SRY gene

X chromosome   Y chromosome

SRY Gene Action Begins Sexual Differentiation

The race to find the male-determining gene was on, now that researchers knew where to look. Researchers at the Imperial Cancer Research Fund in London thought they had discovered it in 1987, but when this gene was not found in the XX males, the researchers knew it could not be the male-determining gene. Three years later, they and a group at the Medical Research Council, also in London, located the male-determining gene. It was named **SRY,** for **sex-determining region of the Y.**

The SRY gene product is a type of protein called a transcription factor that controls other genes. (Transcription factors are discussed in detail in chapter 9.) This protein switches on other genes that direct the development of male structures in the embryo. If the SRY gene is not expressed, the unspecialized gonad develops into an ovary. If the SRY gene is expressed, the gonads specialize as testes, which in turn secrete two types of hormones that begin to mold a male.

The Phenotype Forms

Once SRY has sent the indifferent gonad on the route to maleness, **sustentacular cells** (once called Sertoli cells) in the testis secrete **anti-Müllerian hormone,** which stops the Müllerian ducts from developing further into a uterus, fallopian tubes, and upper vagina. **Interstitial cells** (once called Leydig cells) in the testis secrete testosterone, which stimulates development of internal male reproductive structures—the epididymides, vasa deferentia, seminal vesicles, and ejaculatory ducts. Some testosterone is also converted to **dihydrotestosterone (DHT),** which directs the development of the external male reproductive structures—the urethra, prostate gland, penis, and scrotum.

Because so many steps contribute to male prenatal sexual development, genetic abnormalities can intervene at several different points (figure 6.3). The result may be an individual with an XY sex chromosome constitution, but a block in the gene-controlled elaboration of male structures. A chromosomal he is a phenotypic she.

In a group of disorders called male pseudohermaphroditism, testes are usually

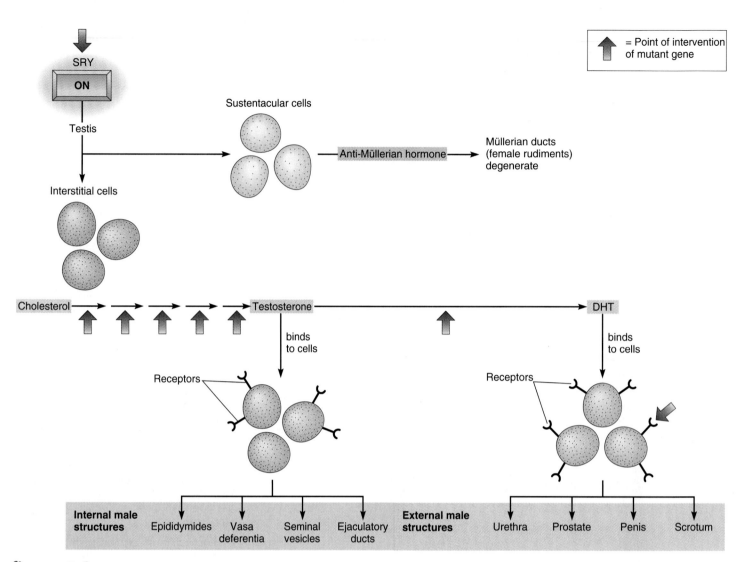

SRY
ON

Testis

Interstitial cells

Sustentacular cells

Anti-Müllerian hormone → Müllerian ducts
(female rudiments)
degenerate

Cholesterol → → → → → Testosterone → DHT

binds
to cells

binds
to cells

Receptors

Receptors

Internal male structures	Epididymides	Vasa deferentia	Seminal vesicles	Ejaculatory ducts	**External male structures**	Urethra	Prostate	Penis	Scrotum

figure 6.3

Male pseudohermaphroditism—a female exterior, but a male interior and chromosome constitution—can arise from mutations in any of several genes, indicated by arrows. Before prenatal testing that determines chromosomal sex became available, pseudohermaphroditism was detected usually after puberty, when masculinization occurred. Today, pseudohermaphroditism is indicated by detecting an XY sex chromosome constitution prenatally, although followed by birth of a phenotypic female.

present (indicating that the SRY gene is functioning) and anti-Müllerian hormone is produced, so the female set of tubes degenerates. However, a block in testosterone synthesis, or the ability of cells to admit testosterone, prevents the fetus from developing external male structures. However, when the individual reaches puberty, testosterone produced in the adrenal glands may lead to masculinization. The voice deepens, and muscles build up into a masculine physique; breasts do not develop, and menstruation does not occur. The clitoris can enlarge so greatly under the testosterone surge that it looks like a penis. Individuals with a form of this con-

dition prevalent in the Dominican Republic are called *guevedoces*, which means "penis at [age] 12."

Gender Identity—Is Homosexuality Inherited?

No one really knows why we have feelings of belonging to one gender or the other, or why we are heterosexual, bisexual, or homosexual. Researchers believe that homosexuality is about 50 percent genetically controlled and 50 percent environmentally controlled (a point we will return to in the next chapter). Homosexuality is

more common than many people think. It is seen in all cultures so far examined and has been observed for thousands of years.

Attitudes toward homosexuality vary greatly. In the Philippines, homosexuality is regarded simply as "nature's way" and is accepted as a natural variant. In the United States, twenty states still have laws punishing homosexual practices as a crime, and several politicians are vocal about their beliefs that homosexuality is an abberation. In contrast, the French Napoleonic code, written in 1810 and followed in many nations today, states that if adults enter into a voluntary behavior with each other, it is not a criminal act. In 1980, the American

Psychiatric Association removed homosexuality from its standard reference book defining behavioral disorders.

Many studies have attempted to estimate the percentage of the population that is homosexual. Noted sex researcher Alfred Kinsey found in a study run from 1948 to 1953 that 4 percent of men and 2 percent of women had homosexual feelings or behaviors that persisted past adolescence. Some have criticized this work as not representative of the general population, but more recent work has produced similar findings. In 1994, the *American Journal of Psychiatry* published a compilation of many studies, concluding that 2 percent of men have homosexual feelings or actions, and an additional 3 percent are bisexual. Data on women are very scarce.

Evidence is accumulating that homosexuality is at least partially inherited. Earlier studies cite the feelings that homosexual individuals have as young children, well before they know of the existence or the meaning of the term. This suggests an inborn influence. A physical explanation for homosexuality currently under investigation is the timing of hormone surges during prenatal development. Rats stressed at certain times during prenatal development later show impaired mating ability, which may reflect alterations in behavior.

Twin studies provide other evidence suggesting a genetic influence on homosexuality. Studies find that identical twins are more likely to both be homosexual than are both members of fraternal same-sex twin pairs, suggesting a genetic component. Also, two brain areas are of different sizes in homosexual versus heterosexual men.

In 1993, National Cancer Institute researcher Dean Hamer brought the tools of molecular biology to bear on the age-old question of whether homosexuality is inherited. Hamer traced the inheritance of 5 DNA sequences on the X chromosome in 40 pairs of brothers who were homosexual. Although these DNA sequences are highly variable in the general population, they were identical in 33 of the sibling pairs. Hamer interpreted the finding to mean that genes causing or predisposing one to homosexuality reside on the X chromosome.

As expected, Hamer's report caused a storm of controversy. One research group

figure 6.4

The ability to genetically alter male fruit flies in a way that causes them to display mating behavior toward each other adds to evidence that homosexuality is at least partially an inherited trait.

confirmed and extended the work, finding that when two brothers are homosexual and have another brother who is heterosexual, the heterosexual brother does not share the X chromosome markers. This study also did not find the X chromosome markers between pairs of lesbian sisters. A third research group has been unable to confirm Hamer's work; however, they selected their participants differently. In 1995, Hamer's laboratory presented additional data supporting their hypothesis that genes on the X chromosome predispose to male homosexuality.

In yet another approach, researchers have been able to genetically engineer what looks like homosexual behavior in male fruit flies. A mutant allele of an eye color gene, called "white," normally causes the flies to have white eyes when expressed in certain cells only. Researchers altered male fly embryos so that the resulting insects express the white gene in every cell. The altered male flies form a "conga line" with each other, displaying mating behavior (figure 6.4), presumably as a result of the altered gene.

The ability to genetically induce homosexual behavior suggests genetic control. The biochemical basis of the phenotype makes sense; the white gene's product, an enzyme that controls a biochemical reaction participating in generating eye color, enables cells to use the amino acid tryptophan, which is required to manufacture the hormone serotonin. When all the fly's cells produce the enzyme, serotonin levels in the brain drop, and this may cause the unusual behavior. In other animals, lowered brain serotonin produces homosexual behavior. Although no direct connection has been made between the fly research and human behavior, some investigators note that the antidepressant drug Prozac, which increases serotonin availability, can dampen or impede sexual desire.

Key Concepts

The human female is homogametic, with two X chromosomes, and the male is heterogametic, with one X and one Y chromosome. Activation of the SRY gene on the Y chromosome causes the undifferentiated gonad to develop into a testis. Then, sustentacular cells in the testis secrete anti-Müllerian hormone, which stops female development, and interstitial cells in the testis secrete testosterone, which stimulates development of internal male reproductive structures. Testosterone is also converted to DHT, which directs development of external male reproductive structures. Evidence is accumulating that indicates that genes contribute to homosexuality.

Sex-linked Recessive Inheritance

A gene on the X chromosome is sex-linked gene. Sex-linked traits affect males and females differently. Any gene on a male's X chromosome is expressed in his phenotype because no second allele for that gene masks its expression. An allele on an X chromosome in a female may or may not be expressed, depending upon whether it is dominant or recessive and on the nature

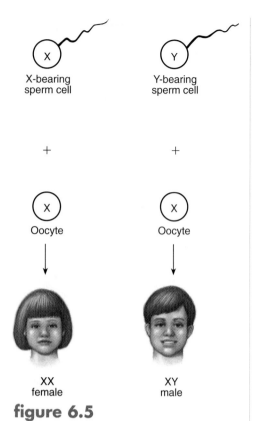

figure 6.5

Sex determination in humans. An oocyte typically contains a single X chromosome. A sperm cell contains either an X chromosome or a Y chromosome. If a Y-bearing sperm cell with a SRY gene fertilizes an oocyte, the zygote is a male (XY). If an X-bearing sperm cell fertilizes an oocyte, then the zygote is a female (XX).

of the allele on the second X chromosome. The human male is thus **hemizygous** for sex-linked traits because he has half the number of sex-linked genes that the female has.

A male always inherits his Y chromosome from his father and his X chromosome from his mother (figure 6.5). A female inherits one X chromosome from each parent. If a mother is heterozygous for a particular sex-linked gene, her son has a 50 percent chance of inheriting either allele from her. Sex-linked traits are always passed on the X chromosome from mother to son or from either parent to daughter; figure 6.6 shows how an unusual sex-linked recessive trait passed in a

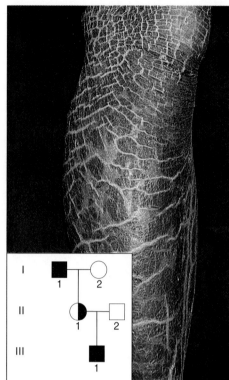

figure 6.6

A middle-aged man who had rough, brown, scaly skin did not realize his condition was inherited until his daughter had a son. By a year of age, the boy's skin resembled his grandfather's. In this sex-linked condition, called ichthyosis, a deficient enzyme interferes with removal of cholesterol from skin cells. As a result, the upper skin layer cannot peel off, as it normally does, and this produces a brown, scaly appearance.

family from grandfather to grandson through a carrier mother. Because a male does not receive an X chromosome from his father (he inherits the Y chromosome from his father), a sex-linked trait is never passed from father to son. Punnett squares can depict transmission of sex-linked traits, as the inset in figure 6.7 shows.

Hemophilia A is a sex-linked recessive disorder. In this condition, absence or deficiency of a specific protein clotting factor greatly slows blood clotting. A cut may take a long time to stop bleeding; a

bump can lead to a large bruise, because broken capillaries leak a great deal of blood before they heal. Most dangerous is internal bleeding, which the individual may not realize is occurring unchecked. Receiving the missing clotting factor can control the illness. Before 1985, when hospitals began screening the blood supply for HIV, many people with hemophilia contracted AIDS from the clotting factor they received, which was pooled from many blood donations.

Hemophilia A is passed from carrier mother to affected son at a risk of 50 percent, because he can inherit either her normal allele or the mutant one. A daughter has a 50 percent chance of inheriting the hemophilia allele and being a carrier like her mother and a 50 percent chance of not carrying the allele.

A daughter can inherit a sex-linked recessive disorder or trait if her father is affected and her mother is a carrier. She inherits one affected X chromosome from each parent. Without a biochemical test, though, an unaffected woman would not know that she is a carrier of a sex-linked recessive trait unless she has an affected son. A genetic counselor can estimate a potential carrier's risk by using probabilities derived from Mendel's laws.

Consider a woman whose brother has hemophilia A. Both her parents are healthy, but her mother is a carrier because her brother is affected. The woman's chance of being a carrier is 1/2 (or 50 percent), which is the chance that she has inherited her mother's hemophilia-allele-bearing X chromosome. The chance of the woman conceiving a son with hemophilia is 1/2 multiplied by 1/2. This is because the chance that she is a carrier is 1/2, and if she is, the chance that her son will inherit the X chromosome bearing the hemophilia allele is also 1/2. Using the product rule, the risk that her son will inherit hemophilia is 1/4, or 25 percent.

A sex-linked recessive trait is more likely to appear in females if it isn't serious enough to prevent a man from fathering children. (This is the case for color blindness, the subject of Reading 6.1.)

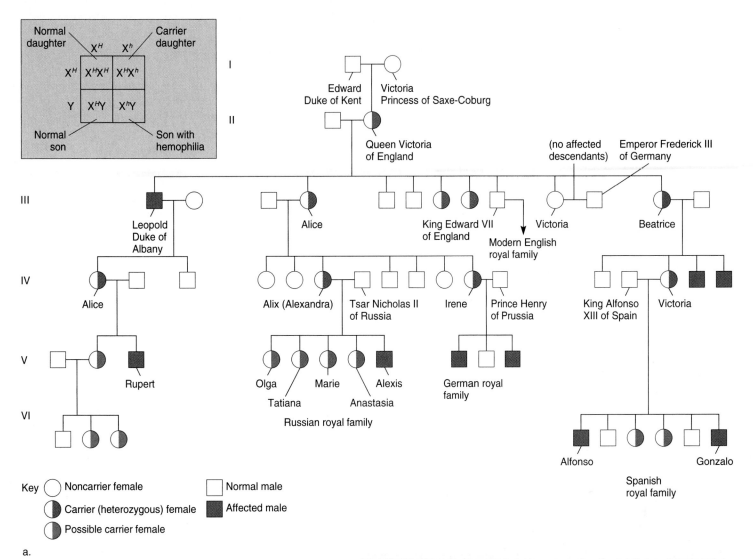

a.

figure 6.7

(a) Sex-linked hemophilia A is usually transmitted from a heterozygous woman (designated $X^H X^h$, where X^h is the hemophilia-causing allele) to heterozygous daughters or hemizygous sons. The disorder has appeared in the royal families of England, Germany, Spain, and Russia. The mutant allele apparently arose in Queen Victoria, who was either a carrier or produced an oocyte with a gene that mutated. She passed the mutant allele to daughters Alice and Beatrice, who were carriers, and to Leopold, who had a case mild enough so that he survived and fathered children. In the fourth generation, Alexandra was a carrier and married Nicholas II, Tsar of Russia, passing the allele to that family. (b) Irene married Prince Henry of Prussia, passing the allele to the German royal family, and Beatrice's descendants passed it to the Spanish royal family. This figure depicts only part of the enormous pedigree. Hemophilia is not present or carried in the modern royal family in England.

b.

Of Preserved Eyeballs and Duplicated Genes—Color Blindness

John Dalton, a famous English chemist, saw things differently than most people (figure 1). In a 1794 lecture, he described his visual world. Sealing wax that appeared red to other people was as green as a leaf to Dalton and his brother. Pink wildflowers were blue, and Dalton perceived the cranesbill plant as "sky blue" in daylight, but "very near yellow, but with a tincture of red," in candlelight. He concluded, ". . . that part of the image which others call red, appears to me little more than a shade, or defect of light." The Dalton brothers had the sex-linked recessive trait of color blindness.

About 8 percent of males of European ancestry are color blind, as are 4 percent of males of African descent. Only 0.4 percent of females are color blind.

Dalton was very curious about the cause of his color blindness, so he made arrangements with his personal physician, Joseph Ransome, to dissect his eyes after he died (figure 2). Ransome snipped off the back of one eye, removing the retina, where the cone cells that provide color vision are nestled among the more abundant rod cells that impart black-and-white vision. Because Ransome could see red and green normally when he peered through the back of his friend's eyeball, he concluded that it was not an abnormal filter in front of the eye that altered color vision.

Fortunately, Ransome stored the eyes in dry air, where they remained relatively undamaged. In 1994, Dalton's eyes underwent DNA analysis at London's Institute of Ophthalmology. The research showed that Dalton's remaining retina lacked one of three types of pigments, called photopigments, that enable cone cells to capture certain incoming wavelengths of light.

figure 1

Chemist John Dalton.

Color Vision Basics

Cone cells are of three types, defined by the presence of any of three types of photopigments. An object appears colored because it reflects certain wavelengths of light, and each cone type captures a particular range of light wavelengths. The brain then interprets the incoming information as a visual perception, much as an artist mixes the three primary colors to create many hues and shadings. Color vision results from the brain's interpretation of information from three types of input cells.

Each photopigment consists of a vitamin A-derived portion called retinal and a protein portion called an opsin. The presence of retinal in photopigments explains why eating vitamin A-rich carrots promotes good vision. The presence of opsins—because they are controlled by genes—explains why color blindness is inherited. The three types of opsins corre-

figure 2

John Dalton donated his eyeballs to science in the hope that studying them would reveal the basis of his color blindness.

spond to short, middle, and long wavelengths of light. Mutations in opsin genes cause the three types of color blindness.

A gene on chromosome 7 encodes shortwave opsins, and mutations in it produce the rare autosomal "blue" form of color blindness. Dalton had deuteranopia (red color blindness), which means his eyes lacked the middle wavelength opsin. In the third type, protanopia (green color blindness), long wavelength opsin is absent. Deuteranopia and protanopia are sex-linked.

Molecular Analysis

John Dalton wasn't the only person interested in color blindness to work on his own tissue. Johns Hopkins University researcher Jeremy Nathans does so today—but not posthumously. Nor is he color blind.

Nathans examined the color vision genes in his own cells. First, he used a cow version of a protein called rhodopsin that provides black-and-white vision to identify the human counterpart of this gene. Guessing that the nucleotide sequence in rhodopsin would be similar to that in the three opsin genes, and therefore able to bind to them, Nathans used the human rhodopsin gene as a "probe" to search his own DNA for genes with similar sequences. Not surprisingly, he found three. One was on chromosome 7, the other two on the X chromosome.

But Nathans's opsin genes were not entirely normal, and this gave him a big clue as to how the trait arises and why it is so common. On his X chromosome, Nathans has one red opsin gene and two green genes, instead of the normal one of each. Because the red and green genes have similar sequences, Nathans reasoned, they can misalign during meiosis in the female (figure 3). The resulting oocytes would then have either two or none of one opsin gene type. An oocyte lacking either a red or a green opsin gene would, when fertilized by a Y-bearing sperm, give rise to a color blind male.

People who are color blind must get along in a multicolored world. To help them overcome the disadvantage of not seeing important color differences, researchers have developed computer algorithms that convert colored video pictures into shades they can see. Figure 4 shows one of the tests typically used to determine whether someone is color blind. Absence of one opsin type prevents affected individuals from seeing a different color in certain of the circles in such a drawing. As a result, their brains cannot perceive a particular embedded pattern that others can see.

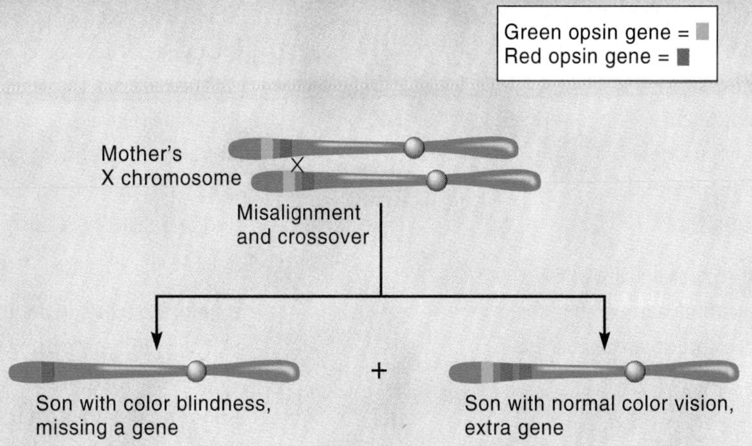

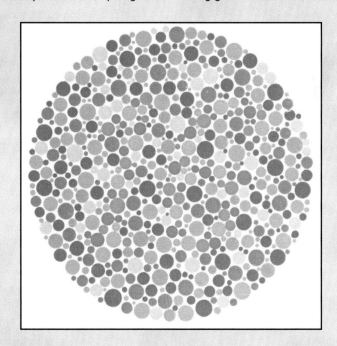

Green opsin gene = ■
Red opsin gene = ■

Mother's X chromosome

Misalignment and crossover

Son with color blindness, missing a gene

+

Son with normal color vision, extra gene

figure 3

The sequence similarities between the opsin genes responsible for color vision that are on the X chromosome may cause unequal crossing over to occur during meiosis in the female. Her sons may inherit too many, or too few, opsin genes. A missing gene causes sex-linked color blindness.

figure 4

Males with red-green color blindness cannot see the number 16 within this pattern of circles, as a person with normal color vision can.

The above has been reproduced from *Ishihara's Tests for Colour Blindness* published by Kanehara & Co. Ltd, Tokyo, Japan, but tests for color blindness cannot be conducted with this material. For accurate testing, the original plates should be used.

table 6.2

Some Disease-related Genes on the Human X Chromosome*

Condition	Description
Eye	
Green color blindness	Abnormal green cone pigments in retina
Megalocornea	Enlarged cornea
Norrie disease	Abnormal growth of retina, eye degeneration
Ocular albinism	Eye lacks pigment
Red color blindness	Abnormal red cone pigments in retina
Retinitis pigmentosa	Constriction of visual field, night blindness, clumps of pigment in eye
Retinoschisis	Retina degenerates and splits
Inborn Errors of Metabolism	
Agammaglobulinemia	Lack of certain antibodies
Chronic granulomatous disease	Skin and lung infections, enlarged liver and spleen
Diabetes insipidus	Copious urination
Fabry disease	Abdominal pain, skin lesions, kidney failure
Gout	Inflamed, painful joints
G6PD deficiency and favism	Hemolytic anemia after eating fava beans
Hemophilia A	Absent clotting factor VIII
Hemophilia B	Absent clotting factor IX
Hypophosphatemia	Vitamin D resistant rickets
Hunter syndrome	Deformed face, dwarfism, deafness, mental retardation, heart defects, enlarged liver and spleen
Ornithine transcarbamylase deficiency	Mental deterioration, ammonia accumulation in blood
Primary adrenal hypoplasia	Great disorganization of adrenal glands and resulting hormone deficiencies
Severe combined immune deficiency	Lack of immune system cells
Wiskott-Aldrich syndrome	Bloody diarrhea, infections, rash, too few platelets
Nerves and Muscles	
Charcot-Marie-Tooth disease	Loss of feeling in ends of arms and legs
Fragile X syndrome	Mental retardation, characteristic face, large testicles
Hydrocephalus	Excess fluid in brain
Lesch-Nyhan syndrome	Mental retardation, self-mutilation, urinary stones, spastic cerebral palsy
Menkes disease	Kinky hair, abnormal copper transport, brain atrophy
Muscular dystrophy, Becker and Duchenne forms	Progressive muscle weakness
Spinal and bulbar muscular atrophy	Muscle weakness and wasting
Other	
Amelogenesis imperfecta	Abnormal tooth enamel
Alport syndrome	Deafness, inflamed kidney tubules
Cleft palate	Opening in roof of mouth
Hypohidrotic ectodermal dysplasia	Absence of teeth, hair, and sweat glands
Ichthyosis	Rough, scaly skin on scalp, ears, neck, abdomen, and legs
Incontinentia pigmenti	Swirls of skin color, hair loss, seizures, abnormal teeth
Kallmann syndrome	Inability to smell, underdeveloped testes
Testicular feminization	Male embryo does not respond to male hormones, appears female

*Some of these conditions may also be inherited through genes on the autosomes.

Table 6.2 presents other sex-linked disorders, and some of the questions at the end of the chapter focus on other sex-linked traits.

Sex-linked Dominant Inheritance

How is a dominant allele on the X chromosome expressed in each of the sexes? A female who inherits a dominant sex-linked allele has the associated trait or illness, but a male who inherits the allele is usually more severely affected because he has no other allele. The children of a normal man and a woman with a dominant, disease-causing gene on the X chromosome face the following risks:

> male, severely affected = 1/4
> male, not affected = 1/4
> female, affected (has phenotype) = 1/4
> female, not affected = 1/4

An example of a sex-linked dominant condition is incontinentia pigmenti. The name derives from the major sign in females with the disorder—swirls of pigment in the skin that resemble swirls of paint or marble cake. The skin pigment melanin leaks down into the deeper skin layers, causing the odd pigmentation pattern. The pattern tends to lessen by adulthood. A newborn girl with incontinentia pigmenti has yellow, pus-filled vesicles on her limbs that come and go over the first few weeks. Then the lesions become warty and are eventually replaced by brown splotches that may remain for life. Other symptoms include hair loss, visual problems, missing or peg-shaped teeth, and seizures. Males with the condition are so severely affected that they die in the uterus. This is consistent with the fact that women with the disorder have a high rate of miscarriage, about 25 percent. Another of the rare sex-linked dominant conditions, vitamin D resistant rickets, is described at the beginning of chapter 9. Reading 6.2 describes a very rare sex-linked dominant condition that causes extremely dense body hair.

Key Concepts

Sex-linked traits are passed on the X chromosome. Because a male is hemizygous, he expresses the genes on his X chromosome, whereas a female expresses dominant alleles but expresses recessive alleles on the X chromosome only if she is homozygous for them. Sex-linked recessive traits pass from carrier mothers to sons at a probability of 50 percent. Sex-linked dominant conditions are expressed in both males and females but are more severe in males.

X Inactivation—Equaling Out the Sexes

Females have two alleles for every gene on the X chromosome, whereas males have only one. In mammals, a mechanism called **X inactivation** balances this inequality. Early in development of a female, one X chromosome in each cell is inactivated. Which X chromosome is turned off in each cell—the one inherited from the mother or from the father—is a matter of chance. As a result, a female mammal expresses the X chromosome genes inherited from her father in some cells and those from her mother in others.

By studying rare human females who have only part of one X chromosome, researchers identified a specific region, the **X inactivation center,** that shuts off the chromosome. A few genes, however, remain active. The inactivation process is under the control of a gene called *XIST*. The *XIST* gene encodes an RNA that binds to a specific site on one X chromosome. From this point, the X chromosome is inactivated, one gene at a time. Experiments in mice demonstrate the central role of the *XIST* gene in silencing the X chromosome. If *XIST* RNA is applied to an autosome, that chromosome is inactivated.

Once an X chromosome is inactivated in one cell, all the cells that form when that cell divides have the same inactivated X chromosome. Because the inactivation occurs early in development, the adult female has patches of tissue that are phenotypically different in their expression of sex-linked genes. But now that each cell in her body has only one active X chromosome, she is numerically equivalent to the male in genetic makeup.

X inactivation alters phenotype (gene expression), not genotype. It is not permanent, because the inactivation reverses in germ-line cells—those destined to become oocytes—so that a fertilized ovum does not have an inactivated X. X inactivation can be observed at the cellular level because the turned-off X chromosome absorbs a stain much faster than the active X chromosome. (The inactivated DNA has chemical methyl groups on it that prevent it from being transcribed into RNA, and this alteration may also be responsible for the differences in staining.) The nucleus of a female cell in interphase has one dark-staining X chromosome called a **Barr body** (named after its discoverer, Murray Barr, a Canadian researcher who noticed these dark bodies in 1949 in nerve cells of female cats). A normal male cell has no Barr body because his one X chromosome remains active (figure 6.8).

In 1961, English geneticist Mary Lyon proposed that the Barr body is the inactivated X chromosome and that the turning off occurs early in development. She reasoned that for homozygous sex-linked genes, X inactivation would have no effect. No matter which X chromosome turns off, the same allele is left to be expressed. For heterozygous genes, however, X inactivation leads to expression of one allele or the other. Usually this doesn't affect health, because enough cells express the functional gene product. However, some traits reveal striking evidence of X inactivation. For example, the swirls of skin color in incontinentia pigmenti patients reflect patterns of X inactivation in cells in the skin layers. Where the wild type allele for melanin pigment is shut off, pale swirls develop. Where pigment is produced, brown swirls result.

A Sex-linked Dominant Condition—Congenital Generalized Hypertrichosis reading 6.2

Since the Middle Ages, medical journals have described about fifty "ape men," "dog men," or "human werewolves." Because of the phenotype of extreme hairiness, these individuals often wound up in circus sideshows. We know today that they have congenital generalized hypertrichosis (CGH), which is sex-linked dominant.

Geneticists know relatively little about hair. We do know that three types of hair grow throughout human development. The early fetus has short, fine hair called vellus, and the older fetus has long, fine hair called lanugo. The long, thick hair that cascades from our scalps and coats our bodies after birth is called terminal hair.

In CGH, a person has more hair follicles than normal, and hence denser and more abundant terminal hair. Unlike hirsutism, caused by a hormonal abnormality that makes a woman grow hair in places where it is usually more pronounced in males (for example, a mustache), CGH causes excess facial and upper body hair that covers extensive areas of skin (figure 1). The hair growth is milder and patchier in females because of hormonal differences and the mitigating presence of a second X chromosome.

Researchers studied a large Mexican family that had nineteen relatives with CGH. The pattern of inheritance was distinctive for sex-linked dominant inheritance, which is quite rare. In one portion of the pedigree, depicted in figure 2, an affected man passed the trait to all four of

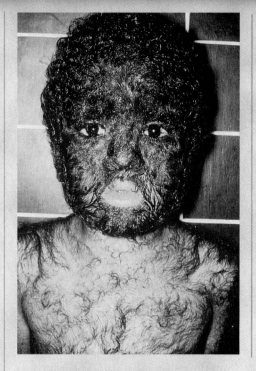

figure 1

This six-year-old boy has congenital generalized hypertrichosis (CGH).

his daughters, but to none of his nine sons. Because sons inherit the X chromosome from their mother, and only the Y from their father, they could not have inherited CGH from their affected father.

The mutant gene that causes CGH is atavistic, which means that it controls a trait also present in ancestral species. A version of the gene is probably present in chimpanzees and other hairy primates. Sometime in our distant past, the wild type form of the gene must have mutated in a way that enables humans to grow dense hair only on their heads and in areas dictated by sex hormones.

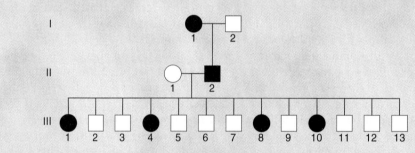

figure 2

Part of the pedigree of the large Mexican family with CGH. Note that the affected male in the second generation has passed the condition to all of his daughters and none of his sons. This is because he transmits his X chromosome only to females.

Sometimes a female who is heterozygous for a sex-linked recessive gene expresses the associated condition because the tissues affected in the illness have the wild type allele inactivated. This can happen in a carrier of hemophilia A. If the X chromosome carrying the normal allele for the clotting factor is turned off in many immature blood platelet cells, then her blood will take longer than normal to clot—causing mild hemophilia. A carrier of a sex-linked trait who expresses the phenotype is called a **manifesting heterozygote.**

A striking and familiar example of X inactivation is seen in the coat colors of tortoiseshell and calico cats. A sex-linked gene confers black, brown, or orange coat color. A male cat with the recessive orange allele has orange fur. However, a female who is heterozygous for this gene has patches of orange and either brown or black, forming a tortoiseshell pattern that reflects different cells expressing the two different alleles (figure 6.9). The earlier the

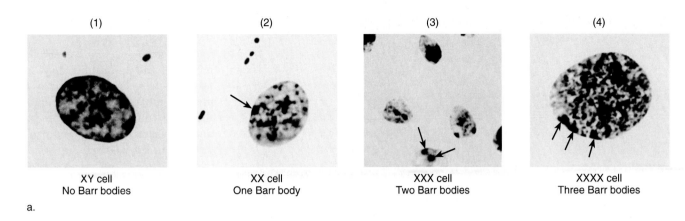

(1)	(2)	(3)	(4)
XY cell No Barr bodies	XX cell One Barr body	XXX cell Two Barr bodies	XXXX cell Three Barr bodies

a.

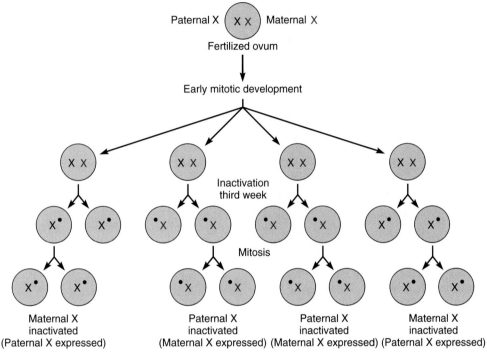

Paternal X (X X) Maternal X

Fertilized ovum

Early mitotic development

Inactivation
third week

Mitosis

Maternal X
inactivated
(Paternal X expressed)

Paternal X
inactivated
(Maternal X expressed)

Paternal X
inactivated
(Maternal X expressed)

Maternal X
inactivated
(Paternal X expressed)

Key
X = Paternally derived X chromosome
X = Maternally derived X chromosome
• = Inactivated X chromosome

b.

figure 6.8

A Barr body marks an inactivated X chromosome. One X chromosome is inactivated in each cell of a female mammal. The turned-off X chromosome absorbs a stain faster than the active X chromosome, forming a dark spot called a Barr body. (*a*) A normal male cell has no Barr body (*1*), and a normal female cell has one (*2*). Individual (*3*) has two Barr bodies and three X chromosomes. She is normal in appearance, behavior, and intellect, but has a lower IQ than her siblings, a slight deficit possibly due to her extra X chromosome. Rarely, a female has two extra X chromosomes, as in (*4*). (*b*) At about the third week of embryonic development in the human female, one X chromosome in each diploid cell is inactivated, and all daughter cells of these cells have the same X chromosome turned off. The inactivated X may come from the mother or father, resulting in a female who is mosaic at the cellular level for X chromosome gene expression.

X inactivation, the larger the patches of color, because more cell divisions can occur afterward. If white patches also appear, due to an autosomal gene, the cat is a calico. Can you see why tortoiseshell and calico cats are nearly always female? The only way a male can have these coat color patterns is if he inherits an extra X chromosome.

X inactivation has a valuable medical application in detecting carriers of some sex-linked disorders. This is the case for Lesch-Nyhan syndrome, in which a child has cerebral palsy, bites his or her fingers and lips to the point of mutilation, is

mentally retarded, and passes painful urinary stones. Mutation results in defective or absent HGPRT, an enzyme. A woman who carries Lesch-Nyhan syndrome can be detected when hairs from widely separated parts of her head are tested for HGPRT. If some hairs have HGPRT but others do not, she is a carrier. The hair cells that lack the enzyme have turned off the X chromosome that carries the normal allele; the hair cells that manufacture the normal enzyme have turned off the X chromosome that carries the disease-causing allele. The woman is healthy

because her brain has enough HGPRT, but her sons have a 50 percent chance of inheriting the disease.

X inactivation is also used to identify carriers of Duchenne muscular dystrophy. A woman who suspects she may be a carrier—for example, whose sister has an affected son—undergoes a muscle biopsy, and the tissue is tested for the presence of dystrophin, the muscle protein missing in the condition. If the woman is a carrier, some muscle cells make dystrophin (cells with the mutant allele inactivated), and some do not (cells with the wild type allele inactivated).

a.

figure 6.9

X inactivation is obvious in tortoiseshell and calico cats. Each orange patch is made up of cells descended from a cell in which the X chromosome carrying the dark coat color allele was inactivated; each dark patch is made of cells descended from a cell in which the X chromosome carrying the orange allele was turned off. In this calico cat (a), an autosomal white gene is expressed. In the tortoiseshell cat (b), it is not. X inactivation is rarely observable in humans because most cells do not remain together during development, as a cat's skin cells do.

Key Concepts

In female mammals, X inactivation compensates for differences in the dosage of genes on the X chromosome. Early in development, one X chromosome in each cell of the female is turned off. Effects of X inactivation can be noticeable for heterozygous alleles expressed in certain tissues.

Gender Effects on Phenotype

A sex-linked recessive trait generally is more prevalent in males than females, as color blindness strikingly illustrates. Other situations, however, can affect gene expression differently in the sexes.

Sex-limited Traits

A **sex-limited trait** affects a structure or function of the body that is present in only males or only females. Such a gene may be sex-linked or autosomal.

Understanding sex-limited inheritance is important in animal breeding. In cattle, for example, milk yield and horn development are traits that affect only one sex, but the genes controlling them can be transmitted by either parent. In humans, beard growth and breast size are sex-limited traits. A woman does not grow a beard because she does not manufacture the hormones required for facial hair growth. She can, however, pass to her sons the genes specifying heavy beard growth.

Sex-influenced Traits

A **sex-influenced trait** results from an allele that is dominant in one sex but recessive in the other. Again, such a gene may be sex-linked or autosomal. This difference in expression can be caused by hormonal differences between the sexes. For example, an autosomal gene for hair growth pattern has two alleles, one that produces hair all over the head and another that causes pattern baldness (figure 6.10). The baldness allele is dominant in males but recessive in females, which is why more men than women are bald. A heterozygous male is bald, but a heterozygous female is not. A bald woman is homozygous recessive.

Genomic Imprinting

In chapter 3, we learned that sexual reproduction—specifically, meiosis—is important for mixing traits in each generation. Genetic contribution from two parents also seems to be critical very early in development. Simply doubling the haploid genetic material in an oocyte or sperm is insufficient to begin development. Evidence suggesting the importance of two parents comes from experiments and human reproductive problems.

In mice, the pronuclei from male and female look slightly different; researchers can recognize and manipulate them. When the female pronucleus is removed from an oocyte and replaced with two male pronuclei, the resulting embryo is too tiny to survive, but the placenta is normal. A zygote with two female pronuclei, on the other hand, develops into an embryo, but the placenta is grossly abnormal.

a.

b.

c.

d.

figure 6.10

Pattern baldness, a sex-influenced trait, was a genetic trademark of the illustrious Adams family. John Adams (1735–1826) (a) was the second president of the United States. He was the father of John Quincy Adams (1767–1848) (b), the sixth president. John Quincy was the father of Charles Francis Adams (1807–1886) (c), a diplomat and the father of Henry Adams (1838–1918) (d), a historian.

In humans, embryos that have two sets of male genes and one set of female genes yield a growth that is largely placenta. An embryo with the reverse genetic constitution—two female genomes and one male genome—is normal, but has an abnormal placenta. A growth called a hydatidiform mole consists of placental tissue but no embryo. Its cells contain two male genomes, presumably caused when a sperm fertilizes an oocyte that lacks a pronucleus, then divides to restore the diploid state. A teratoma is a growth consisting of embryonic tissue whose cells contain two female genomes. It may arise from an oocyte in which the DNA duplicates. (These abnormal fertilized ova arise naturally.)

The parental origin of genes is important after birth too. (Recall from chapter 5 that genomic imprinting is the differing expression of a disorder depending upon which parent transmits the disease-causing gene or chromosome.) A phenotype may vary in expressivity, age of onset, or even in the nature of the symptoms. This last phenomenon occurs in Angelman and Prader-Willi syndromes when one parent's chromosome 15 is missing key genetic material, allowing the corresponding DNA on the other parent's chromosome to predominate. Different sets of signs and symptoms result, depending upon the sex of the parent transmitting the deficient chromosome. Table 6.3 lists some disorders that display genomic imprinting.

Genomic imprinting is also apparent in Turner syndrome, a condition in which females inherit only one X chromosome. If the X chromosome comes from the mother, the affected individual is much more likely to have social problems necessitating special education than if the X chromosome is inherited from the father.

Researchers do not completely understand the mechanism behind genomic imprinting. However, a popular hypothesis is that another layer of meaning—an imprint—is added to genes. Certain genes may be temporarily silenced when methyl (CH_3) groups bind to their nucleotide sequences. Methylation blocks the phenotype (gene expression) but not the genotype. With each new generation, the methyl "imprint" is lifted, only to be applied again, on specific genes, in a pattern that depends upon the new individual's sex.

Key Concepts

A sex-limited trait affects body parts or functions present in only one gender. A sex-influenced allele is dominant in one sex but recessive in the other. In genomic imprinting, the phenotype differs depending on whether a gene is inherited from the mother or the father. Methyl groups may bind to DNA and temporarily suppress gene expression in a pattern determined by the individual's sex.

table 6.3

Conditions that Exhibit Genomic Imprinting

Condition	Description
Allergic rhinitis (hay fever)	Runny nose, itchy eyes
Angelman syndrome	Mental and growth retardation, protruding tongue, floppy muscle tone, large jaw, excessive laughter
Asthma	Difficulty breathing
Beckwith-Wiedemann syndrome	Enlarged tongue, umbilical abnormalities, hypoglycemia, high risk of cancer of adrenal glands and kidneys
Chronic myeloid leukemia	White blood cell cancer
Juvenile diabetes	Lack of insulin leads to high blood sugar level
Huntington disease	Progressive uncontrolled movements, personality changes
Long Q-T syndrome	Heartbeat irregularity
Myotonic dystrophy	Muscle wasting, cataracts, balding
Prader-Willi syndrome	Mental retardation, obesity, small hands and feet, no sexual maturity
Retinoblastoma	Eye cancer
Wilms' tumor	Kidney cancer

summary

1. Sexual identity includes sex chromosome makeup; gonadal specialization; phenotype (reproductive structures); and gender identity.

2. In humans, the male is the **heterogametic sex,** with an X and a Y chromosome. The female, with two X chromosomes, is the **homogametic sex.** The **SRY gene** on the Y chromosome determines sex.

3. Sexual development begins at conception. If the SRY gene is expressed, undifferentiated gonads develop as testes. If SRY is not expressed, the gonads develop as ovaries.

4. Starting at the sixth prenatal week, **sustentacular cells** in the testes secrete **anti-Müllerian hormone,** which prevents development of female structures, and **interstitial cells** produce **testosterone,** which triggers development of male internal reproductive organs. Some

testosterone is converted to **DHT,** which controls development of male external reproductive structures. If SRY doesn't turn on, the Müllerian ducts continue to develop into internal female reproductive structures.

5. Homosexuality is probably about 50 percent inherited. Evidence for an inherited component to homosexuality is accumulating.

6. Males are **hemizygous** for genes on the X chromosome, and thus they express such genes because they do not have another allele on a homolog. A sex-linked trait is passed from mother to son because he inherits his X chromosome from his mother and his Y chromosome from his father. A sex-linked allele may be dominant or recessive.

7. **X inactivation** shuts off one X chromosome in the tissues of female mammals, making

them mosaics for heterozygous genes on the X chromosome. This phenomenon evens out the dosages of genes on the sex chromosomes between the sexes. A female who expresses the phenotype corresponding to a sex-linked gene she carries is a **manifesting heterozygote.**

8. **Sex-limited traits** may be autosomal or sex-linked, but they only affect one sex because of anatomical or hormonal gender differences. A **sex-influenced gene** is dominant in one sex but recessive in the other. In genomic imprinting, the phenotype corresponding to a particular genotype differs depending on whether the parent who passes the gene is female or male. Imprinting is reversible since it affects the phenotype and not the genotype. Methyl groups that temporarily suppress gene expression may be responsible for genomic imprinting.

review questions

1. How is sex expressed at the chromosomal, gonadal, phenotypic, and gender identity levels?

2. What are the phenotypes of the following individuals?

   a. a person with a mutation in the SRY gene, rendering it nonfunctional

   b. a normal XX individual

   c. an XY individual with an autosomal recessive condition that prevents cells from recognizing and binding testosterone

3. List the cell types and hormones that participate in development of male reproductive structures.

4. List the events that must take place for a fetus to develop as a female.

5. Cite evidence that may point to a hereditary component to homosexuality.

6. Why are male calico cats very rare?

7. How might X inactivation cause the patchy hairiness of women who have congenital generalized hypertrichosis (CGH), even though the disease-causing allele is dominant?

8. How does X inactivation even out the "doses" of sex-linked genes between the sexes?

9. Traits that appear more frequently in one sex than the other may be caused by genes that are inherited in a sex-linked, sex-limited, or sex-influenced fashion. How might you distinguish among these possibilities?

10. Cite evidence that genetic contributions from both parents are necessary for normal prenatal development.

11. What evidence suggests that methylation might be involved in a disorder that is more severe and starts earlier in one sex than in the other?

applied questions

1. Comparing human homosexuals to fruit flies may seem insulting, but many homosexual individuals are encouraged by evidence indicating that their sexual preferences are inherited because they believe this will make people less critical of their lifestyles. Do you think such information will change some people's attitudes concerning homosexual behavior?

2. Metacarpal 4–5 fusion is a sex-linked recessive condition in which certain finger bones are fused. It occurs in many members of the Flabudgett family, depicted in this pedigree:

a. Why are three females affected, considering that this is a sex-linked condition?

b. What is the risk that individual III-1 will have an affected son?

c. What is the risk that individual III-5 will have an affected son?

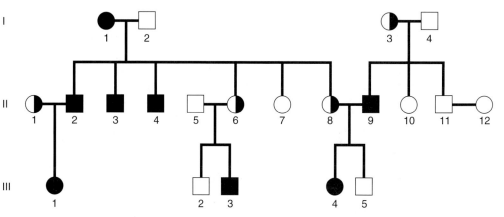

3. The Addams family knows of three relatives who had kinky hair disease, a sex-linked recessive disorder in which a child does not grow, experiences brain degeneration, and dies by the age of two. Affected children have peculiar white stubby hair, from which the disorder takes its name.

   Wanda Addams is hesitant about having children because her two sisters have each had sons who died from kinky hair disease. Her mother had a brother who died of the condition, too. The pedigree for the family is shown to the right.

a. Fill in the symbols for the family members who must be carriers of kinky hair disease.

b. What is the chance that Wanda is a carrier?

c. If Wanda is a carrier, what is the chance that a son of hers would inherit kinky hair disease?

d. Why don't any women in the family have kinky hair disease?

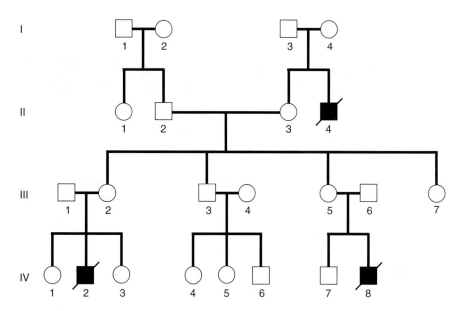

4. A woman with normal color vision has a color-blind father and a color blind brother. She is pregnant, and the fetus's father has the same type of sex-linked recessive color blindness as the woman's father.

   a. What is the risk that a son will be color blind?

   b. What is the risk that a daughter will be color blind?

   c. What is the risk that a daughter will be a carrier of the color blindness allele?

5. A man and woman have a child who has Lesch-Nyhan syndrome. He is profoundly retarded and compulsively bites his lips and fingers to the point that he must be restrained. Lesch-Nyhan is sex-linked.

   a. What are the chances that another son of this couple will inherit Lesch-Nyhan syndrome?

   b. What are the chances that a daughter of this couple will inherit Lesch-Nyhan syndrome?

   c. Why do neither of the parents have symptoms of Lesch-Nyhan syndrome?

6. Herbert is fifty-eight years old and bald. His wife Sheri also has pattern baldness. What is the risk that their son Frank will lose his hair?

7. Reginald has a mild case of hemophilia A that he can control by taking a clotting factor. He marries Lydia, whom he met at the hospital where he and Lydia's brother Marvin receive their treatment. Lydia and Marvin's mother and father, Emma and Clyde, do not have hemophilia. What is the probability that Reginald and Lydia's son will inherit hemophilia A?

8. Harold works in a fish market, but the odor does not bother him because he has a sex-linked recessive lack of sense of smell, a condition called anosmia. Harold's wife Shirley has a normal sense of smell. Harold's sister Maude also has a normal sense of smell, as does her husband Phil and daughter Marsha, but their identical twin boys, Alvin and Simon, cannot detect odors. Harold and Maude's parents, Edgar and Florence, can smell normally. Draw a pedigree for this family, indicating people who must be carriers of the anosmia gene.

suggested readings

Bailey, J. Michael. December 1995. Sexual orientation revolution. *Nature Genetics,* vol. 11. For at least some gay men, their sexual preferences may be traceable to parts of their X chromosomes.

Colapinto, John. December 11, 1997. The true story of John/Joan. *Rolling Stone.* When well-meaning surgeons tried to correct an error by removing an infant's penis, they did not also remove his intense gender identity.

Crowe, Mark A., and William D. James. November 17, 1993. X-linked ichthyosis. *The Journal of the American Medical Association.* A grandfather with bizarre, scaly skin didn't realize he had an inherited condition until his grandson developed the same phenotype.

Hall, Brian K. June 1995. Atavisms and atavistic mutations. *Nature Genetics,* vol. 10. Is congenital generalized hypertrichosis a "throwback" mutation to times when humans were much hairier?

Hamer, D. July 16, 1993. A linkage between DNA markers on the X-chromosome and male sexual orientation. *Science,* vol. 261. Is it coincidence that homosexual brothers have five identical sex-linked DNA sequences far more often than chance would predict? Or does this observation offer proof that homosexuality is inherited? This is the original "genes and homosexuality" report.

Hunt, David M., et al. February 17, 1995. The chemistry of John Dalton's color-blindness. *Science,* vol. 267. The famous chemist requested that his eyeballs be examined after his death to localize the cause of his color blindness.

McGuffin, Peter, and Jane Scourfield. June 12, 1997. A father's imprint on his daughter's thinking. *Nature,* vol. 387. Females with Turner syndrome are affected differently, depending upon which parent transmitted their sole X chromosome.

Neitz, Maureen, and Jay Neitz. February 17, 1995. Numbers and ratios of visual pigment genes for normal red-green color vision. *Science,* vol. 267. Genetics explains how red and green color blindness occur and why they are so common.

Sinclair, Andrew H. November 1995. New genes for boys. *American Journal of Human Genetics.* With the discovery of the SRY gene, researchers began to unravel the genetic controls of maleness.

Stokstad, Erik. November 16, 1996. "Red" genes get the green light. *New Scientist.* Some color blind men can detect some greens because their red cones can respond to some green wavelengths.

Willard, Huntington F., and Helen K. Salz. March 20, 1997. Remodeling chromatin with RNA. *Nature,* vol. 386. A noncoding form of RNA carries out X inactivation.

chapter seven

Complex Traits

"It Runs in the Family"

A woman who is a prolific writer has a daughter who becomes a successful novelist. An overweight man and woman have obese children. A man whose father was an alcoholic is himself an alcoholic. Are these characteristics—writing talent, obesity, and alcoholism—inherited or imitated? Or are they a combination of nature (heredity) and nurture (the environment)?

The traits and medical conditions mentioned so far are single-gene disorders inherited according to Mendel's laws. Geneticists can predict the probability that a certain family member will inherit such a condition. Some traits and diseases, though, seem to "run in families" with no apparent pattern. Sometimes a single-gene problem may appear to follow an unpredictable pattern because of variable expressivity and nonpenetrance. In other cases, however, deviations from a Mendelian ratio can reflect the influence of more than one gene, of the environment—or both.

Characteristics that do not follow Mendel's laws, but still have an inherited component, are termed **complex traits.** Complex traits may be **polygenic** (determined by more than one gene) or **multifactorial** (determined by one or more genes as well as the environment). The term *environment* encompasses many influences, including position in the uterus, experiences, and exposure to infectious agents.

For polygenic (also called quantitative) traits, several genes each contribute to the overall phenotype. The combined actions of many genes produce a continuum, or continuously varying expression, of the trait. The genes do follow Mendel's laws individually, but they don't produce typical ratios because they contribute all to the phenotype and are neither dominant nor recessive with respect to each other.

Table 7.1 shows how the effects of different genes can add up, producing varying degrees of a trait—in this case, skin color. Figure 7.1 illustrates another continuously varying trait—height.

Although skin color and height are traditionally considered examples of polygenic inheritance, they are actually multifactorial, because the environment can influence the phenotype. Constant sun exposure darkens skin, and poor nutrition can prevent a person from realizing his or her genetically determined height.

The number of ridges in a fingerprint pattern is another trait that is largely determined by genes, but also responds to the environment. During weeks 6 through 13 of prenatal development, the ridge pattern can alter as the fetus touches the finger and toe pads to the wall of the amniotic sac. This early environmental effect explains why the fingerprints of identical twins, who share all genes, are not exactly alike.

We can quantify a fingerprint with a measurement called a total ridge count, which tallies the number of ridges comprising a "whorl," "loop," or "arch" part of the pattern for each finger (figure 7.2). Males typically have a total ridge count of 145, and females, 126. Note the similarity between the shapes of the curves in figures 7.1 and 7.2. This is called a bell curve, and we will see it again.

Many illnesses are multifactorial. A person inherits a gene or genes that impart a particular susceptibility but only develops

table 7.1

Polygenic Model of Skin Color Inheritance

Multilocus Genotypes	Number of Pigment Genes
AABBCC	6
AaBBCC, AABbCC, AABBCc	5
aaBBCC, AAbbCC, AABBcc, AaBbCC, AaBBCc, AABbCc	4
AaBbCc, aaBbCC, AAbbCc, AabbCC, AABbcc, aaBBCc, AaBBcc	3
AaBbcc, AabbCc, aaBbCc, AAbbcc, aaBBcc, aabbCC	2
Aabbcc, aaBbcc, aabbCc	1
aabbcc	0

Studies that classify skin color by measuring the amount of light reflected from the skin surface suggest that three or four or more different genes, probably with several alleles each, produce skin pigment. The greater the number of pigment-specifying genes, the darker the skin. Skin color inheritance is most likely even more complicated than this model of three genes.

figure 7.1

Height is a continuously varying trait. When these individuals were asked to line up according to their heights, they formed a characteristic bell-shaped, continuous distribution.

the associated illness if he or she encounters a specific environmental "trigger." For example, inheriting a variant of a gene called p53 predisposes an individual to develop lung cancer, but that fate may not transpire unless the person smokes cigarettes for an extended time.

Other examples of genetic predisposition are more striking. In favism, an inborn error of metabolism, a predisposition to anemia occurs, but the condition develops only if the person takes certain drugs or eats fava beans. Similarly, in malignant hyperthermia, escalating symptoms of fever, muscle contractions, swelling and pressure on the brain, coma, and sometimes death occur only upon exposure to a certain anesthetic drug.

Reading 7.1 discusses several common illnesses that result from complex interactions between gene action and environmental input.

Key Concepts

Complex traits, which do not follow Mendel's laws, may be either polygenic or multifactorial. Polygenic traits are determined by more than one gene and vary continuously in expression. Multifactorial traits are determined by a combination of a gene or genes and the environment.

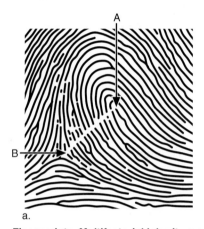

a.

Fingerprints: Multifactorial Inheritance

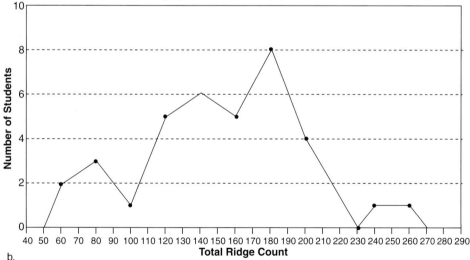

b.

figure 7.2

Anatomy of a fingerprint. (a) The number of ridges between landmark points A and B on this loop pattern is twelve. To calculate total ridge count, the number of ridges in characteristic patterns on each finger is counted and added. (b) Total ridge count plotted on a bar graph forms an approximate bell-shaped curve, signaling a multifactorial trait.

Source: Data and print from Gordon Mendenhall, Thomas Mertens, and Jon Hendrix, "Fingerprint Ridge Count" in *The American Biology Teacher*, vol. 51, no. 4, April 1989, pp. 204–6.

Measuring Multifactorial Traits

Empiric Risk

Geneticists estimate the inherited component of multifactorial traits using information from population studies and from family relationships. Using Mendel's laws, it is possible to predict the risk that a single-gene trait will recur if one knows the mode of inheritance—such as autosomal dominant or recessive. To predict the risk that a multifactorial trait will recur, it is necessary to determine the **empiric risk,** a prediction of recurrence based on the trait's incidence in a specific population. In general, empiric risk increases with the severity of the disorder, the number of affected family members, and how closely related the person is to affected individuals.

Empiric risk may be used to predict the likelihood that a neural tube defect (NTD—see Reading 7.1) will recur. In the United States, the overall population's risk of carrying a fetus with an NTD is about 1 in 1,000 (0.1 percent). However, if a sibling has an NTD, the risk of recurrence increases to 3 percent, and if two siblings are affected, the risk to a third child is even greater (although only about 10 percent of children with this birth defect have an affected older sibling). By determining whether a fetus has any siblings with NTDs, a geneticist can predict the risk to the fetus.

An additional clue to predicting risk of recurrence is possible for multifactorial disorders that affect one sex more often than the other. Pyloric stenosis, for example, an overgrowth of muscle at the juncture between the stomach and the small intestine, is five times more common among males than among females. The condition must be corrected surgically shortly after birth, or the newborn will be unable to digest foods. Empiric data show that the risk of recurrence for the brother of an affected brother is 3.8 percent, but for the brother of an affected sister, the risk is 9.2 percent. Geneticists do not know why this is so for some traits. Table 7.2 summarizes factors that increase the risk that a relative will have a multifactorial trait.

Sometimes it is difficult to determine whether a trait is caused by genes, the environment, or both. The following examples illustrate how important it can be to find out.

Cystic Fibrosis

When researchers realized that cystic fibrosis (CF) was caused by several allele combinations that produce varying degrees of symptom severity, they attempted to see if genotypes correlate to specific phenotypes. Such information would inform people of how sick they would become. Unfortunately, researchers could not establish a direct correlation. Apparently, other unknown genes influence the expression of the cystic fibrosis alleles.

CF held another surprise. In many cases, an environmental input influences the course of an inherited illness; in CF, it was the other way around. The thick mucus that builds up along airway linings provides a very attractive environment for bacteria, most notably a highly transmissible and quick-killing species called *Burkholderia cepacia*. Bacterial infection is familiar to people with CF, but in the past, they have usually been infected by *Pseudomonas aeruginosa*. A *Pseudomonas* infection can be present, on and off, for two decades before it kills, but, *B. cepacia* can do so in weeks. *B. cepacia* have appendages called cable pili that enable them to anchor tenaciously to the mucus-covered cells lining the airway. They resist most antibiotic drugs.

Epidemics of *B. cepacia* were first reported a few years ago from Toronto and Edinburgh, under tragic circumstances. Because the infection transfers so easily from person to person, it swept through summer camps for children with CF. Patients and their families were not prepared for such deadly bacterial infections. The camps and other support services are vitally important to affected families, but suddenly any patient with a *B. cepacia* diagnosis was isolated to avoid spread of the infection to others with CF.

Genetics has helped these patients a little. But rather than determining genotypes for the underlying CF, researchers are typing the DNA of the bacteria. Only patients with the more virulent strains of *B. cepacia* need be isolated. The task now is to correlate all of the information: Which CF genotypes seem to attract which bacterial species, and which genetic variants of those species?

Type I Diabetes

Juvenile diabetes runs in families, but in no particular pattern of recurrence. The reason for the unpredictability may be environmental. In this inborn error in glucose (sugar) metabolism, the immune system attacks the pancreas. As a result, the pancreas does not produce the insulin required to route blood glucose into cells for use.

When studying the pancreases of young people who died suddenly just weeks after being diagnosed with diabetes, researchers observed severe infection of the pancreas plus an unusually strong immune response to the infection. They concluded that certain individuals may inherit a susceptibility to that type of infection or a strong immune response to it, but not develop diabetes unless such an infection occurs.

Neural Tube Defects

Sometimes what appears to be an environmental influence is actually genetic. This may be the case for neural tube defects (NTDs), which are openings in the brain or spinal cord that occur at the end of the first month of prenatal development. Researchers have long attributed these birth defects to a combination of heredity and the environment, based on two observations:

1. A woman who has one affected child is at increased risk of having another affected child (implicating heredity).
2. Recurrence risk diminishes if a woman takes folic acid supplements shortly before and during pregnancy (implicating a vitamin deficiency).

Recent discoveries, however, suggest that an inherited enzyme deficiency may explain why vitamin supplementation prevents some NTDs. A large group of Irish women whose children have NTDs were found to be deficient in both folic acid and vitamin B12. Only one biochemical reaction in the human body requires both of these vitamins; an abnormality in the enzyme that catalyzes that reaction could cause the double vitamin deficiency. Researchers are now trying to determine how disruption of this reaction causes an NTD. Meanwhile, pregnant women routinely take folic acid supplements to reduce the incidence of these birth defects.

Heritability—The Genetic Contribution to a Trait

Heritability is a measurement that estimates the proportion of phenotypic variation in a group that can be attributed to genes. It is calculated as double the difference of the measurable variation between two groups of individuals. Approximately 80 percent of height variance is due to heredity.

However, heritability values are not always reliable. This is because researchers may define different phenotypes, particularly behavioral ones, differently. Also, specific genetic or environmental components may contribute to a complex trait to different degrees.

Heritability describes a particular group of individuals and is not a property of a gene. This means it can vary in different environments. For example, nutrition has a

table 7.2

Factors that Increase Risk for Multifactorial Traits

Close blood relationship to an affected person

Number of affected persons in family

Severity of the disorder

Affected relative of more rarely affected sex (for some traits)

Higher contribution of genes (heritability)

table 7.3

Coefficient of Relationship and Shared Genes

Relationship	Degree of Relationship	Percent Shared Genes
Sibling to sibling	1°	50% (1/2)
Parent to child	1°	50% (1/2)
Uncle/aunt to niece/nephew	2°	25% (1/4)
First cousin to first cousin	3°	12 1/2% (1/8)

greater influence on egg production in a starving population of chickens than in a well-fed one.

Coefficient of Relationship

The **coefficient of relationship** describes the percentage of genes two related individuals share (table 7.3, figure 7.3). The closer the relationship between two individuals, the more genes they have in common, and the greater the probability that they will share a trait. For example, the risk that cleft lip will recur is 40 percent for the identical twin of an affected individual, but only 4 percent for a sibling, and less than 1 percent for a niece, nephew, or first cousin (table 7.4).

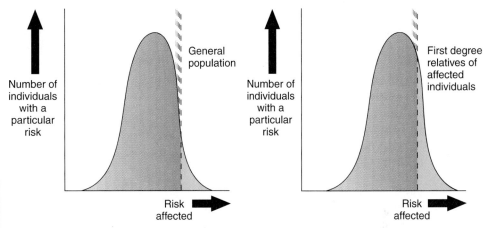

figure 7.3

The risk among the general population of expressing a multifactorial trait follows a bell-shaped curve, with a certain threshold necessary for manifestation. The curve shifts for blood relatives of affected individuals, placing them at greater risk than the general population.

Key Concepts

Researchers measure multifactorial traits by determining empiric risk, heritability, and coefficient of relationship. Empiric risk predicts recurrence of a multifactorial trait. Risk increases with severity of the trait, number of affected relatives, whether a person is of the sex opposite that most often affected, and with increasing relatedness to an affected individual. Heritability estimates the proportion of phenotypic variation of a multifactorial trait in a population due to genetics. Coefficient of relationship indicates the proportion of genes relatives share.

table 7.4

Risk of Recurrence for Cleft Lip

Relationship to Affected Person	Risk of Recurrence
Identical twin	40.0%
Sibling	4.1%
Child	3.5%
Niece/nephew	0.8%
First cousin	0.3%
General population risk (no affected relatives)	0.1%

Studying Multifactorial Traits

Multifactorial inheritance analysis does not easily lend itself to the scientific method, which ideally entails the study of one variable. However, to study humans, geneticists can turn to two types of people to tease apart the genetic and environmental components of complex traits—twins and adopted individuals.

Adopted Individuals

A person adopted by nonrelatives shares environmental influences, but not genes, with his or her adoptive family. Conversely, adopted individuals share genes, but not the exact environment, with their biological parents. Therefore, biologists assume that similarities between adopted people and adoptive parents reflect environmental influences, whereas similarities between adoptees and their biological parents mostly reflect genetic influences. Information on both sets of parents can reveal how heredity and the environment each contribute to the development of a trait.

Many adoption studies use the Danish Adoption Register, a compendium of all adopted Danish children and their families from 1924 to 1947. One study examined correlations between causes of death among biological and adoptive parents and adopted children. If a biological parent died of infection before age fifty, the adopted child was five times more likely to die of infection at a young age than a similar person in the general population. This may be because inherited variants in immune system genes increase susceptibility to certain infectious agents. In support of this hypothesis, the risk that an adopted individual would die young from infection did not correlate with adoptive parents' death from infection before age fifty.

Although researchers concluded that length of life is mostly determined by heredity, they did find evidence of environmental influences. For example, if adoptive parents died before age fifty of cardiovascular disease, their adopted children were three times as likely to die of heart and blood vessel disease as a person in the general population. What environmental factor might account for this correlation?

Separated at birth, the Mallifert twins meet accidentally.

figure 7.4

Drawing by Chas. Addams; ©1981 The New Yorker Magazine, Inc.

Twins

Twins occur in 1 out of 81 births. Identical or **monozygotic** (MZ) **twins** result when a single fertilized ovum splits. Therefore, identical twins are always of the same sex and always have identical genes. Fraternal or **dizygotic** (DZ) **twins** arise from two fertilized ova. Fraternal twins are no more similar genetically than any two siblings, although they share the same prenatal environment.

Using twins to study genetic influence on complex traits dates to 1924, when German dermatologist Hermann Siemens compared school transcripts of identical versus fraternal twins. Noticing that grades and teachers' comments were much more alike for identical twins than for fraternal twins, he proposed that genes contribute to intelligence. Siemens also suggested that a better test would be to study identical twins who were separated at birth, then raised in very different environments. He was ahead of his time.

Since 1979, more than a hundred sets of MZ and DZ twins and triplets who were separated at birth have visited the laboratories of Thomas Bouchard at the University of Minnesota. There, for a week or more, each set of twins undergoes a battery of physical and psychological tests. These "Minnesota twins" have helped unravel how genes and the environment influence an astonishingly wide variety of traits.

Twins separated at birth provide natural experiments for distinguishing nature from nurture. Many of their common traits can be attributed to genetics, especially if their environments have been very different (figure 7.4). By contrast, their differences tend to reflect differences in their upbringing, since their genes are identical (MZ twins) or similar (DZ twins).

A trait that occurs more frequently in both members of identical twin pairs than in both members of fraternal twin pairs is at least partly controlled by heredity. Figure 7.5 illustrates the concept of comparing twins for a variety of hard-to-measure traits. Geneticists calculate the **concordance** of a trait, or the degree to which it is inherited, as the percentage of pairs in which both twins express the trait. Twins can also be used to calculate heritability, which equals approximately double the difference between MZ and DZ concordance values for a trait.

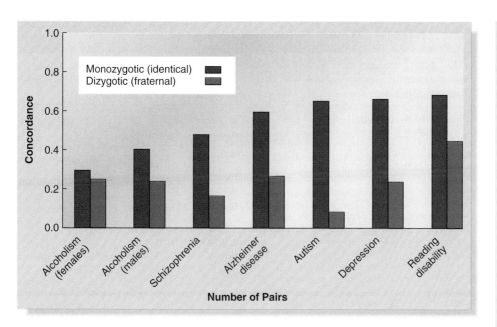

figure 7.5

A trait more often present in both members of MZ twin pairs than in both members of DZ twin pairs has a significant inherited component.

Source: Robert Plomin, et al., The Genetic Basis of Complex Human Behaviors," *Science,* 17 June 1994, vol. 264, p. 1734.

table 7.5

Heritabilities for Cognitive Function

Cognitive Function	Heritability
General cognitive ability	62%
Speed of processing information	62%
Verbal ability	55%
Memory	52%
Spatial ability	32%

Diseases that single genes cause, whether dominant or recessive, are always 100 percent concordant in MZ twins. If one twin has it, so does the other. However, among DZ twins, concordance is 50 percent for a dominant single-gene trait and 25 percent for a recessive trait. These are the Mendelian values that apply to any two siblings. For a trait determined by several genes, concordance values for MZ twins are significantly greater than for DZ twins. A trait molded mostly by the environment exhibits similar concordance values for both types of twins.

Table 7.5 lists heritabilities for aspects of cognitive function (thinking and reasoning) determined in a comparison of these traits among 110 MZ twin pairs and 130 same-sex DZ twin pairs. What was unusual about this study was that the participants were all over age 80! All were healthy and had a lifetime of environmental influences to overshadow inherited contributions to thinking ability. The results indicate that throughout life, the genes we are dealt at conception play a large—but not total—role in our intellectual capabilities.

Twin studies have been useful in assessing personality traits. In one study, a psychologist administered personality tests to 514 MZ twins and 336 DZ twins selected from a national sample of high school seniors. Personality concordance was 50 percent for MZ twins and 28 percent for DZ twins. The heritability for these measures

was calculated to be 44 percent (50 − 28 = 22; 22 × 2 = 44), which means that heredity accounts for slightly less than half of the personality similarities between these twins. This leaves quite a lot of room for environmental influences.

Comparing twin types assumes, perhaps incorrectly, that both types of twins share similar experiences. In fact, identical twins are often closer than fraternal twins, particularly those of opposite sex. This discrepancy led to some misleading results in twin studies conducted in the 1940s. One study concluded that tuberculosis is inherited because concordance among identical twins was higher than among fraternal twins. Actually, the infectious disease was more readily passed between identical twins because their parents kept them in close physical contact.

Today, the Minnesota Study tracks many traits. Each twin pair undergoes six days of tests that measure both physical and behavioral traits, including twenty-four different blood types, handedness, direction of hair growth, fingerprint pattern, height, weight, functioning of all organ systems, intelligence, allergies, and dental patterns. Researchers videotape the twins' facial expressions and body movements in different circumstances and probe their fears, vocational interests, and superstitions.

The researchers have found that identical twins separated at birth and reunited later are remarkably similar, even when they grow up in very different adoptive families. Idiosyncrasies are particularly striking. A pair of identical male twins raised in different countries practicing different religions were astounded, when they were reunited as adults, to find that they both laugh when someone sneezes and flush the toilet before using it. Twins who met for the first time when they were in their thirties responded identically to questions; each paused for 30 seconds, rotated a gold necklace she was wearing three times, and then answered the question. Coincidence, or genetics?

The "twins reared apart" approach is not a perfectly controlled way to separate nature from nurture. Identical twins share an environment in the uterus and possibly in early infancy that may affect later development. Siblings, whether adoptive or biological, do not always share identical home environments. Differences in sex, general health, school and peer experiences, temperament, and personality affect each individual's perception of such environmental influences as parental affection and discipline.

Adoption studies, likewise, are not perfectly controlled experiments. Adoption agencies often search for adoptive families with ethnic, socioeconomic, or religious backgrounds similar to those of the biological parents. Thus, even when different families adopt and raise separated twins, their environments might not be as different as they might be for two unrelated adoptees. However, twins reared apart are still providing intriguing insights into the number of body movements, psychological quirks, interests, and other personality traits that seem to be rooted in our genes.

Key Concepts

Researchers can compare the traits of adopted individuals and their adoptive and biological parents to assess to what degree heredity influences those traits. MZ twins separated at birth provide information on the negative effects of nature and nurture in molding a complex trait.

Some Complex Traits

Cardiovascular Disease

Arthur Ashe was a professional tennis player who suffered a severe heart attack in his early thirties. He was in top physical shape and followed a low-fat diet, but an inherited tendency to deposit lipids on the insides of his coronary arteries led to a heart attack despite his healthy lifestyle. He eventually died of AIDS, which he acquired from a blood transfusion during heart surgery. Table 7.6 lists controllable and uncontrollable risk factors for coronary artery disease, which robs heart muscle of oxygen and nutrients.

In contrast to Arthur Ashe was the case of an eighty-eight-year-old man reported in a medical journal. He ate twenty-five eggs a day yet had a very healthy heart and low serum cholesterol level. The lucky egg eater didn't have a

table 7.6

Risk Factors for Coronary Artery Disease

Uncontrollable	Controllable or Treatable
Family history (genetics)	Fatty diet
Age	Hypertension
Male sex	Smoking
	High serum cholesterol
	Low serum HDL
	High serum LDL
	Stress
	Insufficient exercise
	Obesity
	Diabetes

sky-high cholesterol level or plaque-clogged coronary arteries because his particular metabolism, orchestrated by genes, could handle the large load of dietary lipid. The vastly different heart health status of Arthur Ashe and the elderly egg lover demonstrate the powerful influence of genes—Ashe followed all preventative measures and suffered a heart attack; the eighty-eight-year-old ate a diet oozing with cholesterol and enjoyed good cardiovascular health.

The state of the heart and blood vessels reflects how well the body handles fat levels in the blood. Fats are insoluble in the watery blood, but when bound to proteins and transformed into large molecules called lipoproteins, fats can travel in the circulation.

Several genes encode the protein parts of lipoproteins, called **apolipoproteins** (figure 7.6). Some types of lipoproteins ferry lipids in the blood to tissues, where they are utilized, and other types of lipoproteins take lipids to the liver, where they are dismantled or converted to biochemicals that the body can excrete more easily.

Maintaining a healthy heart and blood vessel system requires a balance: cells require sufficient lipid levels inside but cannot allow too much accumulation on the outside. Several dozen genes control lipid levels in the blood and tissues by specifying other proteins, which are enzymes that process lipids, that transport lipids, or that form receptors that admit lipids into cells.

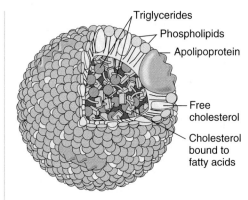

Triglycerides
Phospholipids
Apolipoprotein
Free cholesterol
Cholesterol bound to fatty acids

figure 7.6

Lipoproteins are of different sizes and consist of different proportions of fatty acids, cholesterol, triglycerides, and proteins. High levels of low-density lipoproteins (LDLs) and low levels of high-density lipoproteins (HDLs) are risk factors for coronary artery disease.

Much of what we know about genetic control of cardiovascular health comes from rare inherited conditions that result from a mutation in one of these genes. Often, unraveling a genetic cause of a disease indirectly helps the larger number of people suffering from noninherited forms of the illness. For example, members of a large family living in the remote Italian village of Limone have inherited an apolipoprotein variant, called apo-A1 Milano, that protects heart health even when people eat a very fatty diet. Researchers are trying to develop the apo-A1 Milano protein into a drug that would provide this benefit to others. Similarly, the cholesterol-lowering drugs that millions of people take today grew out of research on people with familial hypercholesterolemia, an inherited high-cholesterol condition.

Hypertension (high blood pressure) is another cardiovascular disease with both genetic and environmental causes (table 7.7). As many as twenty to fifty genes may regulate blood pressure. One is the gene encoding **angiotensinogen,** a protein that is elevated in the blood of hypertension patients. This protein controls blood vessel tone and fluid balance in the body. Certain variants of the gene are found far more frequently among people with hypertension than chance would explain. Even though environmental factors, such as emotional stress, can cause blood pressure to soar, knowing who is genetically susceptible to dangerously high blood pressure can alert doctors to monitor high-risk individuals.

Obesity

A third of all American adults are obese—defined as 20 percent or more above ideal weight. Obesity raises the risk of hypertension, diabetes, stroke, gallstones, sleep apnea, some cancers, and psychological problems. The reason that weight loss can be difficult may reside in the genes.

In 1994, scientists found that a gene long known to cause obesity in mice has a counterpart in humans. The gene, in both species, encodes a protein called **leptin.** Steady infusions of the protein into obese mice cause great weight loss (figure 7.7). Leptin apparently functions by stopping metabolism from slowing when food intake drops. Obese mice cannot respond adequately to leptin. We still do not know leptin's precise role in humans.

Researchers can hardly breed people to study the inheritance of obesity, as they do mice. But they can use techniques such as adoption and twin studies to try to determine the heritability of obesity. Many studies use a measurement called the body mass index (BMI), which equals weight/height^2, with weight measured in kilograms (kg) and height measured in meters (m). BMI provides a measure of weight that takes height into account, a combined characteristic called ponderosity.

One study compared the BMIs of 540 Danish adopted persons to those of their

table 7.7

Risk Factors for Hypertension

Uncontrollable	Controllable or Treatable
Family history	Fatty diet
Age	Salty diet
Male sex	Alcohol intake
African ancestry	Stress
	Insufficient exercise
	Obesity

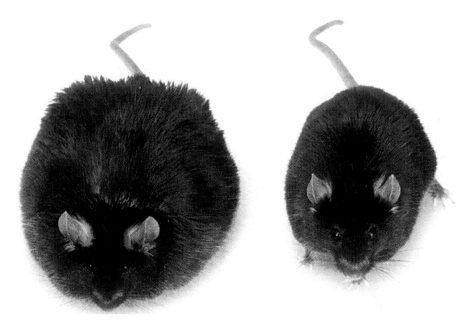

figure 7.7

In 1950, an unusual mouse was born at the Jackson Laboratory in Bar Harbor, Maine, which supplies most of the world's mutant mice for research. The "obese" mouse grew to three times normal mouse weight, developed diabetes, and passed the obesity trait to its offspring. In the 1970s, researchers showed that transfusing an obese mouse's blood into a healthy mouse made the recipient gain weight and concluded that a blood-borne substance—which they called a "satiety factor"—normally helps control fat storage. Today we know the satiety factor is the protein leptin, which maintains level of energy use when food intake drops. Mice that cannot respond to leptin are obese.

adoptive and biological parents. All participants were classified as thin, medium, overweight, or obese, with sex and age factored in. The adopted individuals' BMIs strongly correlated to those of their biological parents, but not to those of their adoptive parents. In fact, adoption and twin studies indicate that about 75 percent of BMI differences later in life are attributable to genes.

In a dormitory at Laval University in Quebec, Canada, twelve pairs of identical male twins have helped shed light on the question of obesity genes as part of the Minnesota Twins Study. The students overate by 1,000 calories a day for 84 of 100 days of observation. Each student thus consumed 84,000 extra calories. Because it takes 3,500 calories of food energy to add a pound of body fat, each participant was expected to gain 24 pounds (84,000 calories/3,500 calories per pound). However, average weight gain was

17.8 pounds, ranging from 9.5 to 29 pounds. Weight gain and percent of body fat varied three times as much between twin pairs as within them. The pattern of fat distribution, determined by CAT scans showing fat deposition, varied six times as much between the pairs as within them. These results support the heritability of .75 for tendency to gain weight. They also indicate that genes specifically influence the body's rate of energy expenditure as well as the degree to which energy is used to build fat or lean (muscle) tissue.

Once adoption and twin studies establish a genetic component to a trait, molecular geneticists often attempt to locate "candidate genes" that might contribute to it. Scientists studying obesity have focused on an enzyme, **lipoprotein lipase,** specified by a gene on chromosome 8. Lipoprotein lipase lines the walls of the smallest blood vessels, where it breaks down fat packets that the small intestine and liver release. Lipoprotein lipase is activated by high-density lipoproteins (HDLs), and it breaks down low-density lipoproteins (LDLs). High HDL levels and low LDL levels are associated with a healthy cardiovascular system.

A group of autosomal recessive inborn errors of metabolism called type I hyperlipoproteinemias cause a deficiency of lipoprotein lipase, which in turn causes triglycerides (a type of fat) to build to dangerously high levels in the blood. Lipoprotein lipase also appears to regulate fat cell size; fat cells usually contribute to obesity by enlarging, rather than by dividing to form more fat cells. Lipoprotein lipase may play a generalized role in utilizing fat stores as well.

Intelligence

Intelligence is a complex trait subject to genetic and environmental influences, and also to intense subjectivity. That is, our definitions of intelligence may be narrower than the true range of human intellectual abilities and talents. One very successful rock musician, for example, was a terrible student who slept through his high-school classes because he was out all night making music. Is he a dullard for failing high-school English or a lyrical genius for writing songs?

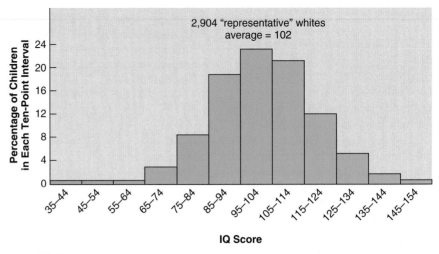

figure 7.8

IQ scores form a continuous distribution, suggesting that a variety of factors influence intelligence.

Source: Terman and Merrill, *Measuring Intelligence.* Copyright © 1937 Houghton Mifflin Co., Boston, MA.

Sir Francis Galton, a half first cousin of Charles Darwin and a contemporary of Gregor Mendel, was obsessed with the study of the inheritance of intelligence. Galton was most noted for his work in eugenics (chapter 11), but he also liked to measure such valuable statistics as the number of fidgets per minute per person in the audience of a Royal Geographic Society meeting.

Galton investigated genius, which he defined as "a man endowed with superior faculties," by first identifying the successful and prominent in Victorian-era English society, and then assessing success among their relatives. In his 1869 book, *Hereditary Genius,* Galton wrote that relatives of eminent people were more likely to also be successful than people in the general population. The closer the blood relationship, he concluded, the more likely the person was to be successful. This, he believed, established a hereditary basis for intelligence as he measured it.

Definitions of intelligence have varied in time and place. The first intelligence tests, developed in the late nineteenth century, assessed sensory perception and reaction times to various stimuli. In 1904, Alfred Binet at the Sorbonne developed a test with verbal, numerical, and pictorial questions. Its purpose was to predict success of developmentally handicapped youngsters in school. The test was subsequently modified at Stanford University to represent white, middle-class Americans. An average score on this "intelligence quotient," or IQ test, was 100, with two-thirds of all people scoring from 85 to 115 in a bell curve or normal distribution (figure 7.8). A 1994 book, *The Bell Curve,* maintained that people in certain population groups score lower on IQ tests because they have a genetically inferior intellect. The treatise was roundly criticized by scientists who cited the limited nature of IQ tests.

Today, twin studies and even molecular biology are used to tackle the age-old question of how heredity and the environment interact to determine or influence intelligence. The results of more than a hundred studies focusing on families, adopted children, or twins generally concur that about 70 percent of IQ variance is due to heredity, allowing parents and educators much leeway to influence intelligence.

The human genome project is likely to provide more objective analyses of intelligence because hundreds of genes are expressed in the human brain. A type of computer program called quantitative trait loci (QTL) association analysis can detect genes that account for as little as 1 percent of the observed variance in a trait. Still, the many environmental influences on intelligence will always make it a challenge to separate the genetic components.

Narcolepsy

Sleep has been called "a vital behavior of unknown function," and indeed without sleep, animals die. We spend a third of our lives in this mysterious state. Genes influence sleep characteristics. When asked about sleep duration, schedule, quality, nap habits, and whether they are "night owls" or "morning people," MZ twins have significantly more in common than do DZ twins, even MZ twins separated at birth. Twin studies of brain wave patterns through four of the five stages of sleep confirm a hereditary influence. The fifth stage, REM sleep, is associated with dreaming and therefore may more closely mirror input of experiences than genes.

Studies of the disorder narcolepsy with cataplexy further illustrate the influence of genes on sleep behavior. Narcolepsy produces daytime sleepiness and the tendency to fall asleep very rapidly, several times a day. Cataplexy is short episodes of muscle weakness, during which the jaw sags, head drops, knees buckle, and the person falls to the ground. This often occurs during a bout of laughter—which can be quite disturbing both to the affected individual and witnesses.

Narcolepsy with cataplexy affects only 0.02 to 0.06 percent of the general populations of North America and Europe. Yet it is much more common within some families. A person with an affected first-degree relative has a 1 to 2 percent chance of developing the condition, which usually begins between the ages of 15 and 25. Concordance for narcolepsy with cataplexy among MZ twins is 25 to 31 percent. Plus, nearly all affected individuals have a rare HLA allele that may be a susceptibility gene.

Dogs may help us understand the complex genetics of narcolepsy. In canines, narcolepsy is a Mendelian trait, inherited as a fully penetrant, autosomal recessive allele, called *canarc-1*. Researchers are searching the corresponding region of the human genome for a possible narcolepsy gene. (We can't tell if dogs also have cataplexy, because they do not laugh! Perhaps they develop dogaplexy.)

Schizophrenia

Schizophrenia is a debilitating loss of the ability to organize thoughts and perceptions,

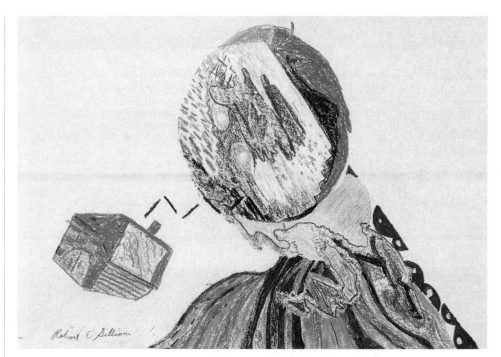

figure 7.9

People with schizophrenia sometimes communicate the disarray of their thoughts by drawing characteristically disjointed pictures.

© Robert E. Gilliam.

which leads to a gradual withdrawal from reality. The condition affects 1 percent of the U.S. population. It often begins in the late teens or early adulthood with delusions and hallucinations—usually auditory, but sometimes visual—that can make everyday events terrifying. A person with schizophrenia may hear a voice in his or her head, or from a television or radio, giving instructions. What others perceive as irrational fears, such as being followed by monsters, are very real to the person with schizophrenia. Speech reflects the garbled thought process; a schizophrenic skips from topic to topic with no obvious thread or logic, or displays inappropriate emotional responses, such as laughing at sad news. Artwork often displays the characteristic fragmentation of the mind (figure 7.9). (Schizophrenia means "split mind," but it does not cause a split personality.)

Schizophrenia has been frequently misdiagnosed since its description a century ago. Because it causes a variety of symptoms that vary in expression, people with schizophrenia are sometimes diagnosed with depression or **bipolar affective disorder** (having extreme mood swings).

However, schizophrenia affects thinking; these other conditions affect mood.

A genetic contribution to schizophrenia is suggested by the increased risk of recurrence in close relatives and by the high concordance between identical twins (table 7.8). Because most of the symptoms are behavioral, however, it is possible to develop some of them—such as disordered thinking—from exposure to people who have schizophrenia. Although concordance is high, a person who has a schizophrenic twin has a 60 percent chance of *not* developing schizophrenia. Therefore, the condition has a significant environmental component, too. Figure 7.10 shows a difference in brain structure between people with schizophrenia and their unaffected identical twins.

Genetic analysis of schizophrenia has been frustrating. Two Chinese brothers with schizophrenia provided a first clue to the genetics of the disorder—they each had a duplication of part of the fifth largest chromosome. This chromosome was also implicated in causing schizophrenia in five families in Iceland and two in England. The mode of inheritance

table 7.8

Risk of Recurrence for Schizophrenia

Relationship to Affected Person	Risk of Recurrence
Identical twin	40%
Sibling	≈10%
Child of one affected parent	≈13%
Child of two affected parents	40%
Niece/nephew	3%
First cousin	2%
General population risk (no affected relatives)	≈1%

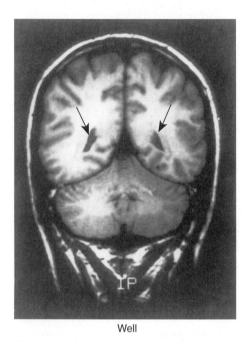
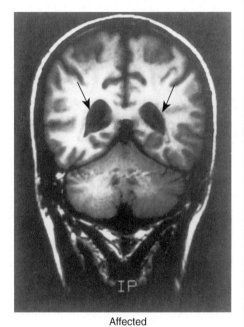

Well   Affected

figure 7.10

The schizophrenic brain. Magnetic resonance images were taken of the brains of sets of identical twins, one of whom has schizophrenia in each set. The brains of the twins with schizophrenia consistently reveal enlarged spaces (ventricles). This difference may hold a clue to the physical basis of this largely behavioral disorder.

appeared to be autosomal dominant. However, in other families, people with schizophrenia did not have an abnormality on chromosome 5. Four subsequent large studies implicated a gene on chromosome 6 in causing schizophrenia. Therefore, there must be more than one way to inherit the disorder. Schizophrenia is a complex trait—it is genetically heterogeneic, multifactorial, and possibly polygenic. It may also possibly be completely environmental, caused when the patient's mother contracted an influenza virus in the second trimester of pregnancy. The evidence for this is that a flu virus can cross the placenta and change brain cells, and the observation that many people with schizophrenia were born in the spring, after winter cases of flu abound.

Alcoholism

In the United States, alcoholism afflicts 10 percent of males and 4 percent of females at some time during their lives. Manifestations of alcoholism are physical as well as behavioral, altering brain wave patterns and activities of certain liver and blood-clotting enzymes. However, it is not clear whether these physical characteristics cause alcohol dependency or result from it.

To what degree is alcoholism inherited, and therefore, somewhat beyond one's control? Empirical data show a two- to threefold increase in alcoholism among adopted persons with one affected biological parent. This suggests, as do twin studies, that genes play a role in alcoholism. Variants of enzymes called alcohol dehydrogenases and protein kinases may explain the large differences among people's reactions to the same amount of alcohol.

Another gene variant that may be implicated in some cases of alcoholism is an autosomal allele called A1. The gene encodes a protein receptor on nerve cells that receives a neurotransmitter (nerve messenger) called dopamine. The receptor returns dopamine to the cell after it has triggered a nerve impulse in a nearby cell. Several studies show that A1 is present in about 45 percent of people with alcoholism who also have physical complications, but in only about 26 percent of people who do not have alcoholism. The suggestion is that the A1 dopamine receptors somehow alter dopamine recycling in a way that predisposes a person to develop alcoholism. The work is controversial because the correlations are so imprecise, and some research groups have been unable to replicate the results.

Nongenetic studies also examine alcoholism. One approach images the dopamine receptors directly in an area of the brain called the striatum. The density of the receptors seems to correlate to phenotype. In one preliminary study, people who become alcoholic later in life and who are sociable and nonviolent have fewer dopamine receptors here than do nonalcoholics. People who develop alcoholism in adolescence, abuse other substances, and are antisocial and violent have slightly more than the normal number of dopamine receptors in this brain area.

Using psychological profiles, dopamine receptor densities, and allele combinations for the dopamine receptor gene to define subtypes of alcoholism may be too simplistic. Alcoholism may be a very heterogeneous disorder, which could explain why some sufferers lack the A1 allele and why some have it. Perhaps A1 causes compulsive behaviors that, in the presence of certain environmental factors, lead to alcoholism. The fact that A1 is more frequent among people with certain behavioral disorders than it is in the general population supports this idea (table 7.9).

The vague association of alcoholism with the A1 allele of the dopamine receptor gene may have practical applications. If alcoholism requires the combined presence of a modifying gene and environmental triggers, people who find out that they have inherited the susceptibility allele can strive to avoid the precipitating events. But many people are aware of the tendency toward alcoholism without a genetic test.

table 7.9

Prevalence of the A1 Allele of the Dopamine Receptor Gene in People with Various Behavioral Disorders

Disorder	Percent with A1 Allele
Alcoholism	42.3%
Attention deficit hyperactivity disorder	46.2%
Autism	54.5%
Posttraumatic stress disorder	45.7%
Tourette syndrome	44.9%
None of these disorders	14.5%

Key Concepts

Genes and environmental risk factors such as exercise and dietary habits control cardiovascular health. Apolipoproteins influence plaque deposition in arteries.

Adoption and twin studies examining BMI and weight gain suggest that heritability of tendency to gain weight is about .75. Leptin is a protein associated with body weight because it maintains energy use. Lipoprotein lipase, an enzyme that breaks down LDL, is a candidate gene in obesity and cardiovascular disease.

Intelligence is a multifactorial trait that is difficult to objectively define and measure. Several studies suggest that differences in intelligence are about 70 percent due to heredity. Several scales assess intelligence and are supplemented with information on genes expressed in the brain.

Genes affect sleep characteristics. Narcolepsy is a complex trait. Schizophrenia causes disorganized thinking. High concordance suggests a genetic component, but the disorder is probably genetically heterogeneic and polygenic. Alcoholism may be associated with a variant dopamine receptor on brain cells.

Behavioral Genetics

Until the 1960s, researchers seeking the roots of human behavior focused on environmental causes, such as attributing schizophrenia to poor parenting. A key 1966 study that demonstrated the role genes play in causing schizophrenia changed the direction of research towards gene discovery. The study followed 47 infants released for adoption by mothers who had schizophrenia. Five of the children developed schizophrenia, which is the same rate of recurrence seen in children raised by biological mothers with schizophrenia.

Since then, twin and adoption studies have revealed genetic components to many behavioral characteristics, including self-esteem, personality traits, intelligence, and academic achievement. Studies on nonhuman animals also demonstrate the role genes play in determining behavior, from fruit flies with homosexual tendencies, to mice that prefer alcohol-tinged water.

Twin and adoption studies provide only a first step in analyzing genetic influences on human behavior. Such investigations identify traits that are likely to have large genetic components and that might be good candidates for gene searches. The second step is to discover genes that cause specific behaviors. Such a gene might encode a protein whose activity affects the nervous system, because this is the organ system that regulates behavior.

One approach to identifying behavior genes is to search within large families for DNA sequences or abnormal chromo-some regions that appear only in the individuals who have the trait under study. These DNA sequences serve as markers. However, such a search can be complicated for a polygenic trait or for a phenotype that can reflect any of several genotypes (genetic heterogeneity). In the 1980s, for example, several research groups sought to pinpoint a gene that causes **bipolar affective disorder,** a condition characterized by mood swings that is also known as manic-depressive illness. Studies on three different populations identified genes on three different chromosomes that predispose a person to this very distinct behavior pattern—all later disproven as more data accumulated. Assignment of a bipolar affective disorder gene to chromosome 11 in a large Old Order Amish family, for example, was disproven when two relatives developed symptoms a few years after the study was completed. The two affected individuals did not have the genetic markers on chromosome 11 that had been associated with inheriting the illness. Today, studies continue to link this disorder to different chromosomal regions in different families. Bipolar affective disorder clearly has a large inherited component, but it is a complex trait, and there may be several different combinations of genes and environmental conditions that trigger symptoms. Reading 7.2 discusses behavioral genetics and its misinterpretations and misuse.

Interactions and contributions of genes and the environment provide some of the greatest challenges in studying

Behavioral Genetics: Blaming Genes

It has become fashionable to blame genes for our shortcomings. A popular magazine's cover shouts "Infidelity: It May Be in Our Genes," advertising an article that actually has little to do with genetics. When researchers identify a gene that plays a role in fat metabolism, people binge on chocolate and forsake exercise, because, after all, if obesity is in their genes, there's nothing they can do to prevent it. Social scientists write in a book on IQ that social welfare programs are of little use, because genes dictate racial differences in intelligence. The resulting uproar has yet to die down.

Geneticists have only recently refocused attention on examining the biological roots of behavior. Early in the century, behavioral genetics was part of eugenics—the idea that humans can improve a population's collection of genes, or gene pool. The horrific experiments and exterminations the Nazis performed in the name of eugenics, however, turned many geneticists away from studying the biology of behavior. For many years, social scientists dominated behavioral research and attributed many behavioral disorders to environmental influences until the 1960s. Then, armed with a clearer idea of what a gene is and what it can do, biologists reentered the debate. Today, researchers attempt to identify specific genes that predispose or cause a clearly defined behavior.

But untangling the causes of human behavior remains highly controversial. One scientific conference to explore genetic aspects of violence was cancelled after a noted psychiatrist objected that "behavioral genetics is the same old stuff in new clothes. It's another way for a violent, racist society to say peoples' problems are their own fault, because they carry 'bad' genes."

figure 1

These air surfers were dropped from a helicopter over a mountain. Does a gene variant make them seek thrills?

Genetic researchers on the trail of physical explanations for behaviors counter that their work can help uncover ways to alter or prevent dangerous behaviors. Attempts to hold meetings discussing the genetics of violence still elicit public protests.

Even in the rare instances when a behavior is linked to a specific mutation, environmental influences remain important. Consider a 1993 study of a Dutch family that had "a syndrome of borderline mental retardation and abnormal behavior." Family members had committed arson, attempted rape, and shown exhibitionism. Researchers found a mutation in a gene that made biological sense. Alteration of a single DNA base in the gene encoding an enzyme called monoamine oxidase A (MAOA) rendered the enzyme nonfunctional. This enzyme normally catalyzes reactions that metabolize the neurotransmitters dopamine, serotonin, and noradrenaline, and it is therefore important in conducting nerve messages. But what is the direct result of this biochemical glitch, and how does it perturb behavior? Perhaps the inherited enzyme deficiency causes slight mental impairment, and this interferes with the person's ability to cope with certain frustrating situations, resulting in violence. Hence, the argument returns once again to how genes interact with the environment.

The study was publicized and applied inappropriately to other situations. An attorney contacted a behavioral geneticist, asking whether he could use the "MAOA deficiency defense" to free a client from a scheduled execution for committing murder. A talk-show host suggested that people who had inherited the "mean gene" be sterilized so they couldn't pass on the tendency. This may have been meant as a joke, but it is frighteningly close to the eugenics practiced earlier in the century.

human genetics. Why does one heavy smoker develop lung cancer, but another does not? Why can one person consistently overeat and never gain weight, while another does so easily? Because we exist in an environment, no gene functions in a vacuum. Subtle interactions of nature and nurture profoundly affect our lives and make us all—even identical twins—unique individuals.

Key Concepts

Twin and adoption studies are useful in identifying behavioral characteristics with large genetic components. Researchers can then search for causative genes. Genes affecting behavior act through the nervous system. More than one gene may cause a particular behavior. Genetic heterogeneity, polygenic inheritance, and environmental influences complicate correlation of specific gene variants with specific behaviors.

summary

1. **Complex traits** do not follow Mendel's laws but do have an inherited component. They may be **multifactorial** or **polygenic.** Multifactorial traits are caused by both the environment and genes. A polygenic trait is determined by more than one gene and varies continuously in its expression.

2. **Empiric risk** measures the likelihood that a multifactorial trait will recur based on its prevalence in a population. The risk rises with genetic closeness to an affected individual, severity of the phenotype, and increasing number of affected relatives.

3. **Heritability** estimates the proportion of variation in a multifactorial trait that is attributable to genetics. It equals twice the difference of the variance for that trait between two groups of individuals. Heritability is not an inherent gene characteristic; it varies among populations.

4. The **coefficient of relationship** describes the proportion of genes different types of relatives share.

5. Characteristics shared by adopted people and their biological parents are mostly inherited, whereas similarities between adopted people and their adoptive parents reflect environmental influences.

6. **Concordance** measures the expression of a trait in MZ or DZ twins. The more influence genes exert over a trait, the higher the concordance value.

7. Many genes as well as environmental factors such as diet and exercise affect the risk of cardiovascular disease. Genes encoding proteins that comprise and control lipoproteins are important in cardiovascular health. **Leptin** is a protein that maintains energy use. Gene variants for **lipoprotein lipase** may increase the

risk of obesity, which has other genetic and environmental causes.

8. Tests to measure intelligence may be subjective and biased. Twin and adoption studies suggest that the heritability of intelligence is about 0.7.

9. **Schizophrenia** is a mental illness that is genetically heterogeneic and multifactorial.

10. Alcoholism variants may be associated with the A1 allele of a dopamine receptor gene and the density of dopamine receptors on nerve cells in the brain's striatum.

11. In the 1960s, adoption and twin studies began to reveal genetic components to conditions previously thought to be mostly environmental in origin. Such studies prodded researchers to search for specific genetic causes of particular traits.

review questions

1. How might abnormalities in the following proteins affect health?
   a. lipoprotein lipase
   b. angiotensinogen
   c. apolipoproteins
   d. dopamine receptors
   e. leptin
   f. monoamine oxidase A

2. How does the risk that a multifactorial disorder will recur differ from the risk that a Mendelian disorder, such as cystic fibrosis, will recur in a family?

3. Suggest a treatment for Type I hyperlipoproteinemia.

4. How can one identical twin express symptoms of malignant hyperthermia, while the other twin does not?

5. Height among Western peoples has increased dramatically over the past century. Do you think this is more likely due to changes in heredity or the environment?

6. What is the coefficient of relationship between a grandparent and a grandchild?

7. Two assumptions underlying adoption and twin studies are that blood relatives share genes, while nonblood relatives do not, and that adoptive families share environments that adopted individuals and their biological parents do not. How can these assumptions be invalid?

8. In the 1960s situation comedy, "The Patty Duke Show," the actress portrayed identical cousins, Patty and Cathy, who looked as alike as identical twins. They differed drastically in their personalities and interests. How likely do you think it is that two first cousins would have identical appearances, considering the proportion of genes they typically share? Can you think of a way that identical first cousins could theoretically occur?

9. What functions do leptin and lipoprotein lipase perform? How do they affect obesity?

10. Explain the evidence that narcolepsy with cataplexy has an inherited component.

applied questions

1. Can a child have darker skin (due to heredity) than his or her parents? Consult table 7.1 for your answer.

2. The Frinks are expecting their third child. Their first two children have neural tube defects. The Rudnicks are also expecting their third child. Their first two children have albinism, which they inherited as an autosomal recessive trait. Why is it that the Frinks' third child is at a greater risk of having a neural tube defect than his or her siblings were, but the Rudnick's third child faces the same risk of having albinism as his or her siblings did?

3. In a family with several cases of alcoholism, a DNA sequence is identified in all the affected adults, but not in any of the unaffected adults. A twelve-year-old family member finds out that she has inherited the DNA variant associated with alcoholism. Is she destined to develop alcoholism? Why or why not?

4. Some psychologists criticize the research techniques behavioral geneticists use, such as relying on family members' reports of characteristics rather than impartial parties' observations. They also question the validity of using statistics to separate environmental from genetic influences, ignoring their interactions. Do you agree with one side or the other? How might they combine approaches?

5. Significantly more people with schizophrenia are born in late winter or spring than at other times of the year. How does this suggest a cause other than genetics for this mental illness?

6. Wolfram syndrome is a rare autosomal recessive disorder that causes severe diabetes, impaired vision, and neurological problems. Examinations of hospital records and self-reports reveal that blood relatives of Wolfram syndrome patients have an eightfold risk over the general population of developing serious psychiatric disorders such as depression, violent behavior, and suicidal tendencies. Can you suggest further experiments and studies to test the hypothesis that these mental manifestations are a less severe expression of Wolfram syndrome?

7. The National Institute on Alcohol Abuse and Alcoholism is working to identify genes that may predispose a person to alcoholism. How should this information be used? How might it be abused?

8. Concordance values for bipolar affective disorder for MZ twins is .79, and for DZ twins, it is .19. For depression, concordance among MZ twins is .54, and among DZ twins, it is .24. Which disorder has a greater inherited component?

suggested readings

Colt, George. April 1998. Were you born that way? *Life.* To what extent do genes dictate behavior?

Friedman, Jeffrey, et al. August 5, 1997. Resistance to leptin contributes to obesity. *Proceedings of the National Academy of Sciences.* Some forms of obesity may be due to an inability of the body to recognize leptin.

Gibbs, W. Wayt. March 1995. Seeking the criminal element. *Scientific American.* Researchers must be very careful when they try to blame violent behavior on genes.

Ginns, Edward I., et al. April 1996. A genome-wide search for chromosomal loci linked to bipolar affective disorder in the Old Order Amish. *Nature Genetics.* Manic-depressive illness is a behavioral disorder that is easier to study among the Amish than other population groups.

Goldman, David. July 1995. Dopamine transporter, alcoholism, and other diseases. *Nature Medicine,* vol. 1. Researchers are investigating biological explanations for alcoholism.

Hamer, Dean, and Peter Copeland. 1998. *Living with our genes.* New York: Doubleday. A highly readable account of behavioral genetics, by the discoverer of the "gay" and "thrill-seeking" genes.

Mignot, Emmanual. June 1997. Genetics of narcolepsy and other sleep disorders. *The American Journal of Human Genetics,* vol. 60. Sleep is a gene-influenced behavior.

Plomin, Robert, and John C. DeFries. May 1998. The genetics of cognitive abilities and disabilities. *Scientific American.* Is dyslexia inherited?

Reus, Victor I., and Nelson B. Freimer. June 1997. Understanding the genetic basis of mood disorders: Where do we stand? *The American Journal of Human Genetics,* vol. 60. Several different genes may predispose to or cause bipolar affective disorder.

Sherman, Stephanie L., et al. June 1997. Recent developments in human behavioral genetics: past accomplishments and future directions. *American Journal of Human Genetics,* vol. 60. Searching the human genome will reveal genes that influence behavior.

The October 1997 issue of *Discover* focuses on behavioral genetics.

chapter eight

DNA Structure and Replication

One night in July 1918, Tsar Nicholas II of Russia and his family met gruesome deaths at the hands of Bolsheviks in a Ural mountain town called Ekaterinburg. Captors led the tsar, tsarina, three of their daughters, the family physician, and three servants to a cellar and shot them, bayoneting those who did not immediately die. The executioners then stripped the bodies and loaded them onto a truck, planning to hurl them down a mine shaft. But the truck broke down, and the killers instead placed the bodies in a shallow grave, then damaged them with sulfuric acid to mask their identities.

In another July—many years later, in 1991—two Russian amateur historians found the grave. Because they were aware that the royal family had spent its last night in Ekaterinburg, they alerted the government that they might have unearthed the long-sought bodies of the Romanov family. An official forensic examination soon determined that the skeletons represented nine individuals. The sizes of the skeletons indicated that three were children, and the porcelain, platinum, and gold in some of the teeth suggested royalty. Unfortunately, the acid had so destroyed the facial bones that some conventional forensic tests were not feasible. But one type of evidence survived—DNA.

British researchers eagerly examined DNA from cells in the skeletal remains. DNA sequences specific to the Y chromosome enabled the investigators to distinguish males from females. Then the genetic material of mitochondria, inherited from mothers only, established one woman as the mother of the children. Another clue was that she had impressive dental work.

But a mother, her children, and companions do not make a royal family. The researchers had to connect the skeletons to known royalty. To do so, they again turned to DNA. However, an inherited quirk proved, at first, to be quite confusing.

The challenge in proving that the male remains with fancy dental work were once Tsar Nicholas II centered around nucleotide position 16169 of a mitochondrial gene that is highly variable in sequence among individuals. About 70 percent of bone cells examined from the remains had cytosine (C) at this position, and the remainder had thymine (T). Skeptics at first suspected contamination or a laboratory error, but when the odd result was repeated, researchers realized that this historical case had revealed a genetic phenomenon not seen before in human DNA. The bone cells apparently harbored two populations of mitochondria, one type with C at this position, the other with T, a phenomenon called heteroplasmy, discussed in chapter 6.

The DNA of a living blood relative of the tsar, Countess Xenia Cheremeteff-Sfiri, had only T at nucleotide site 16169. Xenia is the great-granddaughter of Tsar Nicholas II's sister. However, DNA from Xenia and the murdered man matched at every other site. DNA of another living relative, the Duke of Fife, the great-grandson of Nicholas's maternal aunt, matched Xenia at the famed 16169 site. A closer relative, Nicholas's nephew Tikhon Kulikovsky, refused to lend his DNA, citing anger at the British for not assisting the tsar's family during the Bolshevik revolution.

But the story wasn't over. It would take an event in yet another July, in 1994, to clarify matters.

Attention turned to Nicholas's brother, Grand Duke of Russia Georgij Romanov. Georgij had died at age 28 in 1899 of tuberculosis. He was exhumed in July 1994, and researchers sequenced the troublesome mitochondrial gene in bone cells from his leg. They found a match! Georgij's mitochondrial DNA had the same double-base site as the man murdered in Siberia, who was, therefore, Tsar Nicholas II. The researchers calculated the probability that the remains are truly those of the tsar, rather than resembling Georgij by chance, as 130 million to 1. The murdered Russian royal family can finally rest in peace, thanks to DNA analysis.

A Multitalented Molecule

Of all of the characteristics that distinguish the living from the nonliving, the one most important to the continuance of life is the ability to reproduce. At the cellular level, reproduction entails duplication of a cell—be it a single-celled, early organism on the young Earth billions of years ago, or a cell lining a person's intestine today. At the molecular level, reproduction depends upon a biochemical that has dual abilities: to direct the specific activities of the cell and to manufacture an exact replica of itself so that the instructions can be perpetuated. As Francis H. Crick, codiscoverer of the structure of DNA, pointed out, "A genetic material must carry out two jobs: duplicate itself and control the development of the rest of the cell in a specific way." So familiar is DNA as the genetic material that it often appears in headlines, as chapter 1 points out. DNA analysis is even filling in gaps in our knowledge of history (Reading 8.1) and prehistory (Reading 8.2).

Today we know that deoxyribonucleic acid (DNA) is the molecule that can replicate and orchestrate cellular activities by encoding and controlling protein synthesis (figure 8.1). But the recognition of DNA's vital role in life was a long time coming.

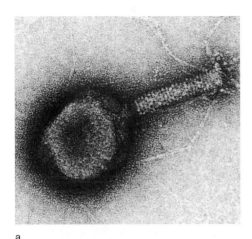

a.

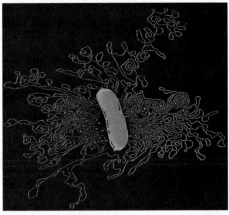

b.

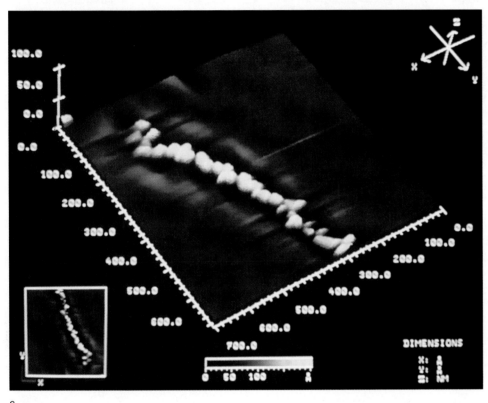

c.

figure 8.1

The genetic material. Gregor Mendel perceptively described the transmission of "characters," but he did not know their chemical composition. Today, we can visualize the genetic material with the aid of powerful microscopes. (*a*) This T4 virus has DNA within its protein head. (*b*) DNA bursts from a bacterial cell. (*c*) DNA structure is revealed in the scanning tunneling microscope, which views complex molecules in the conformations they assume when surrounded by water—just as they would appear in an organism.

Experiments Identify and Describe the Genetic Material

Swiss physician and biochemist Friedrich Miescher was the first investigator to chemically analyze the contents of a cell's nucleus. In 1869, he isolated the nuclei of white blood cells obtained from pus in soiled bandages. In the nuclei, he discovered an unusual acidic substance containing nitrogen and phosphorus. Miescher and others went on to find it in cells from a variety of sources. Because the material resided in cell nuclei, Miescher called it **nuclein** in his 1871 paper; subsequently it was called a nucleic acid.

Few people appreciated Miescher's discovery, like those of his contemporary Gregor Mendel, for some years. Work on inheritance focused for several decades on the association between hereditary diseases and proteins.

In 1909, English physician Archibald Garrod was the first to link inheritance and protein. Garrod noted that certain inherited "inborn errors of metabolism" correlated with missing enzymes. Other researchers added supporting evidence: they associated abnormal or missing enzymes with unusual eye color in fruit flies and nutritional deficiencies in bread mold variants. Although evidence was mounting that proteins are keys to trait expression, new questions arose. Why did enzyme deficiencies occur only in some cells? What controlled protein synthesis? Eventually, investigators were led back to Miescher's discovery of nucleic acids.

DNA Is the Hereditary Molecule

In 1928, English microbiologist Frederick Griffith made an observation that, although he could not explain it, was the first step in identifying DNA as the genetic material. Griffith noticed that mice with a certain type of pneumonia harbored one of two types of *Diplococcus pneumoniae* bacteria. Type R bacteria are rough in texture. Type S bacteria are smooth, because they are enclosed in a polysaccharide capsule. Mice injected with type R bacteria did not develop pneumonia, but mice injected with

figure 8.2

Griffith's experiments showed that a biochemical in a killer strain of bacteria can enable a nonkilling strain to become deadly.

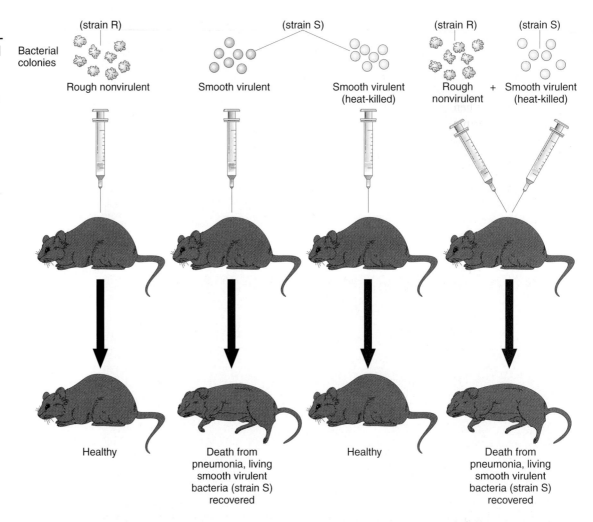

Bacterial colonies

(strain R) — Rough nonvirulent

(strain S) — Smooth virulent

Smooth virulent (heat-killed)

(strain R) Rough nonvirulent + (strain S) Smooth virulent (heat-killed)

Healthy

Death from pneumonia, living smooth virulent bacteria (strain S) recovered

Healthy

Death from pneumonia, living smooth virulent bacteria (strain S) recovered

type S did. The polysaccharide coat seemed to be necessary for infection.

When type S bacteria were heated—which killed them but left their DNA intact—they no longer could cause pneumonia in mice. However, when Griffith injected mice with a mixture of type R bacteria plus heat-killed type S bacteria—each alone not deadly to the mice—the mice died of pneumonia (figure 8.2). Their bodies contained live type S bacteria, encased in polysaccharide. What was happening?

The answer came in the 1930s, with the work of Rockefeller University physicians Oswald Avery, Colin MacLeod, and Maclyn McCarty. They hypothesized that something in the heat-killed type S bacteria "transformed" the normally harmless type R strain into a killer. Could a nucleic acid be the "transforming principle"? They suspected that it might be, because adding an enzyme that dismantles protein (a protease) to Griffith's experiment did not prevent the transformation of a nonkilling to

a killing strain, but adding an enzyme that dismantles DNA only (deoxyribonuclease) disrupted the transformation. Avery, MacLeod, and McCarty confirmed that DNA transformed the bacteria by isolating DNA from heat-killed type S bacteria and injecting it along with type R bacteria into mice (figure 8.3). The mice died, and their bodies contained active type S bacteria. The conclusion: the DNA passed from type S bacteria to type R, enabling it to manufacture the smooth coat necessary for infection.

DNA Is the Hereditary Molecule— And Protein Is Not

In 1953, American microbiologists Alfred Hershey and Martha Chase confirmed that DNA is the genetic material. They used *E. coli* bacteria infected with a virus that consisted of a protein "head" surrounding DNA. Viruses infect bacterial cells by injecting their

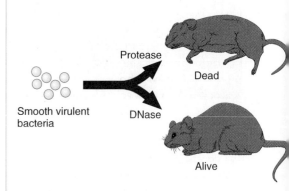

Smooth virulent bacteria

Protease → Dead

DNase → Alive

figure 8.3

In many experiments performed over a decade, Avery, MacLeod, and McCarty identified Griffith's transforming principle as DNA. By adding either a protease or an enzyme that disrupts DNA to Griffith's experiment, they demonstrated the function of DNA in transmitting the ability to kill—and the fact that protein does not have this capacity.

DNA inside them. The viral protein coats remain outside the bacterial cells.

Hershey and Chase first showed that virus grown with radioactive sulfur became radioactive, and the protein coats emitted the radioactivity. When Hershey and Chase repeated the experiment with radioactive phosphorus, the DNA emitted radioactivity. This showed that sulfur is found in protein but not in nucleic acid, and that phosphorus is found in nucleic acid but not in protein. DNA is the only phosphorus-containing biochemical in the virus.

Next, the researchers "labeled" two batches of virus, one with radioactive sulfur (which marked protein), and the other with radioactive phosphorus (which marked DNA). They infected two batches of bacteria, each containing one type of labeled virus. After allowing several minutes for the virus particles to bind to the bacteria and inject their DNA into them, each mixture was agitated in a blender, shaking free the empty virus protein coats. The contents of each blender were collected in test tubes, then centrifuged (spun at high speed). This settled the bacteria at the bottom of each tube because virus coats sediment more slowly than do bacteria.

At the end of the procedure, Hershey and Chase examined fractions containing the virus coats from the top of each test tube and the infected bacteria that had settled to the bottom of each test tube (figure 8.4). In the tube containing virus labeled with sulfur, the virus coats were radioactive, but the virus-infected bacteria were not. In the other tube, where the virus had incorporated radioactive phosphorus, the virus coats carried no radioactive label, but the infected bacteria were radioactive. This meant that the part of the virus that could enter bacteria and direct them to mass produce more virus was the part that had incorporated the phosphorus label—the DNA. The genetic material, therefore, was DNA, and not protein. It is DNA that transmits information from generation to generation.

Deciphering the Structure of DNA

Early in the twentieth century, Russian-American biochemist Phoebus Levene continued the chemical analysis of DNA at Rockefeller University. In 1909, Levene identified the 5-carbon sugar **ribose** as part

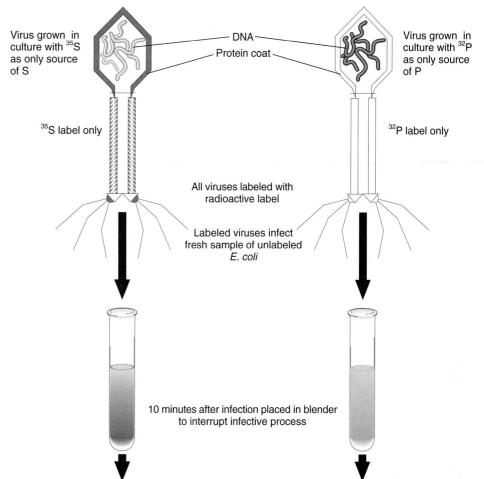

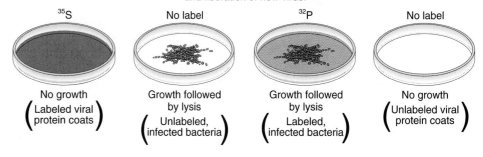

figure 8.4

By labeling either sulfur (found in protein but not in DNA) or phosphorus (found in DNA but not in protein) in viruses used to infect *E. coli,* Hershey and Chase showed that DNA is the hereditary material—and protein is not.

of some nucleic acids, and in 1929, he discovered a new, similar sugar also in other nucleic acids—**deoxyribose.** By identifying these two sugars, Levene had revealed a major chemical distinction between RNA and DNA.

Levene then discovered that the three parts of a nucleic acid—a sugar, a nitrogen-containing group, and a phosphorus-containing component—occur in equal proportions. From this he deduced that a nucleic acid building block must contain one of each component. Furthermore, although the sugar and phosphate portions were always the same, the nitrogen-containing bases were of four types. For

figure 8.5

James Watson (left) and Francis Crick.

several years, scientists erroneously thought that the nitrogen-containing bases occur in equal amounts. If this were the case, DNA could not encode as much information as it could if there were no restrictions on the relative numbers of each base type.

In the 1930s and 1940s, Scottish chemist Alexander Todd confirmed and extended Levene's work by synthesizing DNA building blocks. Others then deciphered the complex three-dimensional conformation of the DNA molecule that would explain its unique role in the perpetuation of life.

In the early 1950s, two lines of experimental evidence converged to provide the direct clues that finally revealed DNA's structure. Chemical analysis by Austrian-American biochemist Erwin Chargaff showed that DNA in several species contains equal amounts of the bases **adenine** and **thymine** and equal amounts of the bases **guanine** and **cytosine**. Next, English physicist Maurice Wilkins and English chemist Rosalind Franklin bombarded DNA with X rays using a technique called X-ray diffraction, then observed the pattern in which the X rays deflected. This pattern revealed a regularly repeating structure of building blocks.

In 1953, American biochemist James Watson and English physicist Francis Crick worked together in England to build a replica of the DNA molecule using ball-and-stick models (figure 8.5). Their model

included equal amounts of guanine and cytosine and equal amounts of adenine and thymine, and it satisfied the symmetry shown in the X-ray diffraction pattern. The result of their insight, which was

based upon the experimental evidence of so many others, was the now-familiar double helix (figure 8.6). Table 8.1 summarizes the experiments that led to the elucidation of the structure of DNA.

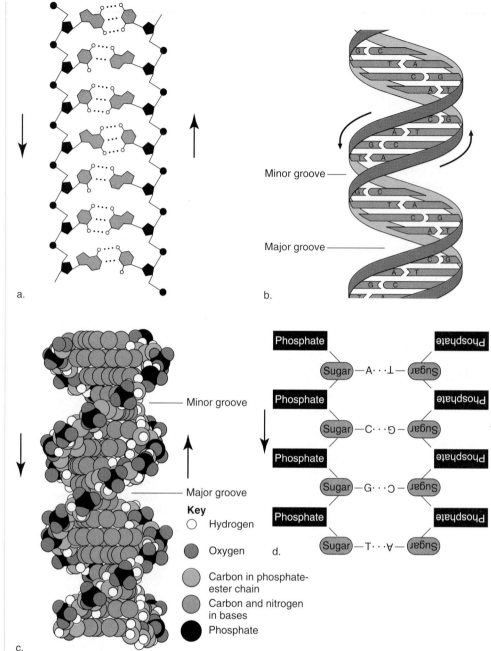

Key
○ Hydrogen
● Oxygen
● Carbon in phosphate-ester chain
● Carbon and nitrogen in bases
● Phosphate

figure 8.6

Different ways to represent the DNA double helix. (*a*) The helix is unwound to show the base pairs in color and the sugar-phosphate backbone in black. (*b*) The sugar-phosphate backbone is emphasized. The two strands run in opposite directions—that is, they are antiparallel. (*c*) This representation shows the relationships of the atoms. (*d*) A schematic representation of an unwound section of the double helix shows the relationship of the sugar-phosphate rails to the base pairs. The informational content of DNA lies in the sequence of bases; the sugar-phosphate rails are identical in all DNA molecules.

Key Concepts

DNA contains the information the cell requires to synthesize protein and to replicate itself. Miescher first isolated DNA in 1869—naming it nuclein. DNA was chemically characterized in the 1940s. Garrod first linked heredity to enzymes. Griffith identified a substance capable of transmitting infectiousness, which Avery, MacLeod, and McCarty showed was DNA. Hershey and Chase showed that DNA is the genetic material, and not protein. Using Chargaff's discovery that the number of adenine bases equals the number of thymines, and the number of guanines equals the number of cytosines, along with Franklin's discovery that DNA is regular and symmetrical in structure, Watson and Crick deciphered the conformation of DNA.

table 8.1

The Road to the Double Helix

Investigator	Contribution
Friedrich Miescher	Isolated nuclein in white blood cell nuclei
Frederick Griffith	Killing ability in bacteria can be transferred between strains
Oswald Avery, Colin MacLeod, and Maclyn McCarty	DNA transmits killing ability in bacteria
Alfred Hershey and Martha Chase	The part of a virus that infects and replicates is its nucleic acid and not its protein
Phoebus Levene, Erwin Chargaff, Maurice Wilkins, and Rosalind Franklin	DNA components, proportions, and positions
James Watson and Francis Crick	DNA's three-dimensional structure

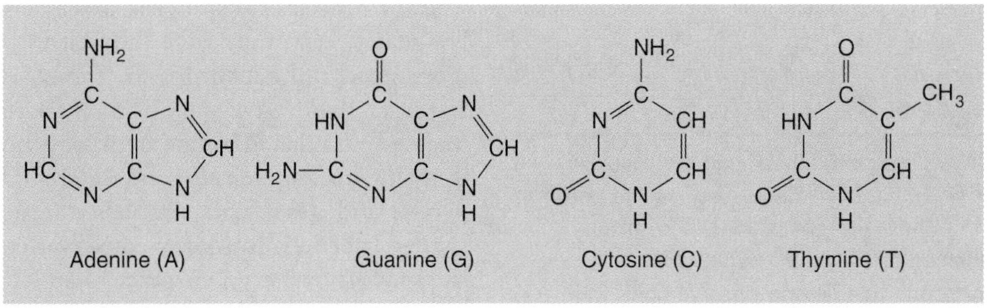

figure 8.7

DNA bases. Adenine and guanine are purines, each composed of a six-member organic ring plus a five-member ring. Cytosine and thymine are pyrimidines, each built of a single six-member ring.

Gene and Protein— An Important Partnership

A gene is a long section of a DNA molecule whose sequence of nucleotides specifies the sequence of amino acids in a particular protein. The activity of the protein is responsible for the trait associated with the gene. The fact that different building blocks combine to form nucleic acids and proteins (4 in RNA, 4 in DNA, and 20 in proteins) enables them to carry information, as the letters of an alphabet combine to form words. In contrast, consider another long molecule, the starch glycogen. It is a string of identical sugars. Like an alphabet consisting of only one letter, glycogen does not encode information.

The connection between inherited traits and the molecular structure and function of the gene is not always apparent, but it probably lies in the many biological functions of proteins. Pea color comes from pigment proteins; a protein hormone controls plant height. In the human body, enzymes catalyze the chemical reactions of metabolism. Proteins such as collagen and elastin provide structural support in connective tissues, and actin and myosin form muscle. Hemoglobin transports oxygen, and antibodies protect against infection. Malfunctioning or inactive proteins, which reflect genetic defects, can devastate health, as we have seen in discussing many hereditary disorders. The amino acids that are assembled into proteins ultimately come from the diet.

The genetic material consists of two long strands of DNA that entwine to form a double helix, which resembles a twisted ladder. The rungs of the ladder are pairs of nitrogenous bases held together by hydrogen bonds. The ladder's rails consist of alternating units of deoxyribose and phosphate (PO_4), joined by covalent bonds. A single building block of DNA—a **nucleotide**—consists of one deoxyribose, one phosphate, and one nitrogenous base.

The DNA Base Sequence Encodes Information

The key to DNA's function as an information molecule lies in the sequence of adenines, thymines, cytosines and guanines (A, T, C, and G for short). Adenine and guanine are **purines,** which have a two-organic-ring structure. Cytosine and thymine are **pyrimidines,** which have a single-organic-ring structure (figure 8.7). The sleek, symmetric double helix of DNA forms when nucleotides containing A pair with those containing T, and nucleotides containing G pair with those containing C. These specific purine-pyrimidine couples are called **complementary base pairs** (figure 8.8).

DNA Is Directional

The two chains of the double helix run in opposite orientation to each other, a little like artist M. C. Escher's depiction of drawing hands (figure 8.9a). This head-to-tail or **antiparallel** arrangement is apparent when the carbons comprising the

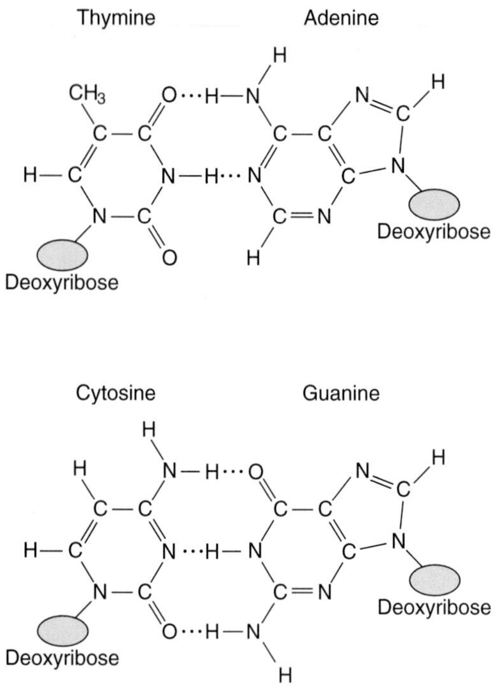

figure 8.8

DNA base pairs. The key to the constant width of the DNA double helix is the pairing of purines with pyrimidines. Specifically, adenine pairs with thymine with two hydrogen bonds, and cytosine pairs with guanine with three hydrogen bonds.

sugars (deoxyribose) are numbered consecutively from right to left according to chemical convention (figure 8.9b) and the specific carbon exposed at each end of each half of the molecule is noted. Where one chain ends in the 3′ (3 prime) carbon, the opposite chain ends in the 5′ (5 prime) carbon (figure 8.9c).(3′ and 5′ refer to the positions of the carbon atoms in the deoxyribose).

DNA Is Highly Coiled

DNA molecules are incredibly long. A human haploid genome—23 chromosomes—stretched out and laid end-to-end would match the height of a person. If all the DNA bases of the human genome were typed as A, C, T, and G, the 3 billion letters would fill 4,000 books of 500 pages each! How can so much material pack into a cell only one millionth of an inch across?

Part of the explanation for how cells contain so much DNA is that DNA tightly coils around proteins. A length of DNA 146

nucleotides long wraps twice around a structure of 8 proteins, each called a **histone** (figure 8.10). Together, DNA and histones constitute **chromatin,** the material that comprises chromosomes; the DNA entwined around eight histones is called a **nucleosome.** A nucleosome is only 10 nanometers (nm, a billionth of a meter) in diameter. Nucleosomes, which resemble beads on a string, are in turn folded to form a structure 30 nm in diameter. The DNA must unwind locally to function. Therefore, as DNA in widely separated 10-nm nucleosomes unwinds and is expressed, the DNA in the remaining 20-nm-wide portion is silent. Whether the DNA is tightly rolled up or rolled entirely off the histone to be transcribed into RNA, it maintains its structural integrity and sequence.

The histones control gene expression. For many years, they were thought to be mere structural backdrops for the DNA. However, the five types of histones are remarkably similar in amino acid sequence in many species, even those as different as people and peas. This similarity across species, called **evolutionary conservation,** is discussed further in chapters 14 and 20. If a protein has not changed much through evolutionary time (indicated by its similarity in diverse modern species), then its function must be very important—certainly more so than serving as a spool to hold DNA, which any other protein of the same general shape could do. Histones also actively participate in controlling gene expression—they turn on some genes and repress others. Gene expression is the subject of the next chapter.

Key Concepts

The DNA double helix is a ladderlike structure, its backbone comprised of alternating deoxyribose and phosphate groups and its rungs formed by complementary pairs of A-T and G-C bases. A and G are purines; T and C are pyrimidines. The DNA double helix is antiparallel, running in an opposite head-to-toe manner. It winds tightly about histone proteins, forming nucleosomes, which in turn wind into a tighter structure to form chromatin. Histones control gene expression, too.

DNA Replication— Maintaining Genetic Information

As soon as Watson and Crick deciphered the structure of DNA, its mechanism for replication became obvious. The two scientists wrote in their classic 1953 paper describing the genetic material, "It has not escaped our notice that the specific pairing we have postulated immediately suggests a possible copying mechanism for the genetic material."

Replication Is Semiconservative

Watson and Crick envisioned a double helix disentangling, with each half serving as a template, or mold, for the assembly of a new half. The new strand would fill in with unattached nucleotides in the cell, supplied from the diet and metabolism. The new bases would dock opposite complementary bases on the parental DNA strand and form hydrogen bonds. Other bonds would cement the sugar-phosphate backbone in the new DNA strand. This mechanism is termed **semiconservative replication,** because half of each double helix comes (is conserved) from a preexisting double helix.

However logical Watson and Crick's idea for the DNA replication mechanism was, an experiment was needed to prove the semiconservative mode of DNA replication, and at the same time disprove other possible mechanisms. What other ways might DNA replicate?

At least two other mechanisms seemed possible. In conservative replication, the double helix would not come apart and remain that way, but instead would be entirely conserved and yet somehow direct the construction of a new double helix. In a third hypothesized mechanism, dispersive replication, a double helix would fall into pieces that would join with new nucleotides to build two new double helices (figure 8.11).

In 1957, Matthew Meselson and Franklin Stahl, at the California Institute of Technology, devised a brilliant experiment to show what Watson and Crick had suspected. To *E. coli* bacteria growing on media in the laboratory, they added nitrogen that was slightly heavier than normal. Newly

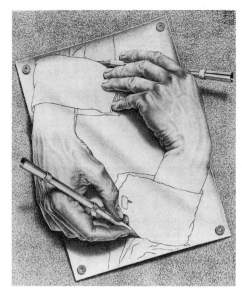

a.

b.

figure 8.9

DNA strands are antiparallel. (*a*) The spatial relationship of these two hands resembles the two DNA chains that comprise the DNA double helix. (*b*) Chemists assign numbers to carbons in different positions in organic molecules. This illustration shows how the carbons are numbered in the sugar of the DNA molecule's sugar-phosphate backbone. (*c*) When several neighboring nucleotide pairs are viewed considering the locations of the 5′ (5 prime) and 3′ (3 prime) carbons in the sugars (deoxyriboses), the opposing directionality of the strands becomes clear. The strand on the left runs from 5′ at the top to 3′ at the bottom. The strand on the right runs oppositely, from 5′ on the bottom to 3′ at the top. The base names on the right are flipped to show the head-to-tail orientation.

c.

figure 8.10

One hundred forty-six DNA nucleotides entwine in two loops around eight histone proteins, forming a nucleosome. Nucleosomes in turn wind into a cable three times thicker than an individual nucleosome. The DNA and associated histone proteins form chromatin, which comprises chromosomes. When DNA is transcribed, it unwinds from its protein support.

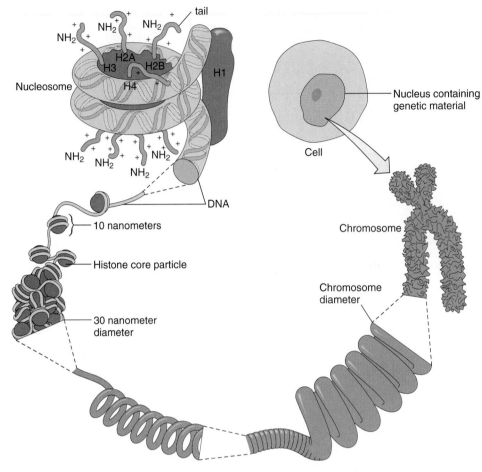

figure 8.11

Three routes to DNA replication—which is correct? New DNA is shown in red.

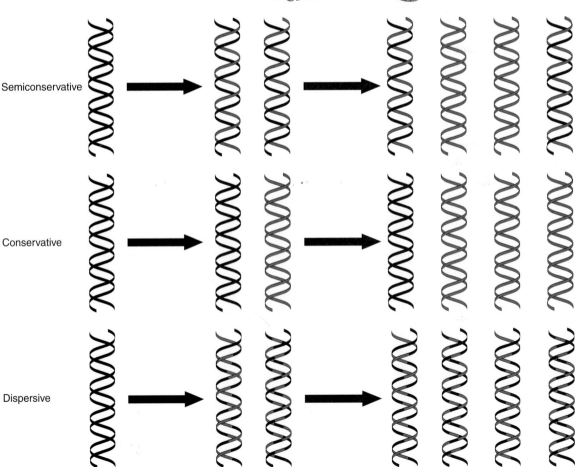

synthesized bacterial DNA incorporating this "heavy" nitrogen isotope, or ^{15}N, would be distinguishable from the previous generation's DNA, which had the more common "light" nitrogen isotope or ^{14}N. (An isotope is an atom with a different number of neutrons than is usual for that element.)

Meselson and Stahl tracked the results using a technique called equilibrium density gradient centrifugation. This entailed spinning DNA in a centrifuge to separate it by density. Very dense DNA would indicate incorporation of ^{15}N; lighter DNA would contain ^{14}N. The experiments came to be called **density shift experiments** because bacterial cultures were shifted to media with either of the two types of nitrogen.

The first step was to grow *E. coli* on medium containing ^{15}N, for several generations. The bacteria had completely heavy DNA (figure 8.12). The researchers knew this because only "heavy-heavy" molecules appeared in the density gradient. They then shifted the bacteria to medium containing ^{14}N, allowing enough time for the bacteria to divide only once (about 30 minutes). The proportions of heavy and light nitrogen over the next two replications would reveal the type of mechanism at play.

When the researchers collected the DNA this time and centrifuged it, the double helices were all of intermediate density, indicating that they contained half ^{14}N and half ^{15}N. This pattern was consistent with semiconservative DNA replication—but it was also consistent with a dispersive mechanism. In contrast, the result of conservative replication would have been one band of material completely labeled with ^{15}N, corresponding to one double helix, and one totally "light" band containing ^{14}N only, corresponding to the other double helix (figure 8.11).

Meselson and Stahl definitively distinguished among the three possible routes to replication, supporting the semiconservative mode and disproving the others, by extending the experiment one more generation. For the semiconservative mechanism to hold up, each hybrid (half ^{14}N and half ^{15}N) double helix present after the first generation following the shift to ^{14}N medium would part and assemble a new half from bases labeled only with ^{14}N. This would produce two double helices with one ^{15}N (heavy) and one ^{14}N (light)

Semiconservative DNA Replication

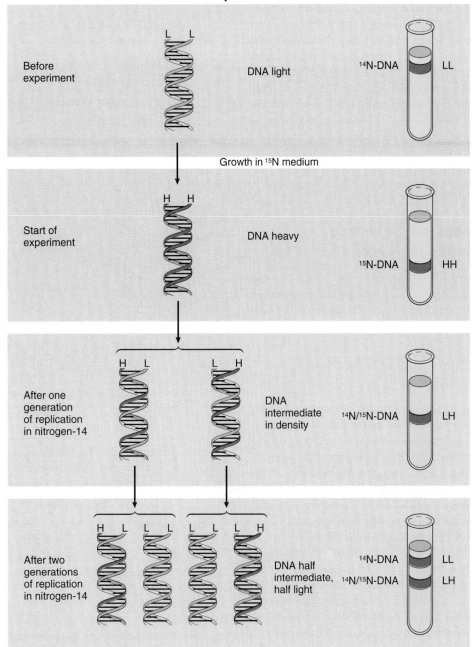

figure 8.12

Meselson and Stahl found that newly synthesized DNA incorporated a label in a pattern consistent with the semiconservative mechanism the molecule's three-dimensional conformation suggested.

chain, plus two double helices containing only ^{14}N. The density gradient would appear as one heavy-light band and one light-light band. This is indeed what Meselson and Stahl saw.

The conservative mechanism would have yielded two bands in the third generation, indicating three completely light

double helices for every completely heavy one. The third generation for the dispersive model would have been a single large band, somewhat higher than the second generation band because additional ^{14}N would have been randomly incorporated.

The semiconservative mode of DNA replication was demonstrated again and again in other species in a similar manner to Meselson and Stahl's density shift experiments. Introducing a radioactive label into growth medium and then removing it and monitoring cell division allows scientists to see replicated chromosomes in which one chromatid (half) displays the radioactivity (by exposing photographic film) and the other does not. These experiments extended Meselson and Stahl's results by demonstrating semiconservative replication in the cells of more complex organisms and at the whole-chromosome level.

Steps and Participants in DNA Replication

With the semiconservative nature of DNA replication predicted and demonstrated, the next challenge was to decipher the steps of the process.

Unraveling and Separating the Strands

Biologists had wondered how the incredibly long DNA molecule might replicate even before they knew its structure. To put the problem of DNA replication into perspective, imagine using a doubled thread the length of a football field to sew a hem on one leg of a pair of jeans! The doubled thread would rapidly become hopelessly tangled. To maintain the length of the thread, you would have to continuously untwist the tangles or periodically cut the thread internally, untwist it locally, and reattach the internal ends.

The latter is conceptually what happens when a long length of DNA replicates—it must break, unwind, replicate, and mend. A contingent of enzymes carries out the process, shown rather whimsically in figure 8.13. Enzymes called **helicases** unwind and hold apart replicating DNA so that other enzymes can guide the assembly of a new DNA strand.

Replication Proceeds at Several Points Simultaneously

A human chromosome replicates at hundreds of points along its length, and then the individual pieces are cemented together. It is like sewing the jean hem in several segments at once, then joining them.

figure 8.13

An army of enzymes carries out DNA replication. This advertisement for a company that sells DNA-cutting enzymes depicts the number of participants required to replicate and repair DNA. How is this depiction of DNA replication incorrect?

Reproduced with the permission of Quadrant Holdings Cambridge Ltd.

The locally opened portion of a replicating DNA double helix is called a **replication fork.** A replicating chromosome has many replication forks.

In the first step in DNA replication, a helicase breaks hydrogen bonds holding together a base pair at an **initiation site** (figure 8.14). Another enzyme, **RNA polymerase,** then attracts complementary RNA nucleotides to build a short piece of RNA, called an **RNA primer,** at the start of each segment of DNA to be replicated. (A polymerase is an enzyme that builds a polymer, which is a chain of chemical building blocks.) The RNA primer is required because DNA cannot initiate a new nucleic acid chain on its own. The RNA primer attracts **DNA polymerase,** which then brings in DNA nucleotides complementary to the exposed bases on the template strand. The new DNA strand grows as hydrogen bonds form between the complementary bases.

The DNA probably moves through the polymerase, rather than the polymerase zipping down the DNA.

DNA polymerase "proofreads" as it goes along, excising mismatched bases and ensuring that the correct ones are inserted. Another enzyme removes the RNA primer and replaces it with the correct DNA bases. (RNA nucleotides differ from those of DNA in that they include ribose rather than deoxyribose, and uracil rather than thymine.) Enzymes called **ligases** (ligase comes from a Latin word meaning "to tie") catalyze the formation of the covalent bonds that hold together the sugar-phosphate backbone.

Replication Is Discontinuous

DNA polymerase works directionally, adding new nucleotides to the exposed 3′ end of the sugar in the growing strand.

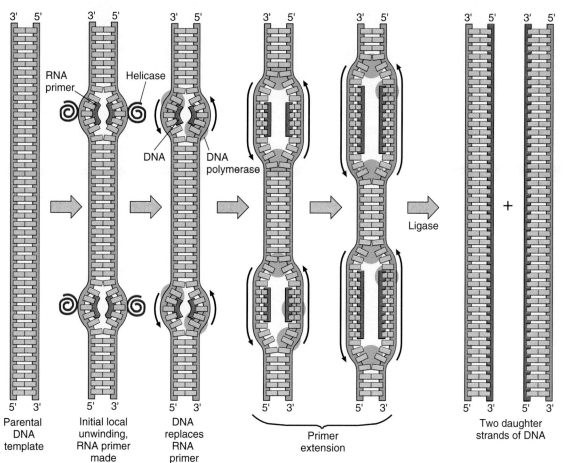

figure 8.14

DNA replication takes several steps. Parental strands are depicted in blue to distinguish them from newly replicated (daughter) DNA, shown in red. Replication begins as the helix unwinds locally at many sites of origin, and RNA primers (purple) are synthesized. DNA polymerase extends the primers, DNA replaces the RNA primer, and the small, replicated portions of the chromosome join as ligase cements the sugar-phosphate backbone.

RNA primer — Helicase — DNA — DNA polymerase — Ligase

Parental DNA template | Initial local unwinding, RNA primer made | DNA replaces RNA primer | Primer extension | Two daughter strands of DNA

Replication proceeds in a 5′ to 3′ direction. How can the growing fork proceed in one direction, when 5′ to 3′ elongation requires movement in both directions? The answer is that on at least one strand, replication is discontinuous. That is, it is accomplished in small pieces from the inner part of the fork outward in a pattern similar to backstitching. The pieces are then ligated to build the new strand (figure 8.15). These smaller pieces, up to 150 nucleotides long, are called Okazaki fragments, after their discoverer.

Gene Amplification—Borrowing the DNA Replication Machinery

At each cell division, all the DNA is replicated. We can borrow the cell's DNA copying machinery and focus it to rapidly replicate millions of copies of DNA sequences of particular interest. The pioneer in gene amplification is the **polymerase chain reaction (PCR)**. Reading 8.2 recounts the story of its beginnings.

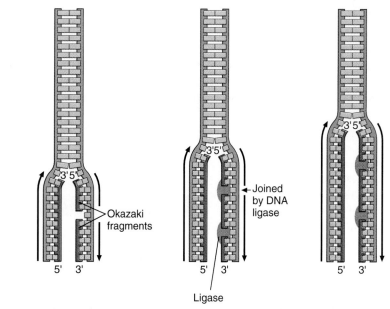

Okazaki fragments — Joined by DNA ligase — Ligase

figure 8.15

To maintain the 5′ to 3′ directionality of DNA replication, at least one strand must be replicated in short pieces, from the inner part of the fork outward. Ligase joins the pieces.

Inspiration on a Starry Night

The polymerase chain reaction (PCR) was born in the mind of Kary Mullis on a moonlit night in northern California in 1983. As he drove up and down the hills, Mullis was thinking about the incredible precision and power of DNA replication and, quite suddenly, a way to tap into that power popped into his mind. He excitedly explained his idea to his girlfriend and then went home to think it through further. "It was difficult for me to sleep with deoxyribonuclear bombs exploding in my brain," he wrote much later, after PCR had revolutionized the life sciences.

The idea behind PCR was so stunningly straightforward that Mullis had trouble convincing his superiors at Cetus Corporation that he was really onto something. He spent the next year using the technique to amplify a well-studied gene so he could prove that his brainstorm was not just a flight of fancy. One by one, other researchers glimpsed Mullis's vision of that starry night. After convincing his colleagues at Cetus, Mullis published a landmark 1985 paper and filed patent applications, launching the era of gene amplification. The technology is a direct application of the DNA replication mechanism.

Surprisingly Simple

PCR rapidly replicates a selected sequence of DNA in a test tube. The requirements include the following:

1. Knowing parts of a target DNA sequence to be amplified.

2. Two types of lab-made, single-stranded, short pieces of DNA called primers. These are complementary in sequence to opposite ends of the target sequence.

3. A large supply of the four types of DNA nucleotide building blocks.

4. Taq1, a DNA polymerase produced by *Thermus aquaticus,* a microbe that inhabits hot springs. This enzyme is adapted to its host's hot surroundings and makes PCR easy because it does not fall apart when DNA is heated. (Other heat-tolerant polymerases can be used, too.)

In the first step of PCR, heat is used to separate the two strands of the target DNA. Next, the temperature is lowered, and the two short DNA primers and Taq1 DNA polymerase are added. The primers bind by complementary base pairing to the separated target strands. In the third step, more DNA nucleotide bases are added. The DNA polymerase adds bases to the primers and builds a sequence complementary to the target sequence. The newly synthesized strands then act as templates in the next round of replication, which is initiated immediately by raising the temperature. All of this is done in an automated device called a thermal cycler that controls the key temperature changes.

The pieces of DNA accumulate geometrically. The number of amplified pieces of DNA equals 2^n, where n equals the number of temperature cycles. After just 20 cycles, one million copies of the original sequence accumulate in the test tube (figure 1). Table 8.1 lists diverse applications of PCR.

PCR's greatest strength is that it works on crude samples of rare and minute sequences, such as a bit of brain tissue on the bumper of a car, which in one criminal case led to identification of a missing person. PCR's greatest weakness, ironically, is its exquisite sensitivity. A blood sample submitted for diagnosis of an infection contaminated by leftover DNA from a previous run, or a stray eyelash dropped from the person running the reaction, can yield a false result. The technique is also limited in that a user must know the sequence to be amplified.

PCR requires two short, lab-made pieces of DNA that, in the organism, bracket the gene of interest. Replicating enzymes are added to repeatedly replicate the primers and the DNA of interest between them. The technology has many applications (table 8.2). PCR is used to amplify genes that cause inherited disease and DNA sequences from viruses that cause infectious diseases. In forensics, PCR can amplify pieces of tissue found at a crime scene sufficiently to either establish or rule out the identity of a suspect. Other gene amplification methods use ligases and different types of replication enzymes.

Key Concepts

Meselson and Stahl, and others, grew cells on media containing labeled DNA precursors. They then followed the distribution of the label to show that DNA replication is semiconservative, not conservative or dispersive.

Enzymes orchestrate DNA replication. In humans, DNA replication occurs simultaneously at several points on each chromosome, and the resulting pieces are joined. At each initiation site, RNA polymerase directs the synthesis of a short RNA primer. DNA eventually replaces this RNA primer; DNA polymerase extends complementary DNA bases to the RNA primer, building a new half of a helix against each template. Finally, ligase joins the sugar-phosphate backbone. DNA is synthesized in a 5' to 3' direction, discontinuously on one or both strands. The polymerase chain reaction is used to replicate selected genes.

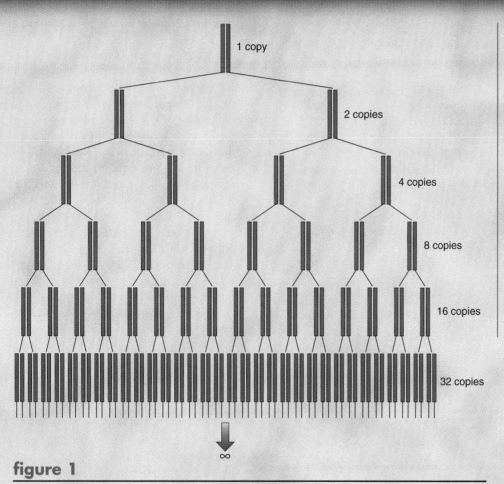

1 copy

2 copies

4 copies

8 copies

16 copies

32 copies

∞

figure 1

DNA amplification using the polymerase chain reaction (PCR) rapidly replicates a selected piece of DNA to a detectable level.

PCR has been applied in an astounding variety of ways (table 8.2), including solving the mystery of the Romanovs (Reading 8.1). PCR shed light on another page of history—the story behind the skeletal remains of one hundred apparently healthy newborn infants discovered in an ancient Roman bathhouse dating from the fourth century. Anthropological investigations had concluded that the babies were all female, and the victims of infanticide in a society that did not value women. By using PCR to detect genes on the Y chromosome only, geneticists found, to their surprise, that the infants were of both sexes. Instead of being the victims of female infanticide, the babies may have been the offspring of courtesans (prostitutes), who simply discarded them—whatever their gender.

DNA Repair

Any manufacturing facility tests a product in several ways to see whether it has been built correctly. Mistakes in production are rectified before the item goes on the market—most of the time. The same is true for a cell's manufacture of DNA.

DNA replication is incredibly accurate—only about one in a million bases is incorrectly incorporated. Just as genes control replication by encoding enzymes such as polymerases and ligases, genes also oversee the fidelity of replication by specifying repair enzymes.

The discovery of DNA repair systems began with observations in the late 1940s that when fungi were exposed to ultraviolet radiation, those cultures nearest a window grew best. The DNA-damaging effect of ultraviolet radiation, and the ability of light to correct it, was soon observed in a variety of organisms.

Three Types of DNA Repair

Ultraviolet radiation damages DNA by causing an extra covalent bond to form between adjacent (same strand) pyrimidines, particularly thymines (figure 8.16). The linked thymines are called thymine dimers. This extra attachment forms a kink in the otherwise sleek double helix, similar to two adjacent steps on an escalator collapsing. The extra bond is enough of an upset to disrupt replication and lead to possible insertion of a noncomplementary base. However, enzymes called **photolyases** absorb energy from visible light and use it to detect and bind to pyrimidine dimers, then break the extra bond. This type of repair, called **photoreactivation,** is what enabled ultraviolet-damaged fungi to recover when exposed to sunlight.

table 8.2

PCR has been used to amplify the following:

- Genetic material from HIV in a human blood sample when infection has been so recent that antibodies are not yet detectable.
- A bit of DNA in a preserved quagga (a relative of the zebra) and a marsupial wolf, which are recently extinct animals.
- DNA in sperm cells found in the body of a rape victim so that specific sequences could be compared to those of a suspect in the crime.
- Genes from microorganisms that cannot be cultured for study.
- Mitochondrial DNA from various modern human populations, indicating that *Homo sapiens* originated in Africa, supporting fossil evidence.
- Similar genes from several species, revealing evolutionary relationships.
- DNA from the brain of a 7,000-year-old human mummy, which indicates that native Americans were not the only people to dwell in North America long ago.
- Genetic material from saliva, hair, skin, and excrement of organisms that we cannot catch to study. The prevalence of a rare DNA sequence among all bird droppings from a certain species in an area can be extrapolated to estimate population size.
- DNA in the digestive tracts of carnivores, to reveal food web interactions.
- DNA in deteriorated road kills and carcasses washed ashore, to identify locally threatened species.
- DNA in products illegally made from endangered species, such as powdered rhinoceros horn, sold as an aphrodisiac.
- DNA sequences in animals indicating that they carry the bacteria that cause Lyme disease, providing clues to how the disease is transmitted.
- DNA from genetically altered microbes that are released in field tests, to follow their dispersion.
- DNA from one cell of an 8-celled human preimplantation embryo to diagnose cystic fibrosis.
- DNA from poached moose meat in hamburger.
- DNA from human remains in Jesse James's grave, to make a positive identification.
- DNA from maggots in a rotting human corpse, to extrapolate the time of murder by determining the time an insect of a particular species deposited its larvae.
- DNA in artificial knee joints, indicating infection.

In the early 1960s, researchers discovered another type of DNA self-mending, called **excision repair,** in mutant *E. coli* that were extra-sensitive to ultraviolet radiation. The enzymes that carry out excision repair cut the bond between the DNA sugar and base and snip out the pyrimidine dimer and surrounding bases. Then, a DNA polymerase fills in the correct nucleotides, using the exposed template as a guide.

A third mechanism of DNA repair is called **mismatch repair.** In this type of repair, enzymes "proofread" newly replicated DNA for small loops emerging from the double helix. These loops indicate an area where the two strands are not precisely aligned, as they should be if complementary base pairing is occurring at every point. Such slippage and mismatching tends to occur in chromosome regions where very short DNA sequences repeat. These sequences, called **microsatellites,** are scattered throughout the genome. Microsatellite lengths can vary from person to person, but within an individual, are usually all the same length.

DNA Repair Disorders

Hereditary nonpolyposis colon cancer, a common form of colon cancer, was linked to a DNA repair defect when researchers discovered that these cancer cells exhibit different-length microsatellites within an individual. Because mismatch repair normally keeps a person's microsatellites all the same length, researchers hypothesized that people with this type of colon cancer might be experiencing a breakdown in this form of DNA repair. Then genetic studies revealed that the causative gene is located on chromosome 2 and that it is remarkably similar to a corresponding mismatch repair gene in *E. coli.*

Hereditary nonpolyposis colon cancer is a common repair disorder, affecting 1 in 200 people. Table 8.3 lists rarer repair disorders. Because the several forms of DNA repair use dozens of different enzymes, and therefore genes, several other disorders reflect faulty repair, too. A given type of repair disorder may reflect different gene actions. This is the case for xeroderma pigmentosum, discussed in Reading 4.2. Nine different forms of xeroderma pigmentosum have been identified, each caused by a different gene.

People with DNA repair disorders often have broken chromosomes and a high susceptibility to certain types of cancer following exposure to ionizing radiation or chemicals that affect cell division. We conclude the chapter with a closer look at one of the more common DNA repair disorders.

Ataxia Telangiectasis—A Closer Look

Gene sequence discoveries can solve medical mysteries. This is true in the continuing tale of the autosomal recessive disorder ataxia telangiectasis (AT). Geneticists have long considered AT to be caused by a defect in DNA repair, because cells from affected individuals grown in culture are unusually sensitive to damage from ionizing radiation such as X rays. Whereas a normal repair system will delay DNA replication until damage is repaired, in AT individuals, cells exposed to X rays proceed with replication, allowing potential cancer cells to remain. Consistent with cell studies is the observation that cancer risk in AT patients exceeds that of the general population some 61 to 184 times. Fifteen percent of patients develop cancer, usually leukemia or lymphoma.

AT is pleiotropic; that is, it has several associated phenotypes. An infant's first symptom is usually ataxia, which is a lack

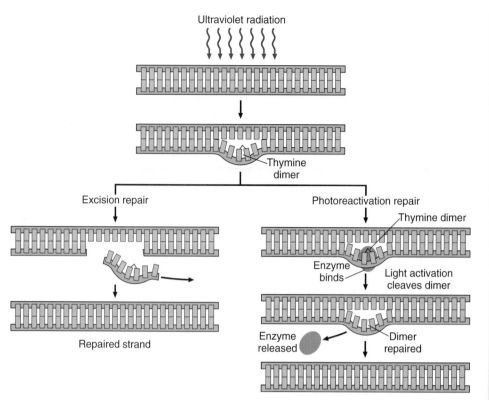

Ultraviolet radiation

Thymine dimer

Excision repair

Repaired strand

Photoreactivation repair

Thymine dimer

Enzyme binds

Light activation cleaves dimer

Enzyme released

Dimer repaired

figure 8.16

DNA is repaired by photoreactivation, in which a pyrimidine dimer is split, or by excision repair, in which the pyrimidine dimer and a few surrounding bases are removed and replaced.

table 8.3

DNA Replication and Repair Disorders

Disorder	Frequency	Defect
Ataxia telangiectasis	1/40,000	Deficiency in kinase that controls the cell cycle
Bloom syndrome (two types)	100 cases since 1950	DNA ligase is inactive or heat sensitive, slowing replication
Fanconi anemia (several types)	As high as 1/22,000 in some populations	Deficient excision repair
Hereditary nonpolyposis colon cancer	1/200	Deficient mismatch repair
Xeroderma pigmentosum (nine types)	1/250,000	Deficient excision repair

of muscle control that worsens as the child begins to walk. An uncontrollable gait soon leads to the need for a wheelchair. The child's eyes also dart about. These symptoms stem from dying cells in the cerebellum, the part of the brain that controls balance, coordination, and posture.

Another symptom of AT—red marks, called telangiectasia, that appear on the face and neck—is caused by dilation of small blood vessels under the skin. This and other symptoms, including increased risk of lung infections and diabetes, and delayed sexual maturation,

seem to have little to do with a DNA repair defect (figure 8.17).

Discovery of the AT gene in 1995 began to explain the phenotype. When researchers knew about half of the gene's sequence, they determined the protein sequence it encoded, and then they ran that sequence against a computer database of known protein sequences—a common way to guess at a logical function of a newly found gene. The database matched the AT gene product to a type of kinase that controls the cell cycle. The kinase is part of the signaling pathway that tells a cell when to divide—or when to die by programmed cell death (apoptosis) to eliminate cells that will become cancerous.

The suggestion that the AT gene product is an enzyme (a kinase) that regulates the cell cycle explained the extreme sensitivity to radiation damage and the resulting increase in cancer risk. But it turned out that the cell cycle isn't the only place where such a kinase might work. Researchers found it is involved in signaling in the cerebellum, and nerve cells do not divide. Here, the AT protein apparently enables growth factors to nourish the cells that control balance and coordination.

Impaired signaling also explains the higher risk of lung infection. In affected individuals, immune system cells in the lungs do not adequately recognize pathogenic bacteria. Similarly, beta cells in the pancreas cannot respond to insulin, causing diabetes. Perhaps defective signaling also explains the failure of certain cells to respond to hormones that oversee sexual maturation. Still a mystery, though, are the facial marks for which the disorder is partially named.

Discovering the gene behind AT may have even more import for heterozygotes, who make up from 0.5 to 1.4 percent of various populations. Carriers may have mild radiation sensitivity, which causes a two- to sixfold increase in cancer risk over the general population. In fact, AT heterozygosity may be the most common genetic cause of breast cancer. It has long been known that female relatives of AT patients have a fivefold increase in risk of breast cancer, and those with the cancer often have had many diagnostic X rays, which may have actually triggered the cancer!

figure 8.17

When researchers identified the protein product of the gene that causes AT, some—but not all—of the symptoms made more sense.

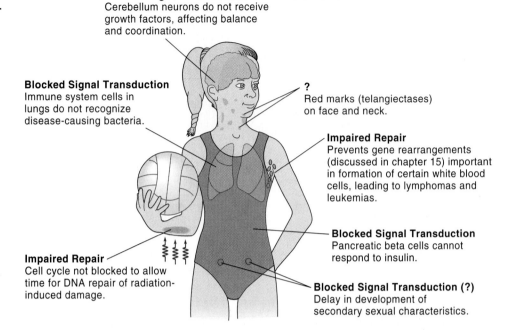

Blocked Signal Transduction
Cerebellum neurons do not receive growth factors, affecting balance and coordination.

Blocked Signal Transduction
Immune system cells in lungs do not recognize disease-causing bacteria.

?
Red marks (telangiectases) on face and neck.

Impaired Repair
Prevents gene rearrangements (discussed in chapter 15) important in formation of certain white blood cells, leading to lymphomas and leukemias.

Blocked Signal Transduction
Pancreatic beta cells cannot respond to insulin.

Impaired Repair
Cell cycle not blocked to allow time for DNA repair of radiation-induced damage.

Blocked Signal Transduction (?)
Delay in development of secondary sexual characteristics.

With the AT gene discovery, researchers now have a tool to identify which individuals in families with AT are carriers and have therefore inherited the greatly increased risk of breast and other cancers. This is of vital importance, because the mammograms and radiation therapy that are often part of breast cancer diagnosis and treatment might make this particular inherited form more likely to occur. Researchers caution, however, that women should not avoid mammograms unless a physician confirms AT in a close blood relative.

Disorders of DNA repair reveal how vital precise DNA replication is to cell survival and proliferation. Once these processes are completed, the cell begins to utilize the informational content of DNA. This is the subject of the next chapter.

Key Concepts

Many genes encode enzymes that search replicating DNA for errors and correct them. A common cause of noncomplementary base insertion is an ultraviolet radiation-induced pyrimidine dimer. Photoreactivation or excision repair can correct pyrimidine dimers. Mismatch repair corrects noncomplementary base pairs. Abnormal repair genes cause disorders characterized by chromosome breaks and predisposition to cancer.

summary

1. The genetic material—DNA—must encode the information a cell requires to survive, to specialize, and to replicate.

2. Many experimenters described DNA and showed it to be the hereditary material. Miescher identified DNA in white blood cell nuclei. Garrod conceptually connected heredity to symptoms caused by enzyme abnormalities. Griffith identified a substance that transmits infectiousness in pneumonia-causing bacteria; Avery, MacLeod, and McCarty discovered that the transforming principle is DNA; Hershey and Chase confirmed that the genetic material is DNA and not protein. Levene described the three components of a nucleotide and found that they appear in DNA in equal amounts. Chargaff discovered that the amount of adenine equals the amount of thymine, and the amount of guanine equals that of cytosine. Watson and Crick put all these clues together to propose DNA's double helix conformation.

3. The rungs of the DNA double helix consist of hydrogen-bonded complementary base pairs (A with T, and C with G). The rails are chains of alternating sugars and phosphates that run **antiparallel** to each other. DNA is highly coiled.

4. Meselson and Stahl proved the **semiconservative** nature of DNA replication with **density shift experiments.** During replication, the DNA unwinds locally at several initiation points. **Replication forks** form as the hydrogen bonds break between an initial base pair. **RNA polymerase** builds a short **RNA primer,** which DNA eventually replaces.

Next, **DNA polymerase** fills in DNA bases, and **ligase** seals the sugar-phosphate backbone. Replication proceeds in a 5′ to 3′ direction, so the process must be discontinuous in short stretches on at least one strand.

5. Gene amplification techniques, such as **PCR,** utilize the power and specificity of DNA replication enzymes to selectively amplify certain sequences.

6. DNA can repair itself in a variety of ways, relying on DNA polymerase proofreading, **excision repair, photoreactivation,** and **mismatch repair.**

review questions

1. The function of DNA is to specify and regulate the cell's synthesis of protein. If a cell contains all the genetic material required to carry out protein synthesis, why must the DNA also be replicated?

2. Match the experiment described on the left to the concept it illustrates on the right.

   1. Density shift experiments

   2. Extracting an acidic substance that includes nitrogen and phosphorus from dirty bandages

   3. "Blender experiments" showed that the part of a virus that infects bacteria contains phosphorus, but not sulfur

   4. DNA contains equal amounts of guanine and cytosine, and of adenine and thymine

   5. Bacteria can transfer a "factor" that transforms a harmless strain into a lethal one

   a. DNA is the hereditary material

   b. Complementary base pairing is part of DNA structure and maintains a symmetrical double helix

   c. Identification of nuclein

   d. DNA is the hereditary material, and protein is not

   e. DNA replication is semiconservative, and not conservative or dispersive

3. What part of the DNA molecule encodes information?

4. Explain how DNA is a directional molecule in a chemical sense.

5. Place the following proteins in the order in which they begin to function in DNA replication.

   ligase

   photolyases

   DNA polymerase

   RNA polymerase

   helicases

6. Write the sequence of a strand of DNA replicated from each of the following base sequences:

   a. T C G A G A A T C T C G A T T

   b. C C G T A T A G C C G G T A C

   c. A T C G G A T C G C T A C T G

7. Place in increasing size order:

   nucleosome

   histone protein

   chromatin

applied questions

1. In Bloom syndrome, ligase malfunctions. As a result, replication forks move too slowly. Why does this happen?

2. A biotechnology company has encapsulated DNA repair enzymes in fatty bubbles called liposomes. Why would this be a valuable addition to a suntanning lotion?

3. To diagnose a rare form of encephalitis (brain inflammation), a researcher needs a million copies of a viral gene. She decides to use the polymerase chain reaction on a sample of the patient's cerebrospinal fluid, which bathes his infected brain. If 1 cycle of PCR takes 2 minutes, how long will it take the researcher to obtain her millionfold amplification?

4. Two young people with skin cancer resulting from xeroderma pigmentosum meet at an event held for teenagers with cancer. The young man's XP results from faulty excision repair, and the young woman's from defective mismatch repair. They decide to marry but will not have children because they believe that each child would have a 25 percent chance of inheriting XP because it is autosomal recessive. Are they correct to be so concerned? Why or why not?

5. A person with deficient or abnormal ligase or excision repair may have an increased cancer risk and chromosomes that cannot heal breaks. The person is, nevertheless, alive. How long would an individual lacking DNA polymerase be likely to survive?

6. Until recently, HIV infection was diagnosed by detecting antibodies in a person's blood or documenting a decline in the number of the type of white blood cell that HIV initially infects. Why is PCR detection more accurate?

7. Cancerous cells from a person with hereditary nonpolyposis colon cancer have different length microsatellite sequences. What is the nature of the defect in DNA repair underlying the cancer?

suggested readings

Debenham, Paul G. April 11, 1996. Heteroplasmy and the Tsar. *Nature,* vol. 380. A DNA quirk solved a royal mystery.

Faerman, Marina, et al. January 17, 1997. DNA analysis reveals the sex of infanticide victims. *Nature,* vol. 385. DNA evidence can solve historical mysteries.

Jaroff, Leon. March 15, 1993. Happy birthday, double helix. *Time.* Watson and Crick shared a rare visit on the fortieth anniversary of their monumental deciphering of DNA structure.

Lewis, Ricki. September 1995. Correcting sun damage the biotech way. *Photonics Spectra.* New gene-containing sunblocks boost DNA repair to lessen sun-induced skin damage.

Lewis, Ricki. March 1996. Using technology to teach difficult genetic concepts. *The American Biology Teacher.* PCR provides entertaining applications of understanding DNA replication.

Lewis, Ricki. May 1, 1996. PCR technology makes additional inroads in the clinic and in the field. *Genetic Engineering News.* PCR, the technique that borrows the DNA replication mechanism, continues to find new applications.

Lewis, Ricki. August 1996. UV damage to DNA revisited. *Photonics Spectra.* In some situations, cells ignore signals to repair UV-induced DNA damage. The result can be cancer.

Liv, B., et al. February 1996. Analysis of mismatch repair genes in hereditary non-polyposis colorectal cancer patients. *Nature Medicine,* vol. 2. Faulty DNA repair causes this inherited cancer.

Marx, Jean. November 4, 1994. DNA repair comes into its own. *Science,* vol. 266. Geneticists are identifying the many genes that enable DNA to repair itself.

Morell, Virginia. February 3, 1995. Getting the poop on baboon DNA. *Science,* vol. 267. Field biologists study baboon populations by examining DNA sequences from cells in excrement.

Mullis, Kary B. April 1990. The unusual origin of the polymerase chain reaction. *Scientific American.* How the technique of gene amplification arose from a brainstorm.

Nelms, B. E. et al. April 24, 1998. In situ visualization of DNA double-stranded break repair in human fibroblasts. *Science,* vol. 280. DNA repair revealed.

Nowack, Rachel. June 23, 1995. Discovery of AT gene sparks biomedical research bonanza. *Science,* vol. 268. Having the AT gene in hand explains observations in cell culture and epidemiology made years ago.

Pennisi, Elizabeth. October 25, 1996. Linker histones, DNA's protein custodians, gain new respect. *Science,* vol. 274. Histone proteins were once thought to be mere structural supports, then to repress gene action. Now they are known to activate genes, too.

Watson, James D., and F. H. C. Crick. April 25, 1953. Molecular structure of nucleic acids: A structure for deoxyribose nucleic acid. *Nature,* vol. 171, no. 4356. The original paper describing the structure of DNA.

Watson, James D. 1968. *The Double Helix.* New York: New American Library. An exciting, personal account of the discovery of DNA structure.

chapter nine

Gene Function

Anatomy of an Illness

Gene expression is very much a matter of communication. Many inherited disorders are the consequence of a breakdown in this communication process. This was the case for two young sisters whose illness at first puzzled doctors.

At seven and three years of age, the girls' too-soft leg bones bowed outwards, and the ends were bearing so much strain that their knees protruded like knobs. Their rib cages caved in. These were the unmistakable symptoms of rickets, a bone weakening that usually results from vitamin D deficiency (figure 9.1). But the children followed a healthy diet.

Even before the skeletal deformities became apparent, all was not right. As infants, the girls' growth lagged. The soft spot on the tops of their skulls did not close and harden by eighteen months, as it normally does. This was the first sign of the underlying lack of vitamin D. The sisters' teeth erupted late and were soon lost to decay. By two years of age, when most children's hair is growing in nicely, the sisters had lost most of theirs.

A hint that the girls' medical problem could be inherited was that their parents were second cousins. The parents could have inherited the same rare autosomal recessive disease-causing gene from a common ancestor. Each girl had inherited two copies of a disease-causing allele, one from each carrier parent.

A second clue came from analyzing the relative amounts of intermediate biochemicals resulting from the girls' cells using vitamin D. Even though the girls ate foods rich in vitamin D, received vitamin supplements, and got plenty of sunshine (needed to activate vitamin D precursors in the skin), they were still sick because their bodies could not use the abundant vitamin. The diagnosis: a very rare inherited form of vitamin D refractory rickets. But at what point in the cell's utilization of vitamin D did things go wrong? There were many possibilities.

Vitamin D may have hit a roadblock in the small intestine, unable to cross into the bloodstream. Or, one of the enzymes that modifies the vitamin into an accessible form may have been absent or defective. Perhaps the problem was in the receptor

figure 9.1

In this child with dietary rickets, lack of vitamin D prevents the leg bones from hardening normally, and they bend under stress. In another case, in two sisters with a rare inherited form of rickets, genes encoding bone proteins never receive vitamin D's message to function. Their rickets is a genetic communication failure.

protein that normally binds the vitamin D derivative in the cell and ferries it to the DNA, where it turns on genes that encode bone-building proteins. The error could prevent the receptor from binding to either the vitamin derivative or to the DNA.

The answer finally came from laboratory studies of the girls' connective tissue cells (fibroblasts). Their vitamin D receptors were isolated and mixed with activated vitamin D, simulating what was happening—or not happening—in their bodies. Like a ferry able to pick up passengers but not able to dock at the destination, the receptors picked up the activated vitamin and could transport it within the cell, but they could not bind to the DNA. The activated vitamin D, plentiful in the girls' bodies, couldn't interact with their DNA. Since the genes never received vitamin D's message, they never stimulated synthesis of important bone proteins. With the girls' skeletal systems awash in the vitamin, rickets resulted not from a lack of vitamin D, but from a failure to communicate at the molecular level.

Transcription—Gene Expression Begins

Hereditary rickets blocks gene expression in its very first stage—when a gene's DNA sequence is copied into a sequence of RNA, a process called **transcription.** DNA must remain in the nucleus for further use of its information. Transcription is a way to utilize that information.

RNA is copied from DNA in the nucleus. It then exits the nucleus through nuclear pores. In the cytoplasm, in the second stage of gene expression, the information in an RNA sequence is used to link, or polymerize, **amino acid** building blocks into polypeptides. One or more polypeptides form a protein. Protein synthesis occurs in a process called **translation.** RNA, then, is the bridging language that transcribes and translates a gene into a protein. Figure 9.2 shows where in a cell transcription and translation occur.

What Is RNA?

Ribonucleic acid (RNA) is similar to deoxyribonucleic acid (DNA) in that both are nucleic acids, consisting of sequences of nitrogen-containing bases joined by a sugar-phosphate backbone. However, structural and functional differences distinguish RNA from DNA.

Structurally, RNA is single-stranded, whereas DNA is double-stranded. Also, RNA has the pyrimidine base uracil, whereas DNA has thymine. And as their names imply, RNA nucleotides include the sugar ribose, rather than the deoxyribose that is part of DNA.

Functionally, DNA maintains genetic information, whereas RNA utilizes that information to enable the cell to synthesize a particular protein. Different types of RNA contribute to this process. Table 9.1 and figure 9.3 summarize the distinctions between RNA and DNA.

The Complexity of Transcription

When Watson and Crick determined the structure of DNA, they envisioned RNA as

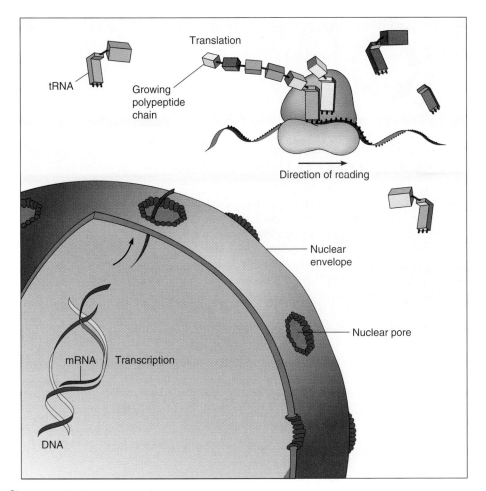

figure 9.2

An mRNA molecule transcribed from a section of DNA exits the nucleus and enters the cytoplasm, where it associates with a ribosome to begin translation.

table 9.1

Distinctions Between RNA and DNA

RNA	DNA
Single-stranded	Double-stranded
Has uracil as a base	Has thymine as a base
Ribose as the sugar	Deoxyribose as the sugar
Uses protein-encoding information	Maintains protein-encoding information

a stepping-stone between a gene's nucleotide base language and a protein's amino acid language (figure 9.4). This paradigm became known as the "central dogma of molecular biology." Although correct, the central dogma outlines only the mechanics of transcription—how a gene's information enables a cell to manufacture protein. It does not explain the more difficult question of how a cell "knows" which genes to express and when to express them. For example, what directs a bone cell to transcribe the genes that control the synthesis of collagen protein and not to transcribe those that instruct the cell to produce muscle-specific proteins?

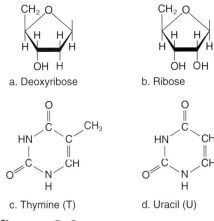

figure 9.3

DNA and RNA differ structurally from each other in three ways. DNA nucleotides have the sugar deoxyribose (a), whereas RNA contains ribose (b). DNA nucleotides include the pyrimidine thymine (c), whereas RNA has uracil (d). DNA is double-stranded and RNA is generally single-stranded. The two types of nucleic acids have different functions.

The central dogma did not include the "backward" flow of genetic information seen among the **retroviruses,** such as HIV, which inject RNA into a host cell, where it is copied into DNA. The tips of chromosomes in most species are also maintained by a mechanism that "reverse transcribes" DNA from RNA. But usually, the flow of genetic information is DNA to RNA to protein.

RNA may be the most important molecule in life. It is far more than a go-between connecting gene to protein. It partakes in all aspects of gene expression. RNA is such an information-packed, versatile molecule that many biologists hypothesize it may have been the long-ago link between the nonliving and the living, an idea explored later in the chapter.

Control of Transcription

In organisms consisting of complex (eukaryotic) cells, transcription is under exquisitely precise control. Researchers have spent four decades unraveling the sequence of protein interactions that occurs in the vicinity of a gene about to be expressed. Work on transcription control began in a much simpler living system: bacteria.

The Lac Operon

We began to appreciate the complexity of gene expression in 1961. At that time, French biologists François Jacob and Jacques Monod described the remarkable ability of *E. coli* to produce enzymes needed to metabolize the sugar lactose precisely when lactose is in the cell's surroundings, but not otherwise. What could be "telling" a simple bacterial cell to transcribe exactly the genes it requires, precisely when it needs them?

The lactose itself is the trigger. It binds to a protein that normally sits atop the DNA sequence that contains the signal to begin transcription of the three enzymes required to break down the sugar. The lactose removes the protein, called a repressor, and the enzymes are synthesized (figure 9.5). Lactose, in a sense, makes its own dismantling possible.

Jacob and Monod termed the trio of genes whose enzyme products are required for lactose metabolism and their controls an **operon.** Soon, operons were discovered for the metabolism of other nutrients and in other bacteria. Some, like the lac operon, negatively control transcription by removing a block. Others act positively, producing factors that turn on transcription. As Jacob and Monod stated in 1961, "The genome contains not only a series of blueprints, but a coordinated program of protein synthesis and means of controlling its execution." In bacteria, operons control these functions.

Transcription Factors

Operons in bacteria function like switches, turning on or off gene transcription. In multicellular organisms like ourselves, genetic control is more complex because different cell types express different subsets of genes. Here, groups of proteins called **transcription factors** come together to form a transcription apparatus that binds DNA and initiates transcription at specific sites on the DNA. The transcription factors, activated by extracellular signals, set the stage for transcription to begin by forming a pocket for **RNA polymerase (RNAP)**—the enzyme that actually builds an RNA chain.

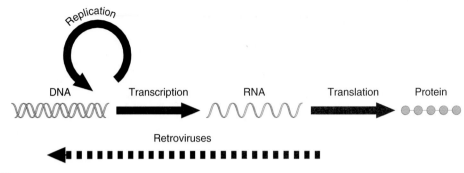

figure 9.4

The central dogma of molecular biology, circa 1965, envisioned DNA replicated and transcribed into RNA, some of which was then translated into protein. All organisms and most viruses exhibit this directional flow of genetic information. Retroviruses, including HIV, have RNA as the genetic material. Once in a host cell, these viruses use an enzyme, reverse transcriptase, to manufacture DNA from RNA, transmitting information in the opposite direction from that proposed by the central dogma. The original central dogma also oversimplified the role of RNA. This versatile nucleic acid assists in DNA replication, and we are still discovering new RNA functions in the control of gene expression.

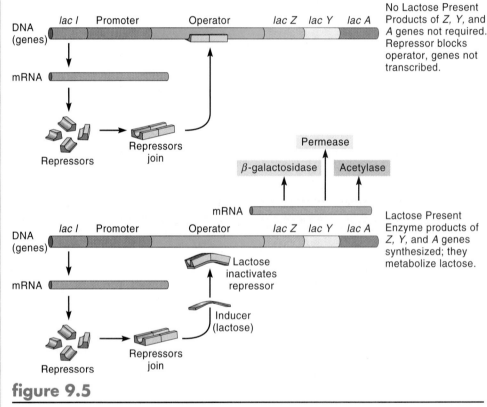

figure 9.5

The lac operon is a group of genes whose actions are coordinated to enable bacterial cells to utilize the nutrient lactose. An operon, although appearing complex, is far simpler than genetic controls in human cells.

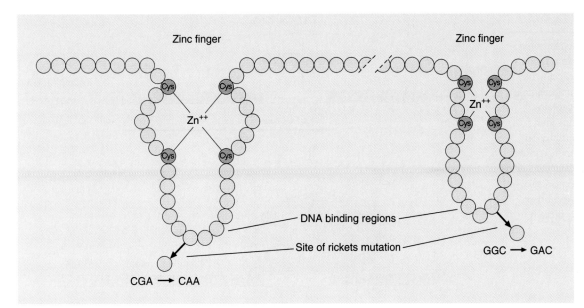

figure 9.6

Vitamin D refractory rickets can be due to a mutation in the gene encoding zinc finger regions of the receptor protein, which prevents it from binding to DNA. The fingers form as a result of four strategically located cysteines. These amino acids attract each other because they contain sulfur. The attraction creates a pocket that entraps zinc, which in turn stabilizes the finger formation.

Zinc finger

Zinc finger

DNA binding regions

Site of rickets mutation

CGA → CAA

GGC → GAC

Several types of transcription factors are required to transcribe a eukaryotic gene. Because transcription factors are proteins, they are gene-encoded. Genes for transcription factors may be near the genes they control, or as far away as 40,000 bases. The DNA of a chromosome may form loops so that genes for transcription factors that act together come near each other. Yet other proteins organize the nucleus so that genes actively being transcribed, and transcription factors in use, are partitioned off together.

Hundreds of transcription factors are known. Many of them have localized regions in common that fold into similar three-dimensional shapes or conformations. These areas are called **motifs.** They often have very descriptive names, such as "helix-loop-helix" and "leucine zipper."

The abnormality in the vitamin D receptor protein that causes the rickets described earlier in the chapter is in a motif called a zinc finger (figure 9.6). The affected vitamin D receptors can bind the activated vitamin D derivative, but they have "broken" zinc fingers, which are the parts of the receptors that bind DNA by extending outward, like fingers.

Initiation of Transcription

How do transcription factors and RNA polymerase "know" where to bind to DNA to initiate transcription? They are attracted to certain control sequences near the start of the gene, which form a region called the **promoter.** The first transcription factor to bind, called a TATA binding protein, is attracted to a sequence called a TATA box, which consists of the sequence TATA surrounded by stretches of 25 bases that are mostly G and C (figure 9.7). The bound first transcription factor attracts others and finally contorts the area so that RNA polymerase joins the complex. Other sequences in or near the promoter regulate the frequency of transcription. Figure 9.7 depicts these interactions in sequence. The complex formed by transcription factors guides RNA polymerase to bind just before the gene sequence starts.

Building an RNA Chain

As in DNA replication, complementary base pairing is the basis of transcription. Enzymes unwind the DNA double helix and RNA nucleotides bond with the exposed complementary bases on one strand of the DNA double helix (figure 9.8). RNA polymerase knits together the RNA nucleotides in the sequence that the DNA specifies, moving along the DNA strand in a 3′ to 5′ direction. For example, the DNA sequence GCGTATG is transcribed into RNA with the sequence CGCAUAC.

A terminator sequence in the DNA indicates where the gene's RNA encoding region ends.

For any gene, RNA is transcribed from only one strand of the DNA double helix. But a portion of that same strand may be transcribed several times simultaneously (figure 9.9). This DNA strand is called the **coding** (or sense or template) **strand** and the RNA transcribed from it is called **sense RNA.** The DNA strand that, for a particular gene, is not transcribed is called the noncoding or antisense strand of DNA. Figure 9.10 shows these relationships.

To determine the sequence of sense RNA bases transcribed from a gene, write the RNA bases that are complementary to the coding DNA strand, substituting uracil for thymine. For example, if a DNA coding strand is the sequence:

C C T A G C T A C

then it is transcribed into sense RNA with the sequence:

G G A U C G A U G

Note the relationship between the sense RNA and the noncoding side of the DNA double helix—the sequences are the same, with T in the DNA wherever U is in the RNA:

noncoding DNA sequence:

G G A T C G A T G

figure 9.7

Transcription begins. (*a*) To set the stage for transcription, a TATA binding protein binds the TATA box in the promoter of a particular gene. (*b*) Next, coactivator proteins assemble around the bound TATA binding protein. (*c*) Activators and repressor proteins then bind. These control the rate of transcription, and their presence is transmitted to the gene to be expressed through the coactivators already bound to the TATA binding protein. (*d*) Finally, a series of proteins called basal factors attach to the TATA binding protein in a way that clears a space for RNA polymerase to bind.

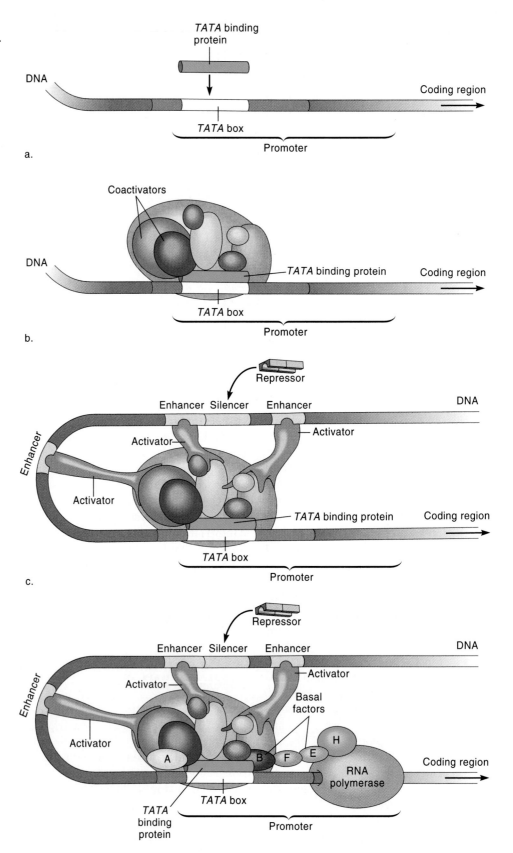

d. Final transcription initiation complex

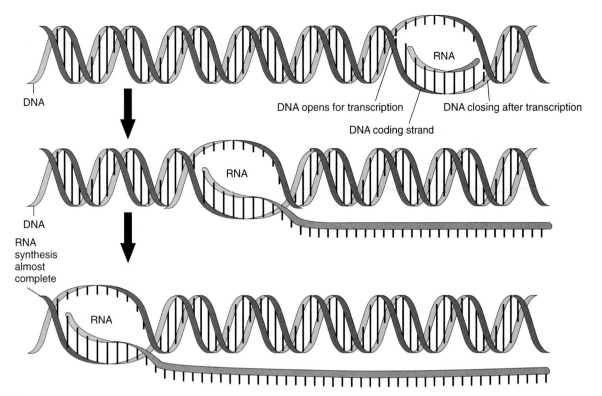

figure 9.8

Transcription of RNA from DNA. The DNA double helix opens and closes, allowing RNA polymerase access to the DNA coding strand, from which RNA is transcribed.

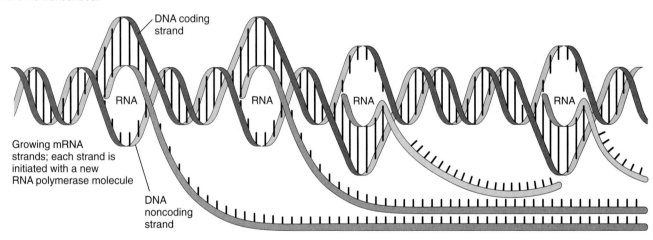

figure 9.9

The same DNA coding sequence can be transcribed several times simultaneously.

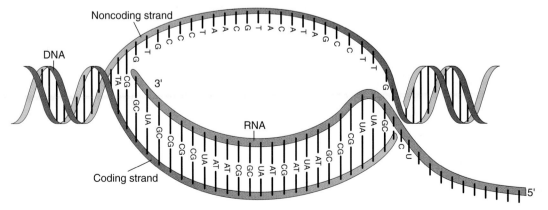

figure 9.10

A single strand of mRNA is transcribed against the coding strand of a DNA double helix. Note that the RNA sequence is complementary to that of the DNA coding strand and, therefore, is the same sequence as the DNA noncoding (antisense) strand, with uracil (U) in place of thymine (T).

Table 9.2 lists more examples of the relationship between DNA and RNA.

A biotechnology called **antisense technology** intentionally blocks expression of a particular gene by introducing RNA complementary to a sense RNA into a cell. This manufactured RNA is called antisense RNA. The antisense RNA sequence binds to RNA from the gene in question, blocking it so it cannot be used in the cytoplasm to build a protein. This halts the gene's action.

Antisense RNA may be useful as an antiviral drug. When a virus infects a human cell, it brings in its genetic material, which may then become part of a human chromosome. Antisense RNA with a sequence complementary to that of viral coding DNA would bind to the viral RNA, stopping the expression of viral genes and therefore the infection. Figure 9.11 shows another application of antisense technology—a tomato that stays fresh longer because an antisense RNA squelches activity of a key ripening enzyme. Figure 1.2 pokes fun at the public's misplaced fear of such genetically altered tomatoes. Ironically, these tomatoes failed in the marketplace because of undesirable characteristics unrelated to ripening.

table 9.2

The RNA Sense Strand—Complementary to the DNA Coding Strand

DNA coding sequence:	GCCCTATAAGACAGT
RNA sense sequence:	CGGGAUAUUCUGUCA
DNA coding sequence:	ATGGAGTCTCTTCAAGTC
RNA sense sequence:	UACCUCAGAGAAGUUCAG
DNA coding sequence:	GAGGTAACACCCGGTTAT
RNA sense sequence:	CUCCAUUGUGGGCCAAUA

Sense mRNA ∘∘∘UGACGCGAUUAGCCGAU∘∘∘

Antisense sequence —ACUGCGCUAAUCGGCUA

a.

figure 9.11

Antisense RNA blocks gene action. (*a*) The sense mRNA depicted on top cannot be translated into protein because an antisense sequence blocks it. (*b*) These tomatoes harbor an antisense gene that silences a ripening enzyme, allowing the fruit to remain longer on the vine, gaining a better flavor and texture.

b.

table 9.3

Major Type of RNA

Type of RNA	Size (number of nucleotides)	Function
mRNA	500–1,000	Codons encode amino acid sequence
rRNA	100–3,000	Associates with proteins to form ribosomes, which structurally support and catalyze protein synthesis
tRNA	75–80	Binds mRNA codon on one end, amino acid on the other, linking a gene's message to the amino acid sequence it encodes

Types of RNA

As RNA is synthesized along DNA, it curls into three-dimensional shapes, or **conformations,** that are determined by complementary base pairing within the same RNA molecule. These shapes are very important for RNA's functioning. Several types of RNA have characteristic conformations. Table 9.3 summarizes RNA types.

Messenger RNA (mRNA) Carries the Genetic Information

Messenger RNA (mRNA) carries the information specifying a particular protein product. Each three mRNA bases in a row form a genetic code word, or **codon,** that specifies a certain amino acid. Because genes vary in length, so do mRNA molecules. Most mRNAs are 500 to 1,000 bases long.

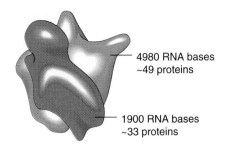

4980 RNA bases
~49 proteins

1900 RNA bases
~33 proteins

figure 9.12

A ribosome in a eukaryote, such as a human, consists of about half protein and half ribosomal RNA.

Transfer and Ribosomal RNAs Help Translate the Message

The information an mRNA sequence carries cannot be utilized without the participation of two other major classes of RNA. **Ribosomal RNA (rRNA)** ranges from 100 to nearly 3,000 nucleotides in length. It associates with certain proteins to form a **ribosome.** Recall from chapter 3 that a ribosome is a structural support for protein synthesis (figure 9.12). A ribosome has two subunits that are separate in the cytoplasm, but which join at the site of protein synthesis. Certain rRNAs catalyze formation of bonds between amino acids. Such an RNA with enzymatic function is called a **ribozyme.**

Transfer RNA (tRNA) molecules are connectors. They bind to mRNA codons at one end and to specific amino acids at the other. A tRNA molecule is only 75 to 80 nucleotides long. Some of its bases weakly bond with each other, folding the tRNA into loops that form a characteristic cloverleaf shape (figure 9.13). One loop of the tRNA has three bases in a row, called the **anticodon,** which is complementary to an mRNA codon. The end of the tRNA opposite the anticodon strongly bonds to a specific amino acid (figure 9.13 inset). A tRNA with a particular anticodon sequence always attracts the same amino acid. (There are 20 types of amino acids in organisms.) For example, a tRNA with the anticodon sequence AAG always picks up the amino acid phenylalanine. Special enzymes attach amino acids to tRNAs bearing the appropriate anticodons.

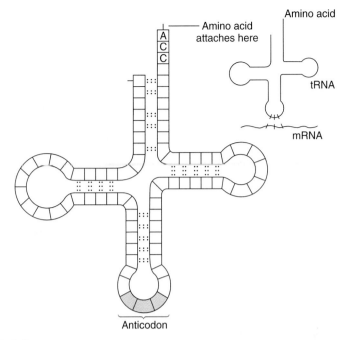

figure 9.13

Transfer RNA. Certain nucleotides within a tRNA molecule form complementary base pairs with each other, imparting a cloverleaflike conformation. The dotted lines indicate complementary base pairing, and the filled-in bases at the bottom denote the anticodon sequence. Each tRNA terminates with the sequence CCA. A particular amino acid bonds with the RNA at this end.

Key Concepts

Messenger RNA transmits information in a gene to cellular structures that build proteins. Each three mRNA bases in a row forms a codon that specifies a particular amino acid. Ribosomal RNA and proteins form ribosomes, which physically support the other participants in protein synthesis and help catalyze formation of bonds between amino acids. Transfer RNAs connect particular mRNA codons to particular amino acids.

After Transcription—RNA Is Processed, Spliced, and Edited

In simple bacteria, RNA begins functioning in protein synthesis as it is transcribed from DNA because these cells lack nuclei. The RNA is already in the cytoplasm. In our cells, mRNA must first exit the nucleus to enter the cytoplasm, where protein synthesis occurs. RNA is altered in several ways before it participates in protein synthesis in more complex cells.

Messenger RNA Processing

While mRNA is being transcribed, a short sequence of modified nucleotides called a cap is added to the 5' end. Then 100 to 200 adenines, forming a "poly A tail," are added to the 3' end as the mRNA moves away from the DNA, but while it is still in the nucleus. The cap and tail assist mRNA's journey from the nucleus to the cytoplasm. These features "tell" the cell which messages should be exported from the nucleus and read.

Genes in Pieces

The ability to determine the sequences of nucleic acids made it possible to compare DNA and RNA molecules base by base. However, rather than the expected direct correspondence between the numbers of bases in a gene and its RNA, the RNA was sometimes altered. RNA could either include bases the gene did not specify, or lack stretches of bases in the corresponding gene.

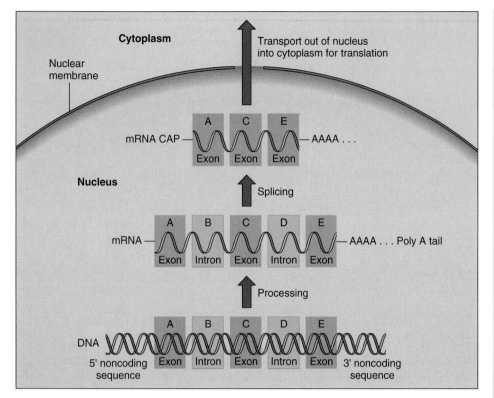

figure 9.14

Messenger RNA processing—the maturing of the message. Several steps carve the mature mRNA. First, noncoding surrounding bases in the DNA are not transcribed. A cap head and poly A tail are added, introns are excised, and exons spliced together.

A gene might be 10,000 bases long, for example, but its corresponding RNA only 6,000 bases long. These "extra" noncoding regions of a gene are called **introns;** the sequences of DNA bases that do appear in the mature RNA are called **exons** (figure 9.14).

Introns were discovered in mRNA. They are transcribed, but they are cut out and the ends of the molecule are spliced together before the mRNA is translated. The mRNA prior to intron removal is called pre-mRNA. Introns are excised by small RNA molecules that are ribozymes, and they associate with proteins to form small nuclear ribonucleoproteins (snRNPs), or "snurps." Several snurps work together to form a complex that cuts introns out and knits exons together to form the mature mRNA that exits the nucleus. Reading 9.1 chronicles the discoveries of introns and ribozymes and tells how they altered earlier views of the gene.

Introns range in size from 65 to 100,000 bases. While the average exon is 100 to 300 bases long, the average intron is about 1,000 bases long. Many genes are riddled with introns—the human collagen gene, for example, contains 50 of them. The number, size, and arrangement of introns varies from gene to gene. Once regarded as an oddity because their existence was unexpected, introns are now known to comprise about 95 percent of the 3 billion bases of the human genome.

The functions of introns remain a puzzle. Introns may control how exons are spliced together, or they may be ancient genes that have lost their original function. Another possibility is that introns are remnants of the genetic material of viruses that once infected the cell. We do not know why some genes have introns and some do not.

RNA Editing

RNA editing refers to changes in RNA bases that happen just after transcription.

Still poorly understood, RNA editing may help explain how cells that make up different tissues use the same protein in slightly different ways. This is the case for apolipoprotein B (apo B). Recall that apolipoproteins transport fats.

In the small intestine, an RNA change shortens the RNA encoding apo B, shortening the protein. In this shortened form, apo B can bind and carry dietary fat. However, in the liver, the RNA encoding apo B is not shortened. The longer version here has a different function than its counterpart in the intestine—it transports fats manufactured in the liver, which do not come from the diet. RNA editing determines whether apo B is produced in the shorter or longer form.

Key Concepts

In eukaryotes, RNA is often altered before it is active. Messenger RNA gains a cap of modified nucleotides and a poly A tail. Introns are transcribed and cut out, and exons are reattached by ribozymes. RNA editing introduces base changes that alter the protein product in different cell types.

Translation—Expressing Genetic Information

Transcription copies the information encoded in a DNA base sequence into the complementary language of mRNA. The next step is translating this "message" into the specified sequence of amino acids. Particular mRNA codons (three bases in a row) correspond to particular amino acids (figure 9.15). This correspondence between the chemical languages of mRNA and protein is called the **genetic code.** In the 1960s, many researchers deciphered the code, determining which mRNA codons correspond to which amino acids. They used a combination of logic and experiments, beginning by answering certain questions.

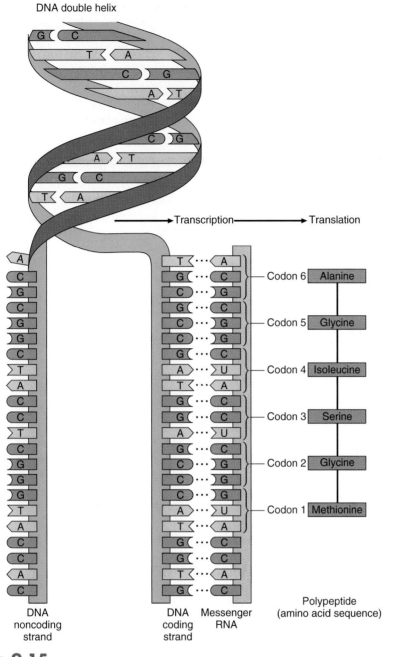

DNA double helix

→ Transcription → → Translation →

Codon 6 — Alanine
Codon 5 — Glycine
Codon 4 — Isoleucine
Codon 3 — Serine
Codon 2 — Glycine
Codon 1 — Methionine

DNA noncoding strand

DNA coding strand

Messenger RNA

Polypeptide (amino acid sequence)

figure 9.15

From DNA to RNA to protein. Messenger RNA is transcribed from a locally unwound portion of DNA. In translation, transfer RNA matches mRNA codons with specific amino acids.

The Genetic Code—From Genetic Message to Protein Product

Question 1—How many RNA bases specify one amino acid?

Because the number of different protein building blocks (20) exceeds the number of different mRNA building blocks (4), each codon must contain more than one mRNA base. In other words, if a codon consisted of only one mRNA base, then codons could specify only 4 different amino acids, with one corresponding to each of the 4 bases: A, C, G, and U (figure 9.16). If each codon consisted of 2 bases, then 16 different amino acids could be specified, one corresponding to each of the 16 possible orders of 2 RNA bases (AA, CC, GG, UU, AC, CA, AU, UA, CG, GC, GU, UG, GA, AG, UC, and CU). This still is inadequate to encode the 20 amino acids. If a codon consisted of 3 bases, then the genetic code could specify as many as 64 different amino acids. Because 20 different amino acids require at least 20 different codons, the minimum number of bases in a codon is 3.

Francis Crick and his coworkers conducted experiments that confirmed the triplet nature of the genetic code. They added 1, 2, or 3 bases within a gene whose sequence and protein product were known. Altering the sequence by 1 or 2 bases greatly disrupted the coded order of amino acids, known as the **reading frame.** This produced a different amino acid sequence. However, adding or deleting 3 contiguous bases added or deleted only one amino acid in the protein product (figure 9.17). The rest of the amino acid sequence was retained. The code, therefore, is triplet.

Question 2—Is the genetic code overlapping?

Consider the hypothetical mRNA sequence AUCAGUCUA. If the genetic code is triplet and nonoverlapping (that is, each three bases in a row form a codon, but any one base is part of only one codon), then this sequence contains only three codons: AUC, AGU, and CUA. If the code is overlapping, the sequence contains seven codons: AUC, UCA, CAG, AGU, GUC, UCU, and CUA.

An overlapping code seems economical in that it packs maximal information into a limited number of bases (figure 9.18). However, an overlapping code constrains protein structure because certain amino acids must always be followed by certain others. For example, the amino acid the first codon specifies, AUC, would always be followed by an amino acid whose codon begins with UC. Experiments that take apart proteins amino acid by amino acid reveal that a specific amino acid does not always follow another specific amino acid. Any amino acid can follow any other amino acid in a protein's sequence. Therefore, the code is not overlapping.

Introns Emerge

The molecular picture of the gene emerged elegantly from Watson and Crick's portrait of the DNA double helix in 1953. The gene was seen as a continuous string of information that specifies another string of information—a protein. By 1969, molecular biologists thought they had thoroughly described the major players in gene expression.

Our straightforward view of the gene changed in 1977, when the ability to sequence DNA revealed genes far too big to account for their respective proteins. The 600-base rabbit beta globin gene, for example, encodes a 146 amino acid chain. Since three DNA bases code for one amino acid, this protein should have been specified by a gene 438 bases long (3 times 146). Why were there 162 extra DNA bases?

In the 1970s, we learned that the extra bases are transcribed into RNA but then removed before the protein is synthesized. Soon, extra DNA was found in the genes of many complex organisms, and even in viruses, but it seemed less common in bacteria.

In 1978, Harvard University's Walter Gilbert named the extra DNA sequences introns, short for "intervening sequences." Introns reside amid expressed DNA sequences called exons. How did these "genes in pieces" fit the central dogma of molecular biology—the idea that genes are transcribed into RNA, which is translated into protein?

Introns explained some genetic mysteries. They accounted for the long precursor forms of mRNA. Introns also explained the excess DNA compared to the number of known proteins, tRNAs, and rRNAs in well-studied bacteria. Introns also provided a mechanism for rapid evolution of a new function. The intron could audition a new activity while the old DNA sequence remained, ensuring survival.

Introns may speed evolution via "exon shuffling," bringing together exon sequences that code for different protein domains. A great variety of proteins could thus be synthesized from relatively few exons, in the same way that a varied wardrobe can be built by combining a few standard items of clothing.

Francis Crick was among the biologists who, for a time, termed introns "parasitic" or "junk" DNA, suggesting that they were molecular stowaways from past viral infections. Today our view of the role of introns—though still a matter of debate—has risen to a comparatively lofty height. RNA transcribed from what was once called "junk" is now considered by many to be the prime candidate for the primordial molecule of life. Biologists have even teamed with linguists to demonstrate that the DNA sequences comprising introns occur in nonrandom patterns resembling a language, suggesting that introns may indeed have a meaning, and therefore a function.

Enter Ribozymes

In the early 1980s, Sidney Altman at Yale University was looking at enzymes that modify RNA. RNase P is an enzyme in *E. coli* that cleaves tRNA precursors to form the shorter, mature tRNA cloverleaf. Altman had discovered RNase P in the early 1970s while working in Francis Crick's lab. It was a peculiar enzyme in that it always had about 377 RNA bases tagging along. Was the persistent presence of the RNA the result of sloppy lab technique, or might it mean something about the enzyme's function? The idea of a nucleic acid assisting an enzyme was radical, because enzymes were thought to be only protein.

Altman showed that the RNA in RNase P was more than a stowaway by adding a nuclease, an enzyme that degrades a nucleic acid, to his preparations. The nuclease destroyed RNA—and it also destroyed the enzyme's function. Altman and Norman Pace of Indiana University then showed that the RNA portion of RNase P, by itself, had catalytic activity.

Two years earlier, Thomas Cech at the University of Colorado in Boulder was trying to demonstrate how introns are spliced out of mRNA molecules. He studied ribosomal RNA (rRNA) in the protozoan *Tetrahymena thermophila*. When Cech added an extract from the nucleus to the rRNA, splicing occurred. However, in the control experiment, he observed the RNA splicing activity without the nuclear extract. Much to his surprise, the intron was still cut out and the bracketing exons linked to form the mature mRNA that would be translated into protein. Cech had found that RNA alone could cut and paste introns.

"It was quite a surprise," Cech recalled. "We had no reason to believe that RNA could catalyze a splicing reaction. We were looking for a protein enzyme, or even multiple enzymes," he added. Cech and Altman shared the 1989 Nobel Prize in chemistry after further showing that these RNA enzymes, or ribozymes, are not consumed by their activity.

Several companies are developing ribozymes as a new type of antiviral treatment. For example, a type of ribozyme called a "hammerhead" cuts DNA at specific three-base sequences. If a particular viral gene has many of these sequences, the hammerhead ribozyme might be a useful drug to cut up viral DNA.

In 1990, researchers discovered that RNA is both a catalyst and a template. Scientists at Massachusetts General Hospital built a multisubunit ribozyme from part of an intron in a well-studied gene of a virus that infects *E. coli*. The ribozyme could replicate new RNA strands using itself, unassembled and unwound, as a template!

RNA therefore both carries genetic information and can replicate. Such a multifunctional molecule fills the requirements for a biochemical first step to life. Figure 1 illustrates how RNA may have been the bridge between an inanimate chemical and life.

figure 1

A scenario for life's beginnings—the RNA world. Chemical evolution in the presence of energy led to formation of nitrogen-containing nucleotide bases in an RNA-like molecule. The phosphate that tied the bases together might have been liberated from rocks when erupting volcanoes released energy. RNA evolved the capabilities to replicate and encode proteins. A protein, perhaps similar to reverse transcriptase, copied the information in RNA into DNA. The DNA then polymerized a complementary strand, fashioning the first DNA double helices. As nucleic acids, proteins, carbohydrates, and lipids formed, the structures that would become parts of cells took shape. At some point, life arose from these structures.

Size of a Genetic Code Word (Codon)
To encode a protein alphabet of 20 amino acids:

Logic

mRNA genetic code of 1 letter

```
U
C
A
G
```

4 combinations:
not sufficient

mRNA genetic code of 2 letters

```
UU CC AA GG UC CU UA
AU UG GU CA AC CG GC
AG GA
```

16 combinations:
not sufficient

mRNA genetic code of 3 letters

```
UUU UUC UUA UUG UCU UCC UCA UCG
UAU UAC UAA UAG UGU UGC UGA UGG
CUU CUC CUA CUG CCU CCC CCA CCG
CAU CAC CAA CAG CGU CGC CGA CGG
AUU AUC AUA AUG ACU ACC ACA ACG
AAU AAC AAA AAG AGU AGC AGA AGG
GUU GUC GUA GUG GCU GCC GCA GCG
GAU GAC GAA GAG GGU GGC GGA GGG
```

64 combinations:
sufficient

figure 9.16

A "thought" experiment in logic reveals the triplet nature of the genetic code.

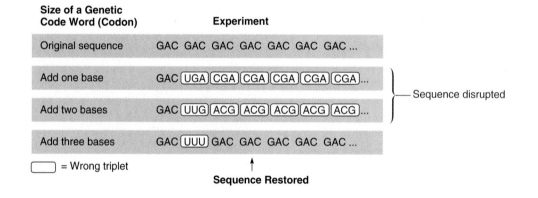

figure 9.17

Francis Crick and his coworkers confirmed the "thought" experiment in figure 9.16, showing that the genetic code is triplet by adding and subtracting 1, 2, and 3 bases to the sequence of a well-studied gene. Adding or subtracting 1 or 2 bases disrupted the reading frame, but adding or subtracting 3 bases restored it. Therefore, the code is triplet.

Question 3—Can mRNA codons signal anything other than amino acids?

Chemical analysis eventually showed that the genetic code contains directions for starting and stopping the translation of a protein. The codon AUG signals "start," and the codons UGA, UAA, and UAG each signify "stop." Another form of "punctuation" is a short sequence of bases at the start of each mRNA, called the **leader sequence,** which enables the mRNA to form attachments called hydrogen bonds with part of the rRNA in a ribosome.

Question 4—Do all species use the same genetic code?

The fact that all types of organisms use the same mRNA codons to specify the same amino acids is part of the abundant evidence that all life on earth evolved from a common ancestor. The genetic code is universal, with the exception of a few genes in the mitochondria of certain single-celled organisms. The ability of mRNA from one species to be translated in a cell of another species has made recombinant DNA technology possible (chapter 17).

The media often mistakenly uses the term "genetic code," stating that we each have our own code, or that the human genome project is deciphering the "human genetic code." This is not the case; the code is universal, like an alphabet used in many different languages. The universality of the genetic code makes the genetic manipulations of biotechnology possible.

Question 5—Which codons specify which amino acids?

In 1961, Marshall Nirenberg and his coworkers at the National Institutes of

The Code Is Not Overlapping

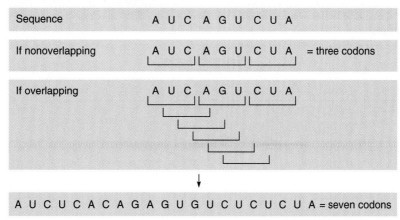

figure 9.18

An overlapping genetic code may seem economical, but it is restrictive, dictating that certain amino acids must follow others in a protein's sequence. This does not happen; therefore, the genetic code is nonoverlapping.

table 9.4

Deciphering RNA Codons and the Amino Acids They Specify

Synthetic RNA	Encoded Amino Acid Chain	Conclusion
U U U U U U U U U U U U U U U U U U	phe-phe-phe-phe-phe-phe	U U U = phe
A A A A A A A A A A A A A A A A A A	lys-lys-lys-lys-lys-lys	A A A = lys
G G G G G G G G G G G G G G G G G G G G G	gly-gly-gly-gly-gly-gly	G G G = gly
C C C C C C C C C C C C C C C C C C C C C C	pro-pro-pro-pro-pro-pro	C C C = pro
A U A U A U A U A U A U A U A U A U	ilu-tyr-ilu-tyr-ilu-tyr-ilu	A U A = ilu or tyr
		U A U = ilu or tyr
U U U A U A U U U A U A U U U A U A	phe-ilu-phe-ilu-phe-ilu	A U A = ilu
		U A U = tyr

Health began the gargantuan task of deciphering which codons specify which amino acids. An elegantly logical series of experiments gave them the answers. The researchers synthesized mRNA molecules in the laboratory and added them to test tubes containing all the chemicals and structures needed for translation, which they had extracted from *E. coli* cells.

The first synthetic mRNA tested had the sequence UUUUUU. . . . In the test tube, this was translated into a polypeptide consisting entirely of the amino acid phenylalanine. Thus, the first entry in the genetic code dictionary was that the codon UUU specifies the amino acid phenylalanine. Interestingly, the number of phenylalanines always equaled one-third the number of mRNA bases, confirming that the genetic code is triplet and nonoverlapping. In the next three experiments, the researchers discovered that AAA codes for the amino acid lysine, GGG for glycine, and CCC for proline.

Next, the researchers synthesized chains of alternating bases. mRNA of the sequence AUAUAU . . . introduced codons AUA and UAU. When translated, this sequence yielded an amino acid sequence of alternating isoleucines and tyrosines. But was AUA the code for isoleucine and UAU for tyrosine, or vice versa? Another experiment was needed.

An mRNA of sequence UUUAUAU-UUAUA proved to encode alternating phenylalanine and isoleucine. Because the scientists knew from the first experiment that UUU codes for phenylalanine, they could now deduce that AUA must code for isoleucine. Going back to the results of the AUAUAU . . . experiment, if AUA codes for isoleucine, then UAU must code for tyrosine. Table 9.4 summarizes some of these experiments.

By the end of the 1960s, researchers had deciphered the entire genetic code (table 9.5). Sixty of the possible 64 codons were found to specify particular amino acids, while the others indicate "stop" or "start." This means that some amino acids are specified by more than one codon. For example, both UUU and UUC encode phenylalanine. Different codons that specify the same amino acid are called **degenerate codons.** They often differ from one another by the base in the third position. The degeneracy of the genetic code provides protection against mutation, because changes in the DNA that cause the substitution of a degenerate codon would not affect the protein's amino acid sequence. We shall return to this point in the next chapter.

table 9.5

The Genetic Code (RNA Triplets)

First Letter	U (Second Letter)		C		A		G		Third Letter
U	UUU, UUC	phenylalanine (phe)	UCU, UCC, UCA, UCG	serine (ser)	UAU, UAC	tyrosine (tyr)	UGU, UGC	cysteine (cys)	U, C
	UUA, UUG	leucine (leu)			UAA	STOP	UGA	STOP	A
					UAG	STOP	UGG	tryptophan (try)	G
C	CUU, CUC, CUA, CUG	leucine (leu)	CCU, CCC, CCA, CCG	proline (pro)	CAU, CAC	histidine (his)	CGU, CGC, CGA, CGG	arginine (arg)	U, C
					CAA, CAG	glutamine (gln)			A, G
A	AUU, AUC, AUA	isoleucine (ilu)	ACU, ACC, ACA, ACG	threonine (thr)	AAU, AAC	asparagine (asn)	AGU, AGC	serine (ser)	U, C
	AUG	methionine (met)			AAA, AAG	lysine (lys)	AGA, AGG	arginine (arg)	A, G
G	GUU, GUC, GUA, GUG	valine (val)	GCU, GCC, GCA, GCG	alanine (ala)	GAU, GAC	aspartic acid (asp)	GGU, GGC, GGA, GGG	glycine (gly)	U, C
					GAA, GAG	glutamic acid (glu)			A, G

Building a Protein

Protein synthesis requires mRNA, tRNA molecules carrying amino acids, ribosomes, energy-storing molecules such as adenosine triphosphate (ATP), and various protein factors. These pieces come together at the beginning of translation, in a stage called **translation initiation.** First, the mRNA leader sequence forms hydrogen bonds with a short sequence of rRNA in a small ribosomal subunit. The first mRNA codon to specify an amino acid is always AUG, which attracts an initiator tRNA that carries the amino acid methionine (abbreviated met) (figure 9.19). Met signifies the start of a polypeptide. The small ribosomal subunit, the mRNA bonded to it, and the initiator tRNA with its attached methionine form the **initiation complex.**

In the next stage, called **translation elongation,** a large ribosomal subunit attaches to the initiation complex. The codon adjacent to the initiating codon (AUG), which is GGA in figure 9.19, then bonds to its complementary anticodon, which is part of a free tRNA that carries the amino acid glycine. The two amino acids (met and glycine in the example), which are still attached to the tRNA molecules that connect them to the mRNA, align. With the help of an enzyme (perhaps a ribozyme), they join, forming a peptide bond. Once the two amino acids bond to each other, the first tRNA is released. It will pick up another amino acid and be used again. The ribosome and its attached mRNA now bind to a single tRNA, with two amino acids extending from it. This is the start of a polypeptide.

Next, the ribosome moves down the mRNA by one codon. A third tRNA enters, carrying its amino acid (cysteine in figure 9.19). This third amino acid aligns with the other two and forms a peptide bond to the second amino acid in the growing chain. The tRNA attached to the second amino acid is released and recycled. The polypeptide builds, one amino acid at a time. Each piece is brought in by a tRNA whose anticodon corresponds to a consecutive mRNA codon.

Elongation halts when one of the mRNA "stop" codons (UGA, UAG, or UAA) is reached, because there are no tRNA molecules that correspond to these codons. The last tRNA is released from the ribosome, the ribosomal subunits separate from each other and are recycled, and the new polypeptide floats away.

Protein Folding

As a protein is synthesized, it folds into a three-dimensional shape (conformation) that helps determine its function. This folding occurs because of attractions and repulsions between the protein's atoms. In addition, thousands of water molecules surround a growing chain of amino acids, and, because some amino acids are attracted to water and some repelled by it, the water contorts the protein's shape. Sulfur atoms also affect overall conformation by bridging the two types of amino acids that contain them.

The conformation of a protein may be described at several levels. The amino acid sequence of a polypeptide chain determines its **primary (1°) structure** (figure 9.20). Chemical attractions between amino acids

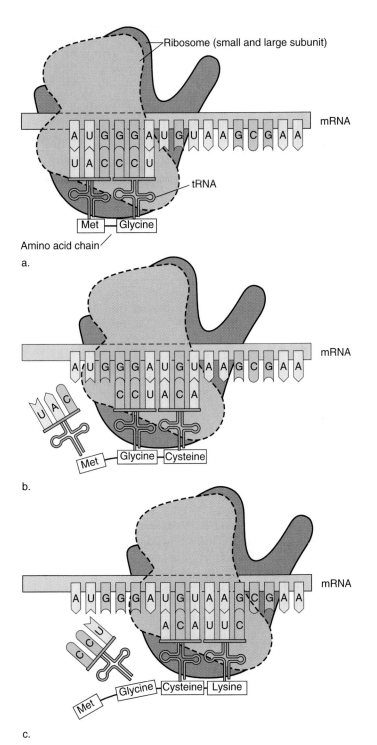

a.

b.

c.

figure 9.19

Translating a polypeptide. (*a*) Translation begins when an mRNA molecule binds to a segment of rRNA that is part of a small ribosomal subunit. The anticodon of a tRNA bearing methionine bonds to the initiation codon (AUG) on the mRNA. These bound structures form the initiation complex. Next, a large ribosomal subunit binds to the complex, and a tRNA bearing a second amino acid (glycine, in this example) bonds between its anticodon and the second mRNA's codon. (*b*) The amino acid brought in by the first tRNA bonds with the amino acid from the second tRNA, and the first tRNA detaches. The ribosome moves down the mRNA by one codon, and a third tRNA arrives, carrying the amino acid cysteine in this example. (*c*) A fourth amino acid is linked to the growing polypeptide chain, and the process continues until a termination codon is reached.

Primary structure

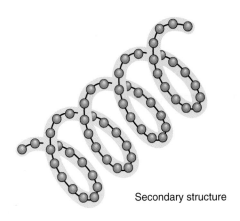

Secondary structure

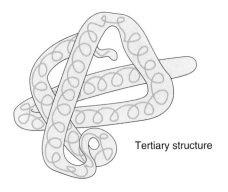

Tertiary structure

Quaternary structure

figure 9.20

Protein conformation. A protein's primary structure is the amino acid sequence of its polypeptide chain. The secondary structure is usually loops, coils, helices, barrels, or sheets created when amino acids close to each other in the primary structure attract. Tertiary structure occurs when amino acids farther apart in the primary structure fold the secondary structures. Finally, a protein consisting of more than one polypeptide chain has a quaternary structure.

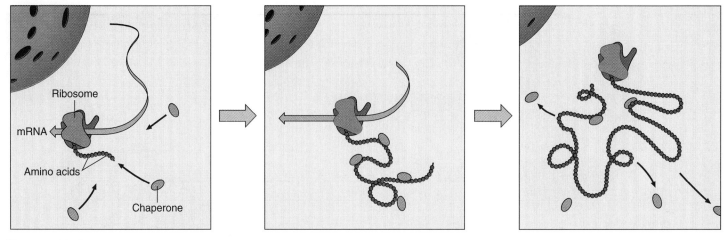

figure 9.21

Protein folding. As this amino acid chain extends from the ribosome on which it is synthesized, chaperone proteins bind the portions that will reside on the molecule's interior, leaving the other regions free to interact. When the final form is assumed, the chaperone proteins depart.

that are close together in the 1° structure fold the polypeptide chain into its **secondary (2°) structure.** Secondary structures wind into larger **tertiary (3°) structures** as amino acids interact with water. Finally, proteins consisting of more than one polypeptide have **quaternary (4°) structure.** For example, hemoglobin, the blood protein that carries oxygen, has four polypeptide chains. The liver protein ferritin has 20 identical polypeptides of 200 amino acids each. In contrast, the muscle protein myoglobin is a single polypeptide chain.

For many years, biochemists thought that protein folding was straightforward, with the amino acid sequence dictating specific attractions and repulsions between parts of a protein and tangling it into its final form as it emerges from the ribosome complex. But the amino acid sequence is not sufficient to ensure that the polypeptide assumes the highly specific form essential to its function. A protein apparently requires help in folding.

An amino acid chain may start to fold as it emerges from the ribosome (figure 9.21). Localized pockets of shape form, and possibly break apart and form again, as translation proceeds. Experiments that isolate proteins as they are synthesized show that other proteins oversee the process. These accessory proteins include enzymes that foster chemical bonds, and **chaperone proteins,** which stabilize partially folded regions that are important to the molecule's final form.

Just as DNA repair enzymes peruse newly replicated DNA for errors, proteins scrutinize a folding protein to detect and dismantle incorrectly folded regions. An incorrectly folded protein can cause illness. In an inherited form of the lung condition emphysema, for example, an enzyme called alpha-1-antitrypsin is misfolded in a way that prevents it from exiting the liver cell where it is synthesized. The enzyme cannot reach the bloodstream, which would normally transport it to the lungs, where it would protect lung connective tissue. Gaps appear in the lung tissue, and the person has difficulty breathing. Chapter 18 discusses gene therapy for alpha-1-antitrypsin deficiency.

In addition to proper folding, certain proteins are modified before becoming functional. Some peptide chains must be shortened by enzymes to become active. The peptide insulin, which is 51 amino acids long, for example, is initially translated as the polypeptide proinsulin, which is 80 amino acids long.

Protein synthesis is economical. A cell can produce large amounts of a particular protein with just one or two copies of a gene. A plasma cell in the immune system, for example, can produce 2,000 identical antibody molecules per second. To mass produce on this scale, RNA, ribosomes, enzymes, and other proteins must be recycled. In addition, many mRNAs can be transcribed from a single gene at once. An mRNA can be translated, in turn, by several ribosomes simultaneously, each at a different point along the message, with polypeptides of different lengths branching from them.

Computers Coax Meaning from Genes

The linguistic nature of molecular genetics makes it an ideal field for computer analysis. The view of DNA sequences as a language emerged in the 1960s, as experiments revealed the linear relationship between nucleic acid sequences in genes and amino acid sequences in proteins. However, researchers' ability to easily translate one language into another awaited two key technological developments. The 1970s brought the power to genetically engineer large numbers of specific DNA sequences (chapter 17). At the same time, computers became accessible, offering the capability of handling long genetic messages with the finesse and flexibility of a word processor.

Determining a gene's sequence was a tedious and cumbersome process in the 1970s, but, in the mid-1980s, automated gene-sequencing devices came on the market. A computer interfaced with a sequencer displays the sequence on a screen and stores gene sequences in databases. Using the rules of the genetic code, computers go from DNA to RNA to protein sequence. Possible protein structures may be depicted, utilizing the protein folding rules just now being worked out; these structures are sometimes called the second genetic code.

Often, the next step after obtaining a gene sequence is to compare it to others stored in databases. A researcher with no idea of what a gene encodes might scan thousands of entries to find a similar sequence that suggests a particular function. Computers are very valuable in comparing the sequences of the same gene in different species, which also provides information on evolutionary relationships. This is especially valuable in mice, which are used as models of human inherited diseases.

Computer programs can also pick up nuances of nucleic acid sequences that suggest functions, such as the distinct conformations of transcription factors. A protein with a series of seven loops formed by certain amino acids hydrogen bonding with each other, for example, indicates a protein that traverses a cell membrane, such as the cystic fibrosis transmembrane regulator (CFTR) protein. A tract of RNA that, if cut out and allowed to base pair with itself, forms a cloverleaf shape, indicates a transfer RNA.

Computers are crucial in molecular genetic research, from single genes analyzed in individual laboratories, to the integration of results from geneticists worldwide participating in large-scale genome projects. No doubt computers will continue to play a critical role in uncovering gene sequences and functions, and in learning about mutations—the subject of the next chapter.

Key Concepts

The genetic code is triplet, nonoverlapping, continuous, universal, and degenerate.

As translation begins, mRNA, tRNA with bound amino acids, ribosomes, energy molecules, and protein factors assemble. The mRNA leader sequence binds to rRNA in the small subunit of a ribosome, and the first codon attracts a tRNA bearing methionine. Next, as the chain elongates, the large ribosomal subunit attaches and the appropriate anticodon parts of tRNAs bind to successive codons in the mRNA. As the amino acids attached to the aligned tRNA molecules form peptide bonds, a polypeptide grows. At a stop codon, protein synthesis ceases. Protein folding begins as translation proceeds, with enzymes and chaperone proteins assisting the amino acid chain in assuming its final functional form. Translation is efficient and economical, as RNA, ribosomes, enzymes, and key proteins are recycled.

summary

1. A gene's information must be transcribed from DNA into ribonucleic acid. RNA is a single-stranded nucleic acid similar to DNA but containing uracil and ribose rather than thymine and deoxyribose.

2. **Transcription factors** regulate which genes or subsets of genes are transcribed in a particular cell type. These factors have certain common regions called **motifs.**

3. Transcription begins when transcription factors help **RNA polymerase** (RNAP) bind to a gene's starting region, or **promoter.** RNAP then adds RNA nucleotides to a growing chain, in a sequence complementary to the DNA **coding strand.**

4. Several types of RNA participate in protein synthesis (**translation**). **Messenger RNA** (mRNA) carries a protein-encoding gene's information. **Ribosomal RNA** (rRNA) associates with certain proteins to form ribosomes, which physically support protein synthesis. **Transfer RNA** (tRNA) is cloverleaf shaped, with a 3-base sequence

complementary to mRNA on one end. It bonds to a particular amino acid at the other end.

5. Each three consecutive mRNA bases form a **codon** that specifies a particular amino acid. The **genetic code** is the correspondence between each codon and the amino acid it specifies. Of the 64 different possible codons, 61 specify amino acids and 3 signal stop. Because 61 codons specify the 20 amino acids, more than one type of codon may encode a single amino acid type. The genetic code is nonoverlapping, triplet, and universal.

6. Translation requires tRNA, **ribosomes,** energy-storage molecules, enzymes, and protein factors. An **initiation complex** forms when mRNA, a small ribosomal subunit, and a tRNA carrying methionine join. The amino acid chain begins to elongate when a large ribosomal subunit joins the small one. Next, a second tRNA binds by its **anticodon** to the next mRNA codon, and its amino acid bonds with the

first amino acid. Transfer RNAs add amino acids, forming a polypeptide. The ribosome moves down the mRNA as the chain grows. When the ribosome reaches a "stop" codon, it falls apart into its two subunits and is released. The new polypeptide breaks free. After translation, some polypeptides are cleaved, and some aggregate to form larger proteins. The cell uses or secretes the protein, which must have a particular **conformation** to be active.

7. A protein's structure determines its function. Its **primary structure** is its amino acid sequence. The **secondary structure** forms as amino acids close in the primary structure attract. **Tertiary structure** occurs as more widely separated amino acids draw together as they are attracted to or repelled by water molecules. **Quaternary structure** forms when a protein consists of more than one polypeptide. **Chaperone proteins** help mold conformation.

review questions

1. Explain how complementary base pairing is responsible for
   a. the structure of the DNA double helix.
   b. DNA replication.
   c. transcription of RNA from DNA.
   d. the attachment of mRNA to a ribosome.
   e. codon/anticodon pairing.
   f. tRNA conformation.

2. Cite two ways in which the central dogma of molecular biology is an oversimplification.

3. Many antibiotic drugs work by interfering with protein synthesis in the bacteria that cause infections. Explain how each of the following antibiotic mechanisms disrupts genetic function in bacteria.
   a. Transfer RNAs misread mRNA codons, binding with the incorrect codon and bringing in the wrong amino acid.
   b. The first amino acid is released from the initiation complex before translation can begin.
   c. Transfer RNA cannot bind to the ribosome.
   d. Ribosomes cannot move.
   e. A tRNA picks up the wrong amino acid.

4. Define and distinguish between transcription and translation.

5. List the differences between RNA and DNA.

6. Where do DNA replication, transcription, and translation occur?

7. How does transcription control cell specialization?

8. How is the function of a retrovirus "backwards" when compared to gene expression in a human?

9. Describe the events of transcription initiation.

10. List the three major types of RNA and their functions.

11. State three ways RNA is altered after it is transcribed.

12. What are the components of a ribosome?

13. Why was the discovery of introns a surprise? of ribozymes?

14. Why would an overlapping genetic code be restrictive?

15. How are the processes of transcription and translation economical?

16. How does the shortening of proinsulin to insulin differ from the shortening of apolipoprotein B?

17. What factors determine how a protein folds into its characteristic conformation?

18. Cite two ways that proteins assist in their own synthesis. How does RNA assist in its own synthesis?

19. Why would two-nucleotide codons be insufficient to encode the number of amino acids in biological proteins?

applied questions

1. List the sequences of the RNA sense strands that would be transcribed from the following DNA coding sequences.
   a. TTACACTTGCTTGAGAGTC
   b. ACTTGGGCTATGCTCATTA
   c. GGCTGCAATAGCCGTAGAT
   d. GGAATACGTCTAGCTAGCA

2. Given the following partial mRNA sequences, reconstruct the corresponding DNA coding sequences.
   a. GCUAUCUGUCAUAAAAGAGGA
   b. GUGGCGUAUUCUUUUCCGGGUAGG
   c. GAGGGAAUUCUUUCUCAACGAAGU
   d. AGGAAAACCCCUCUUAUUAUAGAU

3. State the sequence of an antisense RNA that might be used to fight a virus that has a partial DNA sequence of TTCGCTAAAGACTGT.

4. List three different mRNA sequences that could encode the following amino acid sequence:

   histidine-alanine-arginine-serine-leucine-valine-cysteine

5. Write a DNA sequence that would encode the following amino acid sequence:

   valine-tryptophan-lysine-proline-phenylalanine-threonine

6. In the film *Jurassic Park,* which is about genetically engineered dinosaurs, a cartoon character named Mr. DNA talks about the billions of genetic codes in the DNA. Why is this statement incorrect?

7. When Crick and his coworkers examined synthetic RNA of sequence ACACACACACACACA, they found that it encoded the amino acid sequence thr-his-thr-his-thr-his. How did the researchers determine the codon assignments for ACA and CAC?

8. How might a defect in protein folding cause the cystic fibrosis phenotype at the cellular level?

9. Describe the part of Francis Crick's experiment that confirmed the triplet nature of the genetic code (figure 9.17).

suggested readings

Askari, Frederick, and W. Michael McDonnell. February 1, 1996. Antisense-oligonucleotide therapy. *The New England Journal of Medicine,* vol. 334. Antisense RNAs may make powerful drugs.

Benson, Dennis A. et al. January 1996. GenBank. *Nucleic Acids Research,* vol. 24. Determining protein structures is as much an informational science as it is a life science.

Blalock, J. Edwin. September 1995. Genetic origins of protein shape and interaction rules. *Nature Medicine,* vol. 1. The genetic code holds clues to protein folding, but they are neither simple nor obvious.

Boguski, Mark S. September 7, 1995. Hunting for genes in computer data bases. *The New England Journal of Medicine,* vol. 333. New gene sequences are stored at GenBank, at the National Institutes of Health.

Cleaver, James E., and Michael L. Hultner. June 1995. Transcription-related human disorders. *The American Journal of Human Genetics.* DNA repair disorders can impair RNA synthesis.

Femino, A. F. et al. April 24, 1998. Visualization of single RNA transcripts in situ. *Science,* vol. 280. Using digital imaging and fluoresence microscopy, researchers can view transcription in action.

Gilbert, Walter. February 9, 1978. Why genes in pieces? *Nature,* vol. 271. A classic and insightful look at the enigma of introns.

Lewis, Ricki. February 1996. On cracked codes, cell walls and human fungi. *The American Biology Teacher.* A funny look at errors in genetic code usage.

Lewis, Ricki. July 22, 1996. Software helps researchers in sorting through the human genome. *The Scientist.* Because molecular genetics is informational, computer analysis is a valuable tool.

Lewis, Ricki. March 31, 1997. Scientists debate RNA's role at beginning of life on earth. *The Scientist.* RNA may have been the pivotal chemical at the transition between the nonliving and the living.

Rose, George D. January/February 1996. No assembly required. *The Sciences.* A protein must fold properly to function.

Scott, James. June 16, 1995. A place in the world for RNA editing. *Cell,* vol. 81. RNA editing can make a protein multifunctional.

Shreeve, James. May 1998. The code breaker. *Discover.* Despite misuse of the term "genetic code," this article provides an insightful look at a geneticist who heads an organization that routinely sequences entire genomes.

Sifers, Richard N. May 1995. Defective protein folding as a cause of disease. *Nature Structural Biology,* vol. 2. Secreted proteins most fold properly in order to exit the cell.

Surridge, Christopher. March 28, 1996. The core curriculum. *Nature,* vol. 380. How transcription factors regulate gene expression.

Taubes, Gary. March 15, 1996. Misfolding the way to disease. *Science,* vol. 271. Alzheimer disease may be caused by a misfolded protein.

Tjian, Robert. February 1995. Molecular machines that control genes. *Scientific American.* A complex of sequentially laid down transcription factors begins gene expression.

chapter ten

Gene Mutation

Discovering Mutations That Cause Alzheimer Disease

There are many ways to alter a gene—add, delete, or change a DNA base. Mutations can have varied effects. A mutation can completely halt production of a protein, lower the amount of a protein synthesized, impair the protein's function, introduce a new function—or do nothing at all. Table 10.1 summarizes these effects. Medical geneticists try to identify precisely how a specific mutation alters the phenotype in a way that adversely affects health. New diagnostic tests—and, ultimately, treatments—often begin with studies of mutations. The search for a genetic explanation for a severe form of Alzheimer disease illustrates how discovering mutations can solve biological mysteries.

In the 1880s, a woman named Hannah, born in Latvia, developed Alzheimer disease, the progressive dementia described in chapter 3. Hannah's condition was highly unusual in that she was only in her early forties when the classic forgetfulness that heralds the disease's onset began. Apparently an autosomal dominant form of the illness originated in Hannah. Many of her descendants experienced dementia—some as early as in their thirties.

In 1974, Hannah's grandson and great-grandson, both physicians, constructed an extensive pedigree tracing Alzheimer disease in their family. They circulated the pedigree among geneticists, hoping to elicit interest in identifying the family's mutation. They made available their own and relatives' cells for DNA testing. Research teams in Mexico, the United States, and Canada accepted the challenge, and the search began in earnest in 1983. By 1992, they narrowed the investigation to a portion of chromosome 14, and three years later, they pinpointed the gene that encodes a protein called presenilin 1.

The type of Alzheimer disease in Hannah's family is called AD3 because it was the third variant to be linked to a specific chromosome. Genes on chromosomes 1, 19, and 21 cause other forms of Alzheimer disease. Presenilin 1 is a receptor anchored in the membrane of a Golgi body or a vesicle (figure 10.1). Normally, the protein monitors the cell's storage or use of beta-amyloid, the sticky substance that accumulates in the brains of people with Alzheimer disease. The other forms of Alzheimer disease affect production or storage of beta-amyloid in different ways.

The relationship between beta-amyloid and Alzheimer disease is very similar to that between cholesterol and heart disease. Everyone has beta-amyloid in the brain and elsewhere, but in Alzheimer disease, the sticky protein aggregates into characteristic plaques between brain cells. Similarly, everyone has cholesterol streaks on their artery walls, but it is the abnormal accumulation of the fatty substance that impedes blood flow and causes symptoms. Just as elevated cholesterol in the blood can predict heart disease, people in families that have early-onset Alzheimer disease have elevated levels of presenilin 1 in their bloodstreams before symptoms begin.

So far, researchers have identified more than 30 mutations that substitute one amino acid for another in the gene for presenilin 1. This is a big first step in conquering the illness. Rather than trying existing drugs to alleviate the symptoms of Alzheimer disease, researchers can now focus efforts on correcting particular gene and protein abnormalities. Researchers are also seeking genetic clues to Alzheimer disease by studying populations that rarely develop the disorder. These groups include Cherokee Indians, the Japanese, Nigerians, the Cree Indians in Canada, and the Amish in Indiana.

table 10.1
Effects of Mutations

Effect	Example
Prevents a protein from forming	Lack of dystrophin causes muscle cells to collapse in Duchenne muscular dystrophy
Lowers amount of a protein	Blood clots very slowly due to too little clotting factor in hemophilia A
Alters a protein	Skin blisters because amino acid substitution alters protein filaments that hold skin layers together, in epidermolysis bullosa
Adds a function to a protein	Addition of bases to the Huntington disease gene adds a stretch of amino acids to the protein product that gives it a new function that somehow leads to brain degeneration

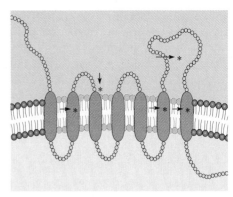

figure 10.1

Homing in on a cause of Alzheimer disease. When geneticists searched the DNA of people with very early-onset inherited Alzheimer disease, they identified a gene on chromosome 14 whose protein product, shown here, fits the well-known pattern of a receptor anchored into a membrane at seven points. This protein resides in vesicles derived from Golgi bodies. When abnormal, it somehow enables amyloid proteins to accumulate outside cells. Amyloid deposits are characteristic of the brains of people who have died of Alzheimer disease. Asterisks indicate sites where mutations in the gene disrupt the protein in a way that causes symptoms.

Of Mutants and Mutations

A mutation is a physical change in the genetic material. This can be a single DNA base substituting for another; one or more DNA bases added to or deleted from a gene; chromosomes that exchange parts; even stretches of bases that move among the chromosomes. A mutation can occur in the part of a gene that encodes a protein, in a sequence controlling transcription, in an intron, or at a site critical to intron removal and exon splicing. The story of fragile X syndrome (Reading 10.1) illustrates how a mutation can have effects at the gene and chromosome level.

The term *mutation* refers to genotype—that is, a change at the DNA level. The familiar term *mutant* refers to an unusual phenotype or expression of a gene. Recall that the unchanged, or "normal," phenotype or allele for a particular gene is the wild type. Whether a mutation causes a mutant phenotype depends upon precisely how the alteration affects the gene's product or activity. Not all mutations are detectable in the organism's appearance or function. Sometimes a biochemical test can detect a mutant phenotype that isn't obvious from the outside. A mutant phenotype usually connotes a clearly abnormal or unusual characteristic. However, it may also mean an unusual variant in a particular population, such as a red-haired child in a class of brunettes and blondes (figure 10.2).

figure 10.2

This child's red curls make her the proud possessor of an unusual genetic variant.

A mutation can occur spontaneously or be induced by exposure to a chemical or radiation. An agent that causes mutation is called a **mutagen.**

A Long-Known Mutation— Sickle Cell Disease

The first genetic illness to be understood at the molecular level was sickle cell disease. We knew in the 1940s that an inherited anemia (weakness and fatigue caused by too few red blood cells) was associated with sickle-shaped red blood cells (figure 10.3). In 1949, Linus Pauling and co-workers discovered that hemoglobin (the oxygen-carrying molecule in red blood cells) from healthy people and from people with the anemia, when placed in a solution in an electrically charged field (a technique called electrophoresis), moved to different positions. Hemoglobin from parents of people with the anemia, who were carriers, showed both movement patterns.

Glutamic acid   Valine
CTC DNA   CAC DNA
GAG RNA $\longrightarrow$ GUG RNA

a.

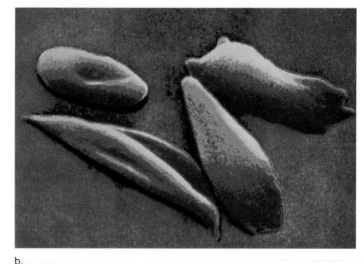

b.

figure 10.3

The first mutation studied causes sickle cell disease. (*a*) A normal red blood cell is a concave disc containing about 200 million molecules of the protein hemoglobin. (*b*) A mutation in the beta globin gene results in abnormal hemoglobin that crystallizes when oxygen tension is low and bends the red blood cells into sickle shapes. These abnormally shaped cells obstruct circulation, causing pain and the loss of function in various organs. A single DNA nucleotide substitution on both homologs causes sickle cell disease.

Fragile X Syndrome—The First of the Triplet Repeat Disorders   reading 10.1

In the 1940s, geneticists noticed that more males than females are mentally retarded, and they hypothesized that a gene on the X chromosome confers the condition. It wasn't until 1969, though, that a clue emerged to the genetic basis of sex-linked mental retardation in a family with two retarded brothers. The brothers and their mother had a most unusual X chromosome. One tip dangled, separated from the rest by a thin thread (figure 1). When grown under culture conditions lacking folic acid, this part of the X chromosome was very prone to breaking—hence, the name fragile X syndrome.

Fragile X syndrome is second only to Down syndrome in genetic or chromosomal causes of mental retardation. It affects 1 in 1,000 individuals.

Youngsters with fragile X syndrome do not appear atypical, but by young adulthood, certain similarities become apparent. The fragile X patient has a very long, narrow face (figure 2)—easily distinguished from the rounder face of the Down syndrome patient (figure 11.1). The ears protrude, the jaw is long, and the testicles are very large. Mental impairment varies a great deal; it may include mental retardation, learning disabilities, poor speech, hyperactivity, shyness, social anxiety, and a short attention span.

An Unusual Mode of Inheritance

Fragile X syndrome is inherited in an unusual pattern. Because the fragile chromosome is the X, the associated syndrome should be transmitted as any sex-linked trait is, from carrier mother to affected son. However, penetrance seemed to be quite low. One-fifth of males known by family history to have inherited the condition (having an affected parent or grandparent and an affected child or grandchild) have no signs or symptoms and have a normal-appearing X chromosome. A common inheritance pattern for fragile X is a symptomless "male carrier" with a severely affected grandchild. Of females bearing one fragile X chromosome, 35 percent are mentally retarded, and 15 percent have milder mental impairment. However, mental problems are more common in a female if she inherits the fragile X from her mother, another example of genomic imprinting (chapter 5).

Researchers in the 1980s were on the right track when they proposed two states of the X chromosome region responsible for fragile X signs and symptoms—a premutation form that does not cause symptoms but transmits the condition, and a full mutation form that causes mental impairment. Still, it took a molecular-level look to begin to unravel the bewildering genetics of fragile X syndrome.

A Molecular View

In 1991, several research teams plunged into the DNA of the fragile X region and found something new in our knowledge of how DNA can mutate. In unaffected individuals, the fragile X area contains a stretch of DNA consisting of 6 to 49 repeats of the sequence CGG. In people who have the fragile chromosome and show its effects, this region is greatly expanded, harboring 230 to more than 1,000 CGG repeats. Symptomless individuals who can

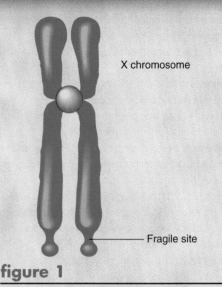

X chromosome

Fragile site

figure 1

When cells from an individual with fragile X syndrome are grown in a medium that lacks thymidine and folic acid, a constriction appears in the X chromosome.

be inferred to have inherited the fragile X chromosome (because the condition affects later generations) have a premutation, which corresponds to an intermediate number (50 to 200) of CGG repeats.

Fragile X syndrome was the first human disorder to be associated with an increase in number of a three-base nucleotide sequence, or triplet. (Other "triplet repeat" disorders are discussed at the end of the chapter.) The discovery of this new type of mutation explains "anticipation," which is the worsening of a phenotype in subsequent generations within a family. The gene actually expands, and, the larger it is, the greater the effect on the phenotype.

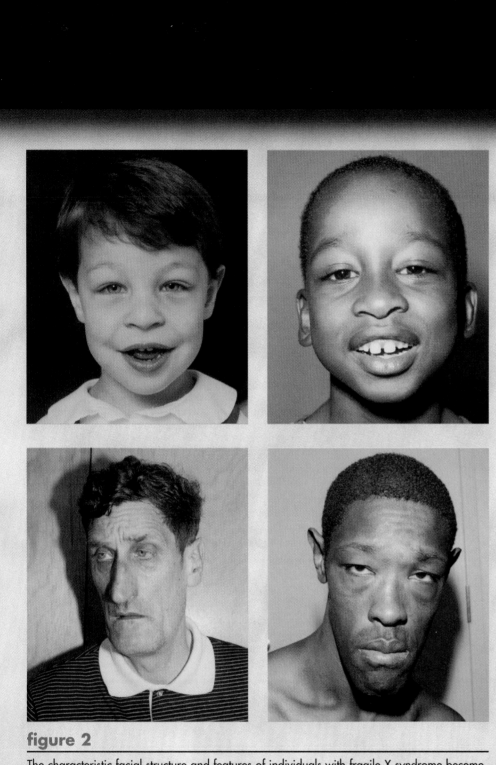

figure 2

The characteristic facial structure and features of individuals with fragile X syndrome become more pronounced with age.

The researchers suspected that a physical difference accounted for the different electrophoretic mobilities of normal versus sickled hemoglobin. But how could they identify the protein portion of hemoglobin affected in sickle cell disease? Hemoglobin is a very large molecule. It consists of four globular-shaped polypeptide chains, each surrounding an iron atom (figure 10.4). Two of the chains are called beta chains, and two alpha chains. Eventually researchers learned that an abnormality in the beta globin polypeptide causes sickle cell disease.

Protein chemist V. M. Ingram cut normal and sickle hemoglobin with a protein-digesting enzyme, separated the resulting pieces, stained them, and displayed them on paper. The patterns of fragments—known as peptide fingerprints—were different. This meant, Ingram deduced, that the two molecules must differ in amino acid sequence. One piece of the molecule in the fingerprint, fragment four, occupied a different position in each of the two types of hemoglobin. Since this peptide was only 8 amino acids long, Ingram needed to decipher only that short sequence—rather than the 146 amino acids of a full beta globin sequence—to find the site of the mutation.

Using newly invented protein sequencing techniques, Ingram identified the tiny mutation responsible for sickle cell disease. It was a substitution of the amino acid valine for the glutamic acid that normally is the sixth amino acid in the beta globin polypeptide chain. At the DNA level, the change was even smaller—a CTC to a CAC, corresponding to RNA codons GAG and GUG. Eventually, scientists found that this mutation causes hemoglobin to crystallize in low-oxygen conditions, bending red blood cells into sickle shapes that cause anemia, joint pain, and organ damage. Table 10.2 offers other examples of how mutations impair health.

figure 10.4

More than three hundred different mutations of the human beta globin gene are known. Mutations can disrupt the binding of the globin chains to each other or to the iron groups; change a stop codon to one specifying an amino acid, elongating the beta globin chain; or change an amino acid-specifying codon into a stop codon, shortening the beta chain. Many beta chain mutations are silent because they change a codon into one specifying the same or a similar amino acid, or they occur in a part of the chain not essential to its function.

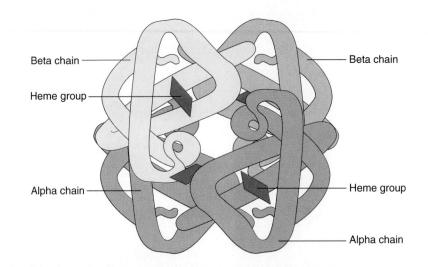

table 10.2

Genotype Explains Phenotype

Disease	Signs and Symptoms (Phenotype)	Protein	Genetic Defect (Genotype)
Cystic fibrosis	Frequent lung infection, pancreatic insufficiency	Cystic fibrosis transmembrane regulator (CFTR)	Missing single amino acid or other defect alters conformation of Cl^- channels in certain epithelial cell membranes. Water enters cells, drying out secretions.
Duchenne muscular dystrophy	Gradual loss of muscle function	Dystrophin	Deletion in dystrophin gene eliminates this protein, which normally binds to inner face of muscle cell membranes, maintaining cellular integrity. Cells and muscles collapse.
Epidermolysis bullosa	Skin blisters very easily	Keratin	Amino acid substitution leads to disturbed network of intermediate filaments in cells of lower epidermis.
Familial hypercholesterolemia	High blood cholesterol, early heart disease	LDL receptor	Deficient LDL receptors cause cholesterol to accumulate in blood.
Hemophilia A	Slow or absent blood clotting	Factor VIII	Absent or deficient clotting factor causes hard-to-control bleeding.
Marfan syndrome	Long limbs, weakened aorta, spindly fingers, sunken chest, lens dislocation	Fibrillin	Too little elastic connective tissue protein depletes it in lens and aorta.
Neurofibromatosis I	Benign tumors of nervous tissue beneath skin	Neurofibromin	Defect in protein that normally suppresses activity of a gene that causes tumor formation.

Key Concepts

Mutations add, delete, or rearrange genetic material. Learning exactly how a mutation alters a protein can help explain how disease arises. In one form of Alzheimer disease, a mutation in a receptor protein may lead to beta-amyloid buildup. In sickle cell disease, a mutation causes hemoglobin to crystallize in a low-oxygen environment, bending red blood cells into sickle shapes and impairing circulation.

Spontaneous Mutation

Two healthy people of normal height have a child of extremely short stature. The parents are surprised to learn that their child's achondroplasia (a form of dwarfism) is caused by an autosomal dominant mutation; therefore, each of the son's children will face a 50 percent chance of inheriting the condition. How could this happen when there are no other affected family members?

The boy with achondroplasia arose from a *de novo*, or new, mutation in either his mother's egg cell or father's sperm cell. Such a **spontaneous mutation** usually originates as an error in DNA replication. One cause of spontaneous mutation stems from the chemical tendency of free nitrogenous bases to exist in two slightly different forms called **tautomers**. For a short time, each base is in an unstable tautomeric form. If, by chance, such an unstable base is inserted into newly forming

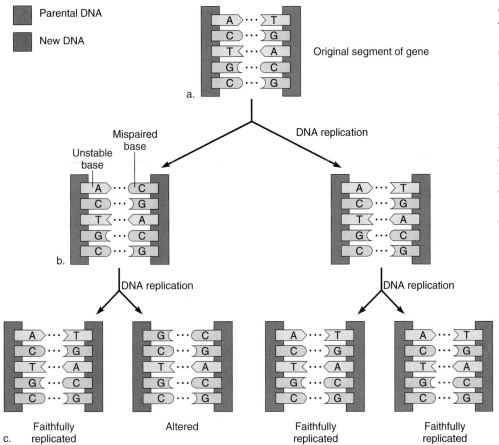

Parental DNA

New DNA

a. Original segment of gene

DNA replication

b.

Unstable base

Mispaired base

DNA replication

DNA replication

c. Faithfully replicated

Altered

Faithfully replicated

Faithfully replicated

figure 10.5

Spontaneous mutation. (*a*) In DNA, A nearly always pairs with T, and C with G. However, DNA bases are very slightly unstable chemically, and for brief moments they exist in altered forms. (*b*) If a replication fork encounters a tautomer (a base in its unstable form), a mismatched base pair can result. (*c*) After another round of replication, one of the daughter cells has a different base pair than the one in the corresponding position in the original DNA segment. This substituted base pair can alter the structure of a gene. If it affects the gene's function, the individual's phenotype may change.

DNA, an error will be generated and perpetuated (figure 10.5).

Spontaneous Mutation Rate

The spontaneous mutation rate varies for different genes. The dominant gene that causes neurofibromatosis type I, for example, has one of the highest mutation rates known, arising in 40 to 100 of every million gametes (table 10.3). The large size of this gene may contribute to its high mutability— there are more ways for its sequence to change, just as there are more opportunities for a misspelling to occur in a long sentence than in a short one. Based on the prevalence of certain disease-causing genes, geneticists estimate that each human gene has about a 1 in 100,000 chance of mutating. Each of us probably carries a few new spontaneously mutated genes. Mitochondrial genes mutate at a high rate because they lack DNA repair mechanisms.

Estimates of the spontaneous mutation rate usually derive from observations

table 10.3

Mutation Rates of Genes that Cause Inherited Disease

	Mutations per Million Gametes	Signs and Symptoms
Sex-linked		
Duchenne muscular dystrophy	40–105	Muscle atrophy
Hemophilia A	30–60	Severe impairment of blood clotting
Hemophilia B	0.5–10	Mild impairment of blood clotting
Autosomal dominant		
Achondroplasia	10	Dwarfism
Aniridia	2.6	Absence of iris
Huntington disease	<1	Uncontrollable movements, personality changes
Marfan syndrome	4–6	Long limbs, weakened blood vessels
Neurofibromatosis I	40–100	Brown skin spots, benign tumors under skin
Osteogenesis imperfecta	10	Easily broken bones
Polycystic kidney disease	60–120	Benign growths in kidneys
Retinoblastoma	5–12	Malignant tumor of retina

figure 10.6

DNA symmetry may increase the likelihood of mutation. These examples show repetitive DNA sequences that may "confuse" replication enzymes, causing errors.

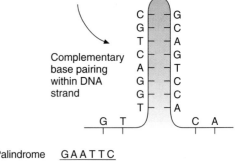

Repeat of a nucleotide   A A A A A A A A   Inverted repeat   G T T G G A C T G C G C A G T C C A C A

Direct repeat of a dinucleotide   G C G C G C G C

Direct repeat of a trinucleotide   T A C T A C T A C

Complementary base pairing within DNA strand

Palindrome   G A A T T C
                C T T A A G

of new (*de novo*), dominant conditions. This is possible because a new dominant mutation is detectable simply by observing the phenotype. In contrast, a new recessive mutation would not be obvious until two heterozygotes produced a homozygous recessive individual with a noticeable phenotype.

We estimate the spontaneous mutation rate using the formula: number of *de novo* cases/2X, where X is the number of individuals examined. The denominator has a factor of 2 to account for the nonmutated homologous chromosome.

Even though recessive mutations are harder to detect because dominant alleles on homologous chromosomes mask their presence, technology can reveal them. Knowing the sequence of a mutated gene enables geneticists to detect *de novo* recessive mutations that have no observable effect on phenotype, as well as to identify the parent in whose gamete a spontaneous mutation originated.

Spontaneous mutation rates in humans are difficult to assess because our generation time is long—usually 20 to 30 years! In bacteria, a new generation arises every half hour or so, and genetic change is therefore much more rapid. This ability to rapidly mutate can be harmful to human health when disease-causing bacteria mutate and become resistant to the antibiotic drugs we use to destroy them. Chapter 13 addresses this pressing health concern from an evolutionary viewpoint.

The genetic material of viruses also spontaneously mutates rapidly. This is why an influenza vaccine manufactured to fight one year's predominant strain may be ineffective by the next flu season. Genetic changes can alter the virus surface

to such an extent that the vaccine no longer recognizes the virus.

One example of rapid viral mutation occurs in HIV, a fact that has stymied efforts to create a vaccine. Mutations are also responsible for HIV's ability to quickly resist the drugs we develop to fight it. For example, four distinct mutations in the gene that encodes reverse transcriptase, the enzyme that the virus uses to convert its RNA to DNA, enable HIV to resist the drug AZT. These mutations lead to drug resistance by encoding versions of the enzyme the drug cannot affect. Interestingly, a fifth mutation renders the virus resistant to another drug, 3TC, but this mutation removes the resistance to AZT! In practical terms, this means that giving an AIDS patient both drugs is more successful than administering either drug alone.

Mutational Hot Spots

Mutations may occur anywhere in a gene, but in some genes they are more likely to occur in certain regions called hot spots, such as in the tail at the right end of the presenilin protein in figure 10.1. Sequences that are mutational hot spots are often not random. For example, many hot spots occur where the DNA sequence is repetitive. It is as if the molecules that guide and carry out replication become "confused" by short repeated sequences, as an editor scanning a manuscript might miss the spelling errors in the words "happpiness" and "bananana" (figure 10.6).

The increased incidence of mutations in repeated DNA sequences has a physical basis. Within a gene, when DNA strands locally unwind to permit replication, symmetrical or repeated sequences allow

base pairing to occur within the same strand. This action interferes with replication and repair enzymes, increasing the chance of an error. (Recall that this is the basis of mismatch repair, discussed in chapter 8.) Mutations in the gene for clotting factor IX, which causes hemophilia B, for example, occur 10 to 100 times as often at any of 11 sites in the gene that have extensive direct repeats of the dinucleotide CG. Inverted repeats can cause base pairing within the same DNA strand, which can disrupt replication and lead to mutation.

Small additions and deletions of DNA are more likely to occur near sequences called **palindromes.** These sequences read the same, in a 5' to 3' direction, on complementary strands. Put another way, the sequence on one strand is the reverse of the sequence on the complementary strand. Palindromes probably increase the spontaneous mutation rate by disturbing replication.

The blood disorder alpha thalassemia illustrates the confusing effect of direct repeats of an entire gene. A normal person has four genes that specify alpha globin chains, two next to each other on each chromosome 16. Homologs with repeated genes can misalign during meiosis, the first sequence on one chromosome lying opposite the second sequence on the homolog. If crossing over occurs, a sperm or oocyte can form that has zero, one, three, or four alpha globin genes instead of the normal two (figure 10.7). Fertilization then results in a zygote with an abnormal number of these genes.

If a sperm with two alpha globin genes fertilizes an oocyte with one, the zygote has only three alpha globin genes. A person

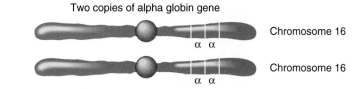

Two copies of alpha globin gene

Chromosome 16

α α

Chromosome 16

α α

Normal chromosome arrangement of alpha globin genes

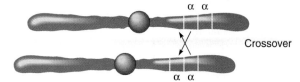

α α

Crossover

α α

Misalignment of alpha globin genes during meiosis I

α α α

Chromosome resulting from crossover with three alpha globin genes

α

Chromosome resulting from crossover with one alpha globin gene

figure 10.7

The repetitive nature of alpha globin genes makes them prone to mutation by mispairing during meiosis.

with at least three such genes produces enough hemoglobin to be healthy, but someone with only two copies of the gene is mildly anemic and tires easily. A person with a single alpha globin gene is severely anemic, and a fetus lacking alpha globin genes does not survive.

Key Concepts

Genes have different mutation rates. Spontaneous mutations result when unusual tautomers of bases are opposite noncomplementary bases during DNA replication. Spontaneous mutations occur more frequently in microorganisms and viruses because they reproduce often. Mutations are more likely to happen when the nearby DNA is repetitive or symmetrical.

Induced Mutations

Researchers can sometimes infer a gene's normal function by observing what happens when mutation alters it. But the spontaneous mutation rate is far too low to be a practical source of genetic variants for experiments.

Mutagens

To obtain mutants for study, geneticists often use chemicals or radiation that induce mutation. Chemicals called alkylating agents, for example, remove a DNA base, which is replaced with any of the four bases—three of which will be a mismatch against the template strand. Dyes called acridines can either add or remove a single DNA base. Because the genetic code is read three bases in a row, adding or deleting a single base can destroy a gene's information, altering the amino acid sequence of the encoded protein. Several other mutagenic chemicals alter base pairs, so that an A-T replaces a G-C, or vice versa, changing a gene's sequence. X rays and other forms of radiation delete just a few bases or break chromosomes.

Researchers have developed several in vitro (in the test tube) protocols for testing the mutagenicity of a substance. The most famous of these, the Ames test, developed by Bruce Ames of the University of California, assesses how likely a substance is to harm the DNA of rapidly reproducing bacteria. One version of the test uses a strain of *Salmonella* that cannot grow when the amino acid histidine is absent from its media. If exposure to a substance enables the bacteria to grow on the deficient media, then it has undergone a mutation that allows it to do so. Another variation of the Ames test incorporates mammalian liver tissue into the media to make the results more applicable to the response of a multicellular organism. Because many mutagens are also carcinogens (cancer-causing agents), scientists often study the substances the Ames test identifies as mutagens to see if they cause cancer. Common mutagens include caffeine; hair dye components; certain food additives and pesticides; chemicals in cigarette smoke; and aflatoxin, a fungus that grows on peanuts.

Accidental Exposures to Mutagens

Researchers use mutagens intentionally in experimental organisms. Unintentional mutagen exposure comes from accidents and weapons that emit radiation, as well as from natural sources such as cosmic rays and radioactive isotopes in rocks.

An example of an environmental disaster that released mutagenic radiation was a nuclear reactor explosion in the former Soviet Union on April 25, 1986. Between 1:23 and 1:24 A.M., Reactor 4 at the Chernobyl Nuclear Power Station in Ukraine exploded, sending a great plume of radioactive isotopes into the air that spread for thousands of miles. The reactor had been undergoing a test, its safety systems temporarily disabled, when it became overloaded and rapidly raged out of control (figure 10.8). Thirty-one people died instantly, and several hundred others died in the following weeks of acute radiation sickness.

Rates of thyroid cancer among children living in nearby Belarus have risen tenfold. This effect was not surprising, because the thyroid glands of young people soak up iodine, which in a radioactive form bathed the area in the first days after the explosion. What was unexpected was the great effect of the disaster on the mutation rate.

figure 10.8

Protective gear shields investigators in the destroyed nuclear reactor at Chernobyl. Ten years after the disaster, mutation rate increases were already evident in nearby rodent and human populations.

The first studies assessing genetic effects focused on voles (a type of rodent) and humans. In voles living right next to the reactor, researchers examined the amino acid sequence of cytochrome b, a protein encoded by a mitochondrial gene. The sequence of cytochrome b is usually the same among individuals, but it differed in every Chernobyl vole studied! This is not the case for voles living elsewhere. The mutation rate calculated for this mitochondrial gene is two base changes for every 10,000 bases—100 times the normal rate for mitochondrial genes.

To study humans, researchers compared lengths of minisatellite sequences in children born in 1994 and their parents, who lived in the Mogilev district of Belarus at the time of the accident and have remained there. Minisatellites are highly repeated DNA sequences that are the same length within an individual. A minisatellite size in a child that does not match the size of either parent indicates that a mutation occurred in a parent's gamete. This was twice as likely to occur in exposed families than in control families living elsewhere. Like mitochondrial genes, minisatellite sequences mutate faster than genes in the nucleus and therefore enable researchers to chart genetic change.

More time has elapsed since the atomic bombing of Hiroshima and Nagasaki at the end of the second world war on August 6 and 9, 1945. Although it was estimated that the radiation would cause enough mutations to double the spontaneous mutation rate, childhood cancer incidence has not borne this out. (Cancer rate is an estimate of mutation rate because certain common childhood cancers result from inheriting one mutation and then undergoing a second mutation in the affected tissues. Therefore, if the mutation rate increases, the incidence of these cancers would be expected to rise.) In fact, 31,150 children of parents directly exposed to the bombs had fewer cancers than 41,066 other Japanese children whose parents were not exposed.

The atomic bombs did cause genetic damage, however. In the general exposed population, leukemia rates increased ten years after the detonations, and lung cancer rates increased twenty years later, indicating definite short-term (less than a generation) effects. Mutations in somatic cells can cause these cancers. Researchers studying blood cell characteristics among bomb survivors found an increase in the mutation rate of some genes. It will take many more generations before we see the effects of recessive mutations the blasts in-

duced. As individuals with the same mutations have children together, the recessive alleles will be expressed in the phenotypes of homozygotes.

Engineered Mutation

Until the polymerase chain reaction (PCR) and DNA sequencing became basic tools of molecular biology, using mutants to understand gene function was unpredictable and imprecise. A researcher would expose an experimental organism to a mutagen, develop screening protocols to select a subset of the resulting mutants, and hope that something interesting would show up.

Today, researchers can create specific gene sequences base by base so that they know exactly what they are studying. For example, primers for the polymerase chain reaction (Reading 8.2) that bracket a gene of interest can be fashioned to include a specific base change. The primer is still alike enough in sequence to base pair with the gene of interest in the DNA sample. However, when the gene is amplified, the intentional change is replicated from it, just as an error in a manuscript is printed in every copy of a book. Tailoring a mutation is called **site-directed mutagenesis.**

Site-directed mutagenesis is a powerful tool to alter proteins one amino acid at a time, and it is faster and more precise than waiting for nature or a mutagen to produce a useful variant. It also makes possible studying mutations that can theoretically exist, but never do because they are too drastic to permit life to continue. Such mutations can be scrutinized at very early stages of development.

Key Concepts

Mutagens are chemicals or radiation that increase the likelihood of mutation. Researchers use mutagens to more quickly obtain mutants, which they study to reveal normal gene function. Organisms may be exposed to mutagens accidentally or intentionally. Accidental exposure may come from nuclear accidents, weapons, drugs, or from natural sources. Site-directed mutagenesis uses PCR primers with intentional base mismatches to engineer and amplify specific mutations.

Natural Protection Against Mutation

The natural repair systems discussed in chapter 8 were only some of the built-in protections against mutation.

The Genetic Code

The genetic code seems at first glance to have too much information—61 codons specify only 20 amino acids. This redundancy (degeneracy) of the genetic code protects against mutation. Degenerate codons ensure that many alterations in the third codon position are "silent." For example, a change from RNA codons CAA to CAG does not alter the designated amino acid, glutamine, so a protein containing the change would not be altered.

Mutations in the second codon position sometimes replace one amino acid with another that has a similar conformation. Often, this does not disrupt the protein's form too drastically. For example, a GCC mutated to GGC replaces alanine with glycine; both are very small amino acids.

Position in the Protein

The degree to which a mutation alters the phenotype depends greatly upon where in the gene the change occurs and how the mutation affects the conformation of the gene's product. A mutation that replaces an amino acid with a very dissimilar one may not affect the phenotype if the change is in part of the protein not critical to its function. Certain mutations in the beta globin gene, for example, do not cause anemia, but they may slightly alter how the protein migrates in an electric field.

Some proteins are more vulnerable to disruption by mutation than others. For example, collagen, a major constituent of connective tissue, is unusually symmetrical. The slightest change in the DNA sequence can greatly deform the overall structure, leading to a connective tissue disorder (Reading 10.2).

Recessive Inheritance Protects

Most inborn errors of metabolism are autosomal recessive, which means that one functional allele supplies 50 percent of the normal amount of the gene product, which is sufficient for health. In this way, the normal allele protects against mutation. Sometimes, however, even the presence of a functioning allele is insufficient to mask the effects of a mutation. The abnormal collagen produced in the "brittle bone disease" osteogenesis imperfecta, for example, is also manufactured in carriers, where it associates with the normal collagen in a way that disrupts its functioning. This causes slightly weak bones, even if a person has only one copy of the mutant allele.

Conditional Mutations

A **conditional** mutation affects the phenotype only under certain conditions. This is the case for a fairly common variant of the X-linked gene that encodes glucose 6-phosphate dehydrogenase (G6PD), an enzyme that immature red blood cells use to extract energy from glucose.

One hundred million people worldwide have G6PD deficiency. The phenotype is severe—life-threatening hemolytic anemia, in which red blood cells burst. Fortunately, anemia develops only under rather unusual conditions—when one is eating fava beans, inhaling pollen in Baghdad, or taking an antimalarial drug.

In the fifth century B.C., Greek mathematician Pythagorus wouldn't allow his followers to consume broad beans—he had discovered that it would make some of them ill. During the second world war, several soldiers taking the antimalarial drug primaquine died of hemolytic anemia. A study began shortly after the war to investigate the effects of the drug on volunteers at the Stateville Penitentiary in Joliet, Illinois, and researchers soon identified abnormal G6PD in people who developed anemia when they took the drug.

What do fava beans, antimalarial drugs, and dozens of other triggering substances have in common? They "stress" red blood cells by exposing them to oxidants, chemicals that strip electrons from other compounds. Without the G6PD enzyme, the stress causes the red blood cells to burst.

Key Concepts

Many natural protections minimize the effects of mutation. A change in DNA, for example, does not always affect protein function. Genetic code degeneracy ensures that some third-codon-position mutations do not alter the specified amino acid. Changes in the second codon position often replace an amino acid with a structurally similar one. A substituted amino acid may not exert a noticeable effect if it is in a nonessential part of a protein. A recessive mutation may not affect the phenotype if the wild type allele is expressed. Conditional mutations are expressed only under certain conditions.

Types of Mutations

Mutation can affect all cells in the body, or only certain cells.

Somatic Versus Germinal Mutations

A mutation that occurs during DNA replication preceding meiosis is present in the resulting gamete and in all the cells that descend from it if it leads to formation of a new individual. This is a **germinal (or constitutional) mutation.** A mutation can also occur during DNA replication before mitosis. (Recall that mitosis occurs in somatic, or nonsex cells.) This is a **somatic mutation.** It affects only cells that descend from the originally mutated cell.

Somatic mutation may be detected prenatally. In amniocentesis (see figure 11.4), 20 or 30 fetal cells are typically examined for chromosome number and structure. Sometimes, a chromosomal anomaly appears in only some of the cells. This is usually associated with a milder form of whatever syndrome arises when all cells have the mutation. For example, a person may have the extra chromosome that causes Down syndrome in 5 of 20 sampled fetal cells. This individual would probably not be as severely mentally retarded as a person who has the extra chromosome in every cell. The phenotype of such a mosaic individual ultimately

Much of the human body consists of the protein collagen. It accounts for more than 60 percent of the protein in bone and cartilage and provides 50–90 percent of the dry weight of skin, ligaments, tendons, and the dentine of teeth. Collagen is in the eyes, the blood vessel linings, and the basement membranes that separate cell types in tissues, and it is a major component of connective tissue. It is not surprising that mutations in the genes encoding collagen lead to a variety of medical problems.

Structure of Collagen

Mutations affecting collagen are particularly devastating because this protein has an extremely precise conformation that is easily disrupted, even by slight alterations that might exert little noticeable effect in other proteins. Collagen is sculpted from a precursor molecule called procollagen (figure 1). Procollagen consists of many repeats of the tripeptide sequence "glycine-X-Y," where X is typically proline, and Y is a form of proline with a hydroxyl (OH) group added. Three procollagen chains coil and entwine to form a triple helix, with two strands identical and manufactured

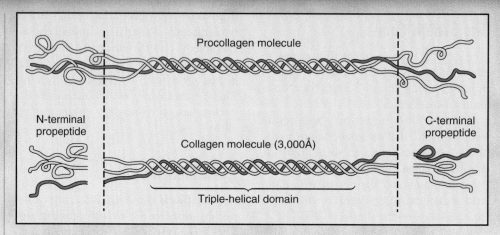

figure 1

The α 1 collagen gene encodes the two light-colored polypeptide chains, and the α 2 procollagen gene encodes the third. The procollagen triple helix is shortened before it becomes functional, forming the fibrils and networks that comprise much of the human body.

from the α 1 (alpha-1) gene, and the other from a second gene, designated α 2 (alpha-2). The electrical charges and water interactions of these amino acids cause the polypeptide chains to coil into a very regular triple helix, with space in the middle only for glycine, a very small amino acid.

Triple helices form as the procollagen is synthesized, but once secreted from the cell, the helices are trimmed, yielding a molecule that is 3,000 Å's long. The collagen fibrils continue to associate outside the cell, building the fibrils and networks that hold the body together. Collagen is rapidly synthesized and assembled into its

depends upon which cells have the mutation (figure 10.9). A mosaic Down syndrome fetus with affected cells in the brain would have a greater mental impairment than such a fetus with the affected cells mostly in the skin. Unfortunately, amniocentesis cannot tell which cells are affected.

A somatic mutation is necessary for the development of some cancers. In retinoblastoma, a childhood eye cancer, an affected child inherits a germinal mutation from a parent, which predisposes him or her to develop the disease. However, an eye tumor does not develop until a somatic mutation in a second gene affects retina cells (Reading 16.2).

Point Mutations

A **point mutation** is a change in a single DNA base. It is a **transition** if a purine replaces a purine (A to G or G to A) or a pyrimidine replaces a pyrimidine (C to T or T to C). It is a **transversion** if a purine stands in for a pyrimidine or vice versa (A or G to T or C). A point mutation can have any of several consequences—or it may have none at all, if it leads to a silent mutation.

Missense Mutations

A **missense mutation** changes a codon that normally specifies a particular amino acid

into one that codes for a different amino acid. If the substituted amino acid alters the protein's conformation sufficiently or at a site critical to its function, signs or symptoms of disease result.

A missense mutation can profoundly affect a gene's product if it alters a site where introns are snipped out of the mRNA. Retaining an intron would add bases to a gene. For example, in one family with severe cystic fibrosis, a missense mutation alters an intron site so that it cannot be removed. Instead, the intron is translated, and the resulting protein has too many amino acids. The protein is too bulky to make its way to its normal position in the rigid architecture. Many types of mutations can disrupt the process, including missing procollagen chains, kinks in the triple helix, failure to cut mature collagen, and defects in aggregation outside the cell. Table 1 shows some collagen defects.

Knowing which specific mutations cause disorders offers a way to diagnose the condition before symptoms arise. This can be helpful if early diagnosis leads to early treatment. A woman who is told that she will develop hereditary osteoporosis, for example, might take calcium supplements or begin estrogen replacement (hormone) therapy before symptoms appear.

Aortic aneurysm is a more serious connective tissue disorder that can be diagnosed presymptomatically if the underlying mutation is detected. A weakened aorta (the largest blood vessel in the body, which emerges from the heart) bursts. Knowing that one has not inherited the mutant gene can ease worries—and knowing that one has inherited it can warn an individual to have frequent ultrasound exams to detect aortic weakening early enough to treat it surgically.

table 1
Collagen Disorders

Disorder	Defect	Signs and Symptoms
Alport syndrome	Not known	Deafness and inflamed kidneys
Aortic aneurysm	Missense mutation substitutes an arg for gly in α 1 gene	Aorta bursts
Chondrodysplasia	Deletion, insertion, or missense mutation replaces gly with bulky amino acids	Stunted growth, deformed joints
Dystrophic epidermolysis bullosa	Collagen fibrils that attach epidermis to dermis break down	Skin blisters on any touch
Ehlers-Danlos syndrome	Missense mutations replace gly with bulky amino acids; deletions or missense mutations disrupt intron/exon splicing	Stretchy, easily scarred skin, lax joints
Osteoarthritis	Missense mutation substitutes cys for arg in α 1 gene	Painful joints
Osteogenesis imperfecta type I	Inactivation of α allele reduces collagen triple helices by 50%	Easily broken bones; blue eye whites; deafness
Osteoporosis	Missense mutation substitutes one ser for gly in α 2 gene, kinking collagen triple helix	Weakened bones
Stickler syndrome	Nonsense mutation in procollagen	Joint pain, degeneration of vitreous gel and retina

cell membrane, where it should enable salt to exit the cell. As a result, chloride (a component of salt) accumulates in the cell, causing the thick, sticky mucus characteristic of this illness.

The reverse situation occurs in a form of the inborn error of metabolism PKU. A mutation changing a G to an A establishes an intron cutting site not usually present in the mRNA. A shortened protein product results, which is nonfunctional.

Missense mutations can affect proteins synthesized as larger precursors from which active proteins are cleaved after translation. In one form of Ehlers-Danlos syndrome, for example, a single base is changed in a gene that encodes procollagen, a precursor of a type of collagen. Because the site where procollagen is normally cleaved is gone, the shortened, functional collagen is not produced. A person with this mutation has very stretchy skin, loose joints, and hip dislocation at birth (figure 10.10).

A missense mutation in a DNA sequence that controls a gene's expression can also affect the phenotype. For 15 percent of people who have Becker muscular dystrophy—the milder adult form of the condition—the muscle protein dystrophin is normal, but its levels are reduced. The missense mutation causing the protein shortage is in the promoter for the dystrophin gene, which affects the transcription rate.

Nonsense Mutations

A point mutation that changes a codon specifying an amino acid into a "stop" codon—UAA, UAG, or UGA in RNA—is a **nonsense mutation.** This shortens the protein product, which can profoundly influence the phenotype. Nonsense mutations are predictable by consulting the genetic code.

The most common cause of factor XI deficiency, a blood clotting disorder, is a nonsense mutation that changes the GAA

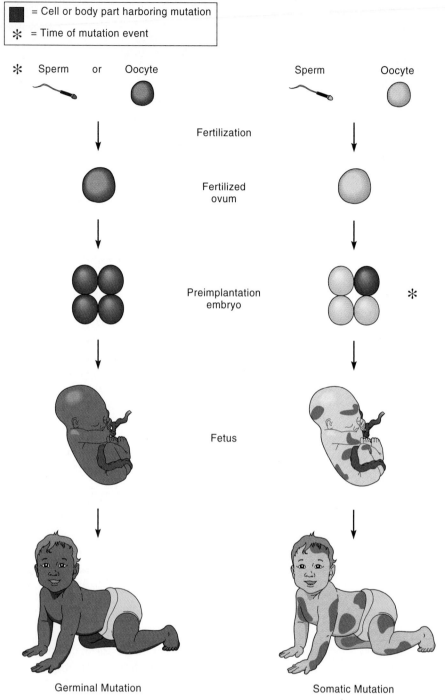

✻ Sperm or Oocyte

Sperm Oocyte

Fertilization

Fertilized ovum

Preimplantation embryo ✻

Fetus

Germinal Mutation

Somatic Mutation

figure 10.9

The phenotype of a somatic mutation depends upon which cells and tissues are affected and on the nature of the gene product.

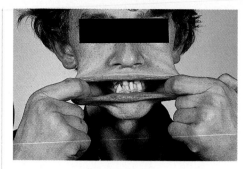

figure 10.10

A mutation in a collagen gene causes the stretchy skin of Ehlers-Danlos syndrome type I.

codon specifying glutamic acid to UAA, signifying stop. The shortened clotting factor causes profuse bleeding during surgery or from injury. In the opposite situation, when a normal stop codon mutates into a codon that specifies an amino acid, the resulting protein is longer than normal.

Altering the Number of DNA Bases

In genes, the number three is very important, because triplets of DNA bases specify amino acids. Adding or deleting a number of bases that is not a multiple of three devastates a gene's function because it disrupts the reading frame, the sequence of DNA codons, and therefore, amino acids. Such a change is called a **frameshift mutation.** Even adding or deleting multiples of three can be drastic enough to alter a phenotype. Figure 10.11 compares the effects on protein sequence of missense, nonsense, and frameshift mutations in the same gene.

Missing Genetic Material

Deletion of genetic material causes many of the more common inherited disorders. Consider the gene for dystrophin, which when mutated causes Duchenne and Becker muscular dystrophies. The gene spans 2.3 million bases and includes more than 75 exons. About two-thirds of patients have deletions, some quite extensive, removing several exons. Smaller mutations are more likely to occur in control (non-amino acid-encoding) regions of the gene, causing shortened proteins or too little protein.

The genes that specify the protein portions of hemoglobin are particularly interesting, because the polypeptide subunits change at different times in development to suit the differing oxygen requirements of the embryo, fetus, and newborn. Our alpha globin chains remain the same throughout these stages, but the embryo has two epsilon chains and the fetus has two gamma chains in place of the two beta chains, which gradually appear in the first six months after birth.

A DNA sequence called the locus control region precedes the embryonic globin gene and controls switching of globin type through development. A deletion in the locus control region leads to a type

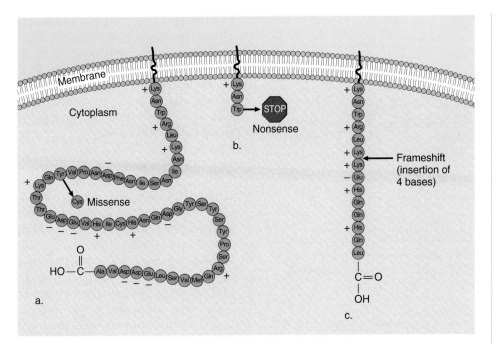

figure 10.11

Different mutations can cause the same disorder. In familial hypercholesterolemia, the low-density lipoprotein (LDL) receptor is unstable, which prevents liver cells from taking up cholesterol. Cholesterol accumulates on artery walls, causing severe heart attacks in childhood for homozygotes or in early adulthood for heterozygotes. The mutations shown here disrupt the portion of the LDL receptor normally anchored in the cytoplasm. LDL receptor (a) bears a missense mutation—a substitution of a cysteine for a tyrosine. The short LDL receptor in (b) results from a nonsense mutation, in which a stop codon replaces an arginine codon. In (c), a 4-base insertion disrupts the gene sequence of the LDL receptor, which throws off the reading frame. A sequence of amino acids not normally in this protein continues until a stop codon occurs.

of anemia called beta thalassemia. In this disorder, the individual has too little beta globin because the control gene does not give the signal to turn on beta globin's transcription.

Extra Genetic Material

Short insertions add genetic material and are rare, but can cause inherited disorders. Just as deleting a DNA base can offset a gene's reading frame, so can adding a base. In a form of Gaucher disease, for example, a base is inserted abnormally at position 84 in the gene. This impairs the gene so that its product, an enzyme that normally breaks down glycolipids, isn't produced. The resulting buildup of glycolipid enlarges the liver and spleen and causes easily fractured bones and neurological impairment. Insertion mutations cause a variety of conditions, including enzyme deficiencies, Tay-Sachs disease, osteoporosis, albinism, and blood disorders.

Another type of added genetic material is a repeat of part of a gene's sequence, usually adjacent or close to the original sequence, like a typographical error repeating a word word. Such a **tandem duplication** causes a form of Charcot-Marie-Tooth disease, an autosomal dominant degeneration of the motor and sensory nerves. Symptoms include numb hands and feet. One and a half million base pairs repeat in the gene!

Remnants of Genes Past— Pseudogenes

For some genes, a stretch of DNA with a sequence very similar to the gene lies nearby on the chromosome. This second gene, which in a sense is a ghost of the first, is called a **pseudogene.** It is not translated into protein, although it may be transcribed. The pseudogene may actually descend from the original gene sequence, which was duplicated, creating an extra copy of the sequence, when DNA strands misaligned during replication. The original gene then mutated to such an extent that it was no longer functional and became a pseudogene. Its duplicate sequence, though, lived on as the functional gene.

Although a pseudogene is not translated, its presence can interfere with the expression of the functional gene and cause a mutation. Gaucher disease can result from a crossover between the working gene and its pseudogene, which has 95 percent of the same sequence located 16,000 bases away. The result is a **fusion gene,** which is a sequence containing part of the functional gene and part of the pseudogene. The fusion gene does not preserve enough of the wild type gene sequence for an enzyme to be manufactured. Gaucher disease results.

Triplet Repeats and Expanding Genes

Until 1992, myotonic dystrophy was a very puzzling disorder. This autosomal dominant disease, the most common adult form of muscular dystrophy, worsens as it passes from one generation to the next, a phenomenon called "anticipation." A grandfather might experience only mild weakness in his forearms. In the next generation, a daughter might have more noticeable arm and leg weakness. By the third generation, children inheriting the genes might experience severe muscle impairment—worse if the affected parent was the mother.

With the ability to sequence genes, researchers found startling evidence that myotonic dystrophy was worsening with each generation because the gene was expanding! The gene for the disorder, on chromosome 19, has an area rich in repeats of the DNA trinucleotide CTG. A person who does not have myotonic dystrophy usually has from 5 to 37 copies of the repeat, whereas a person with the disorder has from 50 to thousands of copies (figure 10.12).

So far, **expanding triplet repeats** have been found in more than a dozen human

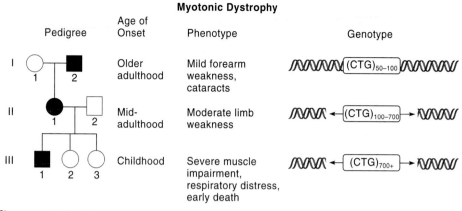

figure 10.12

Expanding genes explain anticipation. In some disorders, symptoms worsening from one generation to the next—termed anticipation—has a physical basis: the gene is expanding.

inherited disorders, many of them affecting the nervous system. Usually, a repeat number of less than 40 copies is stably transmitted to the next generation and doesn't produce symptoms. Larger repeats are unstable, increasing in number each generation and causing symptoms. This is the physical basis of anticipation.

The relationship between repeat number and phenotype may be all-or-none or progressive. In fragile X syndrome (Reading 10.1), for example, it is all-or-none—a male must have at least 220 repeats of the triplet to have symptoms. In myotonic dystrophy, the relationship is progressive. The greater the number of repeats, the more severe the illness.

The nature of triplet repeat mutation is well studied in Huntington disease (HD). Symptoms of HD include worsening loss of muscle control and coordination, slurring and loss of speech, depression, and mental impairment, with death on average eighteen years following diagnosis. In HD, the RNA codon CAG, which encodes the amino acid glutamine, repeats (figure 10.13). The average number of repeats in a normal chromosome 4 is 6 to 37; in an HD chromosome, it ranges from 35 to 121. The rare juvenile-onset form of the illness is associated with the largest number of repeats.

The protein implicated in HD is called huntingtin, and a second protein, called huntington-associated protein (HAP-1), normally binds huntingtin. When huntingtin contains the extra glutamines, HAP-1 binds much more strongly. The mutated HD gene adds a function, rather than destroying a normal function, because all people with HD have the expanded triplet repeat. People who are missing a copy of the wild type gene do *not* have symptoms of HD—implying that nothing essential is missing even when the wild type allele is absent, but something goes wrong when the expanded triplet repeat is present.

A convergence of experiments conducted two decades apart connected the cellular and molecular bases of HD in 1997 (see Technology Timeline). In 1979, researchers at Columbia University detected fibrous clumps in cell nuclei from certain parts of the brains of people who had died of HD. In 1997, researchers from London and Berlin bred mice that had the human expanded (mutant) HD gene. (The mice were transgenic, discussed in chapter 17.) The same fibrous clumps appeared in brain cell nuclei and using technology not available in 1979, the researchers identified the clumps as huntingtin protein! Before symptoms develop

in adult mice, the protein is in the cytoplasm. Once the protein enters the nuclei, symptoms ensue. The mice reveal the beginnings of the illness. Work is now focusing on discovering ways to break up the protein clumps in the test tube in hopes that we will soon be able to do so in affected individuals' brains.

Movable Genes

In the 1940s, corn geneticist Barbara McClintock proposed that the dots that appear on some corn kernels result from genes that "jump" into pigment genes, causing mutations that provide color. It took many years for people to take her work seriously, but McClintock was eventually awarded the Nobel Prize for her discovery. "Jumping genes," or **transposons,** have since been identified in many species.

About 10 percent of the human genome is transposons. About half of these are called alu sequences, each consisting of three hundred bases. Transposons can alter gene function in several ways. They can disrupt the site they jump from, shut off transcription of the gene they jump into, or alter the reading frame of their destination if they are not a multiple of three. For example, a boy with X-linked hemophilia A was found to have a transposable element in his factor VIII gene—a sequence found in his carrier mother, but on her chromosome 22. Apparently, in the oocyte, the transposable element jumped into the factor VIII gene on the X chromosome, causing the boy's hemophilia.

Viruses are, in a sense, jumping genes. A virus's nucleic acid inserts into a host chromosome, sometimes impairing gene function. Bacteria acquire resistance to antibiotic drugs through genes that jump into them. Movable genetic material is also responsible for the incredible diversity of the human immune response and for some cancers, as we shall see in chapters 15 and 16.

Table 10.4 summarizes types of mutations, using an analogy to an English sentence.

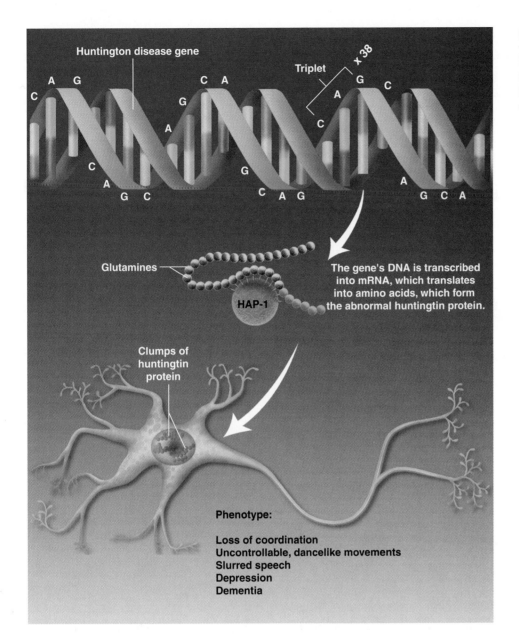

figure 10.13

Huntington disease gene

Triplet

x 38

C A G

C A

G

A

C

A

G C

C A G

C A

G

A

C

A G C

G C A

The gene's DNA is transcribed into mRNA, which translates into amino acids, which form the abnormal huntingtin protein.

Glutamines

HAP-1

Clumps of huntingtin protein

Phenotype:

Loss of coordination
Uncontrollable, dancelike movements
Slurred speech
Depression
Dementia

Huntington disease is caused by a triplet repeat mutation that causes huntingtin protein to abnormally enter and accumulate in certain brain nerve cell nuclei.

Key Concepts

A germinal mutation originates during meiosis and affects all cells of an individual. A somatic mutation originates during mitosis and affects a subset of an individual's cells.

Several types of mutations may affect the DNA sequence or protein products. A point mutation, which alters a single DNA base, can occur in a part of a gene that encodes protein, in a control region, or in a splicing junction between introns and exons. In a transversion, a purine replaces a pyrimidine, or vice versa; in a transition, a purine replaces a purine or a pyrimidine replaces a pyrimidine. A missense mutation replaces one amino acid with another. A nonsense mutation alters an amino-acid-coding codon into a nonsense codon, shortening the gene product. A stop codon that changes to an amino-acid-coding codon lengthens the gene product.

Altering the number of DNA bases may have dramatic effects. Inserting or deleting bases upsets the DNA reading frame, causing a frameshift mutation. Tandem duplications repeat a section of a gene, and pseudogenes are nonfunctional sequences very similar to a nearby functional gene. Expanded triplet repeats cause some disorders. Transposable elements can move, insert into genes, and cause illness.

Technology TIMELINE

1979 Columbia University researchers discover characteristic fibrous clumps in brains of deceased HD patients.

1983 Genetic marker discovered on chromosome 4 that makes presymptomatic diagnosis in some families possible.

1993 Gene for HD discovered and shown to include expanded triplet repeat. Protein product named huntingtin.

1997 Transgenic mice harboring human mutant HD gene have clumps of huntingtin in brain cell nuclei.

table 10.4

Types of Mutations

A sentence comprised of three-letter words can provide an analogy to the effect of mutations on a gene's sequence:

Wild type		THE ONE BIG FLY HAD ONE RED EYE
Missense		THQ ONE BIG FLY HAD ONE RED EYE
Nonsense		THE ONE BIG
Frameshift		THE ONE QBI GFL YHA DON ERE DEY
Deletion		THE ONE BIG HAD ONE RED EYE
Duplication		THE ONE BIG FLY FLY HAD ONE RED EYE
Insertion		THE ONE BIG WET FLY HAD ONE RED EYE
Expanding mutation	P_1	THE ONE BIG FLY HAD ONE RED EYE
	F_1	THE ONE BIG FLY FLY FLY HAD ONE RED EYE
	F_2	THE ONE BIG FLY FLY FLY FLY FLY FLY HAD ONE RED EYE

summary

1. A mutation is a change in DNA (genotype), and a mutant is the corresponding phenotype. A mutation can be spontaneous or induced. In mutations, DNA bases are changed, added, deleted, or moved. Large or repetitive DNA sequences are more likely to mutate. **Mutagens** are chemicals or radiation that increase the mutation rate.

2. Some mutations are silent. A mutation in the third position of a degenerate codon can substitute the same amino acid. A mutation in the second codon position can replace an amino acid with a similarly shaped one. A mutation in a nonvital part of a protein may not affect its function.

3. Researchers classify mutations by the type of tissue they affect and by their specific nature. A **germinal mutation** originates in meiosis and affects all cells of an individual. A **somatic mutation** originates in mitosis and affects a subset of cells. A **point mutation** alters a single DNA base. This mutation may be a **transition** (purine replacing purine or pyrimidine replacing pyrimidine) or a **transversion** (purine replacing pyrimidine, or vice versa). It may also be **missense** (substituting one amino acid for another) or **nonsense** (substituting a "stop" codon for an amino-acid-coding codon). Altering the number of bases in a gene may delete or add genetic material, which may disrupt the reading frame. **Expanding triplet repeats** cause some inherited illnesses, and mobile DNA can disrupt the function of a gene that it enters.

review questions

1. Describe how a spontaneous mutation can arise.

2. What is the physical basis of mutational hot spots?

3. Why is using site-directed mutagenesis more efficient and more valuable to research than exposing experimental organisms to mutagens?

4. Cite three ways in which the genetic code protects against mutation.

5. List four ways that DNA can mutate without affecting the phenotype.

6. What is a conditional mutation?

7. Distinguish between a germinal and a somatic mutation. Which is likely to be more severe? Which is more likely to be transmitted to offspring?

8. Why is the collagen gene particularly prone to mutation?

9. List three types of mutations that can disrupt the reading frame.

10. Why can a mutation that retains an intron's sequence and a triplet repeat mutation have a similar effect on a gene's product?

11. Cite two ways that a jumping gene can disrupt gene function.

12. Cite two reasons it takes many years to detect induction of recessive mutations in a human population.

13. What is a physical, molecular explanation for anticipation, the worsening of an inherited illness over successive generations?

14. Cite two types of mutational mechanisms that can cause Gaucher disease.

applied questions

1. Two teenage boys meet at a clinic set up to treat muscular dystrophy. The boy who is more severely affected has a two-base insertion at the start of his dystrophin gene. The other boy has the same two-base insertion but also has a third base inserted a few bases away. Explain why the second boy's illness is milder.

2. About 10 percent of cases of amyotrophic lateral sclerosis (also known as ALS and Lou Gehrig disease) are inherited. This disorder causes loss of neurological function over a five-year period. Two missense mutations cause ALS. One alters the amino acid asparagine (asn) to lysine (lys). The other changes an isoleucine (ile) to a threonine (thr). List the codons involved and show how single base mutations alter the amino acids they specify.

3. In one family, Tay-Sachs disease stems from a four-base insertion, which changes an amino-acid encoding codon into a stop codon. What type of mutation is this?

4. Epidermolytic hyperkeratosis is an autosomal dominant condition that produces scaly skin. It can be caused by a missense mutation that substitutes a histidine (his) amino acid for an arginine (arg). Write the mRNA codons that could account for this change.

5. Fanconi anemia is an autosomal recessive condition that causes bone marrow abnormalities and an increased risk of certain cancers. It is caused by a transversion mutation that substitutes a valine (val) for an aspartic acid (asp) in the amino acid sequence. Which mRNA codons are involved?

6. A three-year-old boy who suffered from frequent, serious infections was diagnosed with a form of inherited immune deficiency when fibroblast cells and white blood cells grown in the laboratory were found to lack an enzyme called ADA, which activates immunity. In these cells, the boy's ADA gene harbored a missense mutation. Children with ADA deficiency usually die, but this boy grew up, and at age 16, seemed cured. When puzzled geneticists sampled several of the boy's tissues, they found that his fibroblasts and white blood cells still lacked ADA, but several other types of cells produced the enzyme. Explain what had probably happened in the young man's body.

7. Two English geneticists recently published a book suggesting that Queen Victoria originated the hemophilia mutation passed to some of her descendants because Edward, Duke of Kent, was not her biological father, and she inherited the mutation from a man her mother had an affair with. Suggest another explanation for the fact that the mutation first appears in Queen Victoria.

8. Tuberous sclerosis causes noncancerous tumors to form in the heart, brain, skin, lungs, and kidneys. One of the two genes known to cause the condition, on chromosome 16, has 23 exons. No mutations have ever been seen in 13 of these exons. What are two reasons that mutations in these exons are not seen?

9. Aniridia is an autosomal dominant eye condition in which the iris is absent. In one family, an eleven-base insertion in the gene causes a very short protein to form. What kind of mutation must the insertion cause?

10. Why would it be difficult to develop a test to screen the general population (that is, testing individuals without testing their relatives) for inherited Alzheimer disease?

Alward, Wallace L. M. et al. April 9, 1998. Clinical features associated with mutations in the chromosome 1 open-angle glaucoma gene (GLC1A). *The New England Journal of Medicine,* vol. 338. Many types of missense mutations cause this eye disorder.

Bonn, Dorothy. March 15, 1997. Anticipating the future by counting DNA triplet repeats. *The Lancet,* vol. 349. Increasing number of triplet repeats correlates to worsening symptoms.

Crook, Richard, et al. April 1998. A variant of Alzheimer's disease with spastic paraparesis and unusual plagues due to deletion of exon 9 of presenilin 1. *Nature Medicine,* vol. 4. Deletion of an entire exon causes severe Alzheimer disease in a Finnish family.

Gahl, William, et al. April 30, 1998. Genetic defects and clinical characteristics of patients with a form of oculocutaneous albinism. *The New England Journal of Medicine,* vol. 338. In a Puerto Rican family, members with albinism have a 16 base pair duplication.

Hillis, David M. April 25, 1996. Life in the hot zone around Chernobyl. *Nature,* vol. 380. Studies on rodents and humans reveal a doubled mutation rate in some genes.

Hodes, M. E., and S. R. Dlouhy. July 1996. The proteolipid protein gene: double, double, . . . and trouble. *The American Journal of Human Genetics,* vol. 59. Genes that control formation of myelin sheaths on nerve cells are especially prone to duplication mutations.

Housman, David. May 1995. Gain of glutamines, gain of function? *Nature Genetics.* Huntington disease may add a function rather than impairing one.

Ingram, V.M. 1957. Gene mutations in human hemoglobin: The chemical difference between normal and sickle cell hemoglobin. *Nature,* vol. 180. The classic paper explaining the molecular basis for sickle cell disease.

Meacham, Jon, and Daniel Pedersen. July 24, 1995. Was Queen Victoria a bastard? *Newsweek.* Hemophilia may have arisen in Queen Victoria because of marital infidelity—but there might also be a genetic explanation.

Neel, James V. December 1995. New approaches to evaluating the genetic effects of the atomic bombs. *The American Journal of Human Genetics,* vol. 57. It will take several generations for the effects of bomb-induced recessive mutations to become noticeable.

O'Brien, Stephen J., and Michael Dean. September 1997. In search of AIDS-resistance genes. *Scientific American.* Some mutations are beneficial.

Paabo, Svante. September 1996. Mutational hot spots in the mitochondrial microcosm. *The American Journal of Human Genetics,* vol. 59. Mitochondrial genes mutate rapidly.

Post, Stephen G. March 12, 1997. The clinical introduction of genetic testing for Alzheimer disease. *Journal of the American Medical Association,* vol. 277. Genetic testing for Alzheimer disease will be complex.

Schwartz, Robert S. April 6, 1995. Jumping genes. *The New England Journal of Medicine,* vol. 332. Jumping genes explain viral infection, immune system function, some cancers, and some inherited illnesses.

Selkoe, Dennis J. January 31, 1997. Alzheimer's disease: genotypes, phenotype, and treatments. *Science,* vol. 275. At least four genes cause the beta-amyloid buildup of Alzheimer disease, and these genes can mutate in several ways.

Shcherbak, Yurim. April 1996. Ten years of the Chernobyl era. *Scientific American.* Cancer rates are soaring in the area around the damaged nuclear plant. Recessive mutations will take longer to become obvious.

Uitterlinden, André G., et al. April 9, 1998. Relation of alleles of the collagen type Iα1 gene to bone density and the risk of osteoporotic fractures in postmenopausal women. *The New England Journal of Medicine,* vol. 338. A collagen mutation underlies a form of osteoporosis.

chapter eleven

Cytogenetics

Portrait of a Chromosome

Genetic health is largely a matter of balance—inheriting the "correct" number of genes, usually on the "correct" number of chromosomes (46). Too much or too little genetic material, particularly of the autosomes, can cause syndromes (groups of signs and symptoms). A person with Down syndrome, for example, usually has an extra chromosome 21 and, therefore, extra copies of all the genes on that chromosome. This causes mental retardation and various medical problems, but, as figure 11.1 illustrates, people with Down syndrome can lead full and productive lives.

In general, excess genetic material has milder effects on health than a deficit. Still, most chromosomal abnormalities are so harmful that prenatal development ceases in the embryo. As a result, only a few—0.65 percent—of all newborns have chromosomal abnormalities that produce symptoms. An additional 0.20 percent have chromosomal rearrangements, when chromosome parts flip or swap but do not produce symptoms unless they disrupt genes crucial to health.

Cytogenetics is the subdiscipline within genetics that links chromosome variations to specific traits, including illnesses. This chapter explores several ways that chromosome structure can deviate from normal and the consequences of these variations.

A chromosome consists of a very long molecule of DNA, its associated RNA, and histone proteins, as well as DNA replication enzymes and transcription factors. During mitotic metaphase, when DNA coils especially tightly, key physical landmarks distinguish the chromosome pairs.

The 24 chromosome types are numbered from largest to smallest—1 to 22—although chromosome 21 is actually the smallest. The other two chromosomes are the X and the Y. Early attempts to size-order chromosomes resulted in generalized groupings because many of the chromosomes are of similar size.

Centromere position is one distinguishing feature of chromosomes. A chromosome is **metacentric** if the centromere (the largest constriction) divides it into two arms of approximately equal length, **submetacentric** if

the centromere establishes one long arm and one short arm, and **acrocentric** if it pinches off only a small amount of material toward one end (figure 11.2). Some species have telocentric chromosomes, consisting of only one arm, but humans do not. The centromere consists of DNA, and it may help orient chromosomes during cell division. The long arm of a chromosome is designated "q," and the short arm "p."

Cytogeneticists use stains to distinguish chromosomes. Dark-staining genetic material, called **heterochromatin,** is more highly coiled and has more repetitive DNA sequences than the lighter-staining **euchromatin** (figure 11.3). Euchromatin includes protein-encoding genes, whereas heterochromatin maintains a chromosome's structural integrity. The tighter coils of heterochromatin may explain how it entraps dye particles and therefore stains more intensely. Stained chromosomes appear to be striped with long stretches of heterochromatin near the centromere and at the tips (telomeres). (Recall from chapter 2 and figure 2.21 that human telomeres consist of many repeats of the sequence TTAGGG.) **DNA probes,** which are labeled pieces of DNA that are complementary to a sequence of interest, are more specific than stains and are increasingly replacing use of chromosome staining both in research and in clinical tests.

Five human chromosomes (13, 14, 15, 21, and 22) are distinguished further by

figure 11.1

Wendy Weisz has trisomy 21. She enjoys studying art at Cuyahoga Community College.

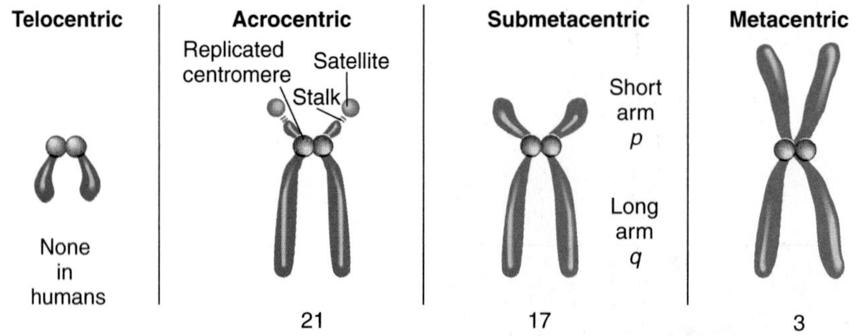

Telocentric	Acrocentric	Submetacentric	Metacentric
None in humans	Replicated centromere / Satellite / Stalk — 21	Short arm p / Long arm q — 17	Short arm p / Long arm q — 3

figure 11.2

Chromosomes can sometimes be distinguished by size and position of the centromere. Telocentric chromosomes have centromeres at one end and do not occur in humans. The smallest chromosomes—21 and 22—are acrocentric, with the centromere near one end and the end portion attached by a stalklike section. A submetacentric chromosome, such as 17 or 18, has a centromere that divides the chromosomes into large and small segments. A metacentric chromosome, such as 3, has an approximately centralized centromere.

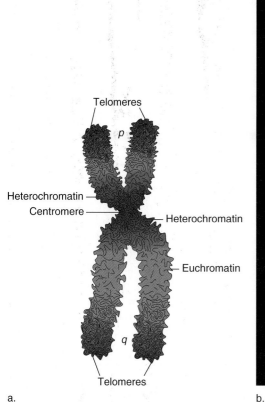

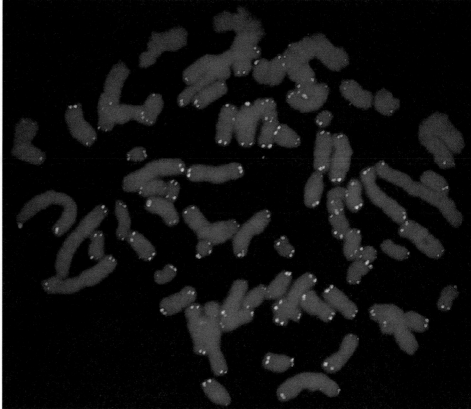

Telomeres

p

Heterochromatin
Centromere

Heterochromatin

Euchromatin

q

Telomeres

a.

b.

figure 11.3

Portrait of a chromosome. (*a*) In a typical chromosome, tightly wound heterochromatin forms the centromere and the telomeres. It is interspersed with euchromatin along the rest of the chromosome. The largest constriction is the centromere, which divides this chromosome into a short arm (p) and a long arm (q). (*b*) In most somatic cells, telomeres shorten with each mitosis, reaching a threshold point that signals cell division to cease.

bloblike ends, called **satellites,** that extend from a thinner, stalklike bridge from the rest of the chromosome. Satellites carry many repeats of genes coding for ribosomal RNA and ribosomal proteins. These regions are called nucleolar organizing regions. They coalesce to form the nucleolus, a structure in the nucleus where ribosomal subunits are produced and assembled into ribosomes.

Visualizing Chromosomes

Extra or missing chromosomes are easily detected by counting a number other than 46. Chromosome rearrangements, such as an inverted sequence or two chromosomes exchanging parts, are more subtle and require a way to distinguish among the 24 different types of human chromosomes. A combination of stains and DNA probes allows this. The chromosomes are then displayed in a size-order chart called a **karyotype.**

Obtaining Cells for Chromosome Study

Any cell other than a mature red blood cell (which lacks a nucleus) can be used to examine chromosomes, but some cells are easier to obtain and culture than others. For adults, white blood cells separated from a blood sample are usually the basis of a chromosome test. A person might require such a test if he or she has a family history of a chromosomal abnormality or is infertile. An extract from kidney beans is added to the sample to make the white blood cells divide, which takes several days. Adding the drug colchicine halts cell division when chromosomes are condensed. They are then stained and observed.

Cancer cells can be checked for chromosomal abnormalities that may indicate which drugs are likely to be the most effective. For blood-borne cancers (leukemias and lymphomas), cytogeneticists examine chromosomes from bone marrow cells, which give rise to blood cells. Some of the earliest chromosome studies in the 1950s used cells from hair roots. Today, Olympic athletes provide lining cells from the insides of their cheeks to confirm the presence or absence of the Y chromosome or the SRY gene. (In the past, officials discovered that some athletes competing as females actually had an XY chromosomal constitution.)

Chromosome tests are most commonly performed on fetal cells to reveal medical problems. Couples who receive a prenatal diagnosis of a chromosome abnormality can arrange for treatment of the newborn, if this is possible; learn more about the condition and perhaps contact support groups and plan care; or terminate the pregnancy. These choices are highly individual and personal and are best made after a genetic counselor or physician provides unbiased information on the particular medical condition and options.

The first successful fetal karyotype was constructed in 1966 by **amniocentesis.** Today, this procedure is a routine part of obstetrical care.

Amniocentesis

The idea of amniocentesis—sampling fetal cells shed into the amniotic fluid that cushions the fetus—arose in the last century, but the procedure was too often harmful to the fetus until the late 1960s. Today, it is very safe.

In amniocentesis, a doctor removes fetal cells and fluids from the uterus with a needle passed through the woman's abdominal wall (figure 11.4). The cells are cultured for several days, and typically 20 cells are karyotyped. Culturing and staining chromosomes takes a week, but DNA probes can detect certain chromosomal anomalies in a day or two. The sampled amniotic fluid is also examined for deficient, excess, or abnormal biochemicals that could indicate particular inborn errors of metabolism. Amniocentesis takes only a minute or two and causes a feeling of pressure. Ultrasound guides the needle placement so that it doesn't harm the fetus (figure 11.5).

Amniocentesis can detect approximately 400 of the more than 5,000 known chromosomal and biochemical problems. It is usually performed at 15 or 16 weeks gesta-

tion, when the fetus isn't yet very large but amniotic fluid is plentiful. Amniocentesis can be carried out anytime after this point.

Doctors recommend amniocentesis if the risk that the fetus has a detectable condition exceeds the risk that the procedure will cause a miscarriage, which is about 1 in 350 (table 11.1). The most common candidate for the test is a pregnant woman over age thirty-five. This "advanced maternal age" statistically increases the risk that the fetus will have an extra or missing chromosome. Amniocentesis is also warranted if a couple has had several spontaneous abortions or children with birth defects or a known chromosome abnormality.

Another reason to seek amniocentesis is if a blood test on the pregnant woman reveals low levels of a fetal liver protein called alpha fetoprotein (AFP) and high levels of human chorionic gonadotropin (hCG). These signs may indicate a fetus with a small liver, which may reflect a condition caused by an extra chromosome, such as Down syndrome. These tests are called maternal serum marker tests. They are useful for pregnant women younger than thirty-five who would not routinely undergo age-related amniocentesis.

Chorionic Villus Sampling

During the 10th week of pregnancy, **chorionic villus sampling** (CVS) obtains cells from the chorionic villi, which develop into the placenta. A karyotype is prepared directly from the collected cells, rather than first culturing them, as in amniocentesis. Results are ready in days.

Because chorionic villus cells descend from the fertilized ovum, their chromo-

somes should be identical to those of the embryo and fetus. Occasionally, **chromosomal mosaicism** occurs, causing the karyotype of a villus cell to differ from that of a cell from the embryo. For this reason, CVS is slightly less accurate than amniocentesis, which examines fetal cells. Also, the sampling procedure in CVS does not include amniotic fluid, so the biochemical tests that amniocentesis allows are not possible.

Fetal Cell Sorting

Amniocentesis and chorionic villus sampling increase risk of miscarriage. **Fetal cell sorting,** a new technique that separates fetal cells from the woman's bloodstream, is safer than anmiocentesis and CVS.

Fetal cell sorting traces its roots to 1957, when a pregnant woman died when cells from a very early embryo lodged in a major blood vessel in her lung, blocking blood flow. By studying the blood of other pregnant women, researchers found that fetal cells enter the maternal circulation in up to 70 percent of pregnancies. Cells from female embryos, however, cannot be distinguished from the cells of the pregnant woman on the basis of sex chromosome analysis.

In fetal cell sorting, a device called a fluorescence-activated cell sorter separates fetal cells by identifying surface characteristics that differ from those on the woman's cells. The fetal cells are karyotyped and fetal DNA extracted and amplified for specific gene tests. Another experimental approach uses PCR (see Reading 8.2) to amplify the SRY gene, present only on the Y chromosome.

table 11.1

Indications for Amniocentesis

"Advanced maternal age" (over age 35)
Repeated spontaneous abortions
Family history of birth defects, stillbirths, or childhood deaths
Family history of inherited illness or chromosome abnormalities
Levels of AFP and hCG in maternal blood serum indicate increased risk of trisomy

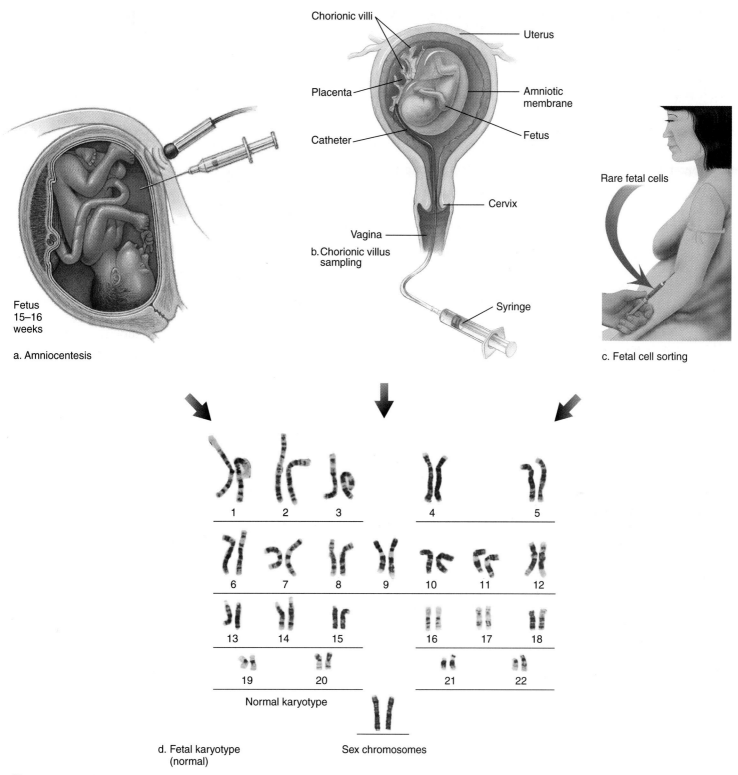

Chorionic villi

Uterus

Placenta

Amniotic membrane

Catheter

Fetus

Cervix

Vagina

b. Chorionic villus sampling

Syringe

Fetus 15–16 weeks

a. Amniocentesis

Rare fetal cells

c. Fetal cell sorting

1	2	3		4	5
6	7	8	9	10	11	12
13	14	15		16	17	18
19	20		21	22

Normal karyotype

d. Fetal karyotype (normal)

Sex chromosomes

figure 11.4

Three ways to check a fetus's chromosomes. (*a*) In amniocentesis, a needle is inserted into the uterus to collect a sample of amniotic fluid, which contains fetal cells. The cells are grown in the laboratory and then dropped onto a microscope slide to spread the chromosomes. The chromosomes are then stained and arranged into a chromosome chart (karyotype). Amniocentesis is performed after the 15th week of gestation. (*b*) Chorionic villus sampling (CVS) removes cells of the chorionic villi, whose chromosomes match those of the fetus because they all descend from the fertilized ovum. CVS is usually performed earlier than amniocentesis. (*c*) Fetal cell sorting (experimental) separates fetal cells in the woman's circulation. A genetic counselor interprets results of these tests—a fetal karyotype (*d*)—for patients.

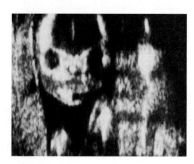

figure 11.5

In an ultrasound exam, sound waves are bounced off the embryo or fetus, and the pattern of deflected sound waves is converted into an image. By 13 weeks, the face can be discerned.

Preparing Cells for Chromosome Observation

Microscopists have tried to describe and display human chromosomes since the late nineteenth century (figure 11.6). Then, the prevailing view held that humans had an XO sex determination system, with females having an extra chromosome. Estimates of the human chromosome number ranged from 30 to 80. In 1923, Theophilus Painter published sketches of human chromosomes from three patients at a Texas state hospital, vacillating at first between 46 and 48, but finally deciding on 48 chromosomes. Painter showed that both sexes have the same chromosome number.

The difficulty in distinguishing between whether there were 46 or 48 chromosomes was physical—visualizing a cell in which chromosomes are not touching one another is challenging. To easily count the chromosomes, scientists had to find a way to capture them when they are the most condensed—during cell division—and spread them apart. Cytogeneticists use colchicine, an extract of the chrysanthemum plant, to arrest cells during division.

Swelling, Squashing, and Untangling

The dilemma of how to untangle the spaghettilike mass of chromosomes in a human cell was solved by accident in 1951. A technician mistakenly washed white blood cells being prepared for chromosome analysis in a salt solution that was less concentrated than the interiors of the cells. Water rushed into the cells, swelling them and separating the chromosomes.

Two years later, cytologists Albert Levan and Joe-Hin Tjio found that when they drew cell-rich fluid into a pipette and dropped it onto a microscope slide prepared with stain, the cells burst open and freed the mass of chromosomes. Addition of a glass coverslip spread the chromosomes enough that the scientists could count them. Another cytogeneticist, a former student of Painter's named John Birsele, suggested that Levan and Tjio use cells from tissue culture, and by 1956, they finally settled the matter of how many chromosomes occupy a diploid human cell—46. In the same year, J. L. Hamerton and C. E. Ford identified the expected 23 chromosomes in human gametes. Researchers could now study specific chromosomes.

Until very recently, a karyotype was constructed using a microscope to locate a cell in which the chromosomes are not touching, photographing the cell, developing a print, and cutting out the individual chromosomes and arranging them into a size-order chart. A computerized approach that produces a chromosome chart in minutes has largely replaced the cut-and-paste method. The device scans the ruptured cells in a drop of stain and selects one in which the chromosomes are the most visible and well spread. Image analysis software recognizes the band patterns of each stained chromosome pair, sorts the structures into a size-order chart, and prints the karyotype. If the software recognizes an abnormal band pattern, a database pulls out identical or similar karyotypes from other patients, providing clinical information on the anomaly.

Staining

The first karyotypes were rather crude because dyes stained the chromosomes a uniform color. Chromosomes were grouped into size classes, designated A through G, in decreasing size order. In 1959, scientists described the first chromosomal abnormalities—Down syndrome (an extra 21st chromosome), Turner syndrome (a female with only one X chromosome), and Klinefelter syndrome (a male with an extra X chromosome). The earliest stains could highlight large deletions and duplications, but more often than not, researchers only vaguely understood the nature of a chromosomal syndrome. In 1967, a mentally retarded child with material missing from chromosome 2 would have been diagnosed as having an "A-group chromosome" disorder.

Describing smaller scale chromosomal aberrations required better ways to distinguish among the chromosomes. In the 1970s, Swedish scientists developed more specific chromosome stains that create banding patterns unique to each chromosome. Combining stains creates even more bands, making it easier to distinguish chromosomes. Stains are specific for AT-rich or GC-rich stretches of DNA, or for heterochromatin, which stains darkly at the centromere and telomeres.

The ability to detect missing, extra, inverted, or misplaced bands allowed researchers to link many more syndromes with specific chromosome aberrations. In the late 1970s, Jorge Yunis at the University of Minnesota improved chromosome staining further by developing a way to synchronize white blood cells in culture, arresting them in early mitosis. His approach, called high-resolution chromosome banding, revealed that many more bands were present for every single band visualized earlier. Today a newer technology, **fluorescence in situ hybridization,** or FISH, is eclipsing even high-resolution chromosome banding, enabling cytogeneticists to focus on individual genes.

FISHing

One drawback of conventional chromosome stains is that they are not specific to particular chromosomes. Rather, they generate different banding patterns among the 24 human chromosome types. FISH is much more specific and provides information on chromosome abnormalities in just one to two days because FISH does not require cell culturing.

FISH begins with DNA probes that are complementary to DNA sequences found only on one chromosome type. The probes are attached to molecules that fluoresce when illuminated, producing a flash of color precisely where the probe binds to a

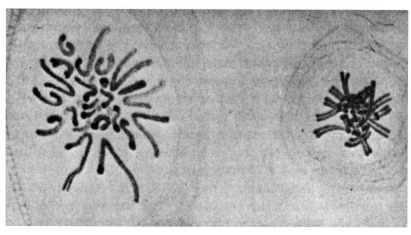

a.

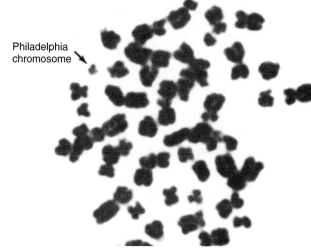

Philadelphia
chromosome

b.

![karyotype c]

1 2 3 4 5
A B

6 7 8 9 10 11 12
C

13 14 15 16 17 18
D E

19 20 21 22 X Y
F G

c.

![karyotype d]

1 2 3 4 5

6 7 8 9 10 11 12

13 14 15 16 17 18

19 20 21 22 X Y

d.

figure 11.6

Evolution of the karyotype. (*a*) The earliest drawings of chromosomes date from 1882, by German biologist Walter Flemming. (*b*) This 1960 chromosome preparation shows the Philadelphia chromosome, which causes leukemia, but reveals little else. (*c*) Stains create banding patterns in this abnormal karyotype. (*d*) This karyotype was constructed using FISH.

chromosome in a patient's sample. A FISH analysis easily identifies an extra chromosome 21 in cells from a fetus with Down syndrome, as figure 11.7 shows. Many laboratories performing amniocentesis or chorionic villus sampling use FISH probes specific to chromosomes 13, 18, 21, and the sex chromosomes to quickly identify the most common chromosome abnormalities. Researchers can now distinguish all 24 chromosomes with FISH probes and can discern levels of detail not possible with conventional staining. Such whole-karyotype FISH

analysis—called "chromosome painting" or "spectral karyotyping"—reveals complex small-scale chromosome aberrations not otherwise detectable.

Chromosomal Shorthand

Geneticists abbreviate the pertinent information in a karyotype. They list the total chromosome number first, followed by the sex chromosome constitution, then any abnormal autosomes. Finally, they use symbols to describe the type of aberration. A

normal male, for example, would be designated as 46,XY, and a female with Turner syndrome as 45,XO. A male who is missing part of the long arm of the 7th largest chromosome is written as 46,XY del(7q), where del means deletion.

Chromosome information is displayed in an **ideogram** (figure 11.8). Bands obtained by staining appear as stripes, and they are divided into numbered major regions and subregions. Specific gene loci appear in a list on the right-hand side. Ideograms are becoming increasingly

figure 11.7

(a) A karyotype of a fetus with trisomy 21 Down syndrome. Note the extra copy of chromosome 21. (b) FISH technology clearly shows the three copies of chromosome 21.

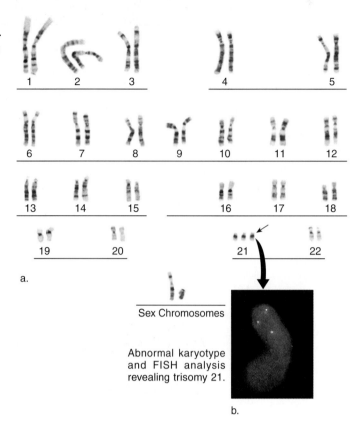

a.

Sex Chromosomes

Abnormal karyotype and FISH analysis revealing trisomy 21.

b.

figure 11.8

An ideogram is a schematic chromosome map. It indicates chromosome arm (p or q), major regions delineated by banding patterns, and the loci of known genes. This is a partial map of human chromosome 3.

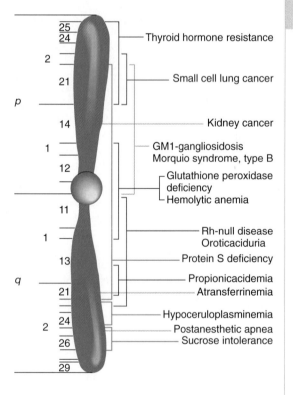

crowded with notations indicating specific genes. We can compare the evolution of cytogenetics in recent years to drawing maps of the United States with increasing detail, from outlines of the states, to major cities, to smaller cities and towns, and eventually even to streets.

Reading 11.1 discusses HACs—human artificial chromosomes.

Karyotypes are charts that display chromosomes in size order. Chromosomes can be obtained from any cell that has a nucleus. Fetal karyotypes are constructed from cells obtained by amniocentesis, chorionic villus sampling, or fetal cell sorting.

To detect a chromosome abnormality, cytogeneticists obtain cells, display, stain, and probe chromosomes, and then arrange them in a karyotype. Chromosomal shorthand summarizes the total number of chromosomes, sex chromosome constitution, and type of aberration present. Ideograms are maps of the distinguishing features of individual chromosomes.

Information from Chromosomes

Karyotypes are useful at several levels. When a baby is born with the distinctive facial characteristics of Down syndrome, only a karyotype can confirm the clinical diagnosis. Within families, karyotypes are used to identify relatives with a particular chromosomal aberration that can cause health problems. For example, in one New England family, several adult members died from a rare form of kidney cancer. Because inheriting the cancer was so unusual, researchers did karyotypes for the affected individuals. They all had an exchange (a translocation) between chromosome 3 and 8. When two young family members proved to have the unusual chromosome exchange, physicians could examine and monitor their kidneys. They detected cancer in these individuals in its very early stages, and because they did so, the operations were successful.

We can sequence genes and analyze genomes, but the basis of a chromosome's integrity remains somewhat mysterious. What are the minimal building blocks necessary to form a chromosome that persists throughout the repeated rounds of DNA replication and reassortment that constitute the life of a cell?

Cytogeneticists knew from work on other species that a chromosome consists of three basic parts:

—telomeres

—origins of replication. These sites, where DNA replication begins, are estimated to occur every 50 to 350 kilobases (kb, or thousands of bases) in human chromosomes

—centromeres (repeated sequences where spindle fibers attach)

The 24 human chromosomes range in size from 50 to 250 megabases (mb, or millions of bases). What would it take to construct a chromosome? There are two ways to tackle this question—pare down an existing chromosome to see how small it can get and still hold together, or build up a new chromosome from DNA pieces.

To cut an existing chromosome down to size, researchers swap in a piece of DNA that includes telomere sequences. New telomeres form at the insertion site, a little like prematurely ending a sentence by adding a period. This technique formed chromosomes as small as 3.5 Mb—but researchers couldn't get them out of cells for further study. The alternative approach, building a chromosome, wasn't feasible because we do not know the sequences of origin of replication sites.

Huntington Willard and colleagues at Case Western Reserve University solved the problem. They sent separately into cultured cells telomere DNA, arrays of a 171-base repeat that is a crucial part of centromeres, and, because they didn't know the origin of replication sites, random pieces of DNA from the human genome. In the cells, these pieces somehow came together in a correct orientation and formed what the researchers called "human artificial microchromosomes." These "HACs" are 6 to 10 Mb long, which is about 5 to 10 times smaller than the smallest natural human chromosome (figure 1). The hardy HACs withstood repeated rounds of cell division.

The next step is to systematically delete parts of the MAC recipe to learn the minimum number of bases necessary to bestow the qualities of chromosomeness—the abil-

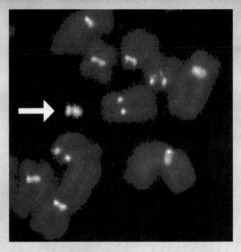

figure 1

Researchers introduced telomere sequences, centromere sequences, and other DNA pieces into cells in culture. The pieces aligned and assembled into human artificial microchromosomes.

(John Harrington, Huntington Willard, et al *Nature Genetics* 4: 345–355, 1997.)

ity of the DNA to remain intact as it replicates and redistributes to the beat of the cell cycle. HACs may also be useful in delivering gene therapy—unlike viruses currently used as vectors, HACs would not cause infection or disrupt genes on other chromosomes.

Karyotypes from individuals within different populations can sometimes reveal the effects of environmental toxins, if abnormalities appear only in a group exposed to a particular contaminant. Because chemicals and radiation that can cause cancer and birth defects often also break chromosomes into fragments or rings, detecting this genetic damage can alert physicians to the possibility that certain conditions will appear in the population.

Karyotypes compared between species can clarify evolutionary relationships. The more recent the divergence of two species from a common ancestor, the more closely related they are, and the more alike their chromosome banding patterns should be. Our closest relative, according to karyotypes, is the chimpanzee. FISH analysis shows that the human karyotype is remarkably similar to that of the domestic cat, and somewhat less similar to the karyotypes of mice, pigs, and cows. Using FISH to compare species is called ZOO-FISH.

The remainder of this chapter considers specific types of chromosome aberrations.

Abnormal Chromosome Number

Chromosomes can be abnormal in several ways. Table 11.2 summarizes types of chromosome anomalies.

Polyploidy

The most drastic upset in chromosome number is an entire extra set. A cell with one or more extra sets of chromosomes is

table 11.2

Chromosome Abnormalities

Type of Abnormality	Definition
Polyploidy	Extra chromosome sets
Aneuploidy	An extra or missing chromosome
Deletion	Part of a chromosome missing
Duplication	Part of a chromosome present twice
Inversion	Gene sequence reversed
Translocation	Two nonhomologous chromosomes join long arms or exchange parts

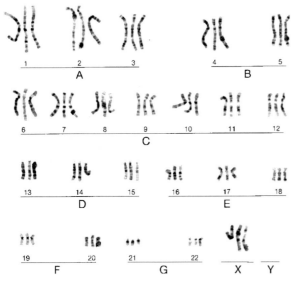

figure 11.9

Individuals with three copies of each chromosome (triploids) account for 17 percent of all spontaneous abortions and 3 percent of stillbirths and newborn deaths.

a **polyploid.** When all cells of an organism have the extra chromosome set, the problem arose from the formation of a diploid (rather than a normal haploid) gamete. If a haploid sperm fertilizes a diploid oocyte, for example, the fertilized ovum is **triploid,** with three copies of each chromosome (figure 11.9).

Most human polyploids die as embryos or fetuses, but occasionally an infant survives for a few days, with defects in nearly all organs. Interestingly, about 30 percent of flowering plant species tolerate polyploidy well. Many agriculturally important plant variants are polyploids.

Aneuploidy

Cells missing a chromosome or having an extra one are **aneuploid** ("not good set"). A normal chromosome number is termed **euploid** ("good set"). Symptoms resulting from aneuploidy depend upon which chromosome is missing or extra. Autosomal aneuploidy often results in mental retardation; this is because development of the central nervous system (brain and spinal cord) is so complex and of such long duration that nearly any large-scale genetic disruption affects it. Sex chromosome aneuploidy is usually less severe.

Most children born with the wrong number of chromosomes have an extra (a **trisomy**) rather than a missing one (a **monosomy**). Most monosomies are so severe that an affected embryo ceases developing. Trisomies and monosomies are named according to the chromosome involved, and the associated syndrome has traditionally been named for the investigator who first described it. Today, cytogenetic terminology is often used instead of names because it is more precise. For example, Down syndrome can result from an extra chromosome 21 (a trisomy) or a translocation.

The meiotic error that causes aneuploidy is called **nondisjunction.** Recall that in normal meiosis, homologs separate, and each of the resulting gametes receives only one member of each chromosome pair. In nondisjunction, a chromosome pair fails to separate at either the first or second meiotic division. This produces a sperm or oocyte that has two copies of a particular chromosome, or none, rather than the normal one copy (figure 11.10). When such a gamete fuses with its mate at fertilization, the zygote has either 45 or 47 chromosomes, instead of the normal 46.

One chromosome can be missing or extra in 49 ways—an extra or missing copy of each of the 22 autosomes, plus the five abnormal types of sex chromosome combinations (YO, XO, XXX, XXY, XYY). (Sometimes individuals are conceived who have 4 or even 5 sex chromosomes.) However, only 9 types of aneuploids appear in newborns, because the others cease developing before birth.

About 50 percent of spontaneous abortions result from extra or missing chromosomes. Most of these are 45, XO individuals (missing an X chromosome), triploids, or trisomy 16. About 9 percent of spontaneous abortions are trisomy 13, 18, or 21. These are also the most common autosomal aneuploids seen in newborns, although they are rare, affecting only 0.1 percent of all children. This means these conditions are usually lethal before birth.

Aneuploidy and polyploidy also arise during mitosis, producing groups of somatic cells with the extra or missing

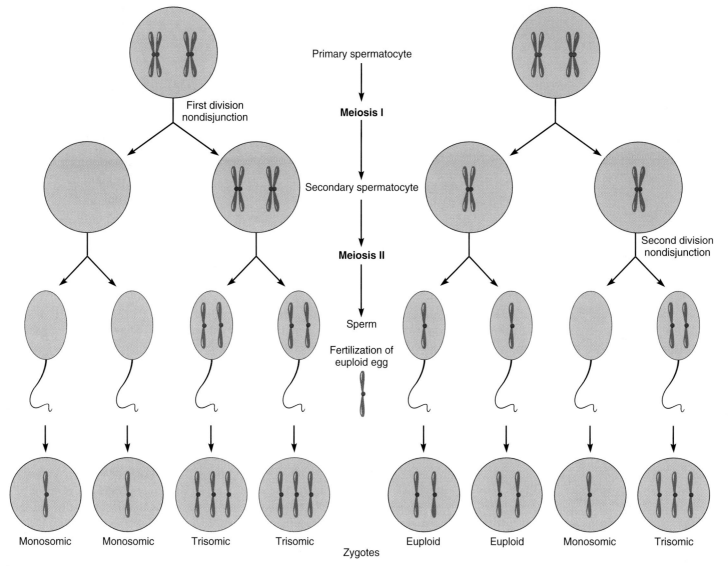

figure 11.10

Extra and missing chromosomes—aneuploidy. Unequal division of chromosome pairs can occur at either the first or second meiotic division. (*a*) A single pair of chromosomes unevenly partitioned into the two cells arising from the first division of meiosis in a male. The result: two sperm cells that have two copies of the chromosome, and two sperm cells that have no copies of that chromosome. When a sperm cell with two copies of the chromosome fertilizes a normal oocyte, the zygote is trisomic for that chromosome; when a sperm cell lacking the chromosome fertilizes a normal oocyte, the zygote is monosomic for that chromosome. Symptoms depend upon which chromosome is involved. (*b*) This nondisjunction occurs at the second meiotic division. Because the two products of the first division are unaffected, two of the mature sperm are normal and two aneuploid. Oocytes can undergo nondisjunction as well, leading to zygotes with extra or missing chromosomes when normal sperm cells fertilize them.

chromosome. If only a few cells are altered, health may not be affected. A mitotic abnormality occurring early in development, so that many cells descend from the unusual one, can seriously affect health. About 1 to 2 percent of Down syndrome cases are mosaic.

Trisomy 21 Down Syndrome— A Closer Look

The most common autosomal aneuploid is trisomy 21. The characteristic slanted eyes and flat face of a person with trisomy 21 prompted Sir John Langdon Haydon Down to coin the inaccurate term *mongolism* when he described the syndrome in 1886. As the medical superintendent of a facility for the profoundly mentally retarded, Down noted that about 10 percent of his patients resembled people of Mongolian heritage. The resemblance is

table 11.3

Signs and Symptoms Used
to Diagnose Down Syndrome
in Newborns

1. Poor muscle tone
2. Flat face
3. Eyes slant upward
4. Abnormally shaped ears
5. Single deep crease across palms
6. Joints extremely flexible
7. Underdeveloped fifth fingers
8. Skin folds in inner corners of eyes (epicanthal folds)
9. Gap between first and second toes
10. Large tongue

coincidental. Males and females of all ethnic groups can have Down syndrome.

A person with Down syndrome is usually short and has straight, sparse hair and a tongue protruding through thick lips. The hands have an abnormal pattern of creases, the joints are loose, and reflexes and muscle tone are poor, resulting in a "floppy" appearance. Developmental milestones (such as sitting, standing, and walking) come slowly, and toilet training may take several years. Intelligence varies greatly, from those with profound mental retardation, to those who can follow simple directions, read, and use a computer. People with Down syndrome have graduated from college and hold jobs. Parents of a child with Down syndrome can help their child reach maximal potential by providing a stimulating environment. Table 11.3 lists criteria used to diagnose Down syndrome in newborns.

Many people with Down syndrome have serious physical problems. Nearly 50 percent of babies with Down syndrome die before their first birthdays, often of heart defects, kidney defects, or a suppressed immune system that can make a bout with influenza deadly. Blockages in the digestive system are common and must be surgically corrected shortly after birth. A child with Down syndrome is fifteen times more likely to develop leukemia than a healthy child. Many of the medical problems that people with

Down syndrome suffer are treatable, so that life expectancy is now 55 years. In 1910, life expectancy was only to age nine!

Persons with Down syndrome who pass age forty often develop the black fibers and tangles of amyloid protein in their brains characteristic of Alzheimer disease. The chance of a person with trisomy 21 Down syndrome developing Alzheimer disease is 25 percent, compared to 6 percent for the general population. A gene on chromosome 21 causes one inherited form of Alzheimer disease. Perhaps the extra copy of the gene in trisomy 21 has a similar effect to a mutation in the gene that causes Alzheimer disease.

By looking at people who have a third copy of only part of chromosome 21, researchers are zeroing in on the genes whose malfunction causes the signs and symptoms of Down syndrome. This tiny chromosome contains only 1.5 percent of the genome, or about 1,500 genes. The distal third of the long arm is consistently present in people with Down syndrome who have only part of the extra chromosome. This region may house a few hundred genes. So far, researchers have identified a few genes that could cause signs and symptoms of Down syndrome: a gene for an enzyme involved in aging; a leukemia-causing gene; and a gene for a lens protein, whose overexpression might cause the cataracts often seen in the eyes of older people with Down syndrome.

The likelihood of giving birth to a child with Down syndrome increases dramatically with the age of the mother. The overall frequency of trisomy 21 Down syndrome is 1 in every 800 to 1,000 births. For women under thirty, the chances are 1 in 3,000. But at age 35, the risk is 1 in 400, and at age 40, 1 in 110. By age 45, risk jumps to 1 in 35, and by age 48, it is 1 in 9. However, 80 percent of children with trisomy 21 are born to women under age 35. This is because younger women are more likely to become pregnant and less likely to undergo amniocentesis. About 5 percent of cases can be traced to nondisjunction in the father.

The age factor in Down syndrome may reflect the fact that meiosis in the female is completed only after conception. The older a woman is, the longer her oocytes have been arrested on the brink of completing meiosis. During this time, the oocytes may have been

figure 11.11

An infant with trisomy 18 clenches its fist in a characteristic manner, with fingers overlapping.

exposed to chromosome-damaging chemicals, viruses, or radiation. Other trisomies are more likely to occur among the offspring of older women, too.

Trisomy 18—Edward Syndrome

Trisomies 18 and 13 were described in the same paper in 1960. Only 1 in 6,000 newborns has trisomy 18, but these individuals account for only 2.5 percent of trisomy 18 conceptions—that is, most affected individuals do not survive to be born. The severe symptoms of trisomy 18 explain why few affected fetuses survive and also make the syndrome relatively easy to diagnose prenatally using ultrasound. The associated major abnormalities include heart defects, a displaced liver, growth retardation, and oddly clenched fists. After birth, additional anomalies are apparent. These include overlapping placement of fingers (figure 11.11), a narrow and flat skull, abnormally shaped and low-set ears, a small mouth and face, unusual or absent fingerprints, short large toes with fused second and third toes, and "rocker-bottom" feet.

At least 90 percent of newborns with trisomy 18 do not survive the first six months, and only 5 percent are alive by one year of age. Affected children have great physical and mental disabilities, with developmental skills stalled at the six-month level. Still, physicians today often encourage parents to keep their babies at home.

Trisomy 13—Patau Syndrome

Trisomy 13 affects 1 in 15,000 births, but, like trisomy 18, this number may reflect only a small percentage of affected conceptions. Trisomy 13 has a different set of signs and symptoms than trisomy 18. Most striking is a fusion of the developing eyes, so that a fetus has one large eyelike structure in the center of the face. Major abnormalities affect the heart, kidneys, brain, face, and limbs. The nose is often malformed, and cleft lip and/or palate is present in a small head. Extra fingers and toes may occur. Appearance of a facial cleft and extra digits on an ultrasound exam are considered sufficient evidence to pursue chromosome analysis of the fetus to detect trisomy 13.

Examinations of affected newborns reveal more extensive anomalies that can be seen with ultrasound, including an extra spleen, abnormal liver structure, rotated intestines, and an abnormal pancreas. More than 80 percent of newborns with trisomy 13 die within the first month of life, with only about 3 percent alive by the sixth month. A few individuals have survived until adulthood, but do not progress developmentally beyond the six-month level.

Sex Chromosome Aneuploids

People with sex chromosome aneuploidy have extra or missing sex chromosomes. Table 11.4 indicates how these aneuploids can arise. Note that some conditions can result from either the male or female undergoing nondisjunction.

XO Turner Syndrome

In 1938, at a medical conference, an endocrinologist named Henry Turner described seven young women, aged fifteen to twenty-three, who were sexually undeveloped, short, had folds of skin on the back of the neck, and had malformed elbows. Alerted to what would become known as Turner syndrome, other physicians soon began identifying such patients in their practices. Everyone assumed the collection of traits reflected a hormonal insufficiency. They were right, but there was more to the story—a chromosomal imbalance caused the hormone deficit.

table 11.4

How Nondisjunction Leads to Sex Chromosome Aneuploids

Situation	Oocyte	Sperm	Consequence
Normal	X	Y	XY normal male
	X	X	XX normal female
Female nondisjunction	XX	Y	XXY Klinefelter syndrome
	XX	X	XXX triplo-X
	O	Y	YO nonviable
	O	X	XO Turner syndrome
Male nondisjunction (meiosis I)	X	O	XO Turner syndrome
	X	XY	XXY Klinefelter syndrome
Male nondisjunction (meiosis II)	X	XX	XXX triplo-X
	X	YY	XYY Jacobs syndrome

In 1954, at a London hospital, P. E. Polani discovered that cells from Turner patients lacked a Barr body, the dark spot that indicates the presence of a second X chromosome. Might the lack of a sex chromosome cause the symptoms, particularly the failure to mature sexually? By 1959, karyotyping confirmed the absence of an X chromosome in cells of Turner syndrome patients.

Like the autosomal aneuploids, Turner syndrome is found more frequently among spontaneously aborted fetuses than among liveborns—99 percent of affected fetuses die before birth. The syndrome accounts for 1 in 2,000 female births. However, those born with the condition are usually not seriously affected, often not knowing they have a chromosome abnormality until they lag behind their classmates in sexual development.

In childhood, the only signs of Turner syndrome are wide-set nipples and skin flaps on the back of the neck. At sexual maturity, sparse body hair develops, but the girls do not ovulate or menstruate and have underdeveloped breasts. Ovaries, fallopian tubes, and the uterus are very small and immature. Intelligence is normal, and these women can lead fairly normal lives if they receive hormone supplements. Although women with Turner syndrome are infertile, individuals who are mosaics may have children. Interestingly, Turner syndrome is the only aneuploid condition that seems unrelated to the age of the mother.

Extra X Chromosomes

About 1 in every 1,000 females has an extra X chromosome in each of her cells, a condition called triplo-X. The only symptom seems to be tallness and menstrual irregularities. Although triplo-X females are rarely mentally retarded, they tend to be less intelligent than their siblings.

A triplo-X individual may produce some oocytes bearing two X chromosomes, which increases her risk of producing daughters who are triplo-X, like herself, or sons who are XXY.

Males with an extra X chromosome have Klinefelter syndrome (XXY). Physicians first described the signs and symptoms in 1942, and geneticists identified the underlying chromosomal anomaly in 1959. Men severely affected with Klinefelter syndrome are underdeveloped sexually, with rudimentary testes and prostate glands and no pubic or facial hair. They have very long arms and legs, large hands and feet, and may develop breast tissue. However, many men do not learn that they have the syndrome until they have fertility problems (Reading 11.2).

Testosterone injections during adolescence can limit limb lengthening and prompt development of secondary sexual characteristics. Boys and men with Klinefelter syndrome may be slow to learn, but they are usually not mentally retarded unless they have more than two X chromosomes, which happens rarely. Klinefelter syndrome occurs in 1 out of 500 male births.

I was diagnosed with Klinefelter syndrome (KS) a little more than a year ago, at age 25, in February 1996. Being diagnosed has been . . . a big sigh of relief after a life of frustrations. Throughout my early childhood, teens, and even somewhat now, I was very shy, reserved, and had trouble making friends. I would fly into rages for no apparent reason. My parents knew when I was very young that there was something about me that wasn't right.

I saw many psychologists, psychiatrists, therapists, and doctors, and their only diagnosis was "learning disabilities." In the seventh grade, I was told by a psychologist that I was stupid and lazy, and I would never amount to anything. After barely graduating high school, I started out at a local community college. I received an associate degree in business administration, and never once sought special help. I transferred to a small liberal arts college to finish up my bachelor of science degree, and spent an extra year to complete a second degree. Then I started a job as a software engineer for an Internet-based company. I have been using computers for 17 years and have learned everything I needed to know on my own.

To find out my KS diagnosis, I had gone to my general physician for a physical. He noticed that my testes were smaller than they should be and sent me for blood work. The karyotype showed Klinefelter syndrome, 47, XXY. After seeing the symptoms of KS and what effects they might have, I found it described me perfectly. But, after getting over the initial shock and dealing with the denial, depression, and anger, I decided that there could be things much worse in life. I decided to take a positive approach.

There are several types of treatments for KS. I give myself a testosterone injection in the thigh once every two weeks. My learning and thought processes have become stronger, and I am much more outgoing and have become more of a leader. Granted, not all of this is due to the increased testosterone level, some of it is from a new confidence level and from maturing.

I feel that parents who are finding out prior to the birth of their son (that he will have Klinefelter syndrome) or parents of affected infants or young children are very lucky. There is so much they can do to help their child have a great life. I have had most all of the symptoms at some time in my life, and I've gotten through and done well.

Stefan Schwarz
sschwarz13@juno.com

(Stefan Schwarz runs a Boston-area support group for KS.)

XYY, or Jacobs Syndrome

One male in 1,000 has an extra Y chromosome. Awareness of this controversial sex chromosome aneuploidy arose in 1961, when a tall, healthy, middle-aged man, known for his boisterous behavior, underwent a routine chromosome check after fathering a child with Down syndrome. The man had an extra Y chromosome. A few other cases were detected over the next several years.

In 1965, researcher Patricia Jacobs published results of a survey among 197 inmates at Carstairs, a high-security mental hospital in Scotland. Of 12 men with unusual chromosomes, 7 had an extra Y! Might their violent or aggressive behavior be linked to their extra Y chromosome? Jacobs thought so, and her findings were repeated in studies in England and Swedish mental institutions. Soon after, Newsweek magazine ran a cover story on "congenital criminals." In 1968, defense attorneys in France and Australia pleaded their violent clients' cases on the basis of an inherited flaw, the extra Y of what became known as Jacobs syndrome. Meanwhile, the National Institute of Mental Health, in Bethesda, Maryland, held a conference on the condition, lending legitimacy to the hypothesis that an extra Y predisposes to violent behavior.

In the early 1970s, newborn screens began in hospital nurseries in England, Canada, Denmark, and Boston. XYY babies were visited by social workers and psychologists who offered "anticipatory guidance" to the parents on how to deal with their toddling future criminals. By 1974, geneticists and others halted the program, pointing out that singling out these boys on the basis of a few statistical studies was inviting self-fulfilling prophecy.

Today, we know that 96 percent of XYY males are apparently normal. The only symptoms attributable to the extra chromosome may be great height, acne, and perhaps speech and reading problems. An explanation of the continued prevalence of XYY among mental-penal institution populations may be more psychological than biological. Large body size may lead teachers, employers, parents, and others to expect more of these people, and a few of them may deal with this stress by becoming aggressive.

Geneticists have never observed a sex chromosome constitution of one Y and no X. Since the Y chromosome carries little genetic material, too much genetic material is probably missing to sustain development beyond a few cell divisions in a YO embryo.

Karyotypes provide information on individuals, families, and populations and help identify chromosome abnormalities such as polyploidy and aneuploidy. Polyploids have extra sets of chromosomes, while aneuploids have an extra or missing chromosome. Nondisjunction during meiosis causes aneuploidy. Trisomics are more likely to survive than monosomics, and sex chromosome aneuploidy is less severe than autosomal aneuploidy. Mitotic nondisjunction produces chromosomal mosaics.

Down syndrome (trisomy 21) is the most common aneuploid, followed by trisomies 18 and 13. Sex chromosome aneuploids include Turner syndrome (XO), triplo-X females, Klinefelter syndrome (XXY), and Jacobs syndrome XYY males.

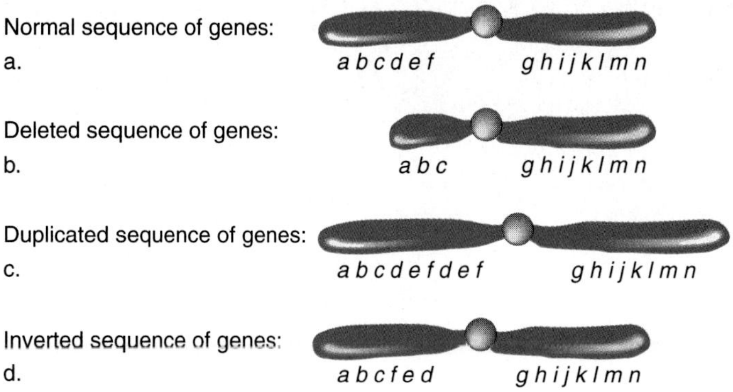

Normal sequence of genes:
a. abcdef ghijklmn

Deleted sequence of genes:
b. abc ghijklmn

Duplicated sequence of genes:
c. abcdefdef ghijklmn

Inverted sequence of genes:
d. abcfed ghijklmn

figure 11.12

If a hypothetical normal gene sequence appears as shown in (*a*), then (*b*) represents a deletion, (*c*) a duplication, and (*d*) an inversion.

Deletions, Duplications, and Rearrangements

Sometimes only part of a chromosome is missing (a **deletion**), extra (a **duplication**), is moved to another chromosome (a **translocation**), or switched around (an **inversion**) (figure 11.12). These are larger-scale versions of the gene deletions and duplications chapter 10 discussed.

Cri-du-chat syndrome (French for "cat's cry") is associated with deletion of the short arm of chromosome 5. It is also called 5p⁻ syndrome. Affected children have a high-pitched cry similar to the mewing of a cat, pinched facial features, and are mentally retarded and developmentally delayed. Researchers studying the extent of the deletions in several families discovered that the chromosome region responsible for the catlike cry is distinct from the region causing mental retardation and developmental delay, confirming the idea that a deletion causes a syndrome by removing more than one gene. This is important because it enables physicians to determine whether a child will have only the catlike cry and perhaps poor weight gain, or will have all of the signs and symptoms. Other symptoms include low birth weight, poor muscle tone, a small head, and impaired language skills. Reading 11.3 describes a child who had 5p⁻ syndrome.

Duplications, like deletions, are more likely to cause symptoms if they are extensive. For example, duplications of chromosome 15 do not produce a phenotype unless they repeat several genes. Figure 11.13 shows three duplicated chromosome 15s, with increasing amounts of material repeated. Many people have the first two types of duplications and have no symptoms. However, several unrelated individuals with the third, larger duplication have seizures and are mentally retarded.

FISH can detect tiny deletions and duplications that are smaller than the bands revealed by conventional staining. Small duplications are generally not dangerous, but some "microdeletions" have been associated with a number of syndromes. Y chromosome microdeletions, for example, cause male infertility. Deletions and duplications can arise from chromosome rearrangements, including translocations, inversions, and ring chromosomes.

Translocations

In a translocation, different (nonhomologous) chromosomes exchange or combine parts. Exposure to certain viruses, drugs, and radiation can cause translocations, but often they arise for no apparent reason.

There are two types of translocations. In a **Robertsonian translocation,** the short arms of two different types of chromosomes break, leaving sticky ends that then cause the two long arms to adhere. This forms a new, large chromosome made of the long arms of the two different chromosomes. The person with the large, translocated chromosome, called a **translocation carrier,** may not have symptoms if a crucial gene has not been deleted or damaged. Even so, he or she may produce unbalanced gametes—sperm or oocytes with too many or too few genes. This can lead to reproductive difficulties, such as spontaneous abortion (miscarriage) or birth defects.

One in twenty cases of Down syndrome arises because a parent has a Robertsonian translocation between chromosome 21 and another, usually chromosome 14. The problem arises because the individual with the translocated chromosome produces some gametes that lack either of the involved chromosomes or has extra material from one of them (figure 11.14). In such a case, each fertilized ovum has a 1 in 2 chance of ending as a spontaneous abortion, and a 1 in 6 chance of developing into an individual with Down syndrome. The other two possibilities—normal chromosomes and a translocation carrier like the parent—have normal phenotypes. Either a male or a female can be a translocation carrier, and the condition is not related to age.

In a **reciprocal translocation,** two different chromosomes exchange parts. FISH can highlight the involved chromosomes

Ashley's Message of Hope

What is it like to have a child born with cri-du-chat syndrome? How does this affect the family and its future? What kinds of assistance can the medical community offer the family?

The birth of any child raises many questions. Will she have my eyes, her dad's smile? What will she want to be when she grows up? But the biggest question for every parent is "Will she be healthy?" If complications occur during birth or if the child is born with a genetic disorder, the questions become more profound and immediate. "How did this happen?" "Where do we go from here?" "Will this happen again?"

Our daughter, Ashley Elizabeth Naylor, was born August 12, 1988. We had a lot of mixed emotions the day of her birth, but mainly we felt fear and despair. The doctors suspected complications, which led to a cesarean section, but the exact problem was not known. Two weeks after her birth, chromosome analysis revealed cri-du-chat (cat cry) syndrome, also known as 5p⁻ syndrome because part of the short arm of one copy of chromosome 5 is missing. The prognosis was uncertain. This is a rare disorder, we were told, and little could be offered to help our daughter. The doctors used the words "profoundly retarded," which cut like a knife through our hearts and our hopes. It wasn't until a few years later that we realized how little the medical community actually knew about cri-du-chat syndrome and especially about our little girl!

Ashley defied all the standard medical labels, as well as her doctors' expectations. Her spirit and determination enabled her to walk with the aid of a walker and express herself using sign language and a communication device. With early intervention and education at United Services for the Handicapped, Ashley found the resources and additional encouragement she needed to succeed. In return, Ashley freely offered one of her best loved and sought after gifts—her hugs. Her bright eyes and glowing smile captured the hearts of everyone she met.

In May of 1992, Ashley's small body could no longer support the spirit that inspired so many. She passed away after a long battle with pneumonia. Her physical presence is gone, but her message remains: hope.

If you are a parent faced with similar profound questions after the birth of your child, do not assume one doctor has all the answers. Search for doctors who respect your child enough to talk to her, not just about her. Above all, find an agency or a school that can help you give your child a chance to succeed. Early education for your child and support for yourself are crucial.

If you are a student in a health field, become as knowledgeable as possible and stay current with the latest research, but most importantly, be sensitive to those

figure 1

Ashley Naylor brought great joy to her family and community during her short life.
Courtesy of Kathy Naylor.

who seek your help. Each word you speak is taken to heart. Information is important, but hope can make all the difference in a family's future.

—Kathy Naylor

(figure 11.15). If the chromosome exchange does not break any genes, then a person who has both translocated chromosomes is healthy and is also a translocation carrier. He or she has the normal amount of genetic material, but it is rearranged.

A reciprocal translocation carrier can have symptoms if the rearrangement affects a gene with a detectable phenotype. Figure 11.16 shows a reciprocal translocation between chromosomes 2 and 20 that causes a condition called Alagille syndrome.

A translocation carrier produces some unbalanced gametes—sperm or oocytes that have deletions or duplications of some of the genes in the translocated chromosomes. The resulting phenotype depends upon the particular genes that the chromosomal rearrangement disrupts. A family with multiple chromosome anomalies and spontaneous abortions might have a translocation. People with translocations are very valuable to medical genetics research. Studies to identify disease-causing genes often begin with people whose translocations literally point the way toward the locus of interest.

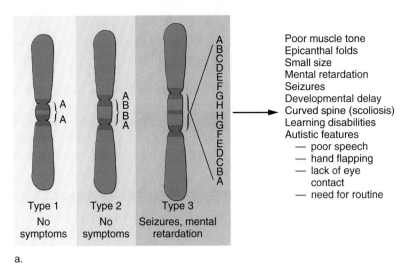

Poor muscle tone
Epicanthal folds
Small size
Mental retardation
Seizures
Developmental delay
Curved spine (scoliosis)
Learning disabilities
Autistic features
— poor speech
— hand flapping
— lack of eye
  contact
— need for routine

Type 1
No
symptoms

Type 2
No
symptoms

Type 3
Seizures, mental
retardation

a.

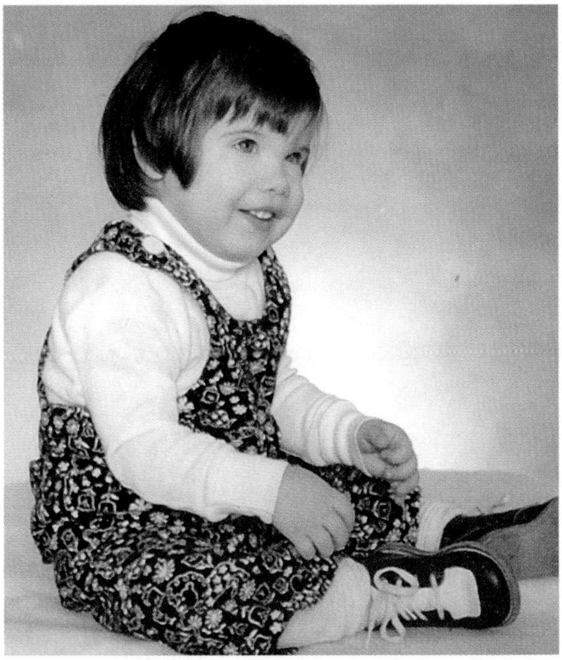

b.

figure 11.13

A study of duplications of parts of chromosome 15 revealed that small duplications do not affect the phenotype, but larger ones may. (*a*) The letters indicate specific DNA sequences, which serve as markers to compare chromosome regions. Note that the duplication is also inverted. (*b*) This child, who had "inv dup (15) syndrome," appears normal but has minor facial anomalies characteristic of the condition.

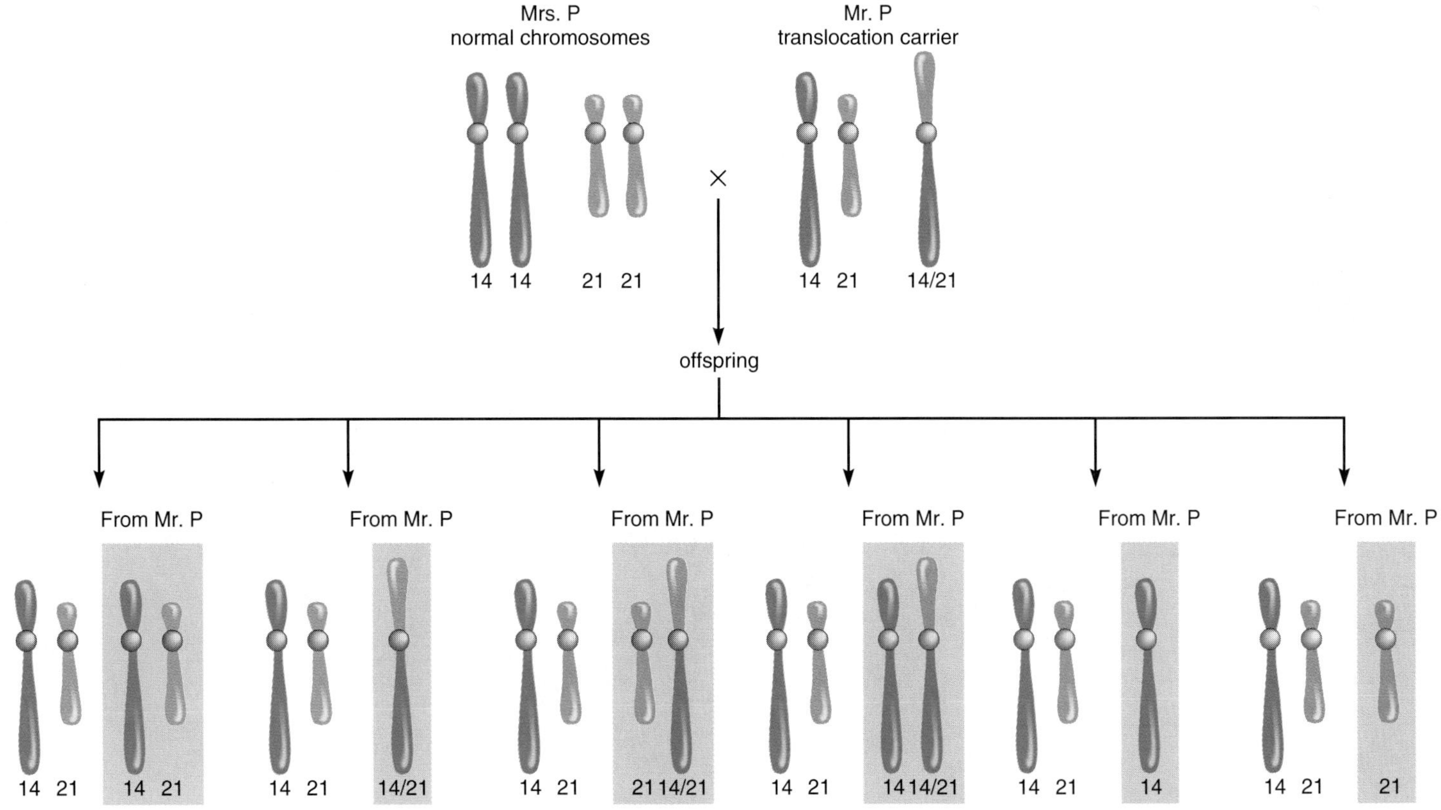

Mrs. P
normal chromosomes

Mr. P
translocation carrier

14 14   21 21

×

14 21   14/21

offspring

From Mr. P

From Mr. P

From Mr. P

From Mr. P

From Mr. P

From Mr. P

14 21   14 21

14 21   14/21

14 21   21 14/21

14 21   14 14/21

14 21   14

14 21   21

a. Balanced
(normal
karyotype)

b. Balanced
(translocation
carrier)

c. Excess 21
(translocation
Down syndrome)

d. Excess 14
(spontaneous
abortion)

e. Deficient 21
(spontaneous
abortion)

f. Deficient 14
(spontaneous
abortion)

figure 11.14

A Robertsonian translocation can cause spontaneous abortion (pregnancy loss) or syndromes. Mr. P. is a translocation carrier. He has only 45 chromosomes because the long arm of one chromosome 14 has joined the long arm of one chromosome 21, with their centromeres joined and short arms lost. He has no symptoms. Mr. P. makes six types of sperm cells, and they determine the fate of his and Mrs. P.'s offspring. (*a*) A sperm with one normal chromosome 14 and one normal 21 yields a chromosomally normal child. (*b*) A sperm carrying the translocated chromosome produces a child who is a translocation carrier, like Mr. P. (*c*) If a sperm contains Mr. P.'s normal 21 and his translocated chromosome, the child receives too much chromosome 21 material, and therefore has Down syndrome. (*d*) A sperm containing the translocated chromosome and a normal 14 leads to excess chromosomal 14 material, which is lethal in the embryo or fetus. (*e*) *and* (*f*) If a sperm lacks either chromosome 14 or 21, it leads to monosomies, which are lethal prenatally.

Inversions

An inverted sequence of chromosome bands indicates that part of the chromosome has flipped around. Empirical studies show that 5 to 10 percent of inversions

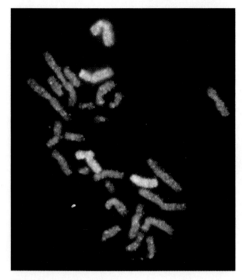

figure 11.15

FISH reveals a translocation by highlighting sequences from two different chromosomes, with two colors, that appear together.

cause health problems, probably because they disrupt important genes. Sometimes inversions are detected in fetal chromosomes, but we do not know whether symptoms are associated. It is distressing for prospective parents to hear that "something showed up on the fetus's chromosomes, but we don't know what it means." When this happens, the parents can have their chromosomes checked. If one of them has the inversion and is healthy, then the child will most likely not have symptoms related to the inversion. If neither parent has the inversion, then the anomaly arose in a gamete that gave rise to the fetus. Effects may not be known.

Like a translocation carrier, an adult can be heterozygous for an inversion and be healthy, but have reproductive problems. One woman had an inversion in the long arm of chromosome 15 and had two spontaneous abortions, two stillbirths, and two children with multiple problems who died within days of birth. She did eventually give birth to a healthy child. How did the inversion cause these problems?

Inversions with such devastating effects can be traced to meiosis, when a crossover occurs between the inverted chromosome and the noninverted homolog. In order for the genes to align, the inverted chromosome contorts and forms a loop.

Two types of inversions are distinguished by the position of the centromere relative to the inverted section. A **paracentric inversion** does not include the centromere. A single crossover gives rise to one normal and one inverted chromosome—but also two very abnormal chromosomes. One has both centromeres and some genes extra and others missing, the other is a small fragment, missing a centromere, lost when the cell divides (figure 11.17).

A **pericentric inversion** includes the centromere. A crossover in it produces one normal and one inverted chromosome, plus two abnormal chromosomes, which have duplications and deletions, but one centromere each (figure 11.18).

Isochromosomes

Another meiotic error that leads to unbalanced genetic material is the formation of an **isochromosome,** or a chromosome with identical arms. This occurs when, during division, the centromeres part in the wrong plane (figure 11.19).

Ring Chromosomes

Chromosomes shaped like rings form in 1 out of 25,000 conceptions. They can involve any chromosome. Ring chromosomes may

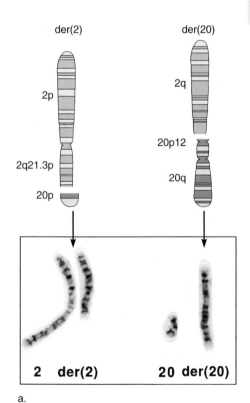

der(2)   der(20)

2p

2q

2q21.3p

20p12

20q

20p

2   der(2)   20   der(20)

a.

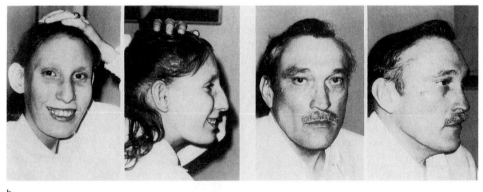

b.

figure 11.16

(a) In one family with Alagille syndrome, a reciprocal translocation occurs between chromosomes 2 and 20. Apparently the exchange disrupts a gene on chromosome 20 that causes the condition, because other families with the syndrome have deletions in this region of the chromosome. ("der" means derivative.) (b) Alagille syndrome produces a characteristic face, absence of bile ducts in the liver, eye and rib abnormalities, heart defects, and severe itching. The condition is so variable that some people do not know that they have it; this father (right) did not realize he had the syndrome until he produced an affected child (left).

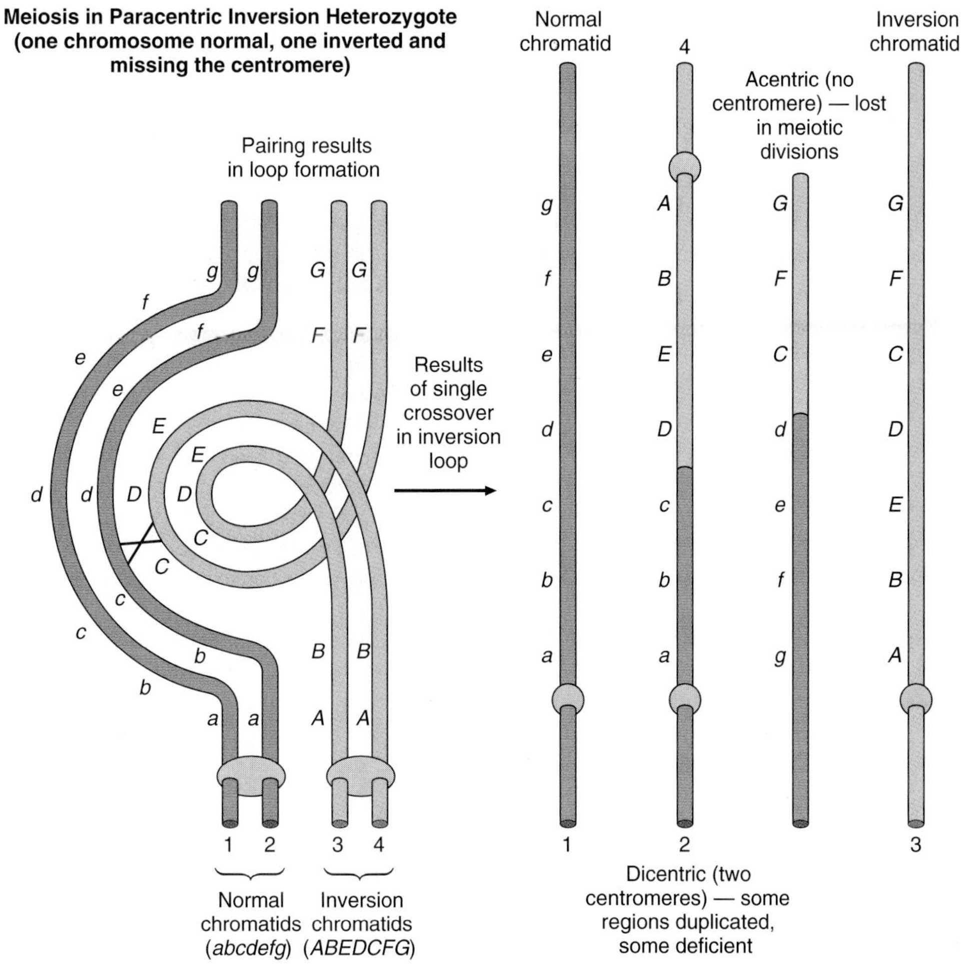

**Meiosis in Paracentric Inversion Heterozygote
(one chromosome normal, one inverted and
missing the centromere)**

Pairing results
in loop formation

Results
of single
crossover
in inversion
loop

Normal
chromatids
(abcdefg)

Inversion
chromatids
(ABEDCFG)

Normal
chromatid

Acentric (no
centromere) — lost
in meiotic
divisions

Inversion
chromatid

Dicentric (two
centromeres) — some
regions duplicated,
some deficient

figure 11.17

A crossover between a chromosome with a
paracentric inversion and its normal
homolog, when in the region of the inversion,
produces one normal chromatid, one
inverted chromatid, one with two centromeres
(called a dicentric), and one with no
centromere (called an acentric fragment). The
letters *a* through *g* denote genes.

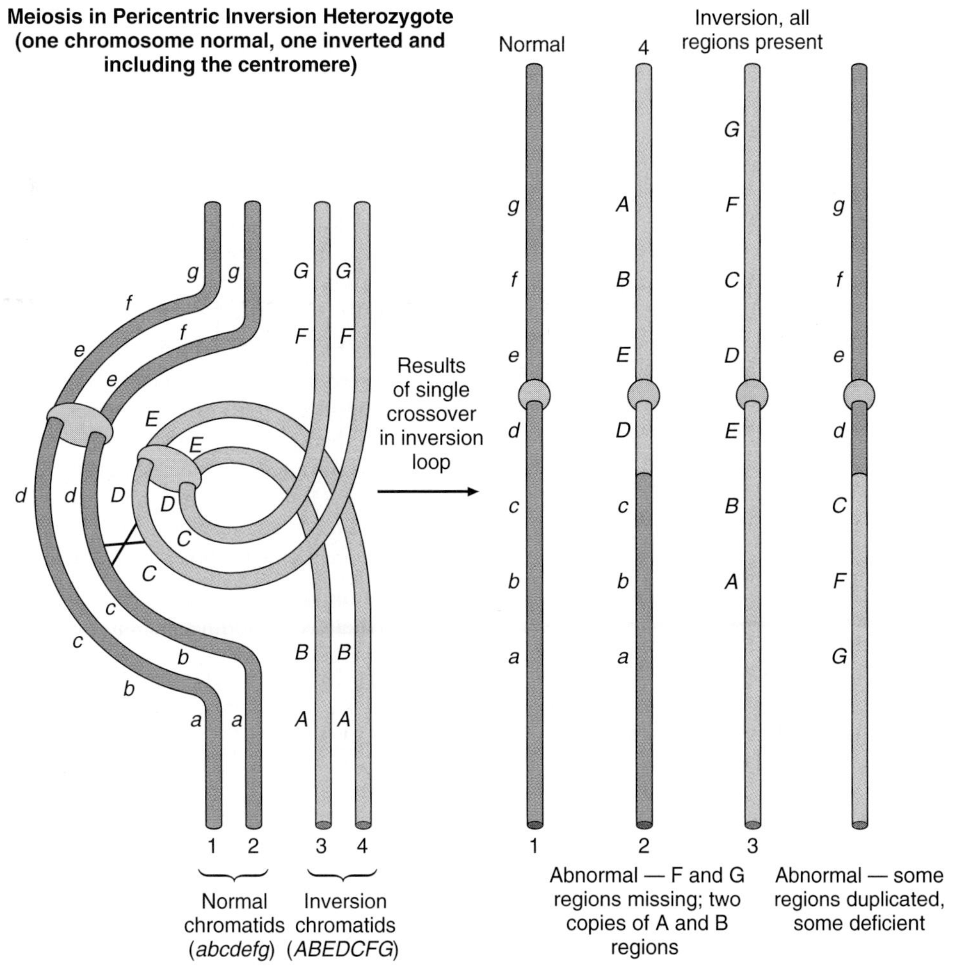

**Meiosis in Pericentric Inversion Heterozygote
(one chromosome normal, one inverted and
including the centromere)**

Normal

Inversion, all
regions present

Results
of single
crossover
in inversion
loop

Normal
chromatids
(abcdefg)

Inversion
chromatids
(ABEDCFG)

Abnormal — F and G
regions missing; two
copies of A and B
regions

Abnormal — some
regions duplicated,
some deficient

figure 11.18

A pericentric inversion in one chromosome
leads to two chromatids with duplications
and deletions, one normal chromatid, and
one inverted chromatid if a crossover occurs.

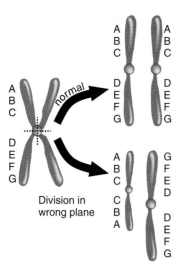

figure 11.19

Isochromosomes have identical arms. They form when chromatids divide along the wrong plane (in this depiction, horizontally rather than vertically).

arise when telomeres are lost, leaving sticky ends that tend to close up. Exposure to radiation can form rings.

Ring chromosomes can produce symptoms when they add genetic material. For example, a small ring chromosome of DNA from chromosome 22 causes cat eye syndrome. Affected children have vertical pupils, are mentally retarded, have heart and urinary tract anomalies, and have skin growing over the anus. They have 47 chromosomes—the normal two chromosome 22 and a ring.

People usually learn their chromosomal makeup only when something is wrong—a family history of reproductive problems, exposure to a toxin, cancer, or symptoms of a known chromosomal disorder. With our rapidly improving ability to peer into the biochemical makeup of our chromosomes, and with the human genome project daily lengthening the list of genes whose chromosomal homes we know, it is very likely that within a decade, consulting chromosomes will be an integral and routine part of medical care—beginning before birth.

summary

1. **Cytogenetics** is the study of chromosome variants and their effects on phenotypes.

2. A chromosome consists of DNA, RNA, and proteins.

3. Chromosomes are distinguishable by size, centromere position, **satellites,** DNA probes to specific sequences, and staining patterns.

4. A **metacentric** chromosome has two fairly equal arms. A **submetacentric** chromosome has a large arm designated "q" and a short arm designated "p." An **acrocentric** chromosome's centromere is near a tip, so that it has one long arm and one very short arm.

5. **Heterochromatin** stains darkly and maintains a chromosome's structural integrity, and light-staining **euchromatin** encodes protein. Heterochromatin surrounds the centromere, comprises telomeres, and is interspersed with euchromatin.

6. Chromosomes can be obtained from any cell that has a nucleus. Prenatal diagnostic techniques that obtain fetal chromosomes include **amniocentesis, chorionic villus sampling,** and **fetal cell sorting.**

7. Hand-cut chromosome charts (**karyotypes**) and classical stains to view chromosomes are giving way to computerized karyotyping and chromosome-specific **fluorescence in situ hybridization** (FISH). **Ideograms** are diagrams that display chromosome bands, FISH data, and gene loci.

8. Chromosomal abnormalities alter the number or arrangement of chromosomes. A **euploid** somatic human cell has 22 pairs of autosomes and a pair of sex chromosomes. **Polyploid** cells have extra chromosome sets, and **aneuploids** have extra or missing individual chromosomes. **Trisomies** (an extra chromosome) are less harmful than **monosomies** (lack of a chromosome), and sex chromosome aneuploidy is less severe than autosomal aneuploidy. **Nondisjunction** (uneven division of chromosomes in meiosis) causes aneuploidy. Most autosomal aneuploids cease developing as embryos.

9. A **deletion** is a chromosome missing some genetic material, and a **duplication** is a repeat of some genetic material. Small duplications may not affect the phenotype, but even a small deletion is usually harmful. Chromosomal rearrangements can generate deletions and duplications when unbalanced gametes form.

10. In a **Robertsonian translocation,** the short arms of two acrocentric chromosomes break, and the long arms join, forming an unusual, large chromosome. In a **reciprocal translocation,** two nonhomologous chromosomes exchange parts. In both types, a **translocation carrier** may have an associated phenotype if the translocation disrupts a vital gene. A translocation carrier also produces a predictable percentage of unbalanced gametes, which can lead to birth defects and spontaneous abortions.

11. A heterozygote for an **inversion** may have reproductive problems if a crossover occurs between the inverted region and the noninverted homolog, generating deletions and duplications. A **paracentric inversion** does not include the centromere; a **pericentric inversion** does.

12. **Isochromosomes** repeat one chromosome arm but delete the other and form when the centromere divides in the wrong plane during meiosis. Ring chromosomes form when telomeres are removed, and may be lost or grow.

review questions

1. What happens during meiosis to produce each of the following?

   a. an aneuploid

   b. a polyploid

   c. the increased risk of Down syndrome in the offspring of a woman over forty at the time of conception

   d. recurrent spontaneous abortions to a couple in which the man has a pericentric inversion

   e. several children with Down syndrome in a family where one parent is a translocation carrier

2. A human liver has patches of cells that are octaploid—that is, they have eight sets of chromosomes. Explain how this might arise.

3. Describe an individual with each of the following chromosome constitutions. Mention the person's sex and possible phenotype.

   a. 47,XXX

   b. 45,XO

   c. 47,XX, trisomy 21

   d. 47,XX

4. Which chromosomal anomaly might you expect to find more frequently among the members of the National Basketball Association than in the general population? Cite a reason for your answer.

5. List three examples illustrating the idea that the extent of genetic material involved in a chromosomal aberration affects the severity of the associated phenotype.

6. List three types of chromosomal aberrations that can cause duplications and/or deletions, and explain how they do so.

7. Why would having the same inversion on both members of a homologous chromosome pair *not* lead to unbalanced gametes, as having the inversion on only one chromosome would?

8. Define or describe the following technologies:

   a. high-resolution chromosome banding

   b. FISH

   c. amniocentesis

   d. chorionic villus sampling

   e. fetal cell sorting

   f. maternal serum markers

applied questions

1. Distinguish among Down syndrome caused by aneuploidy, mosaicism, and translocation.

2. A couple has a son who is diagnosed with Klinefelter syndrome. The man blames the woman. Explain how an abnormality in the man's chromosomes might also cause the condition.

3. Some of Theophilus Painter's early chromosome preparation came from testicular tissue from hospitalized mental patients who were castrated to control their habit of publicly masturbating. How might use of this material have made it difficult to determine the correct human chromosome number?

4. DiGeorge syndrome causes abnormal parathyroid glands, disrupting blood calcium levels; heart defects; and an underdeveloped thymus gland, impairing development of the immune system. About 85 percent of patients have a microdeletion of a particular area of chromosome 22. In one family, a girl, her mother, and a maternal aunt have very mild cases of DiGeorge syndrome, and they also all have a reciprocal translocation involving chromosomes 22 and 2.

   a. How can a microdeletion and a translocation cause the same set of symptoms?

   b. Why were the cases of people with the translocation less severe than those of people with the microdeletion?

   c. What other problems might arise in the translocation family?

5. Two sets of parents who have children with Down syndrome meet at a clinic. The Phelps know that their son has trisomy 21. The Watkins, however, have two affected children, and Mrs. Watkins has had two spontaneous abortions. Why should the Watkins probably be more concerned about future reproductive problems than the Phelps? How are the offspring of the two families different, even though they have the same symptoms?

6. For an exercise in a college genetics laboratory course, a healthy student constructs a karyotype from a cell in a drop of her blood. She finds only one chromosome 3 and one chromosome 21, plus two unusual chromosomes that do not seem to have matching partners.

   a. What type of chromosomal abnormality does she have?

   b. Why doesn't she have any symptoms?

   c. Would you expect any of her relatives to have any particular medical problems? If so, which medical conditions?

7. A fetus dies in the uterus. Several of its cells are karyotyped. Approximately 75 percent of the cells are diploid, and 25 percent are tetraploid (have 4 copies of each chromosome). What do you think happened? When in development did it probably occur?

suggested readings

Bianchi, Diana. April 1998. Fetal DNA in maternal plasma: the plot thickens and the placental barrier thins. *The American Journal of Human Genetics.* PCR using fluorescent primers can spot the few fetal cells in maternal circulation.

Cheng, Sou-De, et al. October 1994. Cytogenetic and molecular characterization of inverted duplicated chromosome 15 from 11 patients. *The American Journal of Human Genetics,* vol. 55. A duplicated and flipped section of chromosome 15 doesn't cause symptoms unless it is extensive.

Gersh, M., et al. June 1995. Evidence for a distinct region causing a catlike cry in patients with 5p deletions. *The American Journal of Human Genetics,* vol. 56. Careful analysis of chromosome 5 correlates specific deletions to specific aspects of cri-du-chat syndrome.

Glover, Thomas W. July 1995. CATCHing a break on 22. *Nature Genetics,* vol. 10. CATCH is an acronym for a syndrome affecting throat structures. This report describes how a microdeletion and a translocation can cause it, with an excellent illustration of a reciprocal translocation.

Lewis, Ricki. January 1991. Genetic imprecision. *BioScience.* Chromosome checks can reveal abnormalities—but they are not necessarily linked to symptoms.

Lewis, Ricki. April 1, 1997. High resolution chromosome maps obtained for X and No. 7. *Genetic Engineering News.* Researchers reveal detailed maps of two human chromosomes.

Lewis, Ricki. September 1998. Telomere tales: elegant experiments confirm 25-year-old theory. *BioScience.* Giving cells telomerase extends life without causing cancer.

Linden, Mary et al. October 1995. Sex chromosome tetrasomy and pentasomy. *Pediatrics,* vol. 96. The more extra sex chromosomes, the more severe the symptoms.

Nicklas, R. Bruce. January 31, 1997. How cells get the right chromosomes. *Science,* vol. 275. One more or less chromosome than normal can have devastating consequences.

Rosenfeld, Melissa. April 15, 1997. Human artificial chromosomes get real. *Nature Genetics,* vol. 15. Telomeres, centromeres, and a few DNA pieces thrown in yield HACs.

Speicher, Michael R. April 1996. Karyotyping human chromosomes by combinatorial multi-fluor FISH. *Nature Genetics,* vol. 12. Using fluorescent dyes and DNA probes, researchers can highlight each human chromosome, all at once.

Willard, Huntington F. May 1998. Human artificial chromosomes coming into focus. *Nature Biotechnology,* vol. 16. HACs may speed development of new gene therapies.

chapter twelve

When Gene Frequencies Stay Constant

DNA Fingerprinting Relies on Population Genetics

So far, we've considered the gene as a "character" that transmits traits, as Mendel did, and as a biochemical blueprint for building a specific protein. It is at the population level that genetics meets history, anthropology and sociology, enabling us to trace our beginnings and our differences today. Population genetics also is the basis of a powerful forensic tool—DNA fingerprinting.

The brutalized body of a young man lies in a dumpster behind a restaurant on a city street. Forensic scientists at the scene recover skin cells and blood beneath the victim's fingernails, put the material in small plastic bags, and carry it to the laboratory. A few hours later, police pick up a man attempting to rob a nearby convenience store. Several people who were dining at the restaurant near the time of the murder later pick the robber out of a lineup as the man they saw near the crime scene.

Meanwhile, at the crime lab, investigators probe the victim's blood, the suspect's blood, and the blood and skin cells from under the victim's nails for five specific DNA sequences. These are not long, protein-encoding genes, but 3-, 4-, or 5-base sequences repeated in tandem (in a row) a different number of times in differ-

ent individuals. The number of repeats provides a way to distinguish people and is considered an allele—a variant of a DNA sequence. As with any gene, each person has two alleles for a particular repeat, which may be the same or different lengths on the two homologs. The five tested DNA sequences also are part of five different chromosomes (nonhomologs).

The gene tests yield a profile, or **DNA fingerprint,** for each sample—2 alleles for each of five loci, or ten points of comparison. We will discuss how the pattern is derived at the end of the chapter, but as figure 12.1 shows, it does match the suspect's blood to the crime scene samples. The victim's blood does not match the skin

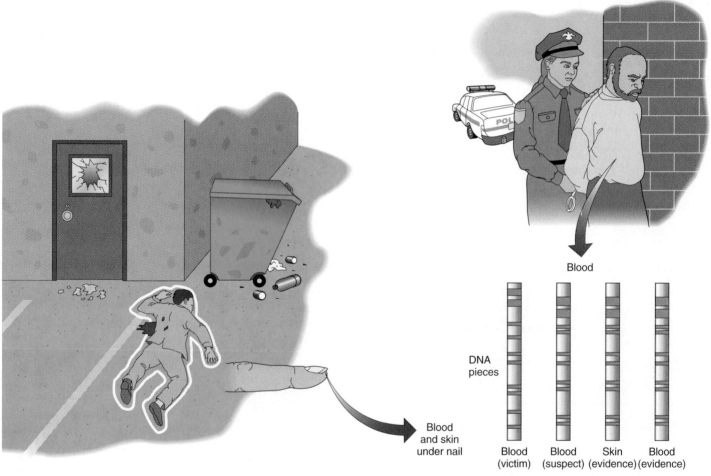

figure 12.1

Population genetics provides the power behind DNA fingerprinting. DNA is collected from evidence at a crime scene and from a suspect. Each sample is cut with enzymes that snip DNA at specific sequences. The DNA pieces are spread out on a sheet of gel-like material, then five repeated DNA sequences are highlighted with DNA probes. The resulting DNA fingerprint resembles a bar code used to scan prices in supermarkets. At a glance, it appears that the bar codes for the suspect and the evidence match. But only population genetics—in the form of multiplied allele frequencies—can place a probability on the likelihood that the suspect's blood genetically matches the blood and skin at the crime scene.

and blood from under his own fingernails. It certainly looks as if the captured man is the murderer.

But perhaps the man in custody did not commit the murder. This is where population genetics enters the forensic picture. Could some other person have the same set of alleles for the five tested DNA sequences? Statistics help place a DNA fingerprint into perspective (figure 12.2). For genetic data to be meaningful, forensic scientists must know how common each allele is.

Just as a perpetrator described as having wavy blond hair, blue eyes, a mole near his nose, and a tattoo on his right arm will be easier to find than one described only as a blue-eyed blond, unusual DNA sequences help narrow a search. If the alleles detected in the crime scene samples and in the suspect's blood are common, then another person may by chance have the same DNA fingerprint for these five sequences. That other person could theoretically have committed the murder. Ideally, a DNA analysis therefore includes the **gene frequency,** or likelihood that each allele appears in other members of the population

group to which the suspect belongs. Because of genetic differences in human populations, an allele that is common among Eskimos, for example, may be very rare among Bantus. However, defining what constitutes a population group is somewhat subjective. This is a major limitation of DNA fingerprinting.

Once the investigators determine the gene frequencies for the 10 alleles (2 each for five DNA sequences) in the suspect's population, they multiply the values. This is because the probability that an individual would inherit all 10 alleles equals the product of the probabilities that the person would inherit each individual allele. The DNA sequences tested must be on different chromosomes so that inheriting one sequence does not increase the likelihood that a person will inherit another. These requirements apply the product rule and Mendel's law of independent assortment. Recall from chapter 4 that geneticists use the product rule to determine the probability of inheriting specific alleles of two or more unlinked genes.

Multiplying the gene frequencies for the suspect's ten DNA sequences leads the

forensic scientists to conclude that the chance is exceedingly low that someone other than the suspect left the skin and blood at the crime scene. They charge the man with murder.

A Population View of the Gene

A **population** is any group of interbreeding organisms. Human populations include the students in a class or the people in a community, state, or nation. The genes in a population comprise its **gene pool,** and movement of alleles between populations is **gene flow.** The study of gene frequencies in different groups of organisms constitutes **population genetics.** Gene frequency refers to the percentage a certain allele represents among all alleles for that gene in a particular population. If the allele conferring a certain blood type, for example, occurs in 12 of every 100 individuals in a population, its frequency is 12 percent.

Differing allele frequencies in a population may be obvious in physical characteristics such as skin color, hair texture, or distinctive facial features. Other genetic differences may be detectable only at a biochemical level, such as blood types more prevalent in one group of people than another, or even in sequences of DNA that have no known protein product but nevertheless vary from person to person. Although we are all human, our differences reflect a staggering diversity of allele combinations.

Determining gene frequencies has important practical implications for genetic counseling. The risk that a particular inherited disorder will occur in an individual when there is no family history of the illness can be predicted by using allele frequencies that apply to the populations the person's parents came from. Certain traits and inherited illnesses are much more common in some population groups than in others. This is striking, for example, among people of eastern European Jewish descent (Ashkenazim), in whom a dozen or so conditions are quite prevalent (see table 13.1). Although it may be "politically incorrect" to single out a particular group of people, when it comes to population genetics, certain disorders are in fact more common in certain groups; this

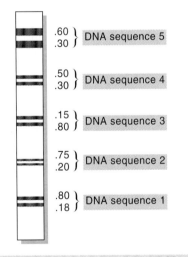

$$0.60 \times 0.30 \times 0.50 \times 0.30 \times 0.15 \times 0.80 \times 0.75 \times 0.20 \times 0.80 \times 0.18 = 0.00007$$

figure 12.2

Each sample from this forensic scene yields 10 bands, representing 2 alleles for each probed DNA sequence. The numbers marking each band are allele frequencies. For DNA sequence 5, for example, the allele represented by the higher band is known to be found in 60 percent of the members of this population; the other allele is present in 30 percent. Other alleles at the locus account for the remaining percentage. Multiplying the 10 allele frequencies provides the probability that another person has this same DNA fingerprint—about 7 in 100,000. Whether this is sufficient to cause reasonable doubt depends on additional factors, such as the size of the population and other evidence.

table 12.1

Frequency of PKU in Various Populations

Population	Frequency of PKU
Chinese	1/16,000
Irish, Scottish, Yemenite Jews	1/5,000
Japanese	1/119,000
Swedes	1/30,000
Turks	1/2,600
United States Caucasians	1/10,000

Algebraic Expression	What It Means
$p + q = 1$ (allele frequencies)	All dominant alleles plus all recessive alleles add up to all alleles for a particular gene in a population.
$p^2 + 2pq + q^2 = 1$ (genotype frequencies)	For a particular gene, all homozygous dominant individuals (p^2) plus all heterozygotes ($2pq$) plus all homozygous recessives (q^2) add up to all of the individuals in the population.

figure 12.3

Using algebra to follow gene frequencies.

is just reality. Several biotechnology companies, for example, offer a battery of tests to screen for carriers of several diseases that are more common in Ashkenazim.

The complexity of human genetic diversity becomes apparent when we compare the varying frequencies of the more common disease-causing mutations in different population groups. Consider myotonic dystrophy, the most prevalent inherited neuromuscular disorder in adults. In western Europe and in North America, 1 in 8,000 people has the disorder. In Japan, only 1 in 20,000 people has myotonic dystrophy. But among a native population in Canada, 1 in 475 people has the illness. Table 12.1 shows similar disease incidences for PKU. Imagine the complexity of tabulating these types of differences for thousands of genes!

Changing Gene Frequencies Underlie Evolution

On a broader level, shifting allele frequencies in populations provide the small steps of change that constitute evolution. The next two chapters consider the genetic changes that drive evolution.

Microevolution occurs when the frequency of an allele in a population changes. This happens when any of the following conditions are met:

1. Mutation introduces new alleles into a population.

2. Individuals migrate between populations.

3. Individuals remain in groups, mating only among themselves.

4. Individuals with a particular phenotype more easily tolerate a specific environmental condition than individuals with other phenotypes.

5. Under particular environmental conditions, individuals with certain genotypes do not produce fertile offspring, eliminating their genes from the population.

These last two situations illustrate a primary force behind evolution called **natural selection.** This is the tendency for individuals with a certain phenotype in a particular environment to produce more fertile offspring than individuals with other phenotypes. Obviously, many conditions must be met if genetic equilibrium is to prevail—that is, if allele frequencies are *not* to change. Thus evolution is not only possible, but also nearly unavoidable.

When microevolutionary changes accumulate sufficiently to keep two fertile organisms of opposite sex from successfully producing fertile offspring, **macroevolution,** the formation of a new species, has occurred. This chapter discusses the interesting, but unusual, situation in which allele frequencies stay constant, called Hardy-Weinberg equilibrium.

Hardy-Weinberg Equilibrium—An Overview

We can calculate changes in gene frequencies in populations from generation to generation and derive the corresponding proportions of phenotypes and genotypes.

In 1908, a mathematician, H. H. Hardy, and a physician who was interested in genetics, W. Weinberg, independently proposed that phenotype and genotype frequencies in sexually reproducing, diploid organisms could be determined by applying a simple algebraic expression. In the binomial expansion $p^2 + 2pq + q^2 = 1.0$, p^2 represents homozygous dominant individuals, q^2 represents homozygous recessive individuals, and $2pq$ represents heterozygotes (figure 12.3). The letter "p" designates the frequency of a dominant allele, and "q" is the frequency of a recessive allele. Note that this Hardy-Weinberg equation is analogous to the genotypic ratio resulting from a monohybrid cross—1 AA : 2 Aa : 1 aa.

The Hardy-Weinberg equation can reveal the single-gene frequency changes that underlie evolution. If the proportion of genotypes remains the same from generation to generation, as the equation indicates, then that gene is not evolving. This situation of **Hardy-Weinberg equilibrium** is an idealized state. It is possible only if the population is large, if its members mate at random, and there is no migration, mutation, or natural selection.

Population genetics—the study of allele frequencies in different groups of individuals—provides the theoretical background for DNA fingerprinting. The genes in a population comprise its gene pool. Microevolution reflects changes in gene frequencies in populations. Microevolution is not occurring if gene frequencies stay constant from generation to generation, a condition called Hardy-Weinberg equilibrium. This happens only if mating is random and the population is large, with no migration, mutation, or natural selection.

table 12.2

Hardy-Weinberg Equilibrium—Allele Frequencies Stay Constant

Male	Female	Proportion in Population	F₁ Genotypes DD	Dd	dd
0.49 DD	0.49 DD	0.2401 ($DD \times DD$)	0.2401		
0.49 DD	0.42 Dd	0.2058 ($DD \times Dd$)	0.1029	0.1029	
0.49 DD	0.09 dd	0.0441 ($DD \times dd$)		0.0441	
0.42 Dd	0.49 DD	0.2058 ($Dd \times DD$)	0.1029	0.1029	
0.42 Dd	0.42 Dd	0.1764 ($Dd \times Dd$)	0.0441	0.0882	0.0441
0.42 Dd	0.09 dd	0.0378 ($Dd \times dd$)		0.0189	0.0189
0.09 dd	0.49 DD	0.0441 ($dd \times DD$)		0.0441	
0.09 dd	0.42 Dd	0.0378 ($dd \times Dd$)		0.0189	0.0189
0.09 dd	0.09 dd	0.0081 ($dd \times dd$)			0.0081
			0.49	0.42	0.09
			DD	Dd	dd

Demonstrating Hardy-Weinberg Equilibrium

To understand the concept of Hardy-Weinberg equilibrium, it helps to follow the frequency of two alleles of a particular gene from one generation to the next. This exercise demonstrates that familiar Mendelian principles underlie population genetics calculations. It also shows how and why dominant traits do not take over a population, as might seem logical.

Consider a gene in a population where the dominant allele D occurs in 70 percent of the gametes, and the recessive allele d occurs in 30 percent of the gametes. According to the Hardy-Weinberg equation, p, the frequency of the dominant allele D, is therefore 0.7, and q, the frequency of the recessive allele d, is 0.3. It is clear that $p + q = 1$.

We can calculate the proportions of each of the three types of genotypes that arise when gametes combine at random to form the next generation:

homozygous dominant = DD = 0.7 × 0.7 = 0.49 = 49 percent in the F₁

homozygous recessive = dd = 0.3 × 0.3 = 0.09 = 9 percent in the F₁

heterozygous = $Dd + dD$ = $2pq$ = (0.3)(0.7) + (0.3)(0.7) = 0.42 = 42 percent in the F₁

The proportion of homozygous individuals is calculated simply by multiplying the allele frequency for the recessive or dominant allele by itself. The heterozygous calculation is $2pq$ because there are two ways of combining a D with a d gamete—a D sperm with a d egg, and a d sperm with a D egg.

Now jump ahead a few decades, and imagine that this theoretical population of 49 percent DD, 9 percent dd, and 42 percent Dd individuals mates randomly among themselves. This means that each gamete combination is equally likely to occur—that is, each genotype of a female (DD, Dd, or dd) is equally likely to mate with each of the three types of males (DD, Dd, or dd), and vice versa. Table 12.2 shows the calculations, which lead to offspring in the now-familiar proportions of 49 percent DD, 42 percent Dd, and 9 percent dd.

In the reverse situation, we can calculate allele frequencies from the proportions of homozygotes and heterozygotes, if we know this information. The frequency of the D allele equals the proportion of homozygous dominants (DD) plus one-half the proportion of heterozygotes (Dd), or:

$$D = p^2 + 1/2(2pq) = 0.49 + 1/2(0.42) = 0.49 + 0.21 = 0.70$$

Similarly, the frequency of the d allele equals the proportion of homozygous recessives (dd) plus one-half the proportion of heterozygotes (Dd), or:

$$d = q^2 + 1/2(2pq) = 0.09 + 1/2(0.42) = 0.09 + 0.21 = 0.30$$

For any 2 alleles in a population, the proportion of homozygous dominants equals the square of the frequency of the dominant allele (p^2), and the proportion of homozygous recessives equals the square of the frequency of the recessive allele (q^2). The proportion of heterozygotes equals $2pq$. If we know the genotype proportions in a population, we can calculate allele frequencies. The frequency of the recessive allele equals the proportion of homozygous recessives plus one-half that of carriers, and the frequency of the dominant allele equals the proportion of homozygous dominants plus that of one-half the carriers.

Calculating Carrier Frequency from Disease Incidence

In a problem in a textbook, the author provides gene frequencies. In real life, gene frequencies are usually estimates calculated from empirical data—specifically, from the frequency of a trait or disorder in a particular population (figure 12.4). For example, researchers compared the number of Ashkenazim in a database called the New York dystonia registry, to the total number

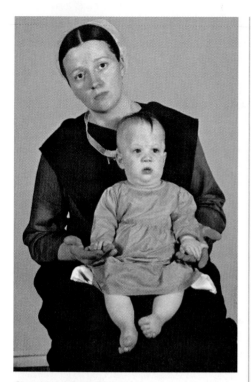

figure 12.4

This Amish child from Lancaster County, Pennsylvania, has inherited Ellis-van Creveld syndrome. He has short-limbed dwarfism, extra fingers, heart disease, fused wrist bones, and had teeth when he was born. The condition is autosomal recessive, but the mutant allele occurs in 7 percent of the people of this Amish community—a high figure, because they marry among themselves.

of Ashkenazim in New York. This revealed the frequency for the gene causing dystonia (a movement disorder) in this population—1 in 1,000 to 1 in 3,000.

Practically, allele frequencies can be used to calculate the probability that a member of the population carries a gene of interest. For example, now that a test is available to detect carriers of cystic fibrosis, researchers have determined gene frequencies for several populations (table 12.3). People can determine how likely they are to be carriers from this information.

Cystic fibrosis affects 1 in 2,000 Caucasian newborns. Therefore, the homozygous recessive frequency—cc if c equals the disease-causing allele—is 1/2,000, or 0.0005 in this population. This equals q^2. The square root of q^2 is about 0.022, which equals the frequency of the c allele. If q equals 0.022, then p, or $1 - q$, equals 0.978.

table 12.3
Carrier Frequency for Cystic Fibrosis

Population Group	Carrier Frequency
African Americans	1 in 66
Asian Americans	1 in 150
Caucasians of European descent	1 in 23
Hispanic Americans	1 in 46

Carrier frequency is equal to $2pq$, which equals $(2)(0.978)(0.022)$, or 0.043—about 1 in 23.

If there is no cystic fibrosis in a family, a person's risk of having an affected child is relatively low. Consider a Caucasian couple with no family history of cystic fibrosis asking a genetic counselor to calculate the risk that they could conceive a child with this illness. The genetic counselor tells them that the chance of *each* being a carrier is about 4.3 percent, or 1 in 23. But this is only part of the picture. The chance that *both* of these people are carriers is 1/23 multiplied by 1/23, because the probability that two events will occur equals the product of the probability that each event will happen. This equals 1 in 529. However, if they *were* both carriers, each of their children would face a 1 in 4 chance of inheriting the illness, based on Mendel's first law of gene segregation. Therefore, the risk for two unrelated Caucasian individuals, neither of whom has a family history of cystic fibrosis, of having an affected child is 1/4 × 1/23 × 1/23, or 1 in 2,116. This couple has learned their chance of producing an affected child from disease incidence and gene frequencies.

Key Concepts

Population calculations are applied to real-life situations by determining the value of q^2 (homozygous recessives) from the incidence of an inherited disease in a population, deducing p and q, and then using the Hardy-Weinberg equation to predict the likelihood that a person is a carrier.

Applications of Hardy-Weinberg Equilibrium

We can modify the Hardy-Weinberg equation to apply to different modes of inheritance.

Autosomal Recessive Traits and Disorders

To determine allele frequencies for autosomal recessively inherited characteristics, we need to know the frequency of one genotype. This is typically the homozygous recessive class, for the same reason that this group is used to do a test cross when tracing inheritance of a single trait—its phenotype indicates its genotype. Consider the ability to taste a bitter substance called phenylthiocarbamide (PTC). This chemical is impregnated into paper strips, which genetics class instructors often give their students to taste.

The ability to taste PTC is a dominant trait that varies in frequency among different populations. In a class of 25 students who take the taste test, approximately 4 students will look about in confusion as their classmates sputter, grimace, and yell. The subdued four are nontasters, so for this population, $q^2 = 4/25 = 0.16$. The frequency of the nontaster allele is the square root of 0.16, or 0.40. Subtracting this from 1 yields a taster allele frequency of 0.60.

Sex-linked Recessive Traits

For sex-linked traits, different predictions of allele frequencies are necessary for males and females. For a female, who can be homozygous recessive, homozygous dominant, or a heterozygote, the standard Hardy-Weinberg equation of $p^2 + 2pq + q^2$ applies as it would to an autosomal recessive trait in either sex. However, in human males, the gene frequency is simply the phenotypic frequency—that is, if a male inherits a sex-linked recessive mutant allele, it is obvious in his phenotype.

The incidence of sex-linked hemophilia, for example, is 1 in 10,000 male births. Therefore, q equals 0.0001. Using the formula $p + q = 1$, the frequency of the wild type allele is 0.9999. The frequency of carriers, who are all female, equals $2pq$, or

(2)(0.0001)(0.9999), which equals 0.00019, which is 0.02 percent, or about 1 in 5,000. The frequency of a female having hemophilia is q^2, or $(0.0001)^2$, or about 1 in 100 million.

Approximations for Very Rare Inherited Diseases

In the real world of inherited disease, gene frequencies, such as 0.6 and 0.4, or 0.7 and 0.3, are most unusual. Genetic diseases are usually very, very rare, and therefore, the q component of the Hardy-Weinberg equation does not contribute much. Because this means that the value of p approaches 1, the carrier frequency, $2pq$, is very close to just $2q$. Therefore, the carrier frequency is approximately twice the frequency of the rare, disease-causing allele.

Consider Tay-Sachs disease, which occurs in 1 in 3,600 Ashkenazim. This means that q^2 equals 1/3,600, or about 0.0003. The square root, q, equals 0.017. The frequency of the dominant wild type allele is then 1 – 0.017, or 0.983. What is the likelihood that an Ashkenazi carries Tay-Sachs disease? It is $2pq$, or (2)(0.983)(0.017), or 0.033. Note that this is very close to double the frequency of the mutant allele, 0.017. We can also adopt the Hardy-Weinberg equation to analyze codominant, multiple allele genes.

DNA Polymorphisms

DNA sequences can vary from person to person, whether they code for a protein and determine a phenotype or not. A DNA sequence that varies between individuals at the same site on a chromosome is a **polymorphism** if it occurs too frequently to be accounted for by new mutation alone. "Frequent" means that the variant is present in at least 1 percent of a population, giving a carrier frequency ($2q$) of 2 percent. Of the 5,000 or so human genes that scientists have described phenotypes for so far, about a third are known to be polymorphic.

Direct DNA sequencing is not necessary to spot a polymorphism. **Restriction enzymes,** which cut DNA at particular short sequences, can reveal DNA polymorphisms. If the DNA variant

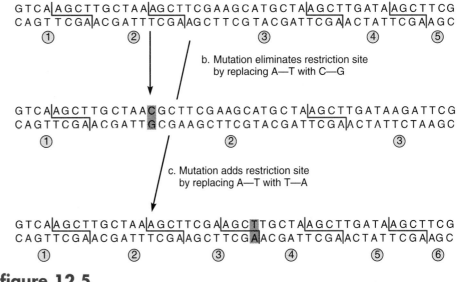

figure 12.5

(a) Hind III is a restriction enzyme that snips DNA between the adenines (AA) of the 6-base sequence AAGCTT. Altering a base by mutation can remove (b) or add (c) a restriction site, changing the numbers and sizes of resulting DNA fragments. Numbers indicate restriction fragments, shown in figure 12.6.

disrupts a restriction enzyme cutting site, then "digesting" (cutting) the DNA with the enzyme yields larger pieces than when the wild type sequence is digested, because here the cutting site is intact (figure 12.5). These **restriction fragment length polymorphisms (RFLPs)** are the basis of several biotechnologies.

Key Concepts

To track the inheritance of sex-linked recessive traits, we must use different values for males and females. The frequency of the recessive phenotype in males is q, whereas in females it is q^2, as in autosomal recessive inheritance. For very rare inherited disorders, the value of p approaches 1, so the carrier frequency is approximately twice the frequency of the disease-causing allele ($2q$). Polymorphisms are DNA sequences that vary among individuals with a frequency of at least 0.01. We can detect polymorphisms using restriction enzymes, producing RFLPs.

DNA Fingerprinting— A Practical Test of Hardy-Weinberg Assumptions

The conditions necessary to maintain gene frequencies rarely happen. Genes change— they mutate. Some genes are disadvantageous in certain environments, so the chance that they will pass to the next generation diminishes because they render the individual unhealthy or infertile. This alters the Hardy-Weinberg equilibrium. Other factors do so, as well; people do not mate at random, nor do they always remain within the same population over many generations. These factors and their influences can be complex and they are addressed in detail in the next chapter. However, Hardy-Weinberg equilibrium does exist for some repetitive DNA sequences. These sequences are used in DNA fingerprinting efforts.

DNA Patterns Distinguish Individuals

DNA fingerprinting is based on a simple fact: since a 3-billion-base sequence of

4 different biochemical building blocks (the DNA nucleotides) can produce more varied combinations than there are humans, each of us (except identical twins) should have a unique DNA sequence. The fingerprinting technique focuses on highly polymorphic stretches of DNA—sequences that vary greatly from individual to individual.

From 5 to 10 percent of the human genome consists of tandem repeats, which range from as few as 2 bases to as many as several thousand. Sir Alec Jeffreys at Leicester University in Great Britain developed DNA fingerprinting in the 1980s. Using long repeats called VNTRs, or **variable number of tandem repeats,** he detected differences in the number of repeats among individuals by cutting DNA with restriction enzymes. Then Jeffreys measured the resulting fragments using a technique called **polyacrylamide gel electrophoresis,** or PAGE.

A polyacrylamide gel is a jellylike material that small pieces of DNA migrate through in response to an electrical field applied to the gel. A positive electrode is placed at one end of the gel, a negative electrode at the other. The DNA pieces, carrying negative charges because of their phosphate groups, move toward the positive pole. The pieces migrate according to size, the shorter pieces moving faster and thus traveling farther in a given amount of time. The pattern that forms from the different sized fragments, with the shorter fragments closer to the positive pole and the longer fragments farther away, is a distinctive DNA fingerprint.

Figure 12.6 shows the electrophoresis patterns obtained for the restriction fragments described in figure 12.5. Now the meaning of "restriction fragment length polymorphism" (RFLP) may be clearer— differences in DNA fragment sizes exist among individuals, and they reflect DNA sequence differences that alter restriction enzyme cutting sites. We will return to RFLPs in the context of genetic disease diagnosis in chapter 20.

Jeffreys's first celebrated cases included proving that a boy was the son of a British citizen so that he could enter the country and freeing a man held in custody for the rape of two schoolgirls. After officials tested the DNA of hundreds of men, yielding no match, conventional sleuthing

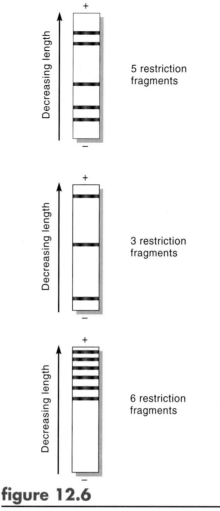

figure 12.6

Polyacrylamide gel electrophoresis (PAGE) is used to separate the DNA fragments in figure 12.5 by length. The shorter fragments move closer to the positive pole.

eventually led to an arrest. Then in 1988, Jeffreys's VNTR approach matched DNA fingerprints from suspect Tommie Lee Andrews's blood cells to sperm cells left on his victim (Reading 12.1). Figure 12.7 describes two other interesting applications of DNA fingerprinting.

Today, many DNA fingerprinting analyses use sequences called **short tandem repeats,** or (STRs), that are shorter than VNTRs. STRs consist of a 2-, 3-, 4-, or 5-base sequence repeated in tandem. One commonly used STR, the dinucleotide sequence AC (TG on the complementary strand), is found in 50,000 to 100,000 sites in the human genome! The function of STRs isn't known, but when expanded, they can cause disease (see chapter 10).

Like VNTRs, the number of STR repeats distinguishes alleles and thus individuals. Unlike VNTRs, which are obtained using restriction enzymes, STRs are analyzed using the polymerase chain reaction (PCR) (Reading 8.2, figure 1). Recall that this method uses sequences (primers) flanking a DNA sequence of interest plus replication enzymes to rapidly mass-produce the sequence.

In STR analysis, the greater the number of repeats, the larger the PCR product, because more genetic material is amplified between the primers. The advantage of PCR over RFLP technology is that PCR works on degraded DNA and requires only a few cells—conditions often found at crime scenes. Figure 12.8 compares the two approaches to collecting DNA fragments. PCR analysis of well-studied protein-encoding genes may also be used to obtain a DNA fingerprint.

Population Statistics Are Used to Interpret DNA Fingerprints

Each VNTR or STR size is assigned a probability value based on its observed frequency in a reference population represented in a database. Typically, several different repeated sequences are evaluated, and their frequencies are multiplied to determine the probability of that particular combination of sequences occurring in the population.

Two basic assumptions underlie applying the product rule to derive probabilities and put a DNA fingerprint into perspective:

1. The DNA sequences examined must assort independently (must be on different chromosomes).

2. The alleles in the population under study should be in or near Hardy-Weinberg equilibrium—that is, the allele frequencies should not dramatically change from generation to generation. Although Hardy-Weinberg equilibrium is an idealized state, some studies have shown certain STRs are in it. The reason may become obvious when we decipher the functions, if any, of these short repeated sequences.

a.

b.

figure 12.7

DNA fingerprinting can clarify kidnappings and disasters. (*a*) As a baby in Israel in 1948, Tsila Levine, then called Saada, vanished from a hospital where her mother, Yemenite immigrant Margalit Omessi, had taken her for a checkup. Israelis of European background adopted the child. Her dark skin made her adoption obvious, and as a teen, Tsila searched in vain for her birth parents. In 1997, after her adoptive parents died, Tsila ran photos of herself as an adult and as an infant in newspapers. Omessi, then living in California, saw the photos and recognized her child. DNA fingerprinting revealed that the probability that they are mother and child exceeds 99.99 percent. (*b*) These aligned coffins represent people who were aboard a Russian plane that crashed into a mountain in Spitsbergen, Norway, in August 1996. DNA fingerprinting enabled forensic scientists to sort out the 257 body parts into the 141 bodies of passengers and crew and identify 139 of them. The other two individuals had distinct DNA patterns but could not be matched to tissue samples given previously or to living relatives. Previously, identifying disaster victims relied on matching X rays, dental patterns, and fingerprints—imprecise, painstaking, and time-consuming methods.

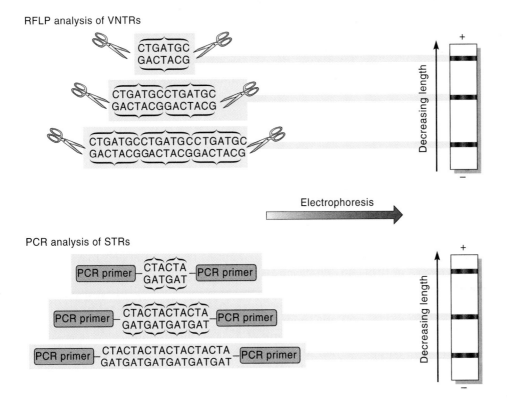

figure 12.8

A simplified comparison between two techniques for obtaining and sizing DNA fragments to construct a DNA fingerprint. Large repeats, called VNTRs, are usually removed by using restriction enzymes to cut the DNA on either side of the repeated sequence. PCR analysis amplifies short repeats (STRs) bracketed by PCR primers. For both approaches, polyacrylamide gel electrophoresis separates the fragments by length.

DNA fingerprinting has rapidly become a standard and powerful forensic tool. Most states maintain DNA files of all convicted felons, and the technique is also enormously helpful in exonerating suspects. The FBI and Scotland Yard release a third of all rape suspects without booking them because DNA analysis shows that their DNA does not match that of sperm on the victims' bodies. So accepted has the method become that in 1992, the U.S. military began a genetic dogtag program. DNA fingerprints derived from blood samples of all servicepeople will make it possible to identify their remains if teeth and conventional fingerprints are not available or destroyed.

Back in 1986, DNA fingerprinting was virtually unheard of outside of scientific circles. So, rapist Tommie Lee Andrews thought he was being very meticulous in planning his crimes. He picked his victims months before he attacked and watched them so that he knew exactly when they would be home alone. On a balmy Sunday night in May 1986, Andrews lay in wait for Nancy Hodge, a young computer operator at Disney World, at her home in Orlando, Florida. The burly man surprised her when she was in the bathroom removing her contact lenses. He covered her face so that she could not see who was attacking her. He then raped and brutalized her repeatedly.

Andrews was very careful not to leave fingerprints, threads, hairs, or any other indication that he had ever been in Hodge's home. But he had not counted on the then-fledgling technology of DNA fingerprinting. Thanks to a clear-thinking crime victim and scientifically informed lawyers, Andrews was soon at the center of a trial not only of himself, but also of the technology that would eventually help convict him.

After the attack, a shaken Nancy Hodge went to the hospital, where she provided a vaginal secretion sample containing the rapist's sperm cells. Then two district attorneys assigned to the case who had read about DNA fingerprinting sent some of the sperm to a biotechnology company that extracted DNA from the sperm cells and cut it with restriction enzymes. The sperm's DNA pieces were then mixed with labeled DNA probes that bound to complementary segments.

The same procedure of extracting, cutting, and probing the DNA was done on white blood cells from Nancy Hodge and Tommie Lee Andrews, who had been apprehended and held as a suspect in several assaults. When the radioactive DNA pieces from each sample, indicating where the probes had bound, were separated and displayed according to size, the resulting pattern of bands—the DNA fingerprint—matched exactly for the sperm sample and Andrews's blood, but differed from Nancy Hodge's DNA. He was the attacker (figure 1).

The sizes of the DNA pieces in a DNA fingerprint vary from person to person because of differences in DNA sequence in the regions surrounding the probed genes. The discriminating power of the technology stems from the fact that there are many more ways for the 3 billion bases of the human genome to vary than there are people. However, this theoretical basis must be tempered by the fact that certain gene combinations are more prevalent in some populations because of marriage, travel, and other social customs. That is, within ethnic groups, some people may be very alike genetically, and distinguishing among them might be more difficult. In one celebrated case, DNA fingerprinting could not reveal whether a man or his father had committed a rape.

Because Tommie Lee Andrews is black, his allele frequencies were compared to those for a representative African American population. At his first trial in November 1987, the judge, perhaps fearful that too much technical information would overwhelm the jury, did not allow the prosecution to cite population-based statistics. Without knowing the appropriate allele frequencies, DNA fingerprinting was reduced to comparing smeary lines on test papers and concluding that the patterns of DNA pieces in the forensic sperm sample looked like those for Andrews's white blood cells. Multiplying the probabilities indicated that the chance that Tommie Lee Andrews's DNA would match the evidence by chance was 1 in 10 billion. But the prosecution could not mention this.

After a mistrial was declared, the prosecution cited the precedent of using population statistics to derive databases on standard blood types. So when Andrews stood trial just three months later for the rape of a different woman, the judge permitted population analysis, and Andrews was convicted. Today, in jail, he keeps a copy of the *Discover* magazine article (written by this author) that describes his role in the first case tried using DNA fingerprinting.

A Call for Ethnic Databases

As DNA fingerprinting grew in popularity, the population statistics started to take on a surrealistic feel because they were too large

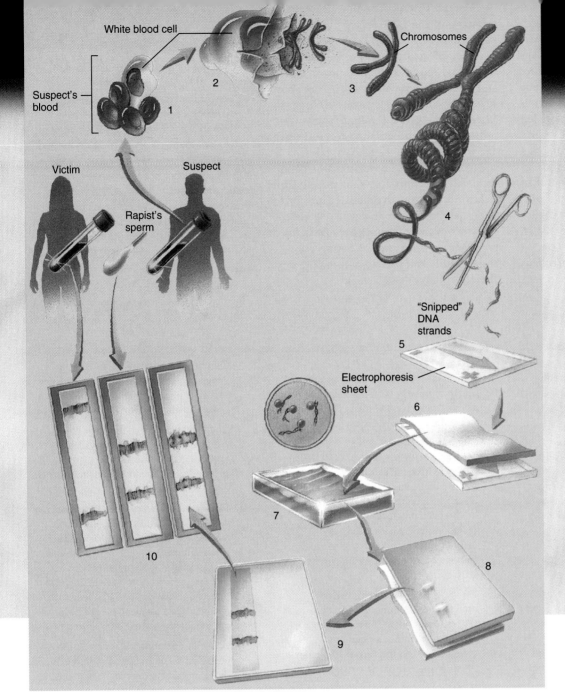

figure 1

DNA fingerprinting. A blood sample (1) is collected from the suspect. White blood cells containing DNA are extracted and burst open (2), releasing the DNA strands (3). The strands are snipped into fragments (4), using scissorlike restriction enzymes. Electrophoresis is used to align the DNA pieces by size—the longest pieces at one end, shortest pieces at the other—in a groove on a sheet of gel (5). The resulting pattern of DNA fragments is transferred to a nylon sheet (6). It is exposed to radioactively tagged probes (7) that home in on the DNA areas used to establish identity. When the nylon sheet is placed against a piece of X-ray film (8) and processed, black bands appear where the probes stuck (9). This pattern of black bands in a white column constitutes a DNA print (10). This print may then be compared to the victim's DNA fingerprint, the rapist's DNA fingerprint obtained from sperm cells, and other biological evidence.

to imagine. In one oft-quoted trial, the prosecutor concluded, "The chance of the DNA fingerprint of the cells in the evidence matching blood of the defendant by chance is 1 in 738 trillion." In figures, this is 1 in 738,000,000,000,000. The numbers themselves were not at fault, but the databases from which they came started to draw questions.

Some population geneticists wondered about the validity of the databases. Did they really reflect the compositions of actual human populations? By 1991, half a dozen judges had rejected DNA evidence because population geneticists had testified that the databases do not correspond directly to true gene frequencies because they greatly oversimplify human population structure.

The first DNA fingerprinting databases neatly shoehorned many different groups into just three seemingly homogenous categories of Caucasian, black, and Hispanic. People from Poland, Greece, or Sweden would all be considered white, and a dark-skinned person from Jamaica and one from Somalia would be lumped together as blacks. Perhaps the most incongruous of all were the Hispanics. Cubans and Puerto Ricans are part African, whereas people from Mexico and Guatemala have mostly native American blood. Spanish and Argentinians have neither black African nor native American genetic backgrounds. Yet these diverse peoples were considered together as a single population! Other groups were left out, such as native Americans and Asians. Ultimately, analysis of these three databases revealed significantly more homozygous recessives for certain polymorphic genes than the Hardy-Weinberg equation would predict, confirming what many had suspected—gene frequencies were not in equilibrium.

To give meaning to the allele frequencies necessary to interpret DNA fingerprints,

we need more restrictive ethnic databases. A frequency of 1 in 1,000 for a particular allele in all whites may actually be much higher or lower in, for example, only Italians, because they (and many others) tend to marry among themselves. On the other hand, narrowly defined ethnic databases may be insufficient to interpret DNA fingerprints from someone whose mother was Scottish/French and whose father was Greek/German.

We may need to develop mathematical models to account for real population structures. Perhaps the first step will be to understand the forces that generate genetic substructures within more broadly defined populations, which means taking into account history and human nature. The next chapter explores these factors.

Key Concepts

DNA fingerprints are based on differences in the sizes of highly repeated DNA sequences. Then population statistics derived from databases are applied to determine the probability that the same pattern would occur in two individuals. A limitation of the method is that databases may not adequately represent real human populations. Developing narrower ethnic databases and considering historical and social factors may help develop more realistic population statistics.

summary

1. A **population** is a group of interbreeding organisms whose genes constitute a **gene pool.**

2. Allele frequencies vary in different populations for a variety of reasons. **Population genetics** is the study of allele frequencies in interbreeding groups. It is used to interpret forensic DNA evidence and predict risk in genetic counseling, and is the basis of **microevolutionary** changes that underlie **macroevolution.**

3. The Hardy-Weinberg equation is a binomial expansion used to represent genotypes in a population. In **Hardy-Weinberg equilibrium,** these genotypes remain constant from generation to generation if evolution is not occurring. When the equation $p^2 + 2pq + q^2$ represents a gene with one dominant and one recessive allele, p^2 corresponds to the frequency of homozygous dominant

individuals; $2pq$ stands for heterozygotes; and q^2 represents the frequency of the homozygous recessive class. The frequency of the dominant allele is p, and of the recessive allele, q.

4. If we know either p or q, we can calculate genotype frequencies. Often such information comes from knowing the q^2 class, which corresponds to the frequency of affected individuals in a population. Hardy-Weinberg equilibrium is demonstrated by following gamete frequencies as they recombine in the next generation.

5. For sex-linked recessive traits, the mutant allele frequency for males equals the trait frequency. For very rare disorders or traits, the value of p approaches 1, so the carrier frequency ($2pq$) is approximately twice the frequency of the rare trait (q).

6. A highly variable gene variant or DNA sequence present in more than 1 percent of a population is called a **polymorphism.**

7. The interpretation of DNA fingerprint patterns depends upon the availability of appropriate databases to calculate the probabilities that certain genetic variants occur in two samples by chance.

8. **Restriction enzymes** or PCR are used to isolate polymorphic repeats such as **VNTRs** and **STRs. Polyacrylamide gel electrophoresis** is used to separate and display labeled DNA fragments by size. The fragment pattern is the DNA fingerprint. To interpret it, scientists multiply allele frequencies specific for the population the sample comes from.

9. DNA fingerprinting will become a more powerful tool when we can more specifically define and analyse human populations.

review questions

1. "We like him, he seems to have a terrific gene pool," say the parents upon meeting their daughter's latest boyfriend. Why doesn't their statement make sense?

2. What is *not* happening in a population in Hardy-Weinberg equilibrium?

3. "The expert witness compared the genetic code of the suspect to that of whomever left the hair at the crime scene," says the television newscaster. Why doesn't this statement make sense?

4. Two couples want to know their risk of conceiving a child with cystic fibrosis. In one couple, neither partner has a family history of the disease; in the other, one partner knows he is a carrier. How do their risks differ?

5. Explain how RFLP analysis and PCR are used to isolate specific DNA fragments.

6. What is the role of polyacrylamide gel electrophoresis in DNA fingerprinting?

7. Why might short tandem repeats (STRs) be more likely to be in Hardy-Weinberg equilibrium than protein-encoding genes that affect phenotype?

8. Why are specific databases necessary to interpret DNA fingerprints?

9. How is the Hardy-Weinberg equation used to predict recurrence of sex-linked recessive traits?

applied questions

1. The Finnish population has a 1 percent carrier frequency for a seizure disorder called myoclonus epilepsy. Two people who have no relatives with the illness ask a genetic counselor to calculate the risk that they will conceive an affected child, based on their belonging to this population group. What is the risk?

2. Factor IX deficiency is a clotting disorder affecting 1 in 190 Ashkenazim living in Israel. It affects 1 in 1,000,000 Japanese, Korean, Chinese, German, Italian, African American, English, Indian, and Arab people.

   a. What is the frequency of the mutant allele in the Israeli population?

   b. What is the frequency of the wild type allele in this population?

   c. Calculate the proportion of carriers in the Israeli population.

   d. Why might the disease incidence be very high in the Israeli population but very low in others?

3. Maple syrup urine disease (MSUD) is an autosomal recessive inborn error of metabolism that causes mental and physical retardation, difficulty feeding, and a sweet odor to urine. In Costa Rica, 1 in 8,000 newborns inherit the condition. Calculate the carrier frequency of MSUD in this population.

4. The amyloidoses are a group of inborn errors of metabolism in which sticky protein builds up in certain organs. Amyloidosis caused by a mutation in the gene encoding a blood protein called transthyretin affects the heart and/or nervous system. It is autosomal recessive. In a population of 177 healthy African Americans, 4 proved, by blood testing, to have one mutant allele of the transthyretin gene. What is the carrier frequency in this population?

5. Ability to taste phenylthiocarbamide (PTC) is determined by the *T* gene. *TT* individuals taste a strong, bitter taste; *Tt* people experience a slightly bitter taste; *tt* individuals taste nothing.

   A fifth-grade class of 20 students tastes PTC papers, rating the experience as "very yucky" (*TT*), "I can taste it" (*Tt*), and "I can't taste it" (*tt*). For homework, the students test their parents, with these results:

   Of 6 *TT* students, 4 have 2 *TT* parents; one has 1 parent who is *TT* and one parent who is *Tt*. The sixth *TT* student has 1 parent who is *Tt* and 1 who is *tt*.

   Of 4 students who are *Tt*, 2 have 2 parents who are *Tt*, and 2 have 1 parent who is *TT* and 1 parent who is *tt*.

   Of the 10 students who can't taste PTC, 4 have 2 parents who also are *tt*, but 4 students have 1 parent who is *Tt* and 1 who is *tt*. The remaining 2 students have 2 *Tt* parents.

   Calculate the frequencies of the *T* and *t* alleles in the two generations. Is Hardy-Weinberg equilibrium maintained, or is this gene evolving?

6. DNA is extracted from blood on a murder victim and from blood taken from a suspect, a white man who reportedly threatened the victim. ABO blood typing reveals that the blood at the crime scene is not that of the victim but does match that of the suspect. However, a large segment of the population has this ABO blood type. The prosecution turns to DNA fingerprinting.

   Four DNA probes are used to construct a DNA fingerprint, corresponding to four unlinked loci where variable repeats occur. The blood on the victim and from the suspect have the same DNA pattern—that is, the same sized repeats correspond to each of the four loci.

   A database of 2,000 male Caucasians indicates that the first DNA repeat occurs in 15 of the subjects; the second DNA repeat is present in 23; the third repeat is in 62; and the fourth is in only 7 people. Assuming that the database accurately represents the suspect's population subgroup, what are the odds that the suspect's blood matches the blood on the victim by chance alone?

suggested readings

Ballantyne, Jack. April 15, 1997. Mass disaster genetics. *Nature Genetics,* vol. 15. DNA fingerprinting can ease the gruesome task of identifying victims of plane crashes.

Chen, Lucian. August 1994. O. J. Simpson case sparks a flurry of interest in DNA fingerprinting methods. *Genetic Engineering News,* vol. 14. This celebrity trial introduced the public to DNA fingerprinting and population genetics.

Deka, Ranjan, et al. February 1995. Population genetics of dinucleotide (dC·dA)$_n$ ·(dG·dT)$_n$ polymorphisms in world populations. *The American Journal of Human Genetics,* vol. 56. Some dinucleotide repeats are in Hardy-Weinberg equilibrium.

Hammond, Holly, et al. July 1994. Evaluation of 13 short tandem repeat loci for use in personal identification applications. *The American Journal of Human Genetics,* vol. 55. Short DNA sequences are useful in distinguishing among individuals.

Koshland, Daniel E., Jr. August 19, 1994. The DNA fingerprint story (continued). *Science,* vol. 265. DNA fingerprinting has gained wide acceptance.

Lewis, Ricki. June 1988. Witness for the prosecution. *Discover.* The story of one of the first DNA fingerprinting cases.

Olaisen, Bjornar, et al. April 15, 1997. Identification by DNA analysis of the victims of the August 1996 Spitsbergen civil aircraft disaster. *Nature Genetics,* vol. 15. A report on how DNA fingerprinting enabled forensic scientists to sort 257 body parts from a plane crash into the 141 victims.

Weir, Bruce S. December 11, 1995. DNA statistics in the Simpson matter. *Nature Genetics,* vol. 11. Reporters called this author's expert testimony "dry as sand and about as digestible." Here, his attempt at easing digestion of some very damning evidence.

chapter
thirteen

Changing Gene Frequencies

Genes and Human Behavior

In 1648, a Ukrainian cossack named Bogdan Chmielnicki led a massacre against the Polish people, including peasants, nobility, and the much-hated Jewish people, in retaliation for a Polish nobleman's seizure of his possessions. By 1654, Russians, Tatars, Swedes, and others joined the Ukrainians in wave after wave of attacks against the Polish people. Thousands perished, only a few thousand Jewish people remaining. The Jewish people have survived many massacres; after this time, like the others, their numbers grew again. From 1800 to 1939, the Jewish population in Eastern Europe swelled to several million.

The Chmielnicki massacre caused a **population bottleneck**—shrinkage of a population, followed by great expansion. A bottleneck is genetically significant because the new population has only those genes present in the small group that survived the catastrophe. An allele present in the small population might become more common in the replenished population than it was in the larger population that existed before the massacre. Population bottlenecks resulting from massacres of Jewish people help explain why several inherited diseases are at least ten times more common among them than in other populations (table 13.1).

Historical records from eighteenth-century Poland may explain another characteristic of the Ashkenazim that may reflect the selection of certain genes—high achievement and intelligence. The records show that under conditions of great discrimination, wealthier Jewish families were more likely to survive than poorer families, producing often from four to nine children that reached adulthood. Well-off girls married scholars and rabbis, who were often the most intelligent men in the population. Some population geneticists speculate that the intellectual successes of today's Ashkenazim (6 million in the United States, 3 million in the former Soviet Union, and 2.5 million in Israel) reflect the nonrandom genetic contributions of survivors of holocausts past.

The slaughter of people of a particular ethnic background is an extreme example of how gene frequencies in populations can drastically change. Recall that nonrandom mating, migration, and medical practices that permit survival of those who might otherwise not live to reproduce also underlie microevolution by countering Hardy-Weinberg equilibrium. This chapter explores several contributing factors to gene frequency changes, delving often into history and anthropology.

Nonrandom Mating

We give great thought to selecting mates—it is hardly a random process. We choose mates based on physical appearance, ethnic background, intelligence, and shared interests. We marry people similar to ourselves about 80 percent of the time. Worldwide, about one-third of all marriages occur between people who were born fewer than ten miles apart! Such nonrandom mating is a major factor in changing human gene frequencies.

Another form of nonrandom mating on a population level occurs when certain individuals contribute disproportionately to the next generation. This is common in agriculture, where an animal or plant with valuable characteristics is bred extensively. Semen from one prize bull may be used to artificially inseminate thousands of cows. Such an extreme situation can arise in a human population when a man fathers many children. In the Cape population of South Africa, for example, a Chinese immigrant known as Arnold had a very rare dominant genetic disease that causes the teeth to fall out before age twenty. Arnold had seven wives. Of his 356 living descendants, 70 have the dental disorder. The frequency of this allele in the Cape population is exceptionally high, thanks to Arnold.

The high frequency of people with albinism among Arizona's Hopi Indians also reflects nonrandom mating. This autosomal recessively inherited lack of skin and hair pigmentation, uncommon in the general U.S. population, occurs in 1 in 200 Hopi Indians. The reason for the trait's prevalence is cultural—men with albinism often stay back and help the women, rather than risk severe sunburn in the fields with the other men. They contribute disproportionately to the next generation because they have more contact with women.

The events of history reflect patterns of nonrandom mating. When a group of people is subservient to another, genes tend to "flow" from the males of the ruling class mating with females of the underclass. Historical records and living records of DNA sequences on the Y chromosome, which indicate gene transmission through the male, reveal this phenomenon of directional gene flow.

Despite our preferences in mate selection, many traits do mix randomly in the next generation. This may be because we

table 13.1

Genetic Diseases Prevalent among Jewish Populations

Condition	Symptoms
Bloom syndrome	Sun sensitivity, poor immunity, increased cancer risk
Breast cancer	Malignant breast tumor caused by mutant BRCA1 genes
Canavan disease	Brain degeneration, death by eighteen months old
Dysautonomia	No tears or sweating, cold hands and feet, skin blotching, drooling
Factor IX deficiency	Poor blood clotting
Gaucher disease	Enlarged liver and spleen, bone degeneration, nervous system impairment
Idiopathic torsion dystonia	Uncontrollable twisting, repetitive motions
Niemann-Pick disease	Lipid accumulation in cells, particularly in the brain. Mental and physical retardation, death by age three. Milder subtypes
Tay-Sachs disease	Brain degeneration causes developmental retardation, paralysis, blindness, death by age four years

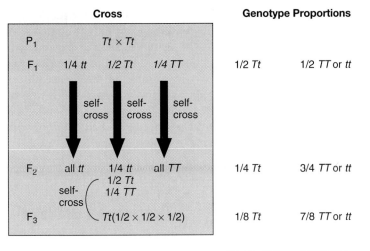

Cross   **Genotype Proportions**

P_1 $Tt \times Tt$

F_1 1/4 tt 1/2 Tt 1/4 TT 1/2 Tt 1/2 TT or tt

self-cross   self-cross   self-cross

F_2 all tt 1/4 tt all TT 1/4 Tt 3/4 TT or tt
             1/2 Tt
self-cross   1/4 TT

F_3 Tt(1/2 × 1/2 × 1/2)   1/8 Tt 7/8 TT or tt

Decreasing   Increasing
heterozygosity   homozygosity

figure 13.1

If a plant heterozygous for a particular gene is crossed to itself, then resulting heterozygous offspring are self-crossed, and this is repeated, the proportion of heterozygotes in the resulting populations will consistently decline by 50 percent.

are unaware of these characteristics, or they are not considered important in choosing a mate. We hardly select life partners, for example, on the basis of blood type! Yet sometimes the opposite occurs. People with uncommon alleles meet more often than might happen by chance when their families participate in a program for people with the same inherited condition, such as sickle cell disease clinics or summer camps for children with cystic fibrosis. In the reverse situation, in a very religious Jewish sect living near New York City, marriages are not permitted between carriers of the same inherited disease. This practice is a curious mix of the old and the new—arranged marriages, but use of genetic testing to identify carriers of specific disorders.

When a child inherits two recessive mutant alleles from unrelated carrier parents, the alleles are said to be "alike in state." In contrast are alleles that are "identical by descent," which appear in an individual because the parents have each inherited a copy of the allele from a shared ancestor.

Consanguinity

Many societies forbid marrying a first cousin and regard incest as a taboo—for solid genetic reasons. When two blood relatives conceive offspring together, each

parent may pass on the same recessive deleterious allele, which would result in a severely ill child. This is why, when a medical geneticist encounters a family with an extremely rare recessive disorder, the question of marriage between blood relatives, or **consanguinity** ("same blood"), arises.

In the United States as a whole, pairings of first cousins account for fewer than 0.1 percent of marriages. However, in small subpopulations, such as the Amish, this proportion may be greater. One of the highest consanguinity rates known is among certain families of the Druze people living in the Golan Heights region of northern Israel, which reaches 49 percent. The Druze are a thousand-year-old, close-knit Islam sect. Certain alleles found in this population are not seen in neighboring Arabs or Jews. Figure 4.10 shows the very contracted pedigree of Egypt's Ptolemy dynasty, with frequent brother-sister and uncle-niece pairings.

Inbreeding refers to the effects on offspring when parents are blood relatives. Trait transmission in plants that can self-fertilize demonstrates how inbreeding reduces heterozygosity (and increases homozygosity) in a population (figure 13.1). In human populations, too, inbreeding results in fewer heterozygotes and more homozygotes.

Inbreeding often occurs in zoo populations and on wildlife preserves, where diminished genetic diversity impairs reproduction. For example, in the panther population of 30 to 50 animals in the Big Cypress swamp ecosystem in south Florida, the animals suffer from many bacterial infections and other parasitic diseases. Eighty percent of them have heart murmurs, and several have died of another heart anomaly. Only 5 percent of the sperm is normal, and in 85 percent of males, one or both testicles never descends, severely hampering fertility. To counter the encroaching homozygosity that lies behind these health problems, reproductive biologists are trying to get the animals to mate with a different subspecies of panther being brought to the area.

When Hardy-Weinberg equilibrium operates, we predict the frequency of an allele based on the assumption of random mating. When blood relatives have children, however, the frequency of the allele appearing in both parents depends on the closeness of their blood relationship. Although each of us inherits several deleterious recessive alleles, the chances that one of these matches one in a nonrelated mate are remote. Table 7.4 shows the different types of relationship (sibling to sibling, parent to child, uncle/aunt to niece/nephew, cousin to cousin) and the proportion of genes they share. This equals the **coefficient of relationship, r.**

Constructing a pedigree helps to calculate the coefficient of relationship. Count the number of parent-child "steps" between the common ancestor and the person for whom the risk of recurrence is being assessed. This equals n. Each step is assigned a probability of 1/2, because the child could inherit either the mutant allele or the wild type allele, assuming we are considering an autosomal recessive trait. Therefore, the coefficient of relationship is $(1/2)^n$. Figure 13.2a shows that grandparents and offspring share 1/4 of their genes. Another way to determine this is to calculate that since each grandchild has four grandparents, a quarter of his or her genes comes from each.

First cousins share, on average, 1/8 of their genes. This is calculated by adding the coefficient of relationships of each cousin to the shared grandparents. In figure 13.2b,

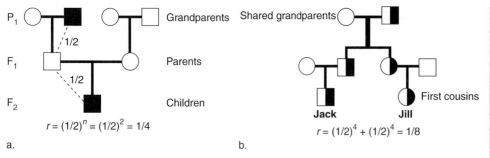

figure 13.2

Alleles from ancestors. (*a*) A child shares 1/4 of his or her genes with each of the four grandparents. The value of 1/2 is assigned to each step because a child has a 1 in 2 chance of inheriting one allele or its mate. (*b*) Should first cousins wed? A geneticist would advise not because each may carry the same deleterious allele from a shared grandparent. Calculation of *r* is based on the fact that each cousin is two "steps" removed from each of two shared grandparents ($1/2 \times 1/2 \times 1/2 \times 1/2$).

if Jack and Jill were to have children, each child would have a 1 in 4 chance of being homozygous recessive for a shared allele, according to Mendel's first law. Therefore, the total risk that first cousins will conceive a child with an autosomal recessive genetic disorder they both carry is 1/8 (the percentage of genes they share) multiplied by 1/4 (the risk of homozygosity), or 1 in 32.

Key Concepts

Genes in human populations are rarely in Hardy-Weinberg equilibrium. We choose mates for a variety of reasons and sometimes contribute disproportionately to the next generation. We also migrate, and our behaviors and historical events affect our gene pool. However, traits lacking obvious phenotypes may be in Hardy-Weinberg equilibrium.

Identical alleles in two unrelated people are alike in state. When two people are related, common alleles are identical by descent. Consanguinity greatly increases the likelihood that an individual will inherit identical deleterious alleles. The closer the blood relationship between two individuals, the more alleles they share.

Migration

Large cities, with their pockets of ethnicity, defy Hardy-Weinberg equilibrium by their very existence. Waves of immigrants formed the population of New York City, for example. The original Dutch settlers of the 1600s lacked many of the alleles in today's metropolis, which were contributed by the English, Irish, Slavics, Africans, Hispanics, Italians, Asians, and many others.

Historical Clues

Much of the immigration that built the population of the modern United States occurred from 1905 to 1924, the year of the Immigration Restriction Act. With a million people entering the nation each of those years, the population grew from 85 million to 110 million. In 1920, 24 percent of the nearly 95 million Caucasians had parents who were born overseas, and 14.5 percent were foreign-born themselves. Even if these diverse groups intermarried often and formed a true "melting pot," only a few generations have passed since then—hardly enough time for recombination to effectively mix linked combinations of traits.

We can trace the genetic effects of migration through history by correlating allele frequencies in present-day populations to events in history. For example, the frequency of ABO blood types in certain parts of the world reflects past Arab rule. The distribution of ABO blood types is very similar in Northern Africa, the Near East, and Southern Spain. These are precisely the regions where Arabs ruled until 1492. Even over half a millenium later, these alleles have not greatly separated.

Directional gene flow also occurred when nomadic peoples with a hunter-gatherer lifestyle encountered a more stable group of people and stayed awhile. For example, in the eighteenth century, European Caucasians called trekboers migrated to the Cape area of South Africa. The men stayed and had children with the native women of the Nama tribe. The mixed society remained fairly isolated, leading to the present-day people of color of the area.

Geographical and Linguistic Clues

Because geographical barriers affect migration patterns, allele frequencies sometimes differ between geographical regions, such as on either side of a mountain range. Across Europe, geographical barriers are important determinants of **clines,** which are allele frequencies that differ greatly in different communities. Another type of gene flow barrier that may be unique to humans is language.

In one study, population geneticists correlated 20 blood types to geographically defined regions of Italy and to areas where a single dialect is spoken. They chose Italy because it is rich in family history records and linguistic variants. Six of the blood types varied more consistently with linguistically defined subregions of the country than with geographical regions. Perhaps differences in language prevent people from socializing, sequestering alleles within groups that speak the same dialect because these people marry.

Key Concepts

Immigration disrupts gene frequencies by introducing new alleles into a population, although it may take many generations for different ethnic groups to intermarry. Distribution of allele frequencies often reflects historical events, geographical barriers, and linguistic differences.

Genetic Drift

In **genetic drift,** gene frequencies change when a small group of individuals is separated from a larger population. By chance, the small group may not represent the whole. Could we estimate the average academic ability of 200 students in a biology class, for example, by considering only the students who earned a grade of F on the final exam—or only those who earned an A?

A common type of genetic drift in human populations is the **founder effect,** which occurs when small groups of people leave their homes to found new settlements. The new colony may have different genotype frequencies than the original population and may amplify traits that were formerly rare. The fact that some populations of native Americans in North America do not have type B blood illustrates the founder effect. Type B blood appears in the Asian population from which they descended, but the founding Asian settlers who crossed the Bering Strait to America thousands of years ago did not include anyone with type B or AB blood, or the people with these blood types did not leave descendants.

The Afrikaners Demonstrate the Founder Effect

The founder effect can also increase the proportion of an allele in a population. Consider the 2.5 million people of the Afrikaner population of South Africa, who descended from a small group of Dutch, French, and German immigrants. Once settled in South Africa, the immigrants had huge families, with ten children not uncommon. In the nineteenth century, some of these Afrikaners migrated northeast to the Transvaal Province, where they lived in isolation until the Boer War in 1902 introduced better transportation.

The founder effect is evident when certain allele frequencies in Afrikaners are compared to those of their ancestral populations in Europe and those of modern South Africans. Today, 30,000 Afrikaners have porphyria variegata, a dominantly inherited enzyme defect that causes a severe reaction to barbiturate anesthetics. (The disorder was unknown until these drugs entered medical practice.) All affected people descend from one couple who came from Holland in the 1680s. Today's gene frequency in South Africa is far higher than that in the Netherlands because this

couple contributed significantly to the early Afrikaner population.

Familial Mediterranean fever (FMF), which causes fever and pain in the chest, joints, and abdomen, illustrates the founder effect. Certain populations living near the Mediterranean have high incidence of the illness. FMF affects 14 percent of Armenians and 17 percent of North African Jews, for example. These people all descend from Spaniards who escaped the Inquisition and settled in nations bordering the sea. DNA analysis reveals that 85 percent of affected individuals in the region have a mutation in the same small area of the causative gene. DNA sequences surrounding this gene are also similar or identical among the people, which provides strong molecular evidence of a founder effect.

People do not have to leave home for genetic drift to occur. It often happens when members of a small community choose to mate only among themselves, keeping genetic variants within their ethnic group. Pittsburgh, Pennsylvania, for example, is made up of many distinct neighborhoods whose residents are more alike genetically than others in the city.

Genetic drift is particularly striking in the Dunker community of Germantown, Pennsylvania. The Dunkers left Germany between 1719 and 1729 to settle in the New World. Today, the frequencies of some genotypes are different among the Dunkers than among their non-Dunker neighbors and among people living in their native German town. For example, the Dunkers

have a different distribution of blood types (table 13.2) and much higher incidences of attached earlobes, hyperextensible thumbs, hairs in the middles of fingers, and left-handedness.

Population Bottlenecks

Genetic drift also results from a population bottleneck. Recall that this occurs when many members of a population die, and numbers are restored as a few individuals mate. The new population has a much more restricted gene pool than the larger ancestral population.

Population bottlenecks sometimes occur when people (or other animals) colonize islands. An extreme example is seen among the Pingelapese people of the eastern Caroline islands. Between 4 and 10 percent of them are born with Pingelapese blindness, an autosomal recessively inherited combination of color blindness, near-sightedness, and cataracts (clouding of the lens). The prevalence of this otherwise very rare condition is traced to a typhoon that decimated the population in 1780. Only 9 males survived, and they founded the present-day population. The effects of this severe population bottleneck, combined with isolation, resulted in the high frequency of the blindness gene.

Figure 13.3 illustrates the dwindling genetic diversity that results from a population bottleneck, against a backdrop of a cheetah. Once 10,000 animals strong and widespread, today's cheetahs live in just two isolated populations of a few

table 13.2
Genetic Drift and the Dunkers

Blood Type	Population		
	U.S.	Dunker	European
ABO system			
A	40%	60%	45%
B, AB	15%	5%	15%
Rh–	15%	11%	15%
MN system			
M	30%	44.5%	30%
MN	50%	42%	50%
N	20%	13.5%	20%

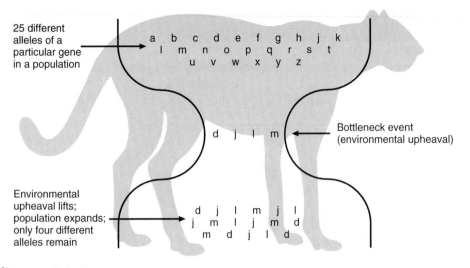

- 25 different alleles of a particular gene in a population

a b c d e f g h j k
l m n o p q r s t
u v w x y z

d j l m

← Bottleneck event (environmental upheaval)

- Environmental upheaval lifts; population expands; only four different alleles remain →

d j l m j l
j m l j m d
m d j l d

figure 13.3

A population bottleneck occurs when the size of a genetically diverse population drastically falls, remains at this level for a time, and then expands again. The rebuilt population loses some genetic diversity if different alleles are lost in the bottleneck event. Cheetahs are difficult to breed in zoos because sperm quality is poor and many newborns die—both due to lack of genetic diversity.

figure 13.4

The strikingly similar facial features and complexions of the Finnish people reflect a restricted gene pool, evidence of a long-ago population bottleneck.

thousand animals in South and East Africa. The South African cheetahs are so alike genetically that even unrelated animals can accept skin grafts from each other. Researchers attribute the cheetahs' genetic uniformity to two bottlenecks—one that occurred at the end of the most recent ice age, when habitats were altered, and another that involved mass slaughter by humans in the nineteenth century.

Evidence of a population bottleneck is apparent among the Finns, who descend from settlers who came to Finland 4,000 years ago. Isolated by both geography and the harsh climate, alleles peculiar to the settlers stayed in the population. Today, the descendants not only have a distinctive appearance and language (figure 13.4), but a unique spectrum of inherited disease. Cystic fibrosis, common in many populations, is practically nonexistent among the Finns, yet they have high incidence of 30 or so genetic disorders that are extremely rare elsewhere. Analysis of mitochondrial DNA, which reflects maternal lineage, and from the Y chromosome, which reflects paternal heritage, provides molecular evidence of a population bottleneck. That is, the Finns show much less genetic variation within their group than do other Europeans.

Key Concepts

Genetic drift occurs when a subset of a population contains different gene frequencies. The founder effect occurs when a few individuals leave a community to start a new settlement. The resulting population may, by chance, either lack some alleles present in the original population or have high frequencies of others. In a population bottleneck, many members of a population die, and only a few individuals contribute genetically to the next generation.

Mutation

A major and continual source of genetic variation is mutation—when one allele changes into another (chapter 10). Genetic variability also arises from crossing over and independent assortment during meiosis, but these events recombine existing traits rather than introduce new ones. If a DNA base change occurs in a part of a gene that encodes a portion of a protein necessary for its function, then an altered trait may result. If the mutation is in a gamete, then the change can pass to future generations and therefore ultimately affect an allele's frequency in the population.

Heterozygotes and further mutational events maintain the frequency of a recessive mutant allele in a population. Such an allele disappears from a population when homozygous individuals who cannot successfully reproduce die. Because heterozygosity and mutation maintain and introduce deleterious alleles, all populations have some alleles that would be harmful if homozygous. The collection of such deleterious alleles in a population is called the **genetic load.**

Natural Selection

Environmental change can alter gene frequencies when individuals with certain phenotypes are more likely to survive and reproduce than others. The effect of natural selection on gene frequencies is vividly revealed by the changing virulence of certain human infectious diseases over many years.

Two such illnesses are tuberculosis and AIDS.

Tuberculosis Ups and Downs— And Ups

The spread of tuberculosis (TB) in the Plains Indians of the Qu'Appelle Valley Reservation in Saskatchewan, Canada, illustrates natural selection. When TB first appeared on the reservation in the mid-1880s, it struck swiftly and lethally, infecting many organs. Ten percent of the population died. By 1921, TB in the Indians tended to affect only the lungs, and only 7 percent of the population died annually from it. By 1950, mortality was down to 0.2 percent.

Outbreaks of TB ran similar courses in other human populations. The disease appeared in crowded settlements where the bacteria easily spread from person to person in exhaled droplets. In the 1700s, TB raged through the cities of Europe. Immigrants brought it to the United States in the early 1800s, where it also swept the cities. Many people thought TB was hereditary until German bacteriologist Robert Koch identified the causative bacterium in 1882.

As in the Plains Indians, TB incidence and virulence fell dramatically in the cities of the industrialized world in the first half of the twentieth century—before antibiotics were discovered. What tamed tuberculosis?

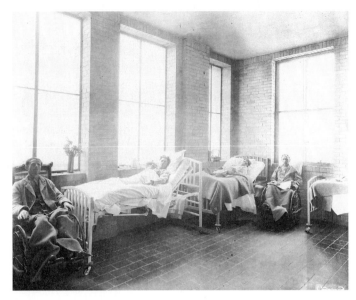

figure 13.5

Earlier in the century, tuberculosis was controlled because many infected people were isolated in sanitaria until they could no longer pass the infection on.

Natural selection, operating on both the bacterial and human populations, may have caused the decline in the virulence of the infection. Some people inherited a resistance and passed this beneficial trait on. The most virulent bacteria killed their hosts so quickly that there was no time to pass on the microbes. As the deadliest bacteria were selected out of the population, and as people who inherited resistance mutations contributed disproportionately to the next generation, the effect of TB on human health gradually became more benign. It evolved from an acute, systemic infection to an increasingly rare chronic lung infection. This was true until the late 1980s.

Over the past few years, a series of unrelated events has created conditions just right for the resurgence of this old foe—but the "new" TB is resistant to many of the eleven drugs that we use to treat it. Some health officials trace the return of tuberculosis to complacency. Researchers turned to other projects when funding became scarce for this seemingly controlled disease, even though the mechanisms of the treatments were never fully understood.

Tuberculosis patients became complacent too. When antibiotics eased symptoms in two to three months, patients felt cured and stopped taking the drugs, even though they unknowingly continued to harbor and spread the live bacteria for up to eighteen months. The *Mycobacterium tuberculosis* bacteria survived in patients who stopped taking antibiotics. The bacteria had time to mutate, eventually evolving the drug resistances that make the newest cases so difficult to treat (Reading 13.1). Tuberculosis treatment in the 1950s was actually more effective; patients were isolated for a year or longer in rest homes called sanitaria and were not released until the bacteria were gone (figure 13.5).

Today, one in seven new tuberculosis cases is resistant to several drugs, and 5 percent of these patients die. People living in crowded, unsanitary conditions with poor health care are especially susceptible to drug-resistant TB. In late 1991, TB became alarmingly prevalent and deadly among prison inmates and the homeless in several large cities. Another reservoir of new TB infection is persons infected with HIV. Tuberculosis develops so quickly in people with suppressed immunity that it can kill before physicians have determined which drugs to use—and some physicians have even died of the infection while trying to treat patients. The resurgence of this killer should remind us never to underestimate the fact that evolution operates in all organisms—and does so unpredictably.

We like to think we have made great medical progress in this century—and we have. But as the century draws to a close, infectious diseases—which we once thought we could control with drugs—are again on the rise. Headlines report new diseases and the return of old ones, playing against a continuing backdrop of the seemingly never-ending story of AIDS.

Infections New and Old

In 1993, the southwestern United States saw an outbreak of a swiftly lethal lung infection caused by hantavirus, which was spread in rodent droppings. In 1994, people in several western states developed bloody diarrhea and kidney failure, some dying after eating meat tainted with *E. coli* bacteria that produce an unusual toxin. In 1995, hundreds of people in Zaire fell ill with Ebola viral hemorrhagic fever, an infection with a nearly 90 percent mortality rate that within days can reduce a human body to liquid.

Meanwhile, infections that were scourges of the past have returned, many more virulent (severe) than before. Multidrug-resistant tuberculosis is spreading in hospitals, perhaps naturally selected in the increasing numbers of people with compromised immune systems. Air travelers brought cholera and malaria from points south to California. Changing weather patterns have also altered where certain infectious diseases occur.

Since 1990, diphtheria has reemerged in Russia. This infection, which coats the throat with a whitish growth and affects the skin, heart, kidneys, and nerves, was under control, since vaccination began more than three decades ago. Reemergence of a highly virulent form of diphtheria may be a response to a combination of factors, including a large number of unvaccinated children and adults, crowding, and forced migration due to political unrest. From 1975 through 1979, there were fewer than 1,000 reported cases a year; by 1993, that number had surged to nearly 50,000! Dengue, cholera, and yellow fever are other old infections reappearing in new places.

Driving Forces—Mutation and Natural Selection

New infections appear and old ones return for two major reasons—mutation and natural selection. Table 1 lists a number of ways that viruses or bacteria mutate and cause illness.

We can't do much to prevent mutation from producing more virulent strains of bacteria and viruses, but because natural selection involves environmental change, we can theoretically alter its effects by changing the environment. The current antibiotic-resistant bacteria crisis illustrates the interplay of mutation and natural selection in the spread of infectious disease. Some infections are now able to resist all antibiotic drugs.

Antibiotic Resistance

The bacteria in a human body, like any population of organisms, include different genetic variants; some confer the ability to survive in the presence of a particular antibiotic drug. The bacteria cause symptoms. The feverish and aching person goes to the doctor, and a course of antibiotics seems to help. But a month later, symptoms return. What happened?

The drug killed most of the bacteria, but a few survived because they have a fortuitous (for them) mutation that enables them to virtually ignore the antibiotic assault. Over a few weeks, those few mutants reproduce, taking over the niche the antibiotic-sensitive bacteria vacated. Soon, the person has enough antibiotic-resistant bacteria to develop signs and symptoms again. The next step is to try a drug that works differently—and hope that the bacteria haven't mutated around that one, too. Antibiotic resistance is, in a sense, a biological arms race.

Antibiotic drugs do not cause mutations in bacteria; they select preexisting resistant variants. Bacteria with drug-resistance mutations circumvent antibiotic actions in several ways. Penicillin, for example, kills bacteria by attaching to and tearing apart their cell walls. Resistant microbes have mutations that enable them to produce enzymes that dismantle penicillin or to alter their cell walls so that the drug cannot bind. Erythromycin, streptomycin, tetracycline, and gentamicin kill bacteria by attacking ribosomes.

Evolving HIV

Because the RNA or DNA of viruses replicates often and is not repaired, mutations accumulate rapidly. In HIV infection, natural selection controls the diversity of HIV genetic variants within a human body. The environmental factors that select resistant viral variants are the human immune system and the drugs we use to slow the infection.

HIV infection can be divided into three stages, both from the human and the viral perspective (figure 13.6). A person infected with HIV may experience an initial acute phase, with symptoms of fever, night sweats, rash, and swollen glands. In a second period, lasting from two to fifteen years, health usually returns. In a third stage, immunity collapses, the virus replicates explosively, and opportunistic infections and cancer eventually cause death.

The HIV population changes and expands throughout the course of infection, even when the patient seems to remain the same for long periods of time. New mutants continuously arise, and alter such traits as

Drug-resistant bacteria have altered ribosomes that the drugs cannot bind.

Bacteria acquire antibiotic resistance in several ways. Their DNA may spontaneously mutate—this is how drug-resistant tuberculosis arose. They may receive a resistance gene from another bacterium in a form of microbial sex called transformation. This is how the sexually transmitted disease gonorrhea gained resistance to penicillin. Bacteria can acquire resistance to several drugs at once by taking up a small circle of DNA, called a plasmid, from another bacterium. Not only can plasmids transmit multiple drug resistances, but they flit freely from one species of bacteria to another. In 1968, a plasmid carrying resistance genes to four commonly used antibiotics caused 12,500 people to die in Guatemala from *Shigella* infection, a severe form of diarrhea.

When we realize that mutation and natural selection underlie many emerging infectious illnesses, we can suggest ways to fight what one book calls "the coming plague":

1. Limit antibiotic use. Many medical experts believe that overuse and inappropriate use of antibiotics encourages the emergence of drug-resistant bacterial strains. Doctors can order laboratory tests to be certain that a patient has a bacterial rather than a viral infection before prescribing antibiotics, which do not work on viruses. Doctors might also not prescribe antibiotics to prevent infection.

table 1

How Mutation Spreads Infectious Disease

Type of Change	Example
Altered host	Until 1978, canine parvovirus killed only minks, cats, foxes, and raccoons. Then the virus changed. Within months, it was killing domestic dogs, apparently spread in droppings carried on the shoes of air travelers.
	HIV may have arisen as a monkey virus that mutated and became able to infect humans.
New toxin	*E. coli* strain 0157:H7 produces a deadly toxin not usually seen in this common gut bacterium.
	The hantavirus that caused illness in the southwestern United States in 1994 differed genetically from strains that caused bleeding and kidney failure in Korea in the 1950s. The new strain also produced a different toxin.
	Two toxins enabled a strain of *Streptococcus A* bacteria to cause "necrotizing fasciitis and myositis"—also known as "flesh-eating bacteria."
New route of transmission	Ebola virus in African monkeys at a facility in Virginia began to be spread not by blood infection, as in the past, but through droplets in the air.
Drug resistance	*Staphylococcus aureus,* a common bacterium that causes blood poisoning, pneumonia, and surgical infections, resists all antibiotic drugs.

2. Improve public health measures. These measures include having health care workers wash their hands frequently and thoroughly, rapidly identifying and isolating patients with drug-resistant infections, improving sewage systems and water purity, and using clean needles.

3. Develop new antibiotics. The cost of developing a new drug, especially when the old ones still worked, kept many companies from exploring new treatments for infectious diseases. Investigating biochemicals in diverse species can yield new natural antibiotics.

speed of replication and the patterns of molecules on the viral surface. Physicians track the course of HIV infection by using DNA amplification to measure viral RNA in blood samples, called the viral load.

In the first stage of HIV infection, as the person battles acute symptoms, viral variants that can replicate very fast have a selective advantage. Soon, most of the viral particles have the same rapidly multiplying genotype. Then the immune system fights back and symptoms abate. Viral replication is no longer unchecked, and many viruses are destroyed. Now natural selection acts—those viral variants that can evade the immune attack survive, then reproduce, until the viral population becomes quite diverse. Therapeutic drugs may further select against the weakest HIV variants. The HIV population gradually overtakes the number of immune system cells the body produces to counter it, but years may pass until immunity begins to shatter.

The third stage, full-blown AIDS, occurs when the viral load reaches a level that overwhelms the immune system. Now, with the selective pressure off, viral diversity

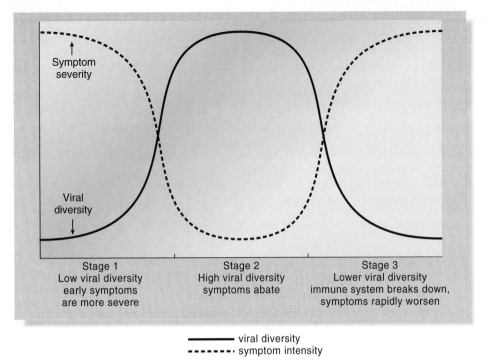

figure 13.6

Natural selection controls the genetic diversity of an HIV population in a person's body. Before the immune system gathers strength, and after it breaks down, HIV diversity is low. A rapidly reproducing viral strain predominates, although new mutations continually arise. During the two- to fifteen-year latency period, viral variants that can evade the immune system gradually accumulate. Eventually, HIV overpowers the immune system. Evolution renders the body's fight against HIV a losing battle—unless the person is one of the lucky few to inherit a mutation that blocks HIV infection.

In the graph legend:
— viral diversity
- - - - - symptom intensity

Within graph:
Symptom severity

Viral diversity

Stage 1
Low viral diversity
early symptoms
are more severe

Stage 2
High viral diversity
symptoms abate

Stage 3
Lower viral diversity
immune system breaks down,
symptoms rapidly worsen

again diminishes, and the fastest-replicating variants predominate. HIV wins.

Knowing that HIV diversifies early in the course of infection has yielded clinical benefits. Patients now start early on combinations of drugs in the hope of squelching several viral variants simultaneously to slow the course of the infection.

Balanced Polymorphism

If natural selection eliminates individuals with detrimental phenotypes from a population, then why do harmful mutant alleles persist in a gene pool? A disease can remain prevalent when heterozygotes have some other advantage over individuals who have two copies of the wild type allele. When carriers have advantages that allow a detrimental allele to persist in a population, **balanced polymorphism** is at work. Being a carrier for an inherited illness may protect against a specific infectious illness or enable an individual to better survive a

certain environmental condition (table 13.3). Examples are fascinating.

Sickle Cell Disease and Malaria

Sickle cell disease is an autosomal recessive disorder that causes anemia, joint pain, a swollen spleen, and frequent, severe infections. It illustrates balanced polymorphism because carriers are resistant to malaria, an infection by the parasite *Plasmodium falciparum* that causes cycles of chills and fever. The parasite spends the first stage of its life cycle in the salivary glands of the mosquito *Anopheles gambiae*. When an infected mosquito bites a human, the malaria parasite enters the red blood cells, which transport it to the liver. The red blood cells burst, releasing the parasite throughout the body.

In 1949, British geneticist Anthony Allison found that the frequency of sickle cell carriers in tropical Africa was higher in regions where malaria raged all year long. Blood tests from children hospitalized with

malaria found that nearly all were homozygous for the wild type sickle cell allele. The few sickle cell carriers among them had the mildest cases of malaria. Was malaria enabling the sickle cell allele to persist by felling people who did not inherit it? The fact that sickle cell disease is far less common where malaria is rare supports the idea that sickle cell heterozygosity protects against the infection.

Further evidence of a sickle cell carrier's advantage in a malaria-ridden environment is the fact that the rise of sickle cell disease parallels the cultivation of crops that provide breeding grounds for *Anopheles* mosquitoes. About 1000 B.C., Malayo-Polynesian sailors from southeast Asia traveled in canoes to East Africa, bringing new crops of bananas, yams, taros, and coconuts. When the jungle was cleared to grow these crops, the open space provided breeding grounds for the mosquitoes. The insects, in turn, offered a habitat for part of the life cycle of the malaria parasite.

The sickle cell gene may have been brought to Africa by people migrating from Southern Arabia and India, or it may have arisen by mutation directly in East Africa. However it happened, people who inherited one copy of the sickle cell allele had red blood cell membranes that did not admit the parasite. Carriers had more children and passed the protective allele to approximately half of them. Gradually, the frequency of the sickle cell allele in East Africa rose from 0.1 percent to 45 percent in thirty-five generations. Carriers paid the price for this genetic protection, however, whenever two produced a child with sickle cell disease.

A cycle set in. Settlements with large numbers of sickle cell carriers escaped debilitating malaria. They were therefore strong enough to clear even more land to grow food—and support the disease-bearing mosquitoes. Even today, sickle cell disease is more prevalent in agricultural societies than among people who hunt and gather their food.

Glucose-6-Phosphate Dehydrogenase Deficiency and Malaria

Recall from chapter 10 that G6PD deficiency is a sex-linked enzyme deficiency that causes life-threatening hemolytic anemia, under specific conditions. Among

table 13.3

Balanced Polymorphism

Inherited Disease	Infectious Disease	Possible Mechanism
Cystic fibrosis	Diarrheal diseases	Carriers have too few chloride channels in intestinal cells, blocking toxin (cholera), or CFTR protein is a receptor typhus-causing bacteria
G6PD deficiency	Malaria	Red blood cells inhospitable to malaria parasite
Phenylketonuria (PKU)	Spontaneous abortion	Excess amino acid (phenylalanine) in carriers inactivates ochratoxin A, a fungal toxin that causes miscarriage
Sickle cell disease	Malaria	Red blood cells inhospitable to malaria parasite
Tay-Sachs disease	Tuberculosis	Unknown

African children with severe malaria, heterozygous females and hemizygous males for G6PD deficiency are underrepresented. This suggests that inheriting the enzyme deficiency gene somehow protects against malaria.

The fact that G6PD deficiency is sex-linked introduces a possibility we do not see with sickle cell disease, which is autosomal recessive. Because both heterozygotes and hemizygotes have an advantage, the mutant allele should eventually predominate in a malaria-exposed population. However, this doesn't happen—there are still males hemizygous and females homozygous for the wild type allele. The reason again relates to natural selection. People with the enzyme deficiency—hemizygous males and homozygous females—are selected out of the population by the fatal anemia. Therefore, natural selection acts in two directions on the hemizygous males—selecting *for* the mutant allele because it protects against malarial infection, yet selecting *against* it because it causes an enzyme deficiency. This is the essence of balanced polymorphism.

PKU and Fungal Infection

In phenylketonuria, a missing enzyme causes the amino acid phenylalanine to build up, which devastates the nervous system unless the individual follows a restrictive diet. Carriers of this autosomal recessive condition have elevated phenylalanine levels—not sufficient to cause symptoms, but high enough to be protective during pregnancy. Women who are PKU carriers have a much lower-than-average incidence of miscarriage. One hypothesis is that excess phenylalanine inactivates a poison, called ochratoxin A, that certain fungi produce and that is known to cause spontaneous abortion.

History provides the evidence that links PKU heterozygosity to protection against a fungal toxin. PKU is most common in Ireland and western Scotland, and many affected families living elsewhere trace their roots to this part of the world. PKU spread eastward in Europe when the Vikings brought wives and slaves back from the Celtic lands. In the moist environment of Ireland and Scotland, the fungi that produce ochratoxin A—*Aspergillis* and *Penicillium*—grow on grains. During the famines that have plagued these nations, starving people ate moldy grain. If PKU carriers were more likely to have children than noncarriers because of the protective effects of the PKU gene, over time, the disease-causing allele would increase in the population.

Tay-Sachs Disease and Tuberculosis

Carrying Tay-Sachs disease may protect against tuberculosis (TB). During World War II, TB ran rampant in Eastern European Jewish settlements. Often, healthy relatives of children with Tay-Sachs disease did not contract TB, even when repeatedly exposed. The protection against TB that Tay-Sachs disease heterozygosity apparently offered remained among the Jewish people because they were prevented from leaving the ghettos. The mutant allele increased in frequency as TB selectively felled those who did not carry it and the carriers had children with each other. Genetic drift may also have helped isolate the Tay-Sachs allele, by chance, in groups of holocaust survivors. Precisely how lowered levels of the gene product, an enzyme called hexoseaminidase A, protect against TB isn't known.

Cystic Fibrosis and Diarrheal Disease

Balanced polymorphism may explain why cystic fibrosis is so common—the anatomical defect that underlies CF protects against diarrheal illnesses, such as cholera and typhus.

Diarrheal disease epidemics have left their mark on many human populations. Severe diarrhea rapidly dehydrates the body and leads to shock, kidney and heart failure, and death in days. In cholera, bacteria produce a toxin that opens chloride channels in cells of the small intestine. As salt (NaCl) leaves the intestinal cells, water rushes out, producing diarrhea. Cholera opens chloride channels, releasing chloride and water. The CFTR protein does just the opposite, closing chloride channels and trapping salt and water in cells, which dries out mucus and other secretions. A person with CF is very unlikely to contract cholera, because the toxin cannot open the chloride channels in the small intestine cells.

Carriers of CF enjoy the mixed blessing of balanced polymorphism. They do not have enough abnormal chloride channels to cause the labored breathing and clogged pancreas of cystic fibrosis, but they do have enough of a defect to prevent the cholera toxin from taking hold. During the devastating cholera epidemics that have peppered history, individuals carrying mutant CF alleles had a selective advantage, and they disproportionately transmitted those alleles to future generations.

However, because CF arose in western Europe and cholera in Africa, perhaps an

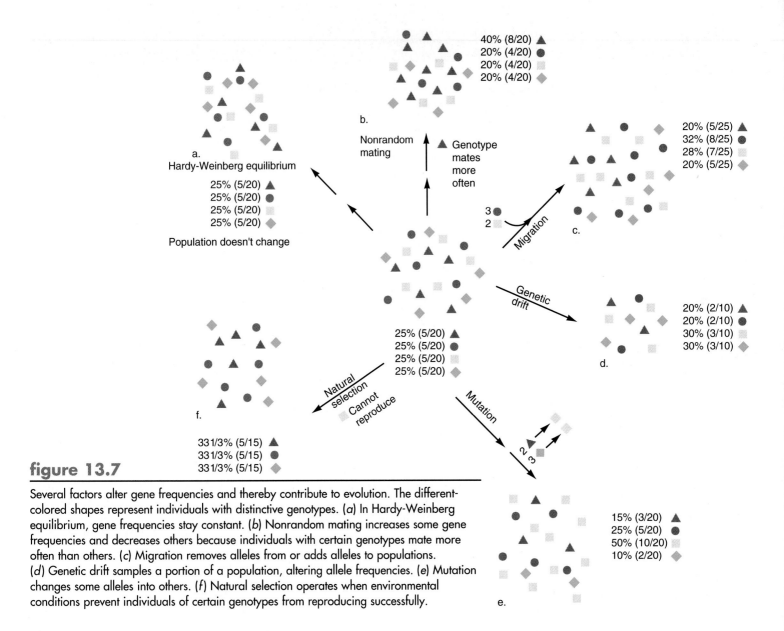

figure 13.7

Several factors alter gene frequencies and thereby contribute to evolution. The different-colored shapes represent individuals with distinctive genotypes. (*a*) In Hardy-Weinberg equilibrium, gene frequencies stay constant. (*b*) Nonrandom mating increases some gene frequencies and decreases others because individuals with certain genotypes mate more often than others. (*c*) Migration removes alleles from or adds alleles to populations. (*d*) Genetic drift samples a portion of a population, altering allele frequencies. (*e*) Mutation changes some alleles into others. (*f*) Natural selection operates when environmental conditions prevent individuals of certain genotypes from reproducing successfully.

initial increase in CF heterozygosity was a response to a different diarrheal infection. This disease may have been typhus, another bacterial infection. Wild type CFTR protein functions as a receptor for the bacterium. Carriers of CF, with half the normal number of functional CFTR proteins, are much less likely to develop typhus.

Diabetes Mellitus and Surviving Famine

Type II (non-insulin-dependent) diabetes mellitus (NIDDM) is a gradual failure of cells to respond to insulin and take up glucose from the bloodstream. It is a complex trait—a first-degree relative has a tenfold increased risk of developing the condition than does the general population. Further evidence for a genetic component comes from populations that once led lives of sparse and intermittent meals and great activity. Then, NIDDM was virtually nonexistent. The disorder arose and became increasingly prevalent as food became more available and lifestyles more sedentary. These observations suggest a preexisting, underlying tendency to develop diabetes under certain environmental conditions.

When Jewish people from Yemen came to Israel in 1949, for example, none had NIDDM. Within two decades, 13 percent of the population was affected. This trend among the Pima Indians of southern Arizona is even more astonishing. Once lean and healthy, the Pimas became overweight and diabetic as their ways became westernized. Today, more than half of the Pimas over age 35 have NIDDM.

Some geneticists suggest that NIDDM is common today because the gene or genes that predispose to it might once have been beneficial, a variation on the balanced polymorphism theme. The reasoning is that NIDDM prevents breakdown of fat and alters the body's ability to store glucose. In times past, extra fat stores and altered glucose metabolism were insurance for surviving famine. Today, they cause weight gain and diabetes.

Figure 13.7 reviews and summarizes the forces that alter gene frequencies and therefore impact on evolution.

Gene Genealogy

Identifying different mutations in a gene is useful in charting the evolution and spread of genetic variants. An assumption in deciphering gene origins is that the more prevalent an allele is, the more ancient it is, because it has had more time to spread and accumulate in a population. Correlating allele frequencies with historical, archeological, and linguistic evidence provides fascinating peeks at the growth of modern peoples.

PKU Revisited

The diversity of PKU mutations suggests that the disease has arisen more than once. Mutations common to many groups of people probably represent more ancient mutational events, which perhaps occurred before many groups spread into disparate populations. In contrast, mutations found only in a small geographical region, or perhaps in a single family, are more likely to be of recent origin. Turks, Norwegians, French Canadians, and Yemenite Jews have their own PKU alleles (Reading 13.2). Analysis of the frequencies of PKU mutations in different populations can reveal the extent of the roles of genetic drift, mutation, and balanced polymorphism in maintaining the illness.

A high mutation rate cannot be the sole reason for the continued prevalence of PKU because some countries, such as Denmark, continue to have only one or two mutations. If the gene were unstable, so that it mutated frequently, all populations would have several different types of PKU mutations. This is not the case.

In some isolated populations, such as the French Canadians and Yemenite Jews, migration and the founder effect have maintained certain PKU alleles. A more recent example of the effect history and politics can have on gene frequency is the influx of families with PKU into northwest Germany after the second world war, when Germans from the east moved westward. Future shifts in allele frequencies may parallel the breakdown of the former Soviet Union.

CF Revisited

Following alleles in modern populations known to have very ancient roots offers clues to how early genetic disorders plagued humankind. For example, the CF allele ΔF508 is very prevalent among northern Europeans, yet not as common in the south (figure 13.8). This distribution might mean that early farmers migrating from the Middle East to Europe in the Neolithic period, up until about 10,000 years ago, brought the allele to Europe. At this time, people were just beginning to give up a hunter-gatherer lifestyle for semipermanent settlements, exhibiting the first activities of agriculture.

The origin, or at least the existence, of ΔF508 may go farther back, to the Paleolithic age before 10,000 years ago. People then were hunter-gatherers who occasionally lived in caves and tents. They used tools of chipped stone, followed a lunar calendar, and created magnificent cave art.

Geneticists were led back to the Paleolithic by an intriguing group of people, the residents of the Basque country in the western part of the Pyrenees Mountains between France and Spain. The Basque

figure 13.8

The most common allele causing cystic fibrosis, ΔF508, occurs with vastly different frequencies in different populations. This map indicates the percentage of CF alleles in these nations that are ΔF508.

Source: Data from European Working Group on Cystic Fibrosis Genetics, "Gradient of Distribution in Europe of the Major CF Mutation and of Its Associated Haplotype," *Human Genetics* 85:436–45, 1990.

resent-day allele frequencies often reflect such cultural influences as economic hardship, religious persecution, and marriage practices. This is true for PKU in modern Israel.

In most populations, point mutations in the phenylalanine hydroxylase (PAH) gene cause PKU. Virtually all of the Yemenite Jews in Israel who have PKU instead have a 6,700-base deletion in the third exon of the PAH gene. With such an unusual mutation to follow, an eclectic group of researchers—including geneticists, cell biologists, scholars in Jewish history, and pediatricians—combined the tools of molecular genetics and historical records to trace the spread of this PKU from North Africa to Israel.

The researchers began by testing for the telltale deletion in the grandparents of the 22 modern Yemenite Jewish families with PKU in Israel. By asking questions and consulting court and religious records, which this close-knit community kept meticulously, the team found that all clues pointed to San'a, the capital of Yemen.

The earliest records identify two families with PKU in San'a, and extrapolating back, indicate the mutation originated in one person before 1800. By 1809, religious persecution and hard economic times led nine families carrying the mutation to migrate north and settle in three towns (figure 1). Four of the families then moved farther northward, into four more towns. Twenty more families spread from San'a to inhabit seventeen other towns. All of this migration took place from 1762 through the mid-1900s, and eventually led to Israel.

The unique PKU mutation of the modern Yemenite Jews in Israel vividly illustrates genetic drift, the founder effect, and possibly heterozygote advantage.

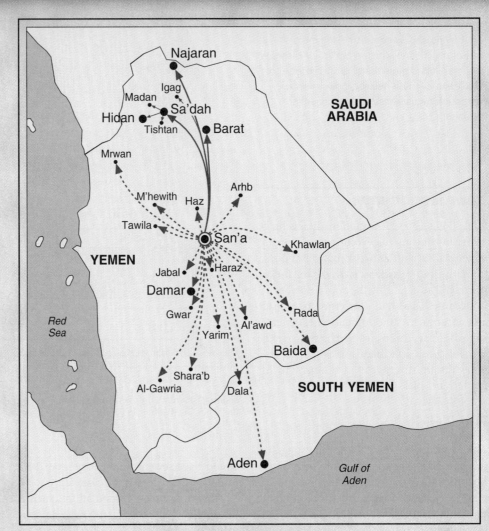

figure 1

The exon 3 deletion in Israeli Yemenite Jews probably arose in San'a, Yemen, in the mid-eighteenth century. The allele spread northward as families moved from San'a in 1809 (solid arrows) and subsequently spread to other regions (broken arrows).

Source: Data from Smadar Avigad, et al., "A Single Origin of Phenylketonuria in Yemenite Jews," *Nature* 344:170. March 8, 1990.

Comparisons of highly polymorphic (variable) DNA sequences among many human populations show that most genetic variability occurs *within* populations, rather than *between* them. Based on several biochemical characteristics, two persons with black skin may be less alike than either is to another person with white skin!

Some traits *are* more common among people of a particular skin color, such as eye color, hair color and texture, and the size and shape of certain bones. However, no single trait always occurs in people of one skin color and never in people of another skin color. Overall, 93 percent of inherited traits that vary (including biochemical differences) are *not* more common in people of any one skin color.

Even as racial distinctions based on skin color continue to cause social problems, people are beginning to rethink accepted definitions of race, if only to recognize more variations of skin color. The U.S. Census plans to expand racial classifications to include multiracial groups as well as native Hawaiians and middle Easterners. The American College of Physicians has suggested that its members refrain from indicating race on medical records, because it does not provide valuable medical information. The International Union of Anthropological and Ethnological Sciences will soon vote on the very existence of races based on skin color. Finally, but perhaps most importantly, a worldwide scientific investigation called the Human Genome Diversity Project plans to study DNA sequences among isolated groups of people from all over the world in an attempt to better describe the genetic variations among us.

Key Concepts

Genetic studies can confirm archeological and linguistic studies of relatedness between populations. Frequencies for HLA alleles were calculated for populations in The Gambia, converted to chord distances and a cluster diagram, then compared to linguistic data. Genetic distance and linguistic distance usually correlate well.

Skin color is just one variable inherited trait in humans. A race is a group of people from one geographic area that share a distinguishing inherited characteristic. Production and distribution of melanin colors the skin. Although humans have long used skin color to define races, two people of the same skin color may actually differ in more genes than either does from a person with another skin color.

summary

1. Human behavior alters the frequency of many genes from Hardy-Weinberg equilibrium. Massacres and discrimination concentrate certain alleles in certain population groups. We choose mates based on certain characteristics, and some individuals have many more children than others. However, DNA sequences that do not cause a phenotype valued in mate selection may exhibit Hardy-Weinberg equilibrium.

2. Identical deleterious recessive alleles are more likely to occur in blood relatives than in two unrelated individuals. Conceiving offspring with a blood relative results in **inbreeding,** which increases the likelihood of homozygosity. When two recessive deleterious alleles that are alike by descent (or, if in nonrelatives, are alike in state) pair in an individual, a phenotype (disease) results. The higher the **coefficient of relationship,** the more alleles two people have in common.

3. Different gene frequencies in communities constitute **clines** and may reflect geographic barriers or linguistic differences. Human migration patterns explain many cline boundaries.

4. **Genetic drift** occurs when small populations leave with a random subset of genotypes not representative of the larger population. A **founder effect** is a type of drift that occurs when a few individuals found a settlement and their genes form the basis of the new gene pool, amplifying whatever alleles they introduce. A **population bottleneck** is a narrowing of genetic diversity that occurs after many members of a population die and the remaining few individuals contribute genetically to rebuild the population.

5. Mutation and heterozygosity maintain deleterious alleles in populations; these alleles are selected against when homozygotes do not reproduce. Environmental conditions influence allele prevalence via natural selection, as the rise and fall of infectious diseases indicates. In **balanced polymorphism,** the frequencies of some deleterious alleles are maintained when heterozygotes have a reproductive advantage.

6. Frequencies of different mutations in different populations provide information on the natural history of alleles and on the relative importance of nonrandom mating, genetic drift, and natural selection in deviations from Hardy-Weinberg equilibrium. Studies on African populations reveal remarkable correlations between allele frequency patterns and language differences.

7. Skin color, one inherited human trait that is highly variable, depends on the production and distribution of melanin in the skin. Though humans have distinguished races according to skin color, two people with the same skin color may be very different genetically.

review questions

1. Give examples of how each of the following can alter gene frequencies from Hardy-Weinberg equilibrium:

   a. nonrandom mating

   b. migration

   c. inbreeding

   d. genetic drift

   e. a population bottleneck

   f. mutation

2. Explain the influence of natural selection on

   a. the virulence of tuberculosis.

   b. bacterial resistance to antibiotics.

   c. the changing degree of genetic diversity of an HIV population during infection.

   d. the prevalence of cystic fibrosis.

3. Why is increasing homozygosity in a population detrimental?

4. Explain how misuse of antibiotics can add to the problem of antibiotic-resistant bacteria.

5. Why might a mutant allele that causes an inherited illness when homozygous persist in a population?

6. Give an example of an inherited disease allele that protects against an infectious illness.

7. State three factors that may contribute to the reemergence of an infectious illness.

8. A disease-causing allele that is very rare in most populations is unusually prevalent in a particular population. What type of information might enable you to determine whether the prevalence reflects a founder effect, balanced polymorphism, or a population bottleneck?

9. Provide two examples of how molecular evidence confirms presence of genetic uniformity.

10. Explain why table 13.2 indicates that genetic drift has occurred among the Dunkers.

11. Would a carrier test to detect the common cystic fibrosis allele ΔF508 be more accurate in France or Finland? Cite a reason for your answer.

12. Balanced polymorphism usually refers to a heterozygous advantage. Why doesn't the homozygote for the mutant allele enjoy the benefit of resisting the infectious disease the allele protects against?

13. According to genetic evidence, are African Americans more closely related to Europeans or to Japanese? to Nigerians or to Wolofs?

applied questions

1. Use the information in chapters 12 and 13 to explain why

   a. some groups of native Americans do not have type B blood.

   b. porphyria variegata is more prevalent among Afrikaners than other South African populations.

   c. many people among the Cape population in South Africa lose their teeth before age twenty.

   d. dwarfism combined with polydactyly and heart defects is more common among the Pennsylvania Amish than in other nearby populations.

   e. cheetah populations are declining.

   f. mongrel dogs are often healthier and live longer than purebreds, which can have characteristic health problems.

   g. the Pingelapese people of the Pacific Islands have a very high incidence of one type of blindness.

2. Which principles discussed in this chapter do the following science fiction film plots illustrate?

   a. In *When Worlds Collide,* the earth is about to be destroyed. One hundred people are selected to colonize a new planet.

   b. In *The Time Machine,* set in the distant future on earth, one group of people is forced to live on the planet's surface while another group is forced to live in caves. Over many years, they come to look and behave differently. The Morlocks that live below ground have dark skin, dark hair, and are very aggressive, whereas the Eloi that live aboveground are blond, fair-skinned, and meek.

   c. In *Children of the Damned,* all of the women in a small town are suddenly made pregnant by genetically identical beings from another planet.

   d. In *The War of the Worlds,* Martians cannot survive on earth because they are vulnerable to infection by terrestrial microbes.

3. Treatment for PKU has been so successful that over the past 30 years, many people who would otherwise have been profoundly mentally retarded have led normal lives and become parents. How has this treatment altered Hardy-Weinberg equilibrium for mutant alleles causing PKU?

4. Researchers identified 100 carriers for cystic fibrosis by consulting pedigrees for 63 families. Seventy-three of the carriers had the most common allele, called ΔF508. Two of these individuals had bronchial asthma (2.7 percent). The other 27 carriers had a different CF mutation, and 6 of them (22.2 percent of the 27) had asthma. Researchers concluded that the ΔF508 allele protects heterozygotes against bronchial asthma.

  a. What other conclusion is consistent with these data?

  b. What other information would help distinguish between the two possible conclusions?

5. Congenital intestinal atresia is more colorfully known as "apple peel syndrome" because the small intestine is twisted in a way that resembles an apple peel. How do you think this rare condition arose in the family depicted in this pedigree?

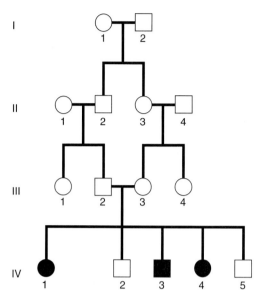

6. By which mechanisms discussed in this chapter do the following situations alter Hardy-Weinberg equilibrium?

  a. Ovalocytosis is a rare genetic abnormality that is not only symptomless, but also seems to be beneficial. A protein that anchors the red blood cell membrane is abnormal, causing the membrane to be unusually rigid. As a result, the parasites that cause malaria cannot enter the red blood cells of individuals who have inherited ovalocytosis.

  b. In the mid-1700s, a multitoed male cat from England crossed the sea and settled in Boston, where he left behind quite a legacy of kittens—about half of whom also had 6, 7, 8, or even 9 digits on their paws. Today, in Boston and nearby regions, multitoed cats are far more common than in other parts of the United States.

  c. Many slaves in the United States arrived in groups from Nigeria, which is an area in Africa with many ethnic subgroups. They landed at a few sites and settled on widely dispersed plantations. Once emancipated, former slaves in the south were free to travel and disperse.

7. People with familial Mediterranean fever have an unusually low incidence of asthma. What force may help maintain FMF in populations?

suggested readings

Armelagos, George J. January/February 1998. The viral superhighway. *The Sciences.* Our own "progress" has spread viral diseases.

Avigad, Smadar, et al. March 8, 1990. A single origin of phenylketonuria in Yemenite Jews. *Nature,* vol. 344. Correlations of allele frequencies with historical information reveal gene flow.

Bowman, James E., and Robert F. Murray, Jr. 1990. *Genetic variation and disorders in people of African origin.* Baltimore and London: Johns Hopkins University Press. Following gene frequencies in Africans may reveal where we all came from.

Chakraborty, Ranajit, et al. January 1992. Caucasian genes in American blacks: New data. *The American Journal of Human Genetics,* vol. 50. About a quarter of the genes in many African Americans are more common among whites.

Diamond, Jared. February 1992. The return of cholera. *Discover.* CF heterozygosity may protect against viral illnesses.

Levy, Stuart B. March 1998. The challenge of antibiotic resistance. *Scientific American.* The antibiotic-resistance problem is now critical.

May, Robert. August 1995. The rise and fall and rise of tuberculosis. *Nature Medicine,* vol. 1. Natural selection has molded the virulence of this reemerging infection.

Motulsky, Arno. February 1995. Jewish diseases and origins. *The American Journal of Human Genetics,* vol. 9. Centuries of discrimination sequestered and selected certain genetic variants in this group, creating "ethnic diseases."

Nowak, Martin A., and Andrew J. McMichael. August 1995. How HIV defeats the immune system. *Scientific American.* Genetic diversity of HIV waxes and wanes during infection in response to the selective pressures of the immune system and therapeutic drugs.

Pier, Gerald B. May 7, 1998. *Salmonella typhi* uses CFTR to enter intestinal epithelial cells. *Nature,* vol. 393. CF remains prevalent because carriers are protected against typhus.

Ruwende, C., et al. July 20, 1995. Natural selection of hemizygotes and heterozygotes for G6PD deficiency in Africa by resistance to severe malaria. *Nature,* vol. 376. G6PD deficiency is a classic example of balanced polymorphism.

Spritz, Richard A. November 1995. A study in scarlet. *Nature Genetics,* vol. 11. A look at control of melanin production.

Waters, Andrew P. January 1998. Chloroquine resistance—discovering the missing link? *Nature Medicine.* A mutation enables the organism that causes malaria to resist certain drugs.

Weissenbach, Jean, et al. September 1997. Mediterranean fever gene identified. *Nature Genetics,* vol. 15. FMF may protect against asthma.

Williams, Dudley H., and Martin S. Westwell. March 1996. *Chemtech.* Some bacteria can survive in the presence of all available antibiotics.

chapter fourteen

Human Origins and Evolution

Fractured Fairytales and Human Origins

Imagine being asked to build a story from the following elements:

1. A pumpkin that turns into a coach

2. A prince who hosts a ball

3. A poor but beautiful young woman with a pleasant voice and dainty feet who has two mean stepsisters who are ugly and have large feet

Chances are that unless you're familiar with the fairytale "Cinderella," you wouldn't come up with that exact story. In fact, ten people given the same pieces of information might construct ten very different tales.

So it is with the sparse evidence we have of our own beginnings—pieces of a puzzle in time, some out of sequence, many missing. Traditionally, paleontologists (scientists who study past life) have consulted the record in the earth's rocks—fossils—to glimpse the ancestors of *Homo sapiens,* our own species. Researchers assign approximate ages to fossils by observing which rock layers they are located in and by extrapolating the passage of time from the ratios of certain radioactive chemicals in surrounding rock.

Other modern organisms also provide intriguing clues to the origins and relationships of species through their chromosomes and through their informational molecules—RNA, DNA, and proteins. Increasingly, genetic evidence is filling in the gaps in our knowledge of the past. In this chapter, we explore human origins, the genetic evidence for evolution, and how we attempt to alter the evolution of our own species and others.

Homo sapiens ("the wise human") probably first appeared during the Pleistocene epoch, about 200,000 years ago. Our ancestry reaches farther back, to about 60 million years ago when rodentlike insect-eaters flourished. These first primates gave rise to many new species. Their ability to grasp and to perceive depth provided the flexibility and coordination necessary to dominate the treetops.

About 30 to 40 million years ago, a monkeylike animal the size of a cat, *Aegyptopithecus,* lived in the lush tropical forests of Africa. Although the animal probably

a. *Dryopithecus*

b. *Australopithecus*

figure 14.1

Human forerunners. *a.* The "oak ape" *Dryopithecus,* who lived from 22 to 33 million years ago, was more dextrous than his predecessors. *b.* Several species of *Australopithecus* lived from 2 to slightly more than 4 million years ago. These hominids walked upright on the plains. *c. Homo erectus* made tools out of bone and stone, used fire, and dwelled communally in caves from 1.6 million years ago to possibly as recently as 35,000 years ago.

c. *Homo erectus*

spent most of its time in the trees, fossilized remains of limb bones indicate that it could run on the ground, too. Fossils of different individuals found together indicate that they were social animals. *Aegyptopithecus* had fangs that it might have used for defense. The large canine teeth seen only in males suggest that males might have provided food for their smaller female mates. *Propliopithecus* was a monkeylike contemporary of *Aegyptopithecus.* Both animals are possible ancestors of gibbons, apes, and humans.

The Hominoids

From 22 to 32 million years ago, Africa was inhabited by the first **hominoids,** animals ancestral to apes and humans only. The earliest hominoid fossils date from 24 to

27 million years ago. More abundant fossils represent the middle-Miocene apes of 11 to 16 million years ago. These apes were about the size of a human seven-year-old and had small brains and pointy snouts. One such resident of southwestern and central Europe was called *Dryopithecus,* meaning "oak ape," because fossilized bones were found with oak leaves (figure 14.1*a*). The way the bones fit together suggests that this animal lived in the trees but could swing and walk farther than *Aegyptopithecus.*

Apelike animals similar to *Dryopithecus* flourished in Europe, Asia, and the Middle East during the same period. Because of the large primate population in the forest, selective pressure to venture onto the grasslands must have been intense. Many primate species probably vanished as the protective forests shrank. Of all of the abundant Miocene apes, one survived to give rise to humans and African apes.

The Hominids

Hominoid and **hominid** (ancestral to humans only) fossils from 4 to 19 million years ago are scarce. This was the time that the stooped, large-brained ape gradually became the upright, smaller-brained ape-human. A 10-million-year-old fossilized face found in northern Greece is from an animal newly named *Ouranopithecus macedoniensis.* Its small canine teeth and thick tooth enamel suggest that it could be an immediate forerunner of hominids.

Walking Upright and Leaving the Forest

Four million years ago, human forebears diversified as **bipedalism**—the ability to walk upright—opened up vast new habitats on the plains. Several species of a hominid called *Australopithecus* lived at this time, until 1 million to 500,000 years ago. Figure 14.2 depicts *Australopithecines* and others.

Australopithecines had flat skull bases, as do all modern primates except humans. They stood about 4 to 5 feet (1.2 to 1.5 meters) tall and had brains about the size of a gorilla's and humanlike teeth. The angle of preserved pelvic bones, plus the discovery of *Australopithecus* fossils with those of animals that grazed, indicate that this ape-human had left the forest.

A. afarensis, represented by the famous fossil "Lucy" (figure 14.3), may have been our direct ancestor. Her skull was shaped more like a human's with a less prominent face and larger brain than her predecessors. These animals probably lived a hunter-gatherer lifestyle during the Pleistocene Ice Age, eating both plants and animals.

Our Species—Homo

By 2 million years ago, *Australopithecus* co-existed with *Homo habilis*—a more human-like primate who lived communally in caves and cared for young intensely. *Habilis* means handy, and this primate is the first to evidence extensive tool use. *H. habilis* may have descended from a group of *Australopithecines* who ate a greater variety of foods

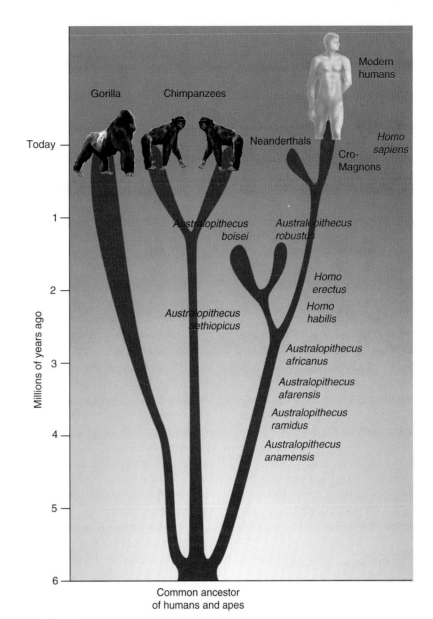

figure 14.2

An evolutionary tree diagram indicates the relationships among primates.

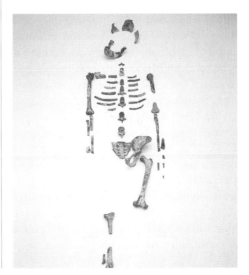

figure 14.3

About 3.6 million years ago, a small-brained human ancestor walked upright in the grasses along a lake in the Afar region of Ethiopia. She skimmed the shores for crabs, turtles, and crocodile eggs to eat. She died at the age of twenty, with severe arthritis in her backbone. Nearly 40 percent of her skeleton was discovered in 1974; her discoverers, Donald Johanson of the Cleveland Museum of Natural History and Timothy White of the University of California at Berkeley, named her "Lucy" because they were listening to the Beatles song "Lucy in the Sky with Diamonds" when they found her.

than other ape-humans, allowing them to adapt to a wider range of habitats.

H. habilis coexisted with and was followed by *Homo erectus*, who left fossil evidence of cooperation, social organization, and tool use, including the use of fire (figure 14.1c). Fossilized teeth and jaws of *H. erectus* suggest that they ate meat. These primates were the first to have an angled skull base that permitted them to make a greater range of sounds, making speech possible. *H. erectus* fossils are widespread. They have been found in China, tropical Africa, and southeast Asia, indicating that these animals could migrate farther than earlier primates. The distribution of fossils suggests that *H. erectus* lived in families of male-female pairs (most primates have harems). The male hunted and the female nurtured young.

H. erectus may have lived as recently as 35,000 years ago and probably coexisted with the very first *Homo sapiens*. Fossilized skulls from Java and China may be from individuals intermediate between *H. erectus* and *Homo sapiens*. These intermediate primates had big brains and robust builds and lived from 30,000 to 50,000 years ago. Several pockets of ancient peoples may have been dispersed throughout the world at that time; fossils have been found in Swanscombe, England, Steinheim, Germany, and the Middle East.

Peoples Overlapping in Time

The Neanderthals, contemporaries of *H. erectus*, appeared in Europe about 150,000 years ago. By 70,000 years ago, the Neanderthals had spread to western Asia. They had slightly larger brains than us, prominent brow ridges, gaps between certain teeth, very muscular jaws, and large, barrel-shaped chests.

The Neanderthals take their name from Neander Valley, Germany, where quarry workers blasting in a limestone cave on a summer day in 1856 discovered the first preserved bones of this hominid that may or may not have been a member of our species. A fossilized, deformed skeleton buried with flowers in Shanidar Cave, Iraq, reveals that the Neanderthals may have been religious hunter-gatherers that were either clever enough or lucky enough to survive a brutal ice age. Anthropologists once thought the Neanderthals were

hunchbacked brutes because the first fossil was from an individual stooped from arthritis.

Fossil evidence indicates that from 30,000 to 40,000 years ago, the Neanderthals coexisted with the lighter-weight, finer-boned, and less hairy Cro-Magnons. The newcomers also had high foreheads and well-developed frontal brain regions. The first Cro-Magnon fossils were found in a French cave. Five adults and a baby were arranged in what appeared to be a communal grave. Nearby were seashells, pierced in a way that suggested they may have been used as jewelry. Intricate art decorated the cave walls.

Anthropologists for a long time thought that the Cro-Magnons replaced the Neanderthals. More recent fossil evidence, however, indicates that these two types of humans actually coexisted, but did not interbreed, in the same region of the mideast that links Africa and Eurasia. What kept them from mating with each other? Perhaps it was incompatible genitalia, or a geographical barrier, such as mountains or water, that kept them apart. Or maybe they migrated, occupying the same areas at different times. Another theory is behavioral—perhaps the great facial differences between the large-boned Neanderthals and more delicate Cro-Magnons made it impossible for them to exchange mating cues. We still don't know how it happened, but by 30,000 years ago, the Neanderthals no longer existed, and the Cro-Magnons presumably continued on the path to humanity.

Modern Humans

Cave art from about 14,000 years ago indicates that by that time, our ancestors had developed fine hand coordination and could use symbols—a milestone in cultural evolution. By 10,000 years ago, people had migrated from the Middle East across Europe, bringing agricultural practices.

In 1991, hikers in the Alps discovered an ancient man frozen in the ice (figure 14.4). After amateurs hacked away at him, causing much damage, the Ice Man, named Otzi, ended up in the hands of several research groups. Unlike other remains that show evidence of intentional burial, the Ice Man was apparently tending sheep high on a mountaintop some 5,300 years ago when

he perished. He was dressed for the weather. Berries found with him place the season as late summer or early fall. The man probably fell into a ditch, where he froze to death and was soon covered by snow. After this safe burial, which preserved his body intact, a glacier sealed the natural tomb. The Ice Man now rests in a simulated glacier (a refrigerator) in the Anatomy Department at the University of Innsbruck.

DNA analyses on Otzi's tissues suggest that he belonged to the same gene pool as modern people living in the area. DNA from a sample of lung tissue held a surprise—it came from a fungus! A lung infection might have contributed to Otzi's death. He was apparently in weakened condition, working hard in a low-oxygen environment.

Anthropologists try to fill in the gaps in our knowledge of what humans were like a few thousand years ago by studying vanishing indigenous peoples, such as the San (bushmen) and pygmies of Africa, the Basques of Spain, the Etas of Japan, the Hill People of New Guinea, the Yanomami of Brazil, and another Brazilian tribe, the Arawete, who number only 130 individuals. Studying DNA sequences within these populations provides information on their origins, as we'll see later in the chapter.

Key Concepts

Monkeylike *Aegyptopithecus* lived about 30 to 40 million years ago and was ancestral to gibbons, apes, and humans. The first hominoid (ape and human ancestor), *Dryopithecus*, lived 22 to 32 million years ago and may have walked onto grasslands.

Hominids (human ancestors) appeared about 19 million years ago. About 4 million years ago, bipedalism opened up new habitats for *Australopithecines* who walked upright and used tools.

By 2 million years ago, *Australopithecus* coexisted with the more humanlike *Homo habilis*. Later, *H. habilis* coexisted with *H. erectus*, who used tools in more complex societies. *H. sapiens* either coexisted with or arose from *H. erectus* 30,000 to 50,000 years ago. The Neanderthals preceded the Cro-Magnons, and modern humans appeared about 40,000 years ago. A preserved man from 5,300 years ago is genetically like us.

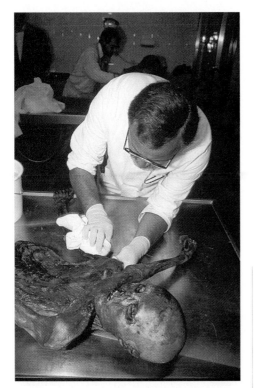

a.

b.

Figure 14.4

a. Hikers discovered Otzi, the Ice Man, in the Austrian/Italian Alps in 1991. He lived 5,300 years ago, recently enough to belong to the same gene pool as people living in the area today. *b.* Otzi wore well-made clothing, including a hat, used intricate arrows displaying familiarity with ballistics and engineering, and carried mushrooms with antibiotic properties. He had tattoos, indentations in his ears that suggest he wore earrings, and evidence of a haircut. This depiction is derived from the evidence found on and near Otzi's preserved body.

Molecular Evolution

Fossils paint an incomplete picture of the past because only certain parts of certain organisms were preserved. Additional information on the past comes from within the cell, where the molecules of life evolve.

Molecular evolution is based on the fact that DNA sequences in nucleic acids and amino acid sequences in proteins change over time as mutations occur. The fewer differences between a gene or protein sequence in two species, the more closely related the two species are presumed to be—that is, the more recently they diverged from a common ancestor. It is highly unlikely that two unrelated species would happen to evolve precisely the same sequence of DNA nucleotides or amino acids simply by chance.

Scientists compare the band patterns and gene orders on stained chromosomes as a measure of species relatedness. Chromosomes, genes, or proteins that are identical or very similar in different species are said to be **highly conserved.**

Comparing Chromosomes

Human chromosome banding patterns match most closely those of chimpanzees, then gorillas, and then orangutans. If human chromosome 2 were broken in half, we would have 48 chromosomes, as the three species of apes do, instead of 46. The banding pattern of chromosome 1 in humans, chimps, gorillas, and orangutans matches that of two small chromosomes in the African green monkey, suggesting that this monkey was ancestral to the other primates.

We can also compare chromosome patterns between species that are not as closely related. All mammals, for example, have identically banded X chromosomes. A section of human chromosome 1 is remarkably similar to parts of the chromosomes of chimpanzees, gorillas, orangutans, African green monkeys, cats, and mice. A human shares several chromosomal segments with a cat (figure 14.5).

Chromosome band patterns, although striking, are not ideal measures of species relatedness because a band can contain many genes that may not be the same as those within a band at a corresponding locus in another species. Direct correspondence of known gene order, or **synteny,** between species is better evidence of close evolutionary relationships. For example, eleven genes are closely linked on the long arm of human chromosome 21, mouse chromosome 16, and on a chromosome called U10 in cows. However, several genes on human chromosome 3 are found near the human chromosome 21 counterpart in mice and cows. Geneticists interpret this to mean that a mammal ancestral to these three species had all of these genes together and that they dispersed to an additional chromosome in humans at some point in time.

Comparing Protein Sequences

The fact that all species utilize the same genetic code to synthesize proteins argues for a common ancestry to all life on earth. In addition, many different types of organisms use the same proteins, with only slight variations in amino acid sequence. The keratin genes that encode a sheep's wool protein, for example, have counterparts on chromosome 11 in humans. The similarities in amino acid sequences in human and chimpanzee proteins are astounding—many proteins are alike in 99 percent of their amino acids. Several are virtually identical.

Cytochrome C

One of the most ancient and well-studied proteins is cytochrome C, which is involved in cellular respiration. Twenty of its 104 amino acids occupy identical

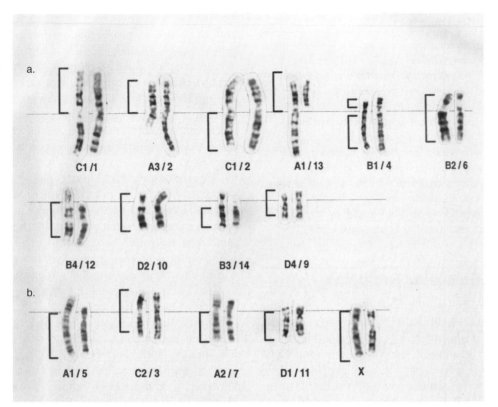

figure 14.5

Conserved regions of human and cat chromosomes. In each pair, the chromosome on the left is from a cat, and the chromosome on the right is from a human. The brackets indicate apparently corresponding areas. The chromosomes in (a) have similar banding patterns generated from traditional stains that do not target specific genes but chromosome regions with generally similar DNA base content. The chromosomes in (b) do not look alike, but DNA probes to specific genes indicate that the pairs do indeed share many specific DNA sequences. (c) The author and one of her cats, Nirvana.

positions in the cytochrome C of all eukaryotes. The more closely related two species are, the more alike their cytochrome C amino acid sequence is. Human cytochrome C, for example, differs from horse cytochrome C by 12 amino acids, and from kangaroo cytochrome C by 8 amino acids. The human protein is identical to that from chimpanzees. Figure 14.6 shows sequence similarities for the antidiuretic hormone gene in various organisms.

Homeobox Proteins

Proteins that are very similar in diverse species probably have a function vital for life, as cytochrome C does. Another vital protein controls the order in which an embryo turns on genes. This cascade of gene action ultimately ensures that anatomical parts—whether a leg, petal, or segment of a larva—develop in the appropriate places. The highly conserved portion of this protein is a 20-amino-acid sequence, encoded by a 60-base DNA sequence called the **homeobox.**

The name homeobox derives from the homeotic mutants of the fruit fly *Drosophila melanogaster,* which have mixed-up body parts. In one mutant, a leg grows where an antenna should be; in another, an antenna grows out of the mouth. Researchers sequenced the fruit fly homeobox gene in 1983 and then found it nearly everywhere—in frogs, mice, beetles, mosquitoes, slime molds, chickens, roundworms, corn, humans, petunias, and many other species. The homeobox protein is a motif in a transcription factor (chapter 8), and this is how it controls the activities of other genes.

Mutations in homeobox genes cause certain human illnesses. One form of leukemia is caused by such a mutation, which shifts certain immature white blood cells onto the wrong developmental pathway. The misguided cells retain the rapid cell division of immature cells, causing the cancer. Although we hardly sprout legs from our heads, as the fly in figure 14.7 did, DiGeorge syndrome is caused by a homeobox gene, and its signs and symptoms are reminiscent of the *Antennapedia* flies. Signs of the syndrome include missing thymus and parathyroid glands and abnormal development of the ears, nose, mouth, and throat—structures corresponding to similar anatomical regions as the sites of abnormalities in the flies.

Experiments that implant genes of one species into another reveal how alike the homeobox is—implying it is essential and ancient. If a mouse version of the *Antennapedia* gene is placed into a fertilized egg of a wild type fly, the adult fly grows legs on its head. The human version of the gene, placed into a mouse's fertilized egg, disrupts the adult mouse's head development. Homeotic genes and the proteins they encode, therefore, are probably

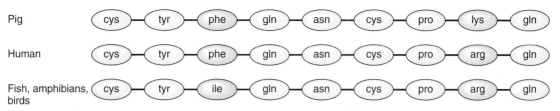

Pig	cys	tyr	phe	gln	asn	cys	pro	lys	gln
Human	cys	tyr	phe	gln	asn	cys	pro	arg	gln
Fish, amphibians, birds	cys	tyr	ile	gln	asn	cys	pro	arg	gln

figure 14.6

Antidiuretic hormone is a peptide hormone eight amino acids long that signals the kidneys to conserve water. Its sequence differs only slightly between major groups of vertebrates (animals with backbones).

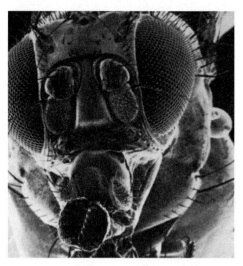

figure 14.7

Homeotic genes and the homeobox protein transcription factors they encode appear in a wide variety of species, indicating that they are vital for life. Mutations in homeotic genes can drastically affect the phenotype, as shown in this *Antennapedia* fly. As its name implies, *Antennapedia's* antennae are transformed into legs.

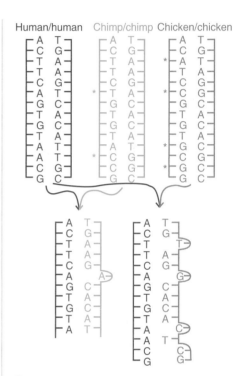

figure 14.8

The rate of DNA hybridization reflects the degree of evolutionary relatedness. This highly schematic diagram shows why DNA from a human hybridizes more rapidly with chimpanzee DNA than with chicken DNA.

genetic instructions basic to the development of all complex organisms.

DNA Hybridization—Comparing DNA Sequences

We can assess similarities in DNA sequences between two species for a single gene or piece of DNA, or for the total genome. A comparison technique called **DNA hybridization** uses complementary base pairing to estimate how similar the genomes of two species are. The scientist unwinds DNA double helices from two species and mixes them. The rate at which hybrid DNA double helices re-form—that is, become DNA molecules containing one helix from each species—is a direct measure of how similar they are in sequence. The faster the DNA from two species forms hybrids, the more of the sequence they share and the more closely related they are (figure 14.8). DNA hybridization shows, for example, that human DNA differs in 1.8 percent of its base pairs from chimpanzee DNA; in 2.3 percent from gorilla DNA; and in 3.7 percent from orangutan DNA. Genes may also be sequenced and compared, but this is much more time-consuming.

Animal Models

Identifying corresponding genes in different species is very important in medical research, where animal models of human diseases are needed to test experimental treatments. For example, researchers are performing muscle cell transplants on golden retrievers who inherit a dog version of Duchenne muscular dystrophy, and brain tissue transplants on mice with a version of Huntington disease. It is important that an animal model of a human disease have the same signs and symptoms.

For some genes, a close correspondence in phenotype exists between species. People with Waardenburg syndrome, for example, have a characteristic white forelock of hair; wide-spaced, light-colored eyes; and hearing impairment (figure 14.9). The responsible gene is very similar in sequence to one in cats who have white coats and blue eyes and are deaf. Horses, mice, and minks also have this combination of traits, which is thought to stem

figure 14.9

A gene in mice, cats, humans, and other species causes light eye color, hearing or other neurological impairment, and a fair forelock in the center of the head.

from abnormal movements of pigment cells in the embryo's outermost layer. So similar are many genes among species that a first step in identifying a newly discovered human gene is to compare its sequence to a database of known gene sequences in other species.

Ancient DNA

When comparing DNA of modern species, a researcher can easily repeat an experiment—there are ample samples of chimp or human DNA directly from the source. This isn't the case with ancient DNA, such as genetic material from insects preserved in amber. Researchers have used the polymerase chain reaction (PCR, Reading 8.2) to amplify DNA from 30-million-year-old termites and stingless bees, a 120-million-year-old weevil, a 40,000-year-old frozen mammoth, a Neanderthal, and a much more recently deceased quagga (figure 14.10).

The exquisite sensitivity of PCR, and the fact that DNA older than 100,000 years sustains oxidative damage, has led some researchers to suggest that analyzing ancient DNA actually amplifies contaminating DNA. One repeat of an experiment found that human and fungal DNA had been amplified, not ancient bee DNA. To better control experiments that amplify preserved DNA, researchers now also test all of the reagents they use. If the reagents lack contaminating DNA, chances are better that what they amplify is really ancient.

figure 14.10

Probing the molecules of extinct organisms. The last quagga, relative of horse and zebra, died in captivity in Amsterdam in 1883. DNA extracted from this preserved quagga is now being deciphered to see how closely related the extinct animal was to modern-day related species.

Key Concepts

Molecular evolution is based on the assumption that the more recently two species shared a common ancestor, the more alike are their stained chromosome bands and protein and DNA sequences. DNA hybridization experiments estimate how closely two species are related by how quickly their DNA forms hybrid double helices. Direct sequencing is also used to compare genes between species. Rarely, scientists can obtain DNA from preserved extinct organisms, amplify it, and compare it to sequences in modern species.

Molecular Clocks

A clock measures the passage of time by moving its hands through a certain degree of a circle in a specific and constant interval of time—a second or a minute. Similarly, a polymeric molecule can be used as a **molecular clock** if its building blocks are replaced at a known and constant rate.

The similarity of nuclear DNA sequences in different species can help scientists estimate the time when the organisms diverged from a common ancestor, if they know the rate of base substitution mutation. For example, many nuclear genes studied in humans and chimpanzees differ in 5 percent of their bases, and substitutions occur at a rate of 1 percent per 1 million years. Therefore, 5 million years have presumably passed since the two species diverged.

A complication of molecular clock studies is that genes change (mutate) at different rates. For example, the gene for a protein receptor on the surface of T cells (a type of white blood cell) is very similar in sequence in the human and the mouse. These mammals diverged from a common ancestor between 65 and 85 million years ago, but the gene has not changed much in that time. In contrast are the DNA sequences surrounding the beta globin gene. These differ between the human and the mouse, suggesting that they evolve faster.

Genes may evolve at different rates if they change in different ways. Whereas the T cell receptor gene differs between human and mouse by single base changes, the differences in sequences surrounding the beta globin gene are the larger-scale insertions, deletions, and duplications. Because a single mutational event can have a drastic effect on the sequences surrounding the beta globin genes, they evolve faster than the T cell receptor gene.

Different mutation rates in different genes or DNA sequences may also reflect natural selection—that is, how important the particular sequence is for survival and successful reproduction. Mutations in a gene may rapidly accumulate in a population if they do not alter the ability to reproduce. However, mutations that block reproduction would be selected against, and the allele would probably disappear from the population.

From Sequence Differences to Evolutionary Trees

Time scales based on fossil evidence and molecular clocks can be superimposed on evolutionary tree diagrams constructed from DNA or protein sequence data. However, evolutionary trees can become complex when a single set of data can be arranged into a large number of different tree configurations. A tree for 17 mammalian species, for example, can be constructed in 10,395 different ways! The sequence in which the data is entered into tree-building computer programs influences

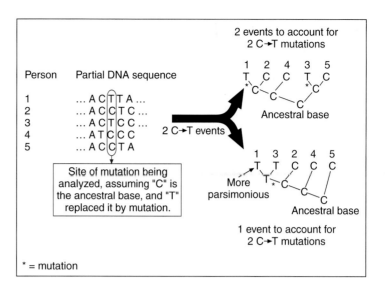

figure 14.11

Parsimony analysis. Even a computer has trouble arranging DNA differences into an evolutionary tree showing species, population, or individual relationships. A parsimonious tree accounts for all data with the fewest number of mutations. Here, the two individuals who have a "T" in place of the ancestral "C" could have arisen as two mutational events or one, assuming that these individuals had a common ancestor.

the tree's shape, which is vital to interpreting species relationships. With every new bit of sequence information, the tree possibilities change.

Parsimony analysis is a statistical method to identify an evolutionary tree likely to represent what really happened. A computer connects all evolutionary tree sequence data using the fewest possible number of mutational events to account for observed DNA base sequence differences. For the 5-base sequence in figure 14.11, for example, the data can be arranged into two possible tree diagrams.

Mitochondrial DNA Clocks

Researchers study recent human ancestry with a special type of molecular clock based on mutations in mitochondrial DNA (mtDNA). Recall from table 5.2 that mtDNA is valuable in tracking recent evolutionary time because it mutates much faster than nuclear DNA and is more abundant.

Like other measures of evolutionary relatedness, the more similar the mtDNA sequence is between two individuals, the more recently they presumably shared a common ancestor. However, following the inheritance of mtDNA is different because

it is passed only from mothers. This fact led to the proposal of a **mitochondrial Eve,** or figurative ancestral mother.

Mitochondrial Eve

Theoretically, if a particular sequence of mtDNA could have given rise—by mutation—to different mtDNA sequences in modern humans, then that ancestral sequence may represent a very early human or humanlike female—a mitochondrial Eve, or first woman. Figure 14.12 shows how one maternal line may come to persist.

When might this theoretical first woman, the most recent female ancestor to us all, have lived? Most fossil evidence points to Africa, but some anthropologists maintain that modern peoples emerged from Asia, too. Berkeley researchers led by the late Allan Wilson compared mtDNA sequences for protein-encoding as well as noncoding DNA regions in a variety of people, including Africans, African Americans, Europeans, New Guineans, Australians, and others. They concluded from several methods that the hypothesized ancestral woman lived about 200,000 years ago.

One way to reach this figure is by comparing how much the mtDNA sequence differs among modern humans to

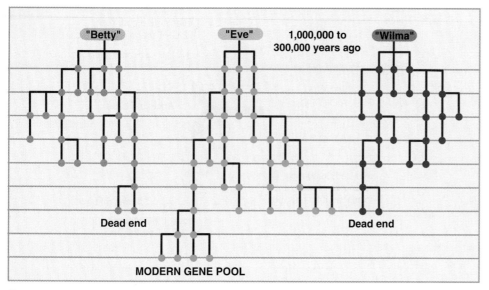

figure 14.12

According to the mitochondrial Eve hypothesis, modern mtDNA retains some sequences from a figurative first woman, "Eve," who lived in Africa 300,000 to 100,000 years ago. In this schematic illustration, lines represent generations, and the circles, females. Lineages cease whenever a woman does not have a daughter to pass on the mtDNA.

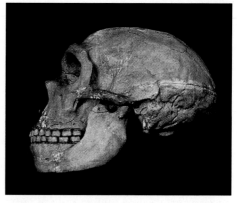

figure 14.13

DNA studies reveal that Neanderthal was less like modern humans than this humanlike skull might suggest.

how much it differs between humans and chimpanzees. Specifically, the differences in mtDNA sequences among contemporary humans is 1/25 the difference between humans and chimpanzees. The two species diverged about 5 million years ago, according to extrapolation from fossil and molecular evidence. Multiplying 1/25 by 5 million gives a value of 200,000 years ago. This estimate assumes that the mtDNA mutation rate has remained constant over that time.

Where did Eve live? Mitochondrial DNA comparisons consistently find that African people have the most numerous and diverse collection of mtDNA mutations. This indicates they have existed longer than other modern peoples, because it takes time for mutations to accumulate. Also, in many evolutionary trees constructed by parsimony analysis, the individuals whose DNA sequences form the bases are from Africa.

The idea of mitochondrial Eve is part of the "out of Africa" view, or **replacement hypothesis** of human origins. It states that *Homo erectus* migrated from Africa to Europe and Asia 1 million to 800,000 years ago, eventually replacing the people living there. An alternate view is the **regional continuity hypothesis,** which maintains that populations all over the world

mixed—including modern humans and Neanderthals. These two ideas were once regarded as so opposite that scientists argued vehemently for one or the other. Today, researchers are recognizing merit to both models and that they may each represent a view of reality.

Neanderthal and Us

A combination of technologies—analyzing ancient DNA and using mitochondrial DNA clocks—provides evidence that Neanderthals were a side branch on the human family tree and diverged from us more than half a million years ago. This is much farther back than is the fossil evidence of Neanderthals.

In 1997, a graduate student, Matthias Krings, ground up a bit of arm bone from the original French Neanderthal skeleton. He then performed PCR on several 100-base-pair-long pieces of a mitochondrial "control" gene that does not encode protein but mutates very rapidly. The pieces were sequenced and double-checked and compared to corresponding sequences from 986 modern *Homo sapiens*. What emerged from the experiment was a DNA profile astonishingly unhumanlike. For this gene, Neanderthal DNA differed from that of modern people at 26 positions. Not only

is this three times the number of differences seen between pairs of the most unrelated modern humans, but the locations of the base differences were completely different from the places where modern genes vary. This genetic distinction is sufficient to suggest that it is highly unlikely that Neanderthals and modern humans ever interbred. Extrapolating from known mutation rates for genes in modern humans and chimps, researchers applied a mitochondrial clock that indicates the last shared ancestor between Neanderthals and humans lived from 690,000 to 550,000 years ago.

On a more philosophical level, the mtDNA evidence distancing us from Neanderthals does make us think about a time when there might have been two types of "people" that roamed the planet (figure 14.13).

Native American Origins

The ancestors of native Americans came to North America across the Beringia land bridge that formed between Siberia and Alaska during low glacial periods (figure 14.14). Anthropologists traditionally dated three waves of such migration based on evidence of ancient human habitation and language differences among modern native populations—the Amerindians about 33,000 years ago, the Nadene 15,000 to 12,000 years ago, and the Eskimo-Aleuts from 7,000 to 5,000 years ago. Remains indicate that modern peoples lived throughout the Americas by 15,000 years ago, and

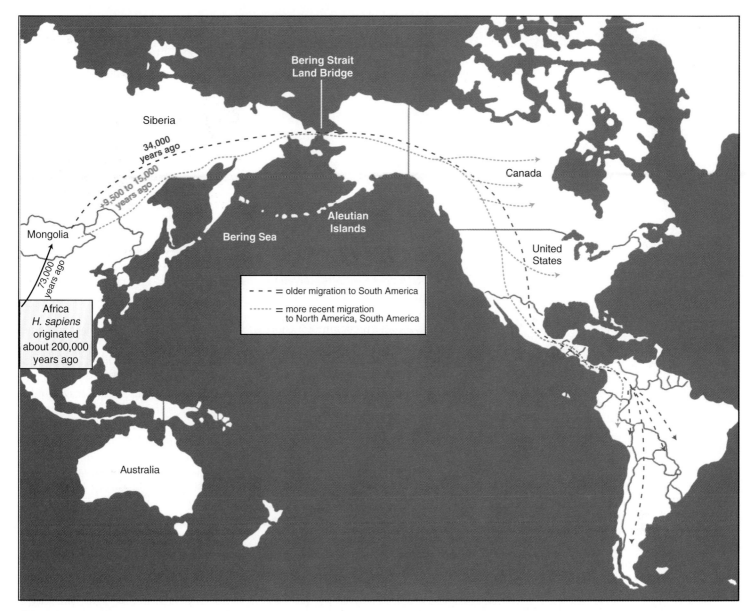

figure 14.14

Analysis of mitochondrial DNA reveals that the ancestors of Americans probably came from Mongolia.

the earliest evidence of human settlements in the New World is in Monte Verde, Chile, dating to 34,000 years ago.

In 1983, anthropologists added mtDNA dating to their toolbox. Since then, researchers have used six mtDNA polymorphisms (DNA sequence variants) that alter restriction enzyme cutting sites, and a deletion of 9 bases that sometimes occurs between two specific mitochondrial genes, as markers. That is, the mtDNA sequence can differ at each of these seven sites. The

pattern of seven markers constitutes a haplotype, which reflects a lineage. Native Americans have 10 distinct haplotypes—that is, 10 ways that their mtDNA differs at these sites. Because most of these haplotypes are seen in modern Asian populations, it is presumed that these gene variants came over the land bridge, possibly at different times. But from where did they come?

The ancestors of native Americans were long thought to have come from

Siberia, since this is the area closest to the land bridge. However, mtDNA analysis tells a different story. One of the haplotypes, B, is widespread in the New World, but it is not in Siberians. Haplotype B is present, however, in people who live in Ulan Bator, the capital city of north central Mongolia. According to mtDNA evidence, the Mongolians were more likely to have been the people who trekked across the land bridge to populate the New World—not the Siberians.

table 14.1

Cultural Ages

Age	Time (years ago)	Defining Skills
Paleolithic	750,000 to 15,000	Earliest chipped tools
Mesolithic	15,000 to 10,000	Cutting tools, bows and arrows
Neolithic	10,000 to present	Complex tools, agriculture

European Origins

Anthropologists consider cultural evolution in ages defined by acquisition of particular skills (table 14.1). A study of mtDNA of 821 modern people from Europe and the Middle East reveals five lineages (haplotypes). By imposing a time scale, anthropologists concluded that most modern Europeans trace their lineage to people arriving in the upper Paleolithic (20,000 to 15,000 years ago). These people persisted, but two waves of gene input from the Middle East occurred somewhat later. Agriculture apparently arose in Europe, too, then added skills were brought by the Middle Easterners. Neanderthals did not contribute to the modern European gene pool.

A much smaller-scale study shed light on a particular European who lived in a region of England now called Cheddar (the site of cheese manufacture) about 9,000 years ago. His skeleton was discovered in a cave in 1903 and now resides in the Natural History Museum in London. Recently, twenty contemporary Cheddar residents had their mtDNA compared to mtDNA from a cell from one of the ancient Cheddar Man's molars. Results of the study directly linked a high school history teacher, Adrian Targett, to Cheddar Man—the mtDNA similarity means that the two descend from a shared female ancestor. Mr. Targett must now withstand caveman jokes from his students—who call him the new Cheddar Man.

Using the Y Chromosome to Trace Paternal Lineage

Just as mitochondrial DNA reflects inheritance from mothers only, DNA sequences unique to the Y chromosome provide a way to trace the paternal line. Unfortunately, many of the Y chromosome sequences studied so far are virtually identical in males from very diverse populations! The lack of diversity among many Y-linked genes may reflect natural selection acting against genes that impair fertility. However, a highly repeated DNA sequence called Alu, studied in eight Africans, two Australians, three Japanese, two Europeans, and four chimpanzees, led to an interpretation of a common Y chromosome forming about 188,000 years ago, which is consistent with mitochondrial evidence of modern human origins.

Key Concepts

Molecular clocks apply mutation rates to time scales to estimate when two individuals or types of organisms most recently shared ancestors. They reveal evolutionary relationships based on similarities and differences in DNA sequences, and they include evolutionary trees, mitochondrial DNA clocks, and Y chromosome sequences. Different genes evolve at different rates. Parsimony analysis selects likely evolutionary trees from data. Mitochondrial DNA provides a clock for dating recent events because it mutates faster than nuclear DNA. Comparing mtDNA sequences among modern peoples provides clues to the time and location of an ancestral first woman who possibly lived in Africa about 200,000 years ago. MtDNA also helps reveal migration routes. Y chromosome sequences can be used to trace paternal lineage.

Eugenics

You wouldn't think twice about pulling out the smaller, weaker plants from a row of baby cucumber plants, or about mating your poodle only with another poodle. Attempting to control human reproduction is another matter.

Eugenics Early in the Twentieth Century

Eugenics is the control of individual reproductive choices in humans to achieve a societal goal. Francis Galton coined the term, meaning "good in birth," in 1883 (table 14.2). Galton was influenced by the idea of natural selection from his cousin, Charles Darwin. Darwin, in turn, was influenced by observations of selective breeding, or **artificial selection,** among pigeon fanciers. (Reading 14.1 discusses artificial selection of dogs and cats.)

Galton's ideas were popular for a time. Eugenics societies formed in several nations and attempted to put his ideas into practice by various means, including sterilization of those deemed "unfit," limitations in immigration, and marriage restrictions. Creating incentives for the reproduction of those considered superior constitutes **positive eugenics.** Interfering with the reproduction of those judged inferior is **negative eugenics.**

One vocal supporter of the eugenics movement was Sir Ronald Aylmer Fisher. In 1930, he published a book, *The Genetical Theory of Natural Selection,* which connected the concepts of Charles Darwin and Gregor Mendel and spelled out the basic tenets of population genetics. Natural selection and Mendelian inheritance provided a framework for eugenics. The final five chapters of Fisher's otherwise highly regarded work tried to apply the principles of population genetics to human society. Fisher maintained that those at the top of a society tend to be "genetically infertile," producing fewer children than the less affluent classes. This, he claimed, was the reason why civilizations ultimately topple. He offered several practical suggestions, including state monetary gifts to high-income families for each child born to them.

Early in the twentieth century, eugenics focused on maintaining purity. One prominent geneticist, Luther Burbank, realized the value of genetic diversity at the beginning of a eugenic effort. Known for selecting interesting plants and crossing them to breed plants with

table 14.2

A Chronology of Eugenics

1883	Francis Galton coins the term *eugenics.*
1889	Francis Galton's writings are published in the book *Natural Inheritance.*
1896	Connecticut enacts law forbidding sex with a person who has epilepsy or is "feebleminded" or an "imbecile."
1904	Galton establishes the Eugenics Record Office at the University of London to keep family records.
1907	First eugenic law in the United States orders sterilization of institutionalized mentally retarded males and criminal males, when experts recommend it.
1910	Eugenics Record Office founded in Cold Spring Harbor, New York, to collect family and institutional data.
1924	Immigration Act limits entry into the United States of "idiots, imbeciles, feebleminded, epileptics, insane persons," and restricts immigration to 7 percent of the U. S. population from a particular country according to the 1890 census—keeping out those from southern and eastern Europe.
1927	Supreme Court (Buck vs. Bell) upholds compulsory sterilization of mentally retarded, 8 to 1, leading to many state laws.
1934	Eugenic sterilization law of Nazi Germany orders sterilization of individuals with conditions thought to be inherited, including epilepsy, schizophrenia, and blindness, depending upon rulings in Genetic Health Courts.
1939	Nazis begin killing 5,000 children with birth defects or mental retardation, then 70,000 "unfit" adults.
1956	U.S. state eugenic sterilization laws are repealed, but 58,000 people have already been sterilized.
1965	U.S. immigration laws reformed, lifting many restrictions.
1980s	California's Center for Germinal Choice is established, where Nobel Prize winners can deposit sperm to inseminate carefully chosen women.
1990s	Laws passed to prevent health insurance or employment discrimination based on genotype.
2000+	Human genome project completed. Many new genetic tests available.

useful characteristics, such as less prickly cacti and a small-pitted plum, Burbank in 1907 applied his agricultural ideas to people. In a book called *The Training of the Human Plant,* he encouraged immigration so that advantageous combinations of traits would appear as the new Americans interbred. Burbank's plan ran into problems, however, at the selection stage, which allowed only those with "desirable" trait combinations to reproduce.

On the east coast, Charles Davenport led the eugenics movement. He established the Eugenics Record Office at Cold Spring Harbor, New York. There he headed a massive effort to compile data from institutions, prisons, and the general society. In the rather simplistic view of genetics at the time, he attributed nearly every trait to a single gene.

Eugenics was practiced in other nations, too. From 1934 until 1976, the Swedish government forced certain individuals to be sterilized as part of a "scientific and modern way of changing society for the better," according to one historian. At first, only mentally ill people were sterilized, but then, poor, single mothers were included, too. Revelation of the Nazi atrocities did not halt eugenics in Sweden, but the women's movement in the 1970s pushed for an end to the forced sterilizations.

Seeking information on human heredity is not, in itself, judgmental. Instead, eugenics uses that information to maximize the genetic contribution from those deemed desirable and minimize the contribution from those considered unacceptable. But a major fallacy of eugenics is its subjectivity. Who decides which traits are desirable? Eugenic thinking arises from time to time, even today.

Eugenics in the 1990s

In 1994, a book called *The Bell Curve* made headlines because of its extreme eugenic assertions. The authors, Richard Herrnstein and Charles Murray, are not geneticists and did not do any genetic research, but they did evaluate others' research. They claimed that intelligence as measured by IQ score is mostly genetically determined and that ethnic groups differ greatly in IQ. They also linked IQ to social problems (such as poverty, crime, and the decline of the two-parent family) and concluded that because genes are responsible for IQ, they also cause these social problems. Echoing Galton, Herrnstein and Murray discussed the "dysgenic" behavior of highly intelligent women, or their tendency to have fewer children, and the high birthrate among poor women.

The recommendations in *The Bell Curve* are even more disturbing than their faulty premises:

1. Eliminating remedial education, because, they claim, the environment cannot help genetically disadvantaged children.

2. Eliminating welfare, to decrease the number of children born into poverty.

3. Encouraging women in higher socioeconomic groups to have more children.

Clearly these ideas are eugenic, because they seek to change the genetic structure of a population by dictating who should and who should not reproduce. They are also disturbing, especially to genetic researchers trying to understand how human genes work, in an effort to improve health and alleviate suffering.

Because genetic technologies affect reproductive choices and can influence which

The pampered poodle and graceful greyhound may win in the show ring, but they are poor specimens in terms of genetics and evolution. Human notions of attractiveness can lead to bizarre breeds that might never have evolved naturally. Behind carefully bred traits lurk small gene pools and extensive inbreeding—all of which spell disaster to the health of many highly prized and highly priced show animals. Purebred dogs suffer from more than 300 types of inherited disorders, although veterinarians know how to test for only 23 of them!

The sad eyes of the basset hound make him a favorite in advertisements, but his runny eyes can be quite painful. His short legs make him prone to arthritis, his long abdomen encourages back injuries, and his characteristic floppy ears often hide ear infections. The eyeballs of the Pekingese protrude so much that a mild bump can pop them out of their sockets. The tiny jaws and massive teeth of pugdogs and bulldogs cause dental and breathing problems, as well as sinusitis, bad colds, and their notorious "dog breath." Folds of skin on their abdomens easily become infected. Larger breeds, such as the Saint Bernard, are plagued by bone problems and short life spans. A Newfoundland or a Great Dane may drop dead at a relatively young age, its heart overworked from years of supporting a large body (table 1).

We artificially select natural oddities in cats, too. One of every ten New England cats has six or seven toes on each paw, thanks to a multitoed ancestor in colonial Boston (figure 1). Elsewhere, these cats are rare. The sizes of the blotched tabby populations in New England, Canada, Australia, and New

figure 1

Multitoed cats are common in New England but rare elsewhere.

Zealand correlate with the time that has passed since cat-loving Britons colonized each region. The Vikings brought the orange tabby to the islands off the coast of Scotland, rural Iceland, and the Isle of Man, where these feline favorites flourish today.

A more modern breed appealing to cat fanciers is the American curl cat, whose origin traces back to a stray female who wandered into the home of a cat-loving family in Lakewood, California, in 1981. She had unusual, curled-up ears, and several of her litters made it obvious that the trait is inherited (figure 2). The cause—a dominant gene that leads to formation of extra cartilage lining the outer ear. Cat breeders, attempting to fashion this natural peculiarity into an official show animal, are hoping that the gene does not have other less lovable effects. Cats with floppy ears, for example, are known to have large feet, stubbed tails, and lazy natures.

figure 2

An American curl cat.

table 1

Purebred Plights

Breed	Health Problems
Cocker spaniel	Nervousness Ear infections Hernias Kidney problems
Collie	Blindness Bald spots Seizures
Dalmation	Deafness
German shepherd	Hip dysplasia
Golden retriever	Lymphatic cancer Muscular dystrophy Skin allergies Hip dysplasia Absence of one testicle
Great Dane	Heart failure Bone cancer
Labrador retriever	Dwarfism Blindness
Shar-pei	Skin disorders

alleles pass to the next generation, the field of modern genetics has sometimes been compared to eugenics. Medical genetics and eugenics differ in their overall goals. Eugenics aims to skew allele frequencies in future generations by allowing people with only certain genotypes perceived as valuable to reproduce, for the supposed benefit of the population as a whole. The goal of medical genetics, in contrast, is usually to skew allele frequencies in order to prevent suffering on a family level. Reading 14.2 contrasts a population view of the blurry distinction between genetic technology and eugenics with a very personal view.

Two Views of Neural Tube Defects

reading 14.2

Genetic technologies permit people to make reproductive choices that can alter allele frequencies in populations. Identifying carriers of a recessive illness, who then decide not to have children together, is one way to remove disease-causing alleles from a population. Screening pregnant women for fetal anomalies, then terminating affected pregnancies, also alters disease prevalence and, if the disorder has a genetic component, allele frequencies. This is the case for neural tube defects (NTDs), which are multifactorial.

An NTD forms at the end of the first month, when the embryo's neural tube does not completely close. If the opening is in the head, the condition is called anencephaly, and usually ends as a miscarriage, stillbirth, or a newborn who dies within days. If the opening is in the spinal cord, the condition is called spina bifida. Usually the individual is paralyzed from the point of the lesion down, but can live into adulthood and have normal intelligence. Sometimes surgery can correct mild cases of spina bifida. People with spina bifida also often have hydrocephalus, or "water on the brain."

Population Screening

In 1974, researchers discovered that pregnant women carrying fetuses with NTDs have an elevated level of a fetal liver protein, AFP, in their blood (Reading 7.1). Amniocentesis has been used to prenatally diagnose NTDs since the late 1960s, and in 1974, development of a blood test led to detection of even more NTDs. The prevalence of these birth defects began to rapidly decline, as pregnancy termination often followed a prenatal diagnosis of an NTD.

In 1992, the Centers for Disease Control and Prevention published a summary of many studies indicating that taking folic acid (a vitamin) supplements in pregnancy lowers the risk of NTD recurrence by 70 percent. Women who had had an affected child began taking large doses of the vitamin in the months before conception.

But when epidemiologists tried to monitor how well the folic acid prevention regimen was working, they faced a problem—the prevalence values of NTDs were greatly underestimated. This happened because the statistics on NTD prevalence—vital to discovering whether folic acid was actually preventing the defect—included only newborns, stillborns, and older fetuses. Most reports did not account for pregnancies terminated following a prenatal diagnosis of an NTD.

In England, France, and Scotland, 80 percent of anencephalic pregnancies are terminated, as are 40 percent of the less severe spina bifida. A preliminary report on six U.S. states found widely varied rates of pregnancy termination. Because of pregnancy termination, prevalence of anencephaly is 60 to 70 percent underreported, and spina bifida, 20 to 30 percent underreported in some states. Screening for NTDs and terminating affected pregnancies alters the allele frequencies by preventing causative genes from passing to new generations.

A Personal View

Blaine Deatherage-Newsom has a different view of population screening for neural tube defects because he has one (figure 1). Blaine was born in 1979 with spina bifida. Paralyzed from the armpits down, he has endured much physical pain, but he has also achieved a great deal. He put the question, "If we had the technology to eliminate disabilities from the population, would that be good public policy?" on the Internet—opening a global discussion. His view on NTD screening is one we do not often hear:

> I was born with spina bifida and hydrocephalus. I hear that when parents have a test and find out that their unborn child has spina bifida, in more than 95 percent of the cases they choose to have an abortion. I also went to an exhibit at the Oregon Museum of Science and Industry several years ago where the exhibit described a child born with spina bifida

figure 1

Blaine Deatherage-Newsom.

> and hydrocephalus, and . . . asked people to vote on whether the child should live or die. I voted that the child should live, but when I voted, the child was losing by quite a few votes.
>
> When these things happen, I get worried. I wonder if people are saying that they think the world would be a better place without me. I wonder if people just think the lives of people with disabilities are so full of misery and suffering that they think we would be better off dead. It's true that my life has suffering (especially when I'm having one of my eleven surgeries so far), but most of the time I am very happy and I like my life very much. My mom says she can't imagine the world without me, and she is convinced that everyone who has a chance to know me thinks that the world is a far better place because I'm in it.

Is eliminating disabilities good public policy? It depends on your point of view.

Excerpt by Blaine Deatherage-Newson, "If we could eliminate disabilities from the population, should we? Results of a survey on the Internet." Reprinted by permission.

One particularly frightening aspect of the eugenics movement early in the century was the vague nature of the traits considered hereditary and undesirable, such as "feeblemindedness," "criminality," and "insanity." Now, as a new century dawns and the human genome is completed, will eugenics resurge? Will we use the abundance of new genetic information to pick and choose the combinations of traits that will make up the next generation?

Many geneticists fear that medical tests that identify carriers and predispositions will be used eugenically. We might not ever again enact forced sterilization laws, but more subtle denials, such as discrimination in insurance coverage or employment based on genetic status, might have the same effect on individuals. Laws are being proposed and implemented in many nations to prevent genetic discrimination. Let's hope that in addition to deciphering our genetic blueprints, we also learn how to apply that information wisely.

Key Concepts

Eugenics is the control of individual human reproduction for societal goals, maximizing the genetic contribution of those deemed acceptable (positive eugenics) and minimizing the contribution from those considered unacceptable (negative eugenics). Some people consider modern genetic screening practices eugenic.

summary

1. Clues about our ancestors come from fossils and comparisons of molecular sequences.

2. The first primates were rodentlike insectivores that lived about 60 million years ago. By 30 to 40 million years ago, monkeylike *Aegyptopithecus* lived. **Hominoids,** ancestral to apes and humans, lived 22 to 32 million years ago. They included *Dryopithecus* and other apes who began to walk upright.

3. **Hominids,** ancestral to humans only, appeared about 4 million years ago. These animals were more upright, dwelled on the plains, and had smaller brains than their forebears. The *Australopithecines* of this time coexisted with *Homo habilis,* who lived in caves and had strong family units and extensive tool use. *Homo erectus* was a contemporary who succeeded *H. habilis,* lived in societies, and used fire. *H. erectus* overlapped in time with our own species. Early *Homo sapiens* included possibly the Neanderthals and Cro-Magnons. Modern humans appeared about 40,000 years ago, and culture was apparent by 14,000 years ago.

4. **Molecular evolution** refers to similarities and differences among sequences of chromosome bands, amino acids, or DNA bases. The rationale is that similarities are more likely to occur because of common descent than to occur by chance. Similar chromosomes, genes, or proteins in different species are **highly conserved.**

5. Closely related species have similar chromosome banding patterns. Genes in the same order on chromosomes in different species are **syntenic.** Genetic similarity can be estimated on a large scale by **DNA hybridization** or by sequencing and comparing individual genes. Amplifying ancient DNA is difficult because contamination may occur.

6. Gene sequence information in several species may be used to construct evolutionary tree diagrams, and a **molecular clock** based on the known mutation rate of the gene applied. Different genes mutate at different rates. Molecular trees indicate when species diverged from shared ancestors.

7. **Parsimony analysis** selects evolutionary trees requiring the fewest mutations and that are therefore the most likely. Molecular clocks based on mitochondrial DNA are used to date recent events—such as human origins—because this DNA mutates faster than nuclear DNA. mtDNA is used to trace an ancestral "Eve," whom fossil evidence places in Africa. mtDNA is also used to trace human migrations into Europe and the Americas, and to study the relationship between modern humans and Neanderthals.

8. Y chromosome genes could be used to trace paternal lineages, but so far this has not been very useful because natural selection has decreased polymorphism.

9. **Eugenics** is the control of individual reproduction to serve a societal goal. **Positive eugenic** measures encourage those deemed acceptable or superior to procreate. **Negative eugenic** measures restrict the reproduction of those considered inferior. Eugenics extends the concept of natural selection and Mendel's laws but does not translate well into practice. Some aspects of genetic technology also affect reproductive choices and allele frequencies, but the goal is to alleviate or prevent suffering, rather than to change society.

review questions

1. What is the difference between a hominoid and a hominid?

2. Several women have offered to be artificially inseminated with sperm from the Ice Man, the human who died 5,300 years ago and was recently found in the Alps. However, he had been castrated. If sperm could have been recovered, and a woman were inseminated, what do you think the child would be like?

3. Why does comparing gene sequences offer more information for molecular evolution studies than comparing protein sequences?

4. Why can comparing the sequences of different genes or proteins lead to different conclusions about when two groups diverged from a common ancestor?

5. Why is comparing the DNA sequence of one gene a less accurate estimate of the evolutionary relationship between two species than a DNA hybridization experiment comparing large portions of the two genomes?

6. Cite a limitation of comparing chromosome banding patterns to estimate species' relationships.

7. Some human and chimp genes are more alike than other genes are from person to person. Does this mean that some chimps are humans, or that humans with different alleles are different species?

8. What types of information are needed to construct an evolutionary tree diagram? What assumptions are necessary? What are the limitations of these diagrams?

9. Cite three examples of eugenic actions or policies.

applied questions

1. A geneticist aboard a federation starship is given the task of determining how closely related Humans, Klingons, Romulans, and Betazoids are. Each organism walks on two legs, lives in complex societies, uses tools and technologies, looks similar, and reproduces in the same manner. Each can interbreed with any of the others. The geneticist finds the following data:

- Klingons and Romulans each have 44 chromosomes. Humans have 46. Human chromosomes 15 and 17 each resemble part of the same large chromosome in Klingons and Romulans.

- Humans and Klingons have 97 percent of their chromosome bands in common. Humans and Romulans have 98 percent of their chromosome bands in common, and Humans and Betazoids show 100 percent correspondence. Humans and Betazoids differ only by an extra segment on chromosome 11, which appears to be a duplication.

- The cytochrome C amino acid sequence is identical in Humans and Betazoids, and differs by 1 amino acid between Humans and Romulans and by 2 amino acids between Humans and Klingons.

- The gene for collagen contains 50 introns in Humans, 50 introns in Betazoids, 62 introns in Romulans, and 74 introns in Klingons.

- Mitochondrial DNA analysis reveals many more individual differences among Klingons and Romulans than among Humans or Betazoids.

  a. Hypothesize the chromosomal aberrations that might explain the karyotypic differences between these four types of organisms.

  b. Which are our closest relatives among the Klingons, Romulans, and Betazoids? What is the evidence for this?

  c. Are Klingons, Romulans, Humans, and Betazoids distinct species? What information reveals this?

  d. Which of the following evolutionary tree diagrams is consistent with the data?

a. Klingons Humans Romulans Betazoids
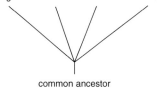
common ancestor

b. Klingons Romulans Humans Betazoids
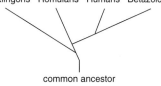
common ancestor

c. Klingons Romulans Humans Betazoids
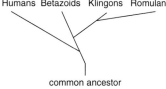
common ancestor

d. Humans Betazoids Klingons Romulans

common ancestor

2. Give three examples of negative eugenic measures and three examples of positive eugenic measures.

3. A molecular anthropologist who is studying diabetes in native Americans feels that he can obtain information on why certain groups are prone to the disorder by analyzing genetic variants in isolated, small populations around the world. Do you think that the goal of understanding disease and alleviating suffering in one group of people justifies obtaining and studying the DNA of other people who have had little contact with cultures outside their own, even if they might be frightened by such attempts? Can you suggest a compromise intervention that might benefit everyone concerned?

4. In 1997, law schools in two states reversed their affirmative action policies and began evaluating all applicants on an equal basis—that is, the same admittance requirements applied to all. In fall, 1997, classrooms of new law students had few, if any, nonwhite faces. How was this action eugenic, and how was it not eugenic?

suggested readings

Boguski, Mark S., M. D., Ph.D. September 7, 1995. Hunting for genes in computer databases. *The New England Journal of Medicine,* vol. 333. Newly discovered human gene sequences are compared to databases of known gene sequences in other species, helping researchers unravel gene functions.

Burrows, Wes, and Oliver A. Ryder. January 9, 1997. Y-chromosome variation in great apes. *Nature,* vol. 385. Natural selection has maintained a fairly uniform Y chromosome in hominids.

Butler, Declan. September 4, 1997. Eugenics scandal reveals silence of Swedish scientists. *Nature,* vol. 389. Until 1976, the Swedish government sterilized people deemed to be unfit.

Darnton, John. *Neanderthal.* New York: Random House. Fiction that pits two groups of Neanderthals, alive today in the Pamir mountains in Tajikstan, against each other. Wonderful reading!

Easton, Ruth D., et al. July 1996. mtDNA variation in the Yanomami: evidence for additional New World founding lineages. *The American Journal of Human Genetics,* vol. 59. The Yanomani, until recently an isolated native American people, exhibit greater than expected genetic diversity.

Gore, Rick. September 1997. Tracking the first of our kind. *National Geographic.* A look at the peoples who preceded us.

Holtzman, Neil A., and Mark A. Rothstein. 1992. Eugenics and genetic discrimination. *The American Journal of Human Genetics,* vol. 50. Eugenics is alive and well—in our attitudes, if not our actions.

Jaroff, Leon. October 26, 1992. Iceman. *Time.* A remarkably well-preserved man who lived 5,300 years ago is providing a wealth of information about life during his time.

Kahn, Patricia, and Ann Gibbons. July 11, 1997. DNA from an extinct human. *Science,* vol. 277. Sequencing Neanderthal DNA surprised us.

Leakey, Meave G., et al. May 7, 1998. New specimens and confirmation of an early age for *Australopithecus anamensis. Nature,* vol. 393. The first australopithecines we know of lived between 4.17 and 4.07 million years ago.

Lyall, Sarah. March 24, 1997. Thanks to DNA, Briton meets really distant relative. *The New York Times.* A history teacher finds genetic links to 9,000-year-old Cheddar Man.

Merriwether, Dr. Andrew, et al. July 1996. mtDNA variation indicates Mongolia may have been the source for the founding population of the New World. *The American Journal of Human Genetics,* vol. 59. Modern Siberians lack a haplotype that is in native Americans and Mongolians, suggesting that Mongolians are the ancestral group.

Paabo, Svante. May 26, 1995. The Y chromosome and the origin of all of us (men). *Science,* vol. 268.

Shreeve, James. 1996. *The Neanderthal enigma: Solving the mystery of modern human origins.* New York: William Morrow & Co. Rather than being isolated in time, the Neanderthals may have overlapped with several other peoples.

Thorne, Alan G., and Milford H. Wolpoff. April 1992. The multiregional evolution of humans. *Scientific American.* Genes descended from *Homo erectus* may still be among us—mitochondrial Eve may not have been the only ancestral woman.

Wallace, Douglas C. August 1997. Mitochondrial DNA in aging and disease. *Scientific American.* A sidebar describes the times of migrations of native Americans.

Wilson, Allan C., and Rebecca L. Cann. April 1992. The recent African genesis of humans. *Scientific American.* Several lines of molecular evidence point to a common ancestor of us all. She lived about 200,000 years ago in Africa.

chapter fifteen

Genetics of Immunity

The Gift of Life

Patti Szuber was a strong supporter of organ donation. She carried an organ donor card and had told her family she wished to donate her organs. But she probably never imagined she would get her wish at age twenty-two. On a brilliant early September day in 1994, Patti was driving in the Smoky Mountains, on vacation before returning to nursing school, when an accident slammed her car into a rock wall. Severely injured, Patti was taken to the University of Tennessee Medical Center, brain dead.

In Michigan, Patti's father Chester was in his fourth year of awaiting a heart transplant, after twenty years of battling heart disease and surviving several surgeries. With his daughter's death, Chester rocketed to the top of the transplant list, because as a close blood relative, chances were good that his body would accept Patti's heart. Doctors in Tennessee removed the young woman's heart, packed it in ice in a picnic cooler, and flew it to Michigan. Within six hours, it was stitched into Chester's chest, where it beats today.

When doctors transplant an organ, they ask the immune system to do something it shouldn't—accept foreign tissue as part of the body. The success of today's transplants rests on our understanding how our immune systems work. To a large extent, genes control that system.

Normal Immunity

We share the planet with plants, microbes, fungi, and other animals. The human immune system keeps potentially harmful organisms out of our bodies. It is a mobile army of about 2 trillion cells and the biochemicals they produce—**antibodies** and **cytokines.** Upon recognizing "foreign" or "nonself" surfaces of viruses, microbial cells, tumor cells, or transplanted cells, the system launches a highly coordinated, multipronged attack.

Although the environment stimulates the immune response, genes control many aspects of immunity. Genes encode antibodies and cytokines and specify the cell surface molecules, or **self antigens,** that mark the body's cells. Genes also encode protein cell surface receptors that bind cytokines. (An antigen is any molecule that elicits an immune response in another individual. Antigens are usually proteins or carbohydrates.) A **foreign antigen,** because it is not of the body, elicits an immune response.

Because genes control immunity, mutations can impair immune function. Health consequences of disturbed immunity include immune deficiencies, autoimmune disorders, allergies, and cancer. But the role genes play in controlling immunity also provides a handle for genetic technologies to enhance or redirect the system's ability to fight disease. Immune illnesses and technologies are discussed in the second half of the chapter. We begin our look at normal immunity with some familiar examples of our personal cellular landscapes.

Self Cell Surfaces

Transplanting an organ as complex as a heart is a major and risky medical procedure. A far simpler type of transplant, although still very dependent on matching cell surfaces, is a blood transfusion (figure 15.1). People have long thought about using one person's blood to restore another's health. It was necessary to understand the genetics of blood types to make transfusions safe.

ABO Blood Groups

The first transfusions, performed in the late 1600s, used lamb blood. By the 1800s, physicians were trying to use human blood. The results were unpredictable—some recipients recovered, but others died when their kidneys failed under the strain of handling red blood cells that clumped when blood types were incompatible. So poor was the success rate that, by the late 1800s, many nations banned transfusions.

Around this time, Austrian physician Karl Landsteiner began investigating why transfusions sometimes worked and sometimes didn't. In 1900, he determined that human blood was of differing types, and that only certain combinations were compatible. In 1910, identification of the ABO blood antigen locus (figure 15.2) explained the observed blood type incompatibilities. Today, we know of 20 different genes whose protein products are part of the surface topography of red blood cells.

Recall from chapter 5 that the I gene alleles encode enzymes that place antigens A, B, both A and B, or neither on sugar chains on red blood cells. Blood type incompatibility occurs when a person's immune system manufactures antibodies that attack the antigens his or her cells do not carry. A person with blood type A, for example, has antibodies against type B antigen. If he or she is transfused with type B blood, the anti-B antibodies cause the transfused red blood cells to clump, blocking circulation and depriving tissues of oxygen. A person with type AB blood doesn't manufacture antibodies against antigen A or B, because if he or she did, the blood would clump. Therefore, someone with type AB blood can receive any ABO blood type. Type O blood has neither A nor B antigens, so it cannot prompt an immune response in a transfusion recipient; people with type O blood can thus donate to anyone. However, the idea that a person with AB blood is a "universal recipient" and one with type O blood is a "universal donor" is more theoretical than practical because antibodies to other donor blood antigens cause slight incompatibilities. For this reason, blood is as closely matched as possible. (An experimental "universal blood type" consists of red blood cells coated with a chemical that masks their surface antigens.)

A person who receives mismatched blood quickly feels the effects—anxiety, difficulty breathing, facial flushing, headache, and severe pain in the neck, chest, and lower back. Red blood cells burst, releasing free hemoglobin that can damage the kidneys. These are the symptoms Landsteiner observed with mismatched transfusions.

The Rh Factor

ABO blood type is often further differentiated by a $^+$ or $^-$, which refers to another blood group antigen called the Rh factor. Whether a person has the Rh factor (Rh^+) or not (Rh^-) is determined by the combination of alleles of three genes called C, D, and E. The antigen was originally identified in rhesus monkeys, hence the name.

Rh type is important when an Rh^+ man and an Rh^- woman conceive a child who is Rh^+. The pregnant woman's immune

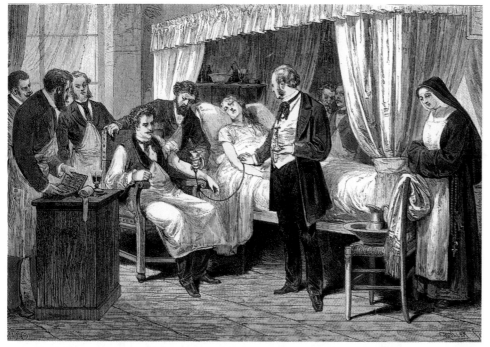

a.

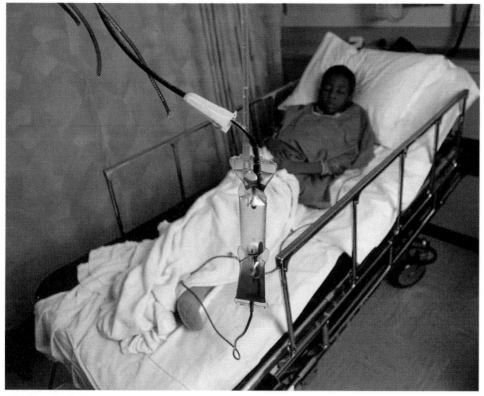

b.

figure 15.1

(a) In the 1500s, physicians believed that draining blood could cure a variety of ills. A century later, transfusion experiments began, but no one could achieve consistent success until Landsteiner described the ABO blood groups in 1900. (b) Today, blood typing takes several blood groups into account, ensuring that donors and recipients match. Donated whole blood is also screened for contaminants such as HIV.

system reacts to the few fetal cells that leak into her bloodstream by manufacturing antibodies against the fetal cells (figure 15.3). Not enough antibodies form to harm the first fetus, but if she carries a second Rh^+ fetus, the woman's now plentiful antibodies attack its blood supply. In the fetus, bilirubin, a breakdown product of red blood cells, accumulates, damaging the brain and turning the skin and whites of the eyes yellow (a condition called jaundice). The fetal liver and spleen swell as they rapidly produce new red blood cells. If the fetus or newborn does not receive a transfusion of Rh^- blood, the heart and blood vessels collapse and fatal respiratory distress sets in. Rh disease that progresses this far is called hydrops fetalis.

Fortunately, natural and medical protections make hydrops fetalis rare. ABO blood types help determine whether an immune reaction against the fetus of an Rh incompatible couple takes place. If the woman has type O blood and the man is A, B, or AB, then her anti-A and anti-B antibodies attack type A or B fetal blood cells in her circulation before her system has a chance to manufacture the anti-Rh antibodies. This blocks the anti-Rh reaction.

Obstetricians routinely determine a pregnant woman's blood type. If she and her partner have Rh incompatibility, doctors inject a drug during pregnancy and after the birth. The drug covers antigens on fetal blood cells in the woman's circulation so that she does not manufacture anti-Rh antibodies. However, events other than pregnancy and childbirth can expose an Rh^- woman's system to Rh^+ cells, placing even her first child at risk. These include amniocentesis, a blood transfusion, an ectopic (tubal) pregnancy, a miscarriage, or an abortion.

Other Blood Groups

Another way of distinguishing red blood cells is by the L gene, whose codominant alleles M, N, and S combine to form ten different genotypes and six different glycoprotein cell surface patterns (the phenotype). Another blood-type determining gene is called Lewis. It encodes an enzyme that adds an antigen to the sugar fucose, which the product of the H gene places on red blood cells. (Recall that the H gene is

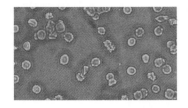
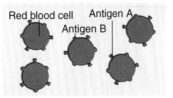

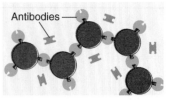

Red blood cell — Antigen A
Antigen B

Antibodies —

Compatible Blood Types (no clumping)		Incompatible Blood Types (clumping)	
Donor	*Recipient*	*Donor*	*Recipient*
O	O, A, B, AB	A	B, O
A	A, AB	B	A, O
B	B, AB	AB	A, B, O
AB	AB		

figure 15.2

Genetics explains blood incompatibilities.

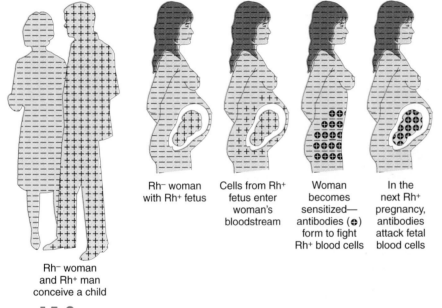

Rh⁻ woman and Rh⁺ man conceive a child

Rh⁻ woman with Rh⁺ fetus

Cells from Rh⁺ fetus enter woman's bloodstream

Woman becomes sensitized— antibodies (⊕) form to fight Rh⁺ blood cells

In the next Rh⁺ pregnancy, antibodies attack fetal blood cells

figure 15.3

If a man who is Rh⁺ and a woman who is Rh⁻ conceive a child who is Rh⁺, the woman's body manufactures antibodies that attack future Rh⁺ offspring.

necessary for ABO expression.) Individuals with genotype *LeLe* or *Lele* have the Lewis antigen on red blood cell membranes and in saliva, whereas *lele* people do not produce the antigen.

Another interesting gene that affects the blood is the secretor gene. People who have the dominant allele *Se* secrete the A, B, and H antigens in body fluids, including semen, saliva, tears, and mucus.

The blood group antigens, as cell surface markers, serve as cellular nametags, clearly delineating "self" to the immune system. Another cell surface antigen system, with important applications in health care and forensics, is the **human leukocyte antigen (HLA)** gene complex. (The name comes from the fact that these antigens were first studied in leukocytes, a broad term for white blood cells.)

The Human Leukocyte Antigens

When Chester Szuber became a candidate for a heart transplant, the tissue typing procedure used to match him with a potential donor heart determined the types of cell surface proteins encoded by a closely linked set of genes on the short arm of chromosome 6. These HLA genes are important in tissue typing because each has a number of easily distinguished alleles, and the pattern of HLA cell surface molecules differs from person to person. The five genes in the HLA complex—A, B, C, D, and DR—have 23, 47, 8, 12, and 12 known alleles, respectively.

Because of the great polymorphism (variability) of the HLA genes, a person's HLA profile is highly individual—only 2 in every 20,000 unrelated people match. Forensic specialists use HLA types to distinguish individuals, but the more powerful DNA fingerprinting (Reading 12.1) is replacing the HLA technique. An HLA type can only rule a suspect out, whereas DNA fingerprinting can identify the person responsible for a crime.

The HLA system did not evolve to help us catch criminals. HLA genes specify proteins, which join sugars to form branchlike glycoproteins on cell surfaces. Some of these HLA glycoproteins latch onto bacterial and viral proteins, displaying them like badges on an immune system cell in a way that alerts other immune system cells. This action, called **antigen processing,** is often the first step in an immune response. The cell that displays the foreign antigen is an **antigen-presenting cell.** Figure 15.4 shows how a large cell called a **macrophage** displays bacterial antigens.

For reasons we do not completely understand, certain HLA combinations are statistically associated with an increased

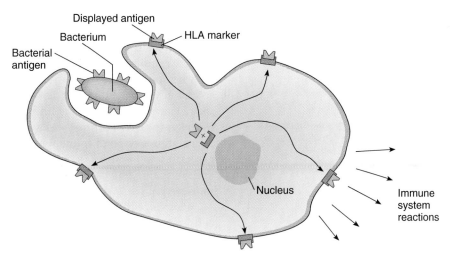

figure 15.4

A macrophage internalizes a bacterium, then dismantles it. A piece of a bacterial antigen attaches to an HLA protein inside the macrophage and gains a sugar, and the complex moves to the cell's surface. The combination of the foreign antigen bound to the self HLA glycoprotein alerts the immune system to make body-wide changes to fight the infection.

table 15.1

Medical Problems Linked to Specific HLA Types

Condition	Description
Ankylosing spondylitis	Inflammation and deformation of vertebrae
Reiter syndrome	Inflammation of joints, eyes, and urinary tract
Rheumatoid arthritis	Inflammation of joints
Psoriasis	Scaly skin lesions
Dermatitis herpetiformia	Burning, itchy skin lesions
Systemic lupus erythematosus	Facial rash; destruction of heart, brain, and kidney cells; very high, persistent fever
Addison disease	Malfunction of adrenal glands, producing anemia, discolored skin, diarrhea, low blood pressure, and stomachache
Grave's disease	Malfunction of thyroid gland, producing goiter
Juvenile-onset diabetes	Defect in beta cells of pancreas, disrupting sugar metabolism
Multiple sclerosis	Degeneration of brain or spinal cord, producing weakness and poor coordination
Myasthenia gravis	Progressive paralysis
Celiac disease	Childhood diarrhea
Gluten-sensitive enteropathy	Sensitivity of intestine to wheat
Chronic active hepatitis	Inflammation of liver

risk of developing one of fifty or so particular diseases. As table 15.1 shows, these HLA-associated disorders affect a range of organ systems, and all involve the immune system. HLA-linked diseases run in families, but not in a predictable manner.

Consider ankylosing spondylitis, which inflames and deforms vertebrae. A person with an HLA antigen called B27 is one hundred times as likely to develop the condition as someone who lacks the antigen. More than 90 percent of people who

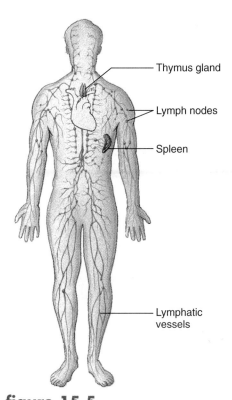

figure 15.5

The immune system.

suffer from ankylosing spondylitis have the B27 antigen, which occurs in only 5 percent of the general population. However, predictions of disease based on HLA tests are not absolute. As the statistics show, 10 percent of people who have ankylosing spondylitis do *not* have the B27 antigen, and some people who have the antigen never develop the disease.

An Overview of Immunity— Structures and Functions

On a macroscopic level, the immune system includes a network of vessels called lymphatics, which transport lymph, a watery fluid, to bean-shaped structures called lymph nodes. The spleen and thymus gland are also part of the immune system (figure 15.5). On a microscopic level, the immune system consists of white blood cells called **lymphocytes** and the wandering, scavenging macrophages that capture and degrade invading bacteria, viruses, and cellular debris.

Lymphocytes are made in the bone marrow and migrate to the lymph nodes,

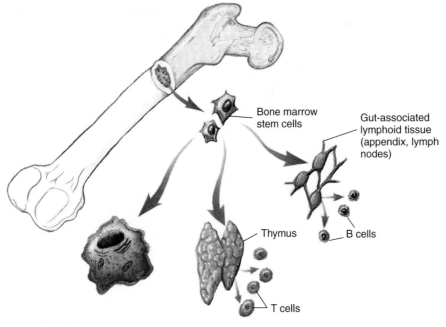

figure 15.6

Macrophages, T cells, and B cells interact to generate immune responses. All three cell types originate in the bone marrow and migrate into the blood. Macrophages engulf bacteria and also stimulate T cells to proliferate and activate B cells. T cells mature in the thymus gland and in the skin, and some manufacture biochemicals released during viral infections. T cells also attack cancer cells and transplanted tissues. B cells are released from the appendix and lymph nodes, and they secrete antibodies.

spleen, and thymus gland, as well as circulate in the blood and tissue fluid (figure 15.6). They are of two types. **B cells** secrete antibody proteins in response to nonself molecules (foreign antigens). **T cells** release cytokines that have a number of functions. They also stimulate B cells to produce antibodies.

The immune system has three basic characteristics. It is *diverse,* vanquishing many types of microscopic foes. It is *specific,* distinguishing the cells and molecules that cause disease from those that are harmless. The immune system also *remembers,* responding faster to a subsequent encounter with a foreign antigen than it did the first time. The first assault constitutes a **primary immune response,** and the second assault, based on the system's "memory," a **secondary immune response.** This is why we get chicken pox only once. However, colds and influenza recur because the causative viruses mutate, literally presenting a different face to our immune systems each season.

The Humoral Immune Response

B cells secreting antibodies into the bloodstream constitute the **humoral immune response.** (*Humor* means fluid.)

B Cell Activation

An antibody response begins when an antigen-presenting macrophage activates a T cell, which in turn contacts a B cell that has surface receptors that have bound the same type of foreign antigen. The immune system has so many B cells, each with different combinations of surface antigens, that there is almost always one or more available that corresponds to a particular foreign antigen. Each day, millions of B cells perish in the lymph nodes and spleen, while millions more form in the bone marrow, each with a unique combination of surface molecules.

Once the activated T cell finds a B cell match, it releases cytokines that prompt the B cell to divide. Soon the B cell gives rise to two types of cells (figure 15.7). The first type of B cell descendants, **plasma cells,** are antibody factories, secreting up to two thousand identical antibodies per second at the height of their few-day lifespan. These cells provide the primary immune response. **Memory cells** remain dormant, but respond to the foreign antigen faster and with more force should it appear again. This is the secondary immune response.

Plasma cells derived from different B cells secrete different antibodies, each antibody type corresponding to a specific portion of the microbe (figure 15.8). This is called a **polyclonal antibody response.** A type of cancer called multiple myeloma illustrates the value of this antibody diversity. In this condition, one B cell out of the body's 10 billion divides out of control, eventually comprising a significant proportion of the total B cell population. The person makes massive amounts of antibody type IgG and suffers frequent bacterial infections because of the lack of antibody diversity. A bacterium whose antigens do not fit the receptors on the overabundant B cells has a selective advantage.

Antibody Structure

Antibodies are among the most complex of proteins, constructed of several polypeptides and therefore encoded by several genes. The simplest antibody molecule is made up of four polypeptide chains connected by disulfide (sulfur-sulfur) bonds, forming a shape like the letter Y (figure 15.9). The two longer polypeptides are called **heavy chains,** and the other two are called **light chains.** The lower portion of each chain is an amino acid sequence that is very similar in all antibody molecules, even in different species. These areas are called **constant regions.** The amino acid sequence of the upper portions of each polypeptide chain, the **variable regions,** can differ a great deal among antibodies.

Antibodies can bind to certain antigens because of the three-dimensional shapes of the tips of the variable regions. These specialized ends of the antibody

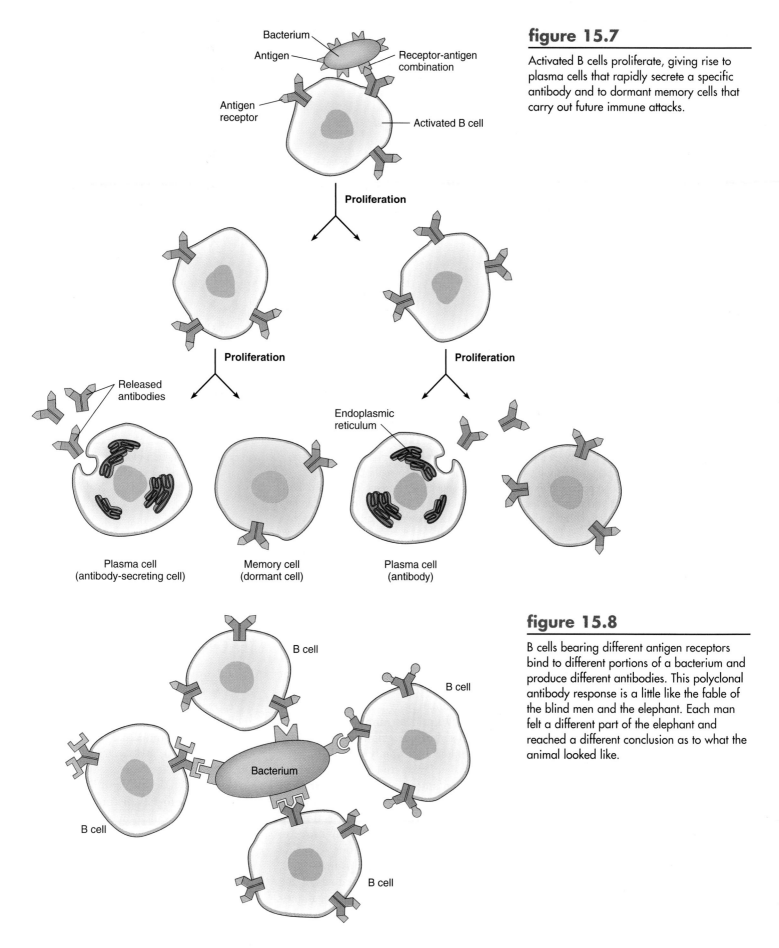

figure 15.7

Activated B cells proliferate, giving rise to plasma cells that rapidly secrete a specific antibody and to dormant memory cells that carry out future immune attacks.

Bacterium
Antigen
Receptor-antigen combination
Antigen receptor
Activated B cell

Proliferation

Proliferation

Proliferation

Released antibodies

Endoplasmic reticulum

Plasma cell (antibody-secreting cell)

Memory cell (dormant cell)

Plasma cell (antibody)

figure 15.8

B cells bearing different antigen receptors bind to different portions of a bacterium and produce different antibodies. This polyclonal antibody response is a little like the fable of the blind men and the elephant. Each man felt a different part of the elephant and reached a different conclusion as to what the animal looked like.

B cell

B cell

B cell

Bacterium

B cell

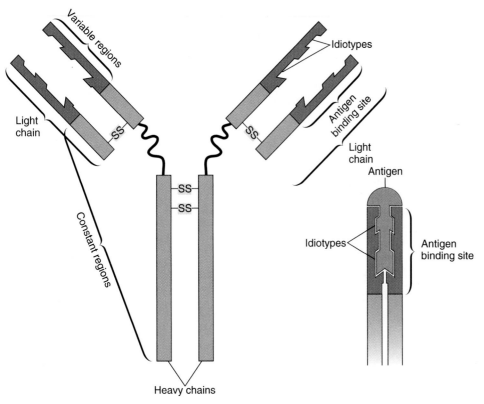

figure 15.9

Antibody structure. The simplest antibody molecule consists of four polypeptide chains, two heavy and two light, held together by disulfide bonds that form between sulfur-containing amino acids. Part of each polypeptide chain has a constant sequence of amino acids, and the remainder of the sequence is variable. The tops of the Y-shaped molecules form antigen binding sites. Four genes encode this simple antibody molecule. The inset shows how an antigen fits the antigen binding site.

figure 15.10

An antibody's antigen binding site hugs an antigen as a hand holds an object.

molecule are called **antigen binding sites,** and the specific parts that actually bind the antigen are called **idiotypes.** An antibody contorts to form a pocket around the antigen, much like a hand grasping an object (figure 15.10).

Antibody-antigen binding inactivates a microbe or neutralizes the toxin it produces. Antibodies can cause pathogens to clump, making them more visible to macrophages, which then destroy them. Antibodies also activate a collection of biochemicals called **complement,** which destroys microbes and transplanted tissue in several complex ways.

Antibody Diversity

Antibodies are diverse in their ability to combine, their locations and roles, and at what point they join in the immune response. Antibody molecules can aggregate into complexes (figure 15.11). Five classes of antibodies are distinguished by location in the body and by function (table 15.2). Antibodies are also called immunoglobulins, abbreviated *Ig.* Different antibody types predominate in different stages of an infection.

The human body can manufacture an apparently limitless number of different antibodies, but our genomes have a limited number of antibody genes. How can this be? The great diversity of antibody types is possible because different antibody gene products combine. During the early development of B cells, sections of their antibody genes randomly move to other chromosomal locations, creating new genetic instructions for antibodies. Shuffling the polypeptide products of 200 genes generates 100 trillion different anti-

bodies! Antibody diversity is like using the limited number of words in a language to compose an infinite variety of stories.

The Cellular Immune Response

T cells provide the **cellular immune response,** so-called because the cells themselves travel to where they are needed, unlike B cells, which secrete antibodies into the bloodstream. Immature cells called thymocytes are "educated" in the thymus, acquiring the ability to recognize self cell surfaces and molecules and becoming T cells. Immunologists distinguish several types of T cells by their functions.

Helper T Cells

Helper T cells recognize foreign antigens presented on macrophages, stimulate

B cells to produce antibodies, secrete cytokines, and activate another type of T cell called a **cytotoxic T cell** (sometimes called a killer T cell). The cytokines that helper T cells secrete include **interleukins, interferons, tumor necrosis factor,** and **colony stimulating factors** (table 15.3). Cytokines interact and signal each other in complex cascades of gene action.

Distinctive surfaces distinguish subsets of helper T cells. Certain antigens called **cluster-of-differentiation antigens,** or CD antigens, enable T cells to recognize foreign antigens displayed on macrophages. One such cell type, called a CD4 helper T cell, is the prime target of HIV. Considering the critical role of helper T cells in coordinating immunity, it is little wonder that HIV infection ultimately topples the entire system, a point we will return to soon.

CD4 helper T cells are further classified by the types of cytokines they secrete. The proportion of these subclasses may influence susceptibility to HIV infection. Specifically, one type of CD4 helper T cell called TH1 seems to protect against infection, while another type, TH2, increases susceptibility. HIV infection may shift the CD4 helper T cell population so that TH2 predominates.

Cytotoxic T Cells

Cytotoxic T cells attack virally infected and cancerous cells by attaching to them and releasing chemicals. They do this by joining two surface peptides to form **T cell receptors** that bind foreign antigens. When a cytotoxic T cell encounters a nonself cell—a cancer cell, for example—the T cell receptors draw the two cells into physical contact. The T cell then releases a protein called perforin, which drills holes in the foreign cell's membrane. This disrupts the flow of chemicals in and out of the foreign cell and kills it (figure 15.12). Cytotoxic T cell receptors also attract body cells that are covered with certain viruses, destroying the cells before the viruses on them can enter, replicate, and spread the infection. In this way, cytotoxic T cells continually monitor cells, recognizing and eliminating virally infected and tumor cells.

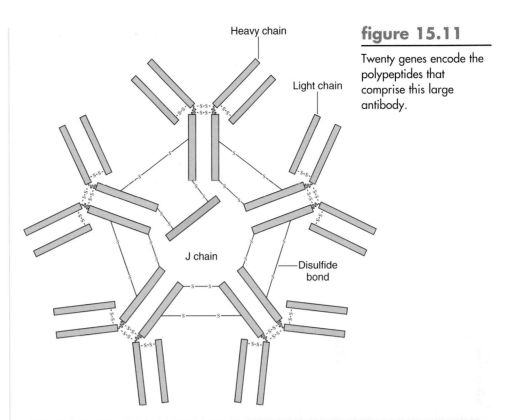

figure 15.11

Twenty genes encode the polypeptides that comprise this large antibody.

table 15.2

Types of Antibodies

Type*	Location	Functions
IgA	Milk, saliva, urine, and tears; respiratory and digestive	Protects against microorganisms at points of entry into body secretions
IgD	On B cells in blood	Stimulates B cells to make other antibodies, particularly in infants
IgE	In secretions with IgA and in mast cells in tissues	Acts as receptor for antigens that cause mast cells to secrete allergy mediators
IgG	Blood plasma and tissue fluid; passes to fetus	Protects against bacteria, viruses, and toxins, especially in secondary immune response
IgM	Blood plasma	Fights bacteria in primary immune response; includes anti-A and anti-B antibodies

*The letters A, D, E, G, and M refer to the specific conformation of heavy chains characteristic of each class of antibody.

table 15.3

Types of Cytokines

Cytokine	Function
Colony stimulating factors	Stimulate bone marrow to produce lymphocytes
Interferons	Block viral replication, stimulate macrophages to engulf viruses, stimulate B cells to produce antibodies, attack cancer cells
Interleukins	Control lymphocyte differentiation and growth
Tumor necrosis factor	Stops tumor growth, releases growth factors, causes fever that accompanies bacterial infection, stimulates lymphocyte differentiation

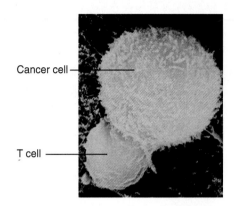

figure 15.12

The smaller cell is a cytotoxic T cell, homing in on the surface topography of the large cancer cell above it. The T cell will literally break the cancer cell apart, leaving nothing behind but scattered fibers.

Key Concepts

The immune system consists of cells and biochemicals that distinguish self from nonself antigens. Blood types result from self antigen patterns on red blood cells. The HLA complex is a highly diverse group of cell surface proteins, some of which display bacterial antigens to other parts of the immune system, triggering a response.

The immune system consists of lymphatic vessels, lymph, the spleen and thymus, macrophages, and lymphocytes (B cells and T cells). B cells secrete antibodies, and T cells secrete cytokines. The immune response is diverse, specific, and it remembers. A primary immune response occurs on a first encounter with a nonself antigen. A secondary immune response occurs more swiftly when the foreign antigen appears again.

In the humoral immune response, stimulated B cells divide and differentiate into plasma cells and memory cells. A plasma cell secretes abundant antibodies of a single type. Antibodies are made of Y-shaped polypeptides, each consisting of two light and two heavy chains. Each chain consists of a constant and a variable region, and the tips of the Y form an antigen binding site with a specific idiotype. Antibodies make foreign antigens more visible to macrophages and stimulate complement. Shuffling gene pieces generates astounding antibody diversity.

T cells, made in bone marrow and "educated" in the thymus, carry out the cellular immune response. Helper T cells stimulate B cells and cytotoxic T cells and secrete cytokines. Using T cell receptors, cytotoxic T cells bind to nonself cells and virus-covered cells and burst them.

Abnormal Immunity

The immune system renews itself daily, continually adapting to environmental change, for the thousands of days in a human lifetime. Reading 15.1 describes how immune system functions change throughout life.

Because the immune response is so diverse, its breakdown affects health in many ways. Immune system malfunction may be inherited or acquired, and immunity too strong, too weak, or misdirected.

Inherited Immune Deficiencies

Mutations in genes that encode cytokines or T cell receptors impair cellular immunity, which primarily targets viruses and cancer cells. But because T cells activate the B cells that manufacture antibodies, abnormal cellular immunity (T cell function) causes some degree of abnormal humoral immunity (B cell function). Defects in the genes encoding antibody segments would impair immunity mostly against bacteria.

More than twenty types of inherited immune deficiencies are recognized. The types classified as **severe combined immune deficiency** (SCID) affect both branches of the immune system, humoral and cellular. About 50 percent of SCID cases are sex-linked, and therefore seen in boys only. In a less severe form, the boy lacks B cells but has T cells. Before the advent of antibiotic drugs, these boys died before the age of ten years of overwhelming bacterial infection. In a more severe form of sex-linked SCID, lack of T cells leads to death by eighteen months of age. Severe thrush (a fungal infection), chronic diarrhea, and recurrent lung infections usually kill these children.

A young man named David Vetter taught the world about the difficulty of life with SCID years before AIDS appeared (figure 15.13). David had an autosomal form of the illness that caused him to be born without a thymus gland. His T cells could not mature and activate B cells, leaving him defenseless in a germ-filled world. Born in Texas in 1971, he spent his short life in a vinyl bubble, awaiting a treatment that never came. As David reached adolescence, he wanted to leave his bubble. An experimental bone marrow transplant was unsuccessful—soon afterwards David began vomiting and developed diarrhea, both signs of infection. David left the bubble but died within days of a massive infection.

For Laura Cay Boren, the first four years of life were an endless bout of severe infections. Her autosomal recessive form of SCID was caused by a lack of an enzyme called adenosine deaminase (ADA). Laura was luckier than David. Enzyme replacement and gene therapy have allowed her to live a near-normal life. (Her story is told in chapter 18.) About 15 percent of all SCID cases are due to ADA deficiency.

Another autosomal recessive form of SCID shows genetic drift (chapter 13). Affected children have a tiny thymus gland

Before Birth

The immune system begins to develop in a fetus by cataloging cells destined to differentiate as lymphocytes. These cells will eventually learn to tell self from nonself. Before this happens, the body will regard any antigen a fetus is exposed to as self. Therefore, first encounters with the antigen after birth will not evoke immune rejection. This is vividly seen in mice. A mouse fetus exposed to another mouse's cells will, as an adult, accept a skin graft from the donor mouse. Similarly, the rare set of human fraternal twins who have different ABO blood types can accept transfusions from each other if each twin's immune system, as it cataloged self antigens before birth, included the blood cell surfaces of the other.

As the fetus is taking inventory of its cells, it is already in a precarious situation. A fetus is totally dependent upon another individual—the pregnant woman—whose cell surfaces, although similar to the fetus's, are not identical. The female immune response, usually stronger than a male's, dampens during pregnancy so that it doesn't reject the embryo and fetus. Pregnant women are more prone to infection while their immune systems rest, but after giving birth, protection returns.

The Newborn

Because some of a pregnant woman's IgG antibodies pass through the placenta, a newborn has temporary immunity against certain illnesses. Human milk provides additional protection. Shortly before and after giving birth, a woman's milk contains a yellow substance called colostrum that is rich in IgA antibodies that protect the baby from certain digestive and respiratory infections. In a few days, mature milk replaces the colostrum, adding antibodies against some intestinal parasites.

Just as the maternal antibody supply falls, the infant begins to manufacture its own. The first antibodies an infant makes are a response to bacteria and viruses transmitted by whoever is in closest physical contact. The mother also makes antibodies to the bacteria and viruses on her baby's skin (faster than the baby can) and passes them to the baby in her milk.

This gradual exposure to foreign antigens seems to be part of the normal development of the immune system. By six months of age, a baby can produce a great enough variety of antibodies to overcome most infections. However, a child cannot fight certain infections, such as those caused by the herpes simplex family of viruses, until the second year of life.

Childhood—Is Early Infection Protective?

The immune system vividly illustrates how the environment can influence gene expression. The immune systems of people in different parts of the world provide protection against different illnesses in response to the particular microbes in the environment. Early exposure to the microbes we share the planet with may be crucial to the continuing development of the immune system.

Consider common acute lymphoblastic leukemia. This white blood cell cancer is much more prevalent among children of developed nations than among those in poorer nations, where it is most often seen in the wealthy. A controversial theory suggests that susceptibility to a leukemia-causing virus is greater in individuals who have led sheltered childhoods because their immune systems are less well developed. Children in developing nations, where sanitation is poor and exposure to pathogens greater, acquire a variety of antibodies early. According to the theory, a virus that triggers leukemia in a five-year-old living in Manhattan who has rarely been ill might be easily destroyed by the immune system of a five-year-old living in a South American village who has had many infections.

The Aging Immune System

The immune system begins to decline early in life. The thymus gland reaches its maximal size in early adolescence and then slowly degenerates. By age seventy, the thymus is one-tenth the size it was at the age of ten, and the immune system is only 25 percent as powerful. The declining strength of the immune response is why elderly persons have a higher risk of developing cancer and succumb more easily to infections that they easily fought off at an earlier age, such as influenza, tuberculosis, and pneumonia. Decline in immune function is mostly due to loss of T cells. B cell activity changes little with age.

and very few lymphocytes. Among the general population, 2 in a million newborns have this SCID variant, but among the Navajo and Apache peoples in the southwestern United States, 1 in 3,340 newborns are affected. Table 15.4 summarizes some inherited immune deficiencies.

Acquired Immune Deficiency Syndrome (AIDS)

Imagine that each day, 3 billion ants appear at your front door. The first day, you kill a billion of them. The next day, 3 billion more ants arrive, but even after you kill another billion, 4 billion still remain. Each day you kill about a third of the ants, yet still they replenish their numbers. Soon you tire. You can only kill a fourth of them, then a fifth. Before long, you can no longer wage the battle, and ants overrun your house. As they come

figure 15.13

David Vetter, the "bubble boy," was born without a thymus gland. Because his T cells could not mature, he was virtually defenseless against infection.

through the windows, under the doors, and down the chimney, they open up routes for other unwanted visitors, who damage the house in other ways. This scenario is not unlike what happens when HIV infects a human body.

HIV first infects macrophages. The virus adheres with its surface protein, called gp120, to two co-receptors on the host cell surface, called CD4 and CCR5. HIV enters macrophages but doesn't kill them—instead, it replicates ferociously, pumping millions of new viruses into the bloodstream.

HIV is a retrovirus; its genetic material is RNA. Once HIV is inside a cell, a viral enzyme, **reverse transcriptase,** catalyzes construction of a DNA strand complementary to the viral RNA. The initial viral DNA strand replicates to form a DNA double helix, which enters the cell's nucleus. HIV replicates, filling the host cell with viral RNA and proteins (figure 15.14).

table 15.4

Some Inherited Immune Deficiencies

Disorder	Phenotype	Defect
Sex-linked recessive		
X-linked immunodeficiency	Severe viral, bacterial, and protozoan infections	Absent glycoprotein on T cell surfaces
Hyper IgM syndrome	Excess IgM, deficient IgA and IgG; disorganized lymphoid tissue; large tonsils; immune system destroys blood cells	Antibody protection can't switch from IgM to IgA and IgG
Duncan disease	Great risk of Epstein-Barr virus infection, causing lethal mononucleosis, death by age 20; B cell cancer; too few antibodies and red blood cells	Progressive loss of T cell function
SCID X2	No lymphoid tissue; deficient IgG; at high risk for viral infections	Lack of CD4 and CD8 helper T cells
Agammaglobulinemia, Bruton type (T^+B^- SCID)	Bacterial infections	Lack of B cells
Agammaglobulinemia, Swiss type (T^-B^+ SCID)	Very small thymus; at high risk for viral, bacterial, fungal infections	Lack of T cells
Autosomal recessive		
ADA deficiency	Bacterial and viral infections	Lack of ADA poisons T cells, which cannot activate B cells
Agammaglobulinemia	Thymocytes do not mature; no lymphocytes in bloodstream or lymph nodes; small thymus; no antibodies; diverse infections	Defect in protein kinase linked with T cell cytokine receptor
Immune defect due to absence of thymus	Viral infections	No thymus gland; no T cells; deficient antibodies
Autosomal dominant		
Immunodeficiency with defective lymphocyte function	Skin and eye infections	Defective antibody production

So genetically diverse is HIV that within days of the initial infection, variants arise that resist the drugs used to treat AIDS. All it takes is a change in a single RNA base for a drug-resistant variant to appear. HIV's changeable nature has important clinical implications. Drugs that block viral replication must be administered as soon as possible. Combining drugs that act in different ways has the greatest chance of slowing the disease process. For example, two types of drugs, protease inhibitors and nucleoside analogs, intervene at different stages of HIV replication, and when teamed early in infection, may greatly slow its progress.

Identifying the CCR5 co-receptor was a decade-long effort that involved many researchers. Epidemiologists searched the DNA of people at high risk of HIV infection—people who had unprotected sex with many partners, and people with hemophilia who had received HIV-tainted blood in the 1980s. What parts of the genome did they share? Then molecular biologists discovered CCR5, and the epidemiologists soon found that people who were homozygous recessive for a 32-base deletion in the CCR5 gene were among those who had, seemingly, miraculously avoided AIDS. They were not saved by a miracle, but by a mutation. The 32-base deletion introduced a premature "stop" codon, which resulted in production of a CCR5 co-receptor that was too stunted to reach the cell's surface (figure 15.15). Like a ferry arriving at shore to find no dock, HIV has nowhere to bind. Unable to enter human cells, the virus cannot reproduce. Heterozygotes, with one copy of the deletion, can become infected, but remain healthy for several years longer than people who do not have the deletion.

Investigating the population genetics of CCR5 may hold clues to past epidemics. The deletion mutation frequency is highest in European and Eurasian Caucasians and slightly less common among Caucasians in the United States, where 1 to 2 percent are homozygous recessive and therefore resistant to HIV infection. The deletion mutation is not seen in Africans but is very rare among African Americans, which may reflect the fact that black people in the United States have, on average, 25 percent of their genes from Caucasians. Native Americans and Asians

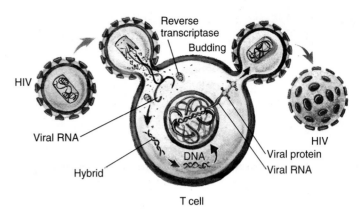

figure 15.14

How HIV infects a helper T cell. HIV sends its RNA and reverse transcriptase into a helper T cell by docking at a CD4 receptor. Once inside, reverse transcriptase builds a complementary DNA chain; after replicating, the viral genetic information, now encoded in DNA, enters the nucleus. When infection by another type of virus stimulates the T cell to divide and manufacture cytokines, the HIV genes are activated too. Instead of assisting B cells and secreting cytokines, the helper T cell becomes an HIV factory.

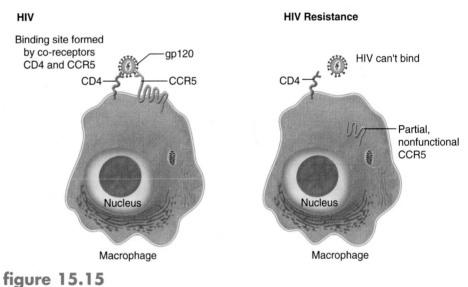

figure 15.15

People who inherit two copies of a deletion mutant of the CCR5 gene are resistant to HIV infection.

do not have the deletion. The fact that the protective mutation is fairly common in European populations and their descendants suggests that the allele was subject to a selective advantage in the past. That is, it offered protection in a past scourge, and therefore increased in the population over time. Human populations may have had AIDS, or something like it, thousands of years ago.

Today, finding the shortened and nonfunctional CCR5 and its critical role in evading AIDS suggests a new target for AIDS therapy and possibly prevention. Until the discovery, most drugs used to treat AIDS impaired viral replication. The focus is now shifting to altering the host. Because people who naturally lack CCR5 resist HIV infection and seem otherwise healthy, finding a way to block the CCR5 co-receptor might block infection. New clinical approaches include searching for drugs to block the CCR5 co-receptor, or giving a person a portion of the CCR5 protein as a vaccine. This would prompt an antibody response that would shield the HIV binding sites on cells. A combination approach that cripples HIV, while wiping out their binding sites, may finally conquer AIDS.

table 15.5

Autoimmune Disorders

Disorder	Signs and Symptoms	Antibodies Against:
Glomerulonephritis	Lower back pain	Kidney cell antigens that resemble strep bacteria antigens
Grave's disease	Restlessness, weight loss, irritability, increased heart rate and blood pressure	Thyroid gland antigens near thyroid-stimulating hormone receptor, causing overactivity
Juvenile diabetes	Thirst, hunger, weakness, emaciation	Pancreatic beta cells
Hemolytic anemia	Fatigue and weakness	Red blood cells
Myasthenia gravis	Muscle weakness	Receptors for nerve messages on skeletal muscle
Pernicious anemia	Fatigue and weakness	Binding site for vitamin B on cells lining stomach
Rheumatic fever	Weakness, shortness of breath	Heart cell antigens that resemble *Streptococcus* bacteria antigens
Rheumatoid arthritis	Joint pain and deformity	Cells lining joints
Scleroderma	Thick, hard, pigmented skin patches	Connective tissue cells
Systemic lupus erythematosus	Red facial rash, prolonged fever, weakness, kidney damage	DNA, neurons, blood cells
Ulcerative colitis	Lower abdominal pain	Colon cells

Autoimmunity

Sometimes the immune system backfires and manufactures antibodies called **autoantibodies** that attack "self"—the body's own cells. The signs and symptoms of this **autoimmunity** depend upon the cell types attacked (table 15.5). Most people who suffer from autoimmune disorders are female. For example, over 90 percent of people with systemic lupus erythematosus are female.

Several types of events might prompt the immune system to turn on itself. Perhaps a virus, while replicating within a human cell, borrows proteins from the host cell's surface and incorporates them onto its own. When the immune system "learns" the surface of the virus to destroy it, it also learns to attack the human cells that normally bear the protein. Alternatively, perhaps thymocytes escape their "education" in the thymus, never learning to distinguish self from nonself.

A third possible route of autoimmunity is when a nonself antigen coincidentally resembles a self antigen. This may explain juvenile diabetes, a deficiency of the pancre-

atic hormone insulin, which normally transports glucose in the blood to cells. Part of a protein on insulin-producing cells matches part of bovine serum albumin (BSA), a protein in cow's milk. Could children with an allergy to cow's milk develop antibodies against BSA, which later attack the similar-appearing pancreas cells, causing juvenile diabetes?

A fourth possible explanation of autoimmunity, which accounts for its prevalence in women, is that fetal cells enter and remain in a woman's circulation, maturing into white blood cells that carry out an inflammatory response years later. Researchers have discovered male cells in white blood cells in the skin of women with scleroderma and are looking to see if other conditions thought to be autoimmune are actually responses to fetal cells.

Allergies

Sometimes the immune system can be overly sensitive and attack substances that pose no health threat. Such an inappropriate

response is an allergy. In an allergic reaction, the offending substances, called allergens, activate IgE antibodies. These antibodies, in turn, bind to circulating cells called **mast cells** and cause them to explosively release substances called allergy mediators, which include histamine and heparin. Allergy mediators cause symptoms that range from the perpetually stuffed nose of an individual with dust mite allergy, to the runny eyes of hay fever, various rashes, and the body-wide overwhelming allergic reaction called anaphylactic shock.

Allergies are multifactorial. That is, they run in families but do not recur with the predictability of a Mendelian trait. This may be because an environmental trigger is necessary for expression of the phenotype. This trigger—an allergen—is a substance that is not threatening, such as chocolate or pollen. The immune system, however, perceives it as such (figure 15.16).

Any gene whose product controls IgE production or the receptor that it binds to on mast cells is a candidate for a genetic cause of allergy. A gene on chromosome 11, for example, encodes a subunit of the IgE receptor. Another possible allergy gene, located on chromosome 5, encodes a cytokine that regulates the level of IgE in the blood.

Key Concepts

HIV replicates very rapidly, and T cell production matches it until the immune response is overwhelmed and AIDS begins. HIV is a retrovirus that injects its RNA into host cells by binding to the co-receptors CD4 and CCR5, first on macrophages, then on T cells. Reverse transcriptase copies viral RNA into DNA. HIV uses the cell's protein synthesis machinery to mass produce itself, then the cell bursts, releasing virus. HIV mutates, becoming resistant to drugs.

In autoimmune disorders, autoantibodies attack healthy tissue. These conditions may be caused by a virus that borrows a self antigen, T cells that never learn to recognize self, healthy cells bearing antigens that resemble nonself antigens, or lingering fetal cells.

An overly sensitive immune system causes allergies. In an allergic reaction, allergens bind to IgE antibodies on mast cells, which release allergy mediators. Genes that control IgE production or its receptors may cause allergies.

Transplantation and Tissue Rejection

When a car breaks down, replacing the damaged or malfunctioning part often fixes the trouble. The same is sometimes true for the human body. Organ transplantation is now the primary treatment for a failing heart, kidney, liver or lung. Corneas, pancreases, skin, and bone marrow are also transplanted often.

Transplant Types

Transplants are classified by the relationship of donor to recipient:

1. An **autograft** transfers tissue from one part of a person's body to another. A skin graft taken from the thigh to replace burned skin on the chest and a leg vein replacing a coronary artery are autografts. The immune system does not reject the graft, because it recognizes the tissue as self. (Technically, an autograft is not a transplant because it involves only one person.)

2. An **isograft** is tissue from an identical twin. Because such twins are genetically identical, the recipient's immune system does not reject the transplant.

3. An **allograft** comes from an individual who is not genetically identical to the recipient, but is a member of the same species. A kidney transplant from a relative or other suitable donor is an allograft. The first allograft was performed a century ago (see the Technology Timeline).

4. A **xenograft** transplants tissue from one species to another. Reading 15.2 explores the topic of pigs genetically engineered so that their hearts can be transplanted into humans.

Rejection Reactions

The immune system recognizes most donor tissue as nonself and attempts to destroy it in a **tissue rejection reaction.** Tissue rejection involves many parts of the immune system, including T cell action, antibody attack, and activation of complement. The greater the difference

a. b.

figure 15.16

Causes of two common allergies: (*a*) ragweed pollen causes hay fever (Magnification ×325), and (*b*) dust mites cause year-round runny nose and eyes, and asthma.

Transplantation

1899	First allograft—a kidney from dog to dog.
1902	Pig kidney is attached to blood vessels of woman dying of kidney failure.
1905	First successful corneal transplant, from a boy who lost an eye in an accident to a man whose cornea is chemically damaged. Works because cornea cells lack antigens.
1940s	First kidney transplants on young people with end-stage kidney failure.
1950s	Blood typing predicts success of donor-recipient pairs for organ transplants.
1960s	First effective immunosuppressant drugs revive interest in human allografts. Kidney xenografts between baboons and chimpanzees.
1967	First human heart transplant. Patient lives eighteen days.
1968	Uniform Anatomical Gift Act passes. Requires informed consent from next of kin before organs or tissues can be used for organ donation.
1970s	Transplant problems: they extend life only briefly and do not correct underlying disease; surgical complications; rejection reactions.
1980s	Improved immunosuppressant drugs, surgical techniques, and tissue matching, plus ability to strip antigens from donor tissue, reawaken interest in transplants.
1984	Doctors transplant a baboon's heart into "Baby Fae," who was born with half a heart. She lives twenty days before rejecting the xenograft.
1992	Surgeons transplant a baboon's liver into a thirty-five-year-old man with hepatitis. The man lives for seventy-one days, dying of an unrelated cause.
1995	An AIDS patient receives bone marrow from an HIV-resistant baboon.
1997	Pig cell implants used to treat pancreatic failure and Parkinson disease.
1998–9	While researchers develop ways for non-human cell surfaces to more closely resemble those of humans, concern rises over risk of xenotransplants introducing retroviral disease.

Xenotransplantation From Pig to Human

In 1902, a German medical journal reported an astonishing experiment. A physician, Emmerich Ullman, had attached the blood vessels of a patient dying of kidney failure to a pig's kidney by her bedside. The experiment failed when her immune system rejected the attachment almost immediately. Today, nearly a century later, interest in using pig organs to heal humans has resurged. Pig heart valves have been used for years. More recently, fetal pig neural tissue has been used to treat Parkinson disease, and islet cells have been used to treat pancreatic failure.

The pig is a good candidate for heart transplants because its heart is about the same size as a human's, and its cardiovascular system is similar to ours. But a pig-to-human heart xenograft puts the immune system on red alert, even in the presence of the strongest immunosuppressive drugs. If we can't make the human body accept pig tissue, then perhaps we can engineer pig tissue to more closely resemble human tissue.

The first step is to understand what happens in a hyperacute rejection reaction, the immune system's response to tissue from another species. When pig tissue is grafted to human tissue, preexisting human antibodies bind to cells lining the pig's blood vessels. This triggers complement, in which a series of proteins in the blood react to cause swelling, bleeding, and clotting at the site of the foreign tissue, destroying it. The reaction is swift, taking from minutes to an hour. However, the human body also produces complement regulatory proteins, which stop the complement reaction.

Using this information, geneticists added genes encoding a key human complement regulatory protein to fertilized pig eggs. The resulting adult transgenic pigs produce the human protein in all of their tissues, yet live a perfectly normal pig existence. (Transgenic organisms are discussed further in chapter 17.) When their hearts are transplanted to a baboon (a stand-in for a human), the hyperacute rejection does not occur, thanks to expression of the human version of the regulatory proteins. The next step will be to genetically alter pigs even further so that they do not produce the cell sur-face molecules human antibodies bind to, preventing the complement reaction.

Porcine replacement parts are not without problems. The recipient would need to be immunosuppressed, possibly becoming vulnerable to pig viruses that might not normally infect a human. Many people might object to intentionally creating and nurturing pigs to be sacrificed for their parts. But development of genetically engineered animals for organ transplants would go a long way to solving the organ shortage problem (figure 1).

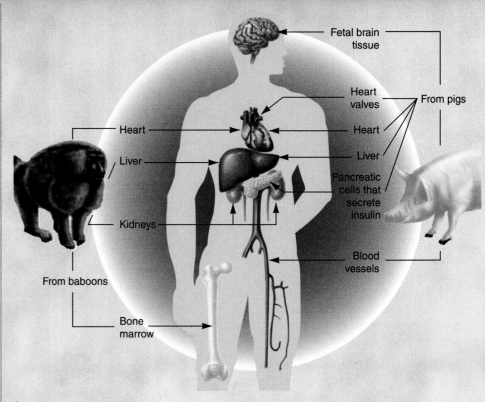

figure 1

Baboons and pigs can provide tissues and organs for transplant.

between recipient and donor cell surfaces, the more rapid and severe the rejection reaction. An extreme example of this is the **hyperacute rejection reaction** that takes place against tissue transplanted from another species—the donor cells are usually destroyed in minutes. By closely matching HLA types between donor and recipient, and stripping donor tissue of antigens, transplant surgeons can minimize the likelihood and intensity of a tissue rejection reaction.

Immunosuppressive drugs are another way to reduce rejection of transplanted tissue. These drugs interfere with the recipient's immune response by suppressing antibody synthesis or T cell production, thereby dampening either humoral or cellular immunity. Several new immunosuppressive drugs improve upon older drugs, such as cyclosporin, by selectively inactivating the parts of the immune response that attack transplanted tissue, while preserving the ability to fight infection.

A different type of immune problem arises sometimes in bone marrow transplants, which are used to correct certain blood deficiencies and cancers. The transplanted bone marrow, which is actually part of the donor's immune system, regards the recipient—its new body—as foreign. The transplant actually attacks the recipient. This condition is called **graft-versus-host disease,** and it is deadly.

Cell Implants

Transplanting smaller amounts of tissue in a **cell implant** may reduce the chance of rejection because fewer foreign antigens provoke the immune system. Cell implants can also make a single donor organ, such as a liver or pancreas that can be subdivided, go a much longer way. Implants of liver cells may treat cirrhosis, and implants of pancreas cells may treat diabetes.

The challenge in using cell implants is to have the healing cells persist and take over the impaired function. For example, several boys who have Duchenne muscular dystrophy were given implants consisting of 10 million immature muscle cells (myoblasts) from a first-degree, HLA-matched relative. On examination six months after the procedure, 3 to 14 percent of the cells were detected, and about half of them had joined the muscle tissue and were producing dystrophin.

In a few years, human tissues may be cultured in laboratories and either altered to be acceptable to anyone, or custom-designed to match a particular individual's cell surfaces. This may be possible because researchers can culture stem cells derived from human embryos and stimulate them to give rise to specialized tissues in laboratory dishes by adding certain growth factors.

Technology TIMELINE

Immunotherapy

1890s New York surgeon William Coley, after noting patients cured of cancer following bacterial infections, intentionally gives other cancer patients killed bacteria. Sometimes it works. The active ingredient the recipients' bodies make in response to the bacteria is an immune system biochemical called tumor necrosis factor.

German bacteriologist Paul Ehrlich develops the concept of the "magic bullet," a substance that destroys diseased cells yet spares healthy cells.

1950s Attempts begin to immunize mice against future cancer by implanting their own tumors back into them. Later, scientists realize these tumors are not accurate models of human cancer because they are induced and small.

1975 Monoclonal antibody technology harnesses the specificity of a single antibody type.

1980s Testing begins using cytokines (interleukins and interferons) to treat a variety of disorders. Researchers work out dosages, delivery protocols, and ways to minimize side effects.

1990s Several cytokines are approved for varied uses. Several cancer immunotherapies are in clinical trials.

Key Concepts

Autografts transfer tissue from one part of a person's body to another; isografts occur between identical twins; an allograft is between two members of the same species; and a xenograft is a cross-species transplant. Allografts can cause tissue rejection reactions, and xenografts can set off hyperacute rejection. Graft-versus-host disease occurs when transplanted bone marrow rejects the tissues of the recipient. Measures to improve transplant success include using immunosuppressive drugs, stripping antigens from donor tissue, and matching donor to recipient. Cell implants and stem cells from embryos may provide new sources of transplant material.

Immunotherapy

The immune system is remarkably effective at keeping potentially infectious bacteria, viruses, and tumor cells from taking over our bodies. Can we improve on nature? The idea of immunotherapy—amplifying or redirecting the immune response—originated in the late nineteenth century (Technology Timeline: Immunotherapy). Today, many immunotherapies are in clinical trials, and a few are already part of medical practice.

Boosting Humoral Immunity— Monoclonal Antibody Technology

When a single B cell recognizes a single foreign antigen, it manufactures a single, or monoclonal, type of antibody in response. A large amount of a single antibody type would make a powerful medicine because of its great specificity. It could be used to target a particular pathogenic microorganism or virus, or cancer.

In 1975, British researchers Cesar Milstein and George Köhler devised **monoclonal antibody** (MAb) technology, which amplifies a single B cell, preserving its specificity. First, they injected a mouse with a sheep's red blood cells (figure 15.17). They then isolated a single B cell from the mouse's spleen and fused it with a

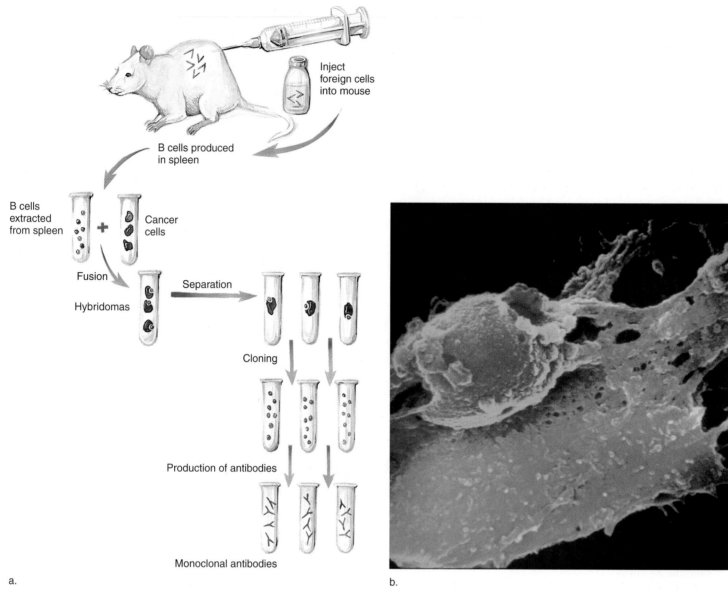

Inject
foreign cells
into mouse

B cells produced
in spleen

B cells
extracted
from spleen

Cancer
cells

Fusion

Hybridomas

Separation

Cloning

Production of antibodies

Monoclonal antibodies

a.

b.

figure 15.17

(a) Steps in making monoclonal antibodies. A foreign cell elicits production of different antibodies because it has several different antigens on its surface. (b) B cell + cancer cell = hybridoma. A hybridoma monoclonal antibody factory is created by fusing a cancer cell (the flat cell) with a B cell (the rounded cell).

cancerous white blood cell from a mouse. The fused cell, called a hybridoma, had a valuable pair of talents. Like the B cell, it produced large amounts of a single antibody type. Like the cancer cell, it divided continuously.

Today, MAbs are used in basic research, veterinary and human health care, agriculture, forestry, and forensics. Scientists have developed techniques to make them more like human antibodies—the original mouse versions cause allergic reactions in many people.

Diagnostic MAb kits that detect tiny amounts of a molecule are used to diagnose everything from strep throat to turf grass disease. One common use is a home pregnancy test. A woman places drops of her urine onto a paper strip impregnated with a MAb that binds to hCG, the hormone present only during pregnancy. A color change ensues if the MAb binds its target. Another MAb inactivates the parts of the immune response that reject transplanted tissue. It is being developed as a new immunosuppressant drug.

MAbs can detect cancer earlier than other methods can. The MAb is attached to a fluorescent dye and injected into a patient or applied to a sample of tissue or body fluid. If the MAb binds its target—an antigen found mostly or only on cancer cells—the fluorescence is detected with a scanning technology or fluorescence microscope. MAbs linked to radioactive isotopes or to drugs can be used in a similar fashion to ferry treatment to cancer cells.

Boosting Cellular Immunity— Harnessing Cytokines

As coordinators of immunity, cytokines are used to treat a variety of conditions. However, it has been difficult to develop these body chemicals into drugs for several reasons. They cause side effects, remain active only for short periods, and must be delivered precisely where they are needed.

Interferon (IF) was the first cytokine to be tested on a large scale. When researchers discovered it in the 1950s, IF was erroneously hailed as a cure-all wonder drug. Although it did not live up to early expectations, IF is used today to treat a dozen or so conditions, including a few types of cancer, genital warts, and multiple sclerosis.

Interleukin-2 (IL-2) is administered intravenously to treat kidney cancer recurrence. In another approach, IL-2 is applied to T cells removed from a patient's tumor; then the stimulated T cells, along with IL-2, are reinfused into the patient. Much ongoing research is focused on discovering uses for the many other interleukins. Colony stimulating factors, which cause immature white blood cells to mature and differentiate, are used to boost white blood cell supplies in people with suppressed immune systems, such as those with AIDS or individuals receiving cancer chemotherapy.

So logical and promising is immunotherapy that cancer treatment may soon consist of administering combinations of immune system cells and biochemicals, plus standard therapies. Immunotherapy can enable a patient to withstand higher doses of a conventional drug or destroy cancer cells that remain after conventional treatment.

The human immune system has had to continually adapt to new challenges. In the past decade, we've seen several new viral and bacterial illnesses arise, and old ones resurge, often in deadly, drug-resistant forms. Let us hope that, when we conquer AIDS, what we learn about immune system functions will have repercussions in treating other conditions—and in understanding how this complex organ system works.

Key Concepts

Immunotherapy uses immune system components to fight disease. Hybridomas, which are artificial cells that consist of a B cell fused with a cancer cell, produce monoclonal antibodies (MAbs) that can target specific antigens. Cytokines boost immune function and destroy cancer cells.

summary

1. The cells and biochemicals of the immune system distinguish self from nonself, protecting the body against infections and cancer.

2. Genetically encoded cell surface molecules determine blood types. A blood incompatibility occurs if a blood recipient manufactures **antibodies** against antigens on donor blood. Blood type systems include ABO and Rh.

3. The **HLA** genes are closely linked on chromosome 6 and are highly polymorphic. They encode cell surface antigens that present foreign antigens to the immune system. Identifying combinations of HLA alleles is useful in tissue typing, establishing identity, and estimating disease risk.

4. Immune system cells include **B cells, T cells, macrophages,** and **mast cells.** Biochemicals include antibodies, **cytokines,** and allergy mediators. An infectious agent, encountered again, triggers an immune response that was initiated during the first encounter.

5. The **humoral immune response** begins when macrophages display foreign antigens near HLA antigens. This activates **helper T cells,** which activate B cells. The B cells, in turn, mature into **plasma cells** and secrete specific antibodies. Some B cells also become **memory cells.**

6. An antibody is Y-shaped and made up of four polypeptide chains, two **heavy** and two **light.** Each antibody molecule has regions of **constant** amino acid sequence and regions of **variable** sequence.

7. The tips of the Y of each subunit form **antigen binding sites,** which include the more specific **idiotypes** that bind foreign antigens.

8. Antibodies bind antigens to form immune complexes, which are large enough for other immune system components to detect and destroy. Antibody genes are rearranged during early B cell development, which provides instructions to produce a great variety of antibodies.

9. T cells carry out the **cellular immune response.** Their precursors, thymocytes, are "educated" in the thymus to recognize self. Helper T cells secrete cytokines that activate other T cells and B cells. A helper T cell's **CD4 antigen** binds macrophages that present foreign antigens. **Cytotoxic T cells** release biochemicals that bore into bacteria and kill them and also destroy body cells covered with viruses.

10. Mutations in antibody or cytokine genes, or in genes encoding **T cell receptors,** cause inherited immune deficiencies. **Severe combined immune deficiencies** affect both branches of the immune system.

11. HIV binds to the co-receptors CD4 and CCR5 on macrophages, then takes over the cell but does not kill it. As HIV replicates, it mutates and eventually infects helper T cells, which the viruses kill. Falling CD4 helper T cell numbers allow opportunistic infections and cancers to occur. People who cannot produce a complete CCR5 protein are resistant to HIV infection.

12. In an **autoimmune disease,** the body manufactures **autoantibodies** against its own cells. Autoimmunity may result from a virus that incorporates and displays a self antigen, from bacteria or cancer cells that have antigens that resemble self antigens, from uneducated T cells, or from lingering fetal cells.

13. In allergies, allergens stimulate IgE antibodies to bind to mast cells, which causes them to release allergy mediators. Genes that control IgE production or IgE receptors may predispose individuals to develop allergies.

14. Transplant types include **autografts** (within oneself), **isografts** (between identical twins), **allografts** (within a species), and **xenografts** (between species). A **tissue rejection reaction** occurs if donor tissue is too unlike recipient tissue. Measures to reduce rejection include stripping donor tissue of antigens, using immunosuppressant drugs, and matching donor to recipient. **Cell implants** are smaller than transplants but may be more effective.

15. **Immunotherapy** enhances or redirects immune function. **Monoclonal antibodies** are useful in diagnosing and treating some diseases because of their abundance and specificity. To create MAbs, individual activated B cells are fused with cancer cells to form **hybridomas.** Cytokines are used to treat various conditions.

review questions

1. What are three basic characteristics of the immune system?

2. What is the physical basis of a blood type? of blood incompatibility?

3. How is the great variability of HLA types similar to the diversity of the antibody response?

4. List the cells and biochemicals that provide the humoral and cellular immune responses.

5. What roles do macrophages and mast cells play in immunity?

6. What part do antibodies play in allergic reactions and in autoimmune disorders?

7. A person is exposed for the first time to Coxsackie virus and develops a painful sore throat. How is the immune system alerted to the exposure to the virus? When the person encounters the virus again, why doesn't she develop symptoms?

8. Describe three manipulations to make a transplant more likely to succeed.

9. List three potential ways to increase the supply of donor tissues.

10. How do each of the following illnesses disturb immunity?

   a. graft-versus-host disease

   b. ADA deficiency

   c. rheumatoid arthritis

   d. AIDS

   e. hayfever

11. Why is a deficiency of T cells more dangerous than a deficiency of B cells?

12. What do a plasma cell and a memory cell descended from the same B cell have in common, and how do they differ?

13. Why is a polyclonal antibody response valuable in the body but a monoclonal antibody valuable as a diagnostic tool?

applied questions

1. A man is flown to an emergency room of a major medical center, near death after massive blood loss in a car accident. There isn't time to match blood types, so the physician orders type O negative blood. Why did she order this type of blood?

2. Rasmussen's encephalitis is a rare and severe form of epilepsy that causes children to have one hundred or more seizures a day. Affected children have antibodies that attack brain cell receptors that normally receive nervous system biochemicals. Is this condition an inherited immune deficiency, an acquired immune deficiency, an autoimmune disorder, or an allergy?

3. In the summer of 1995, baseball legend Mickey Mantle was dying of aggressive and widespread cancer. He received a liver transplant, even though the surgeons realized during the operation that the cancer would soon invade the new liver. Many people objected to using a donor liver for someone who could not benefit from it. However, before he died, Mickey Mantle made several public pleas for people to donate organs; because of this, many organs became available. Do you think that Mickey Mantle should have received the liver?

4. State whether each of the following is an autograft, an isograft, an allograft, or a xenograft.

    a. Two parents each donate part of a lung to increase the respiratory capacity of their child, who has cystic fibrosis.

    b. A woman with infertility receives an ovary transplant from her sister, who is an identical twin. (This is the only way this particular transplant works.)

    c. A man receives a heart valve from a pig.

    d. A woman who has had a breast removed has a new breast reconstructed using fatty tissue from her thigh.

5. Robin has been in day care since the age of six weeks and has had many mild childhood illnesses. Aliki has stayed home with a parent since birth. When Robin and Aliki begin kindergarten, who would you expect to miss fewer days due to illness? Cite a reason for your answer.

6. Explain two ways that scientists can genetically alter a pig's cells so that a human body is more likely to accept a xenograft of its tissues.

7. The HLA profile of blood found at a murder scene is different from that of the victim but matches that of a suspect. Does the match prove that the suspect is guilty? Why or why not?

8. A man and woman are planning to have their first child, but they are concerned because they think that they have an Rh incompatibility. He is Rh^- and she is Rh^+. Will there be a problem? Why or why not?

9. A young woman has aplastic anemia, and she will soon die as her lymphocyte levels drop sharply. What type of cytokine might help her?

10. A couple conceived a child so that she could donate bone marrow to her teenage sister, who had leukemia. The little girl was unharmed and saved her sister's life. The little girl is a very cherished child, but do you think that her intentional conception as a tissue donor was ethical? Why or why not?

11. T cells "learn" to distinguish self from nonself during prenatal development. How could this learning process be altered to enable a person to accept a transplant?

12. In Robin Cook's novel *Chromosome Six*, a geneticist places a portion of human chromosome six into fertilized ova from bonobos (a primate that looks like a chimp). The bonobos that result are used to provide organs for transplant into specific individuals. Explain how this technique would work.

suggested readings

Allan, Jonathan S. January 1996. Xenotransplantation at a crossroads: Prevention versus progress. *Nature Medicine,* vol. 2. Can baboons safely provide organs for transplant into humans?

Bach, F. H. et al. February 1998. Uncertainty in xenotransplantation: individual benefit versus collective risk. *Nature Medicine,* vol. 4. The risks may outweigh potential benefits of transplanting pig parts.

Balter, Michael. February 6, 1998. Virus from 1959 sample marks early years of HIV. *Science,* vol. 279. An old blood plasma sample from Africa pushes the date of the debut of AIDS back to 1959.

Davies, Kevin. June 9, 1995. Allergy by mutation. *Nature,* vol. 369. A gene encoding part of an IgE receptor may cause allergies.

Effros, Rita B. May 1998. Replicative senescence in the immune system: impact of the Hayflick Unit on T-cell function in the elderly. *The American Journal of Human Genetics.* Declining immunity with age may reflect a stopped mitotic clock in T-cells

Gage, Fred. April 30, 1998. Cell therapy. *Nature,* vol. 392 supp. Cell implants may replace organ transplants.

Geha, Raif S., and Fred S. Rosen. April 7, 1994. The genetic basis of immunoglobulin-class switching. *The New England Journal of Medicine,* vol. 330. Two boys prone to severe, persistent infection had too much of one antibody type and none of the others because they were missing a T cell antigen.

Gorman, Christine. February 12, 1996. Battling the AIDS virus. *Time.* A look at how people are living with HIV.

Hull, Jon D. September 5, 1994. A daughter's last gift. *Time.* A father lives with his daughter's heart beating inside him.

Lewis, Ricki. June 15, 1997. New directions in research on blood substitutes. *Genetic Engineering News.* Blocking red blood cell surfaces creates a universal blood type.

Lewis, Ricki. September 29, 1997. Human embryonic stem cells debut to lack of fanfare. *The Scientist.* We may one day be able to grow universal human tissues in the laboratory.

Morell, Virginia. August 11, 1995. Zeroing in on how hormones affect the immune system. *Science,* vol. 269. A woman's immune system is much stronger than a man's, for reproductive reasons.

Negrier, Sylvie et al. April 30, 1998. Recombinant human interleukin-2, recombinant human interferon alfa-2a, or both in metastatic renal-cell carcinoma. *The New England Journal of Medicine,* vol. 338.

Nelson, J. Lee. April 23, 1998. Microchimerism and auto-immune disease. *The New England Journal of Medicine,* vol. 338. Fetal cells remaining in a woman's body may cause illness that resembles an autoimmune attack.

O'Brien, Stephen J. September 1997. In search of AIDS-resistance genes. *Scientific American.* A mutation protects against AIDS.

Platt, Jeffrey L. April 30, 1998. New directions for organ transplantation. *Nature,* vol. 392 suppl. Researchers are finding solutions to the problems inherent in xenotransplantation.

Sachs, David H. September 1997. Xenografts, cloning and the immune system. *Nature Medicine,* vol. 3. Cloned adrenal cells from cows save immunodeficient mice, providing a model system to study xenotransplantation.

Tyndall, Alan and Alois Gratwohl. April 1998. Microchimerism: Friend or foe? *Nature Medicine,* vol. 4. Is scleroderma an autoimmune disorder or rejection of fetal cells?

chapter

Genetics of Cancer

Cancer as a Genetic Disorder

There probably wasn't much comedienne Gilda Radner could have done to prevent the ovarian cancer that killed her in 1989. However, had she connected her persistent feelings of malaise, fatigue, and abdominal bloating to the fact that an aunt, a cousin, and a grandmother had died from ovarian cancer, her doctors might have known to order the blood test and ultrasound scan that would have caught the cancer at an early, treatable stage. With such a strong family history, Gilda's risk for developing cancer of the ovary was not the general population risk of 1 in 70, but possibly as high as 1 in 2 (figure 16.1).

Since Gilda's death, geneticists have made great progress in identifying the genes that cause some cases of ovarian cancer. Specifically, the two recently discovered genes that predispose to breast cancer, BRCA1 and BRCA2, also greatly increase the risk of developing ovarian cancer.

Searches for cancer-causing genes begin with families that have many young members with the same type of cancer. Researchers then identify parts of the genome that the affected individuals share. This may be a chromosomal aberration or a DNA sequence unique to these people. Next, the researchers study specific genes in the region that can affect cell cycle control. Thanks to such studies, people with strong family histories of breast or ovarian cancer can undergo genetic tests that may diagnose cancers in earlier, more treatable stages. Such a test might have saved Gilda Radner's life.

Forty percent of us will develop cancer, some of us more than once. Between publication of the first and second editions of this text, the author had, and overcame, cancer. A million new cases of cancer will be diagnosed in the United States this year, and 10 million people are being treated for some form of the illness right now.

Cancer is actually a large collection of illnesses that have one trait in common: a loss of cell cycle control. Basic research in cell biology and biochemistry, as well as the human genome project, are revealing the genetic causes of cancer. This new knowledge is changing the way we diagnose and treat cancer.

figure 16.1

Gilda Radner was an original member of the *Saturday Night Live* comedy ensemble. For three years she went from doctor to doctor, complaining of sudden and prolonged fatigue and vague abdominal pain. Gilda and her doctors didn't know until it was too late that she had a strong family history of ovarian cancer. Here she is pictured with husband Gene Wilder in happier times. Wilder established the Gilda Radner Ovarian Cancer Registry after her death to help other women avoid her fate by recognizing symptoms early enough to get treatment.

Cancer—A Loss of Cell Cycle Control

Cancer begins with a single abnormal cell that divides to produce others like itself. These cells may either grow into a mass called a cancerous or **malignant tumor** or travel in the bloodstream. Cancer cells probably arise in everyone, because mitosis occurs so frequently that an occasional cell escapes the mechanisms that normally control the process. The immune system probably destroys most cancer cells.

Cancer is a consequence of disruption of the cell cycle (chapter 2). The timing, rate, and number of mitoses depend on protein growth factors and signaling molecules from outside the cell, and transcription factors from within. Because these biochemicals are under genetic control, so is the cell cycle perturbation that is cancer. Defects in DNA repair also cause cancer.

Control of telomere length is another function whose loss may contribute to causing cancer. Recall from chapter 2 that telomeres, or chromosome tips, protect chromosomes from breaking. Human telomeres consist of the DNA sequence TTAGGG repeated thousands of times. The repeats are normally lost as a cell matures, at the rate of about 15 to 40 nucleotides per cell division. The more specialized a cell, the shorter its telomeres. The chromosomes in skin, nerve, and muscle cells, for example, have short telomeres. Chromosomes in a sperm cell or oocyte, however, have long telomeres. This makes sense—as the precursors of a new life, gametes must retain the capacity to divide many times.

Gametes are able to keep their telomeres long thanks to an enzyme called **telomerase.** Telomerase is a complex of RNA and protein. Part of the RNA portion of telomerase—the sequence AAUCCC—serves as a template for the 6 DNA base repeat that builds telomeres (figure 16.2). Telomerase moves down a chromosome tip like a zipper, adding six "teeth" at a time. Telomerase adds telomere material to gametes, keeping their cellular clocks from running down.

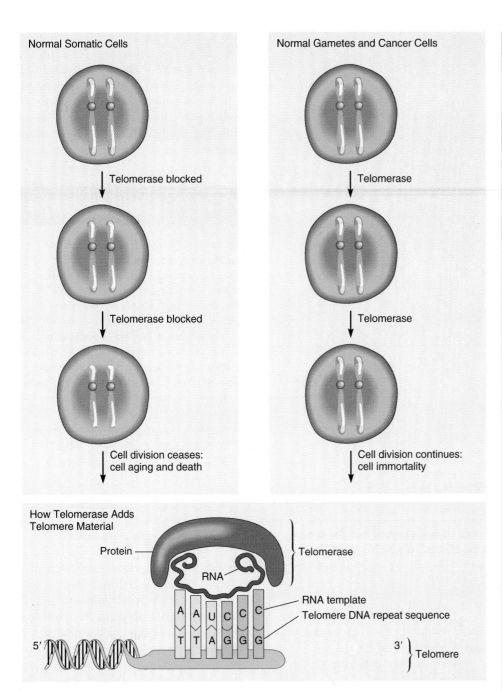

Normal Somatic Cells

Telomerase blocked

Telomerase blocked

Cell division ceases:
cell aging and death

Normal Gametes and Cancer Cells

Telomerase

Telomerase

Cell division continues:
cell immortality

How Telomerase Adds
Telomere Material

Protein

RNA

Telomerase

RNA template
Telomere DNA repeat sequence

5′

3′ } Telomere

figure 16.2

In normal somatic cells, telomeres shorten slightly with each cell division. When they shorten to a certain critical length, the cell stops dividing. In gametes and cancer cells, in contrast, activated telomerase keeps adding DNA to telomeres, continually resetting the cellular clock. The bottom section shows how a chromosome's ends keep extending—telomerase serves as a template and an enzyme.

In normal, specialized cells, telomerase is turned off, and as telomeres are methodically cut down to size, the cell stops dividing. In cancer cells, telomerase is turned back on. Telomeres are extended, and release the normal brake on rapid cell division. A tumor forms, grows, and spreads. The longer the telomeres in cancer cells, usually the more advanced the disease. However, turning on telomerase production in a cell is not sufficient to cause cancer. Still future cancer treatments may focus on inhibiting telomerase.

It took many years for scientists to view cancer as a genetic phenomenon. When President Richard Nixon declared a "war on cancer" in 1971, the targets were radiation, viruses, and chemicals. These agents are still implicated in cancer causation, but today we know that they do so by interfering with the precise genetic controls of cell division. One noted cancer researcher wrote, "A few years ago the question was whether there are genetic changes in cancer cells. Now you find a huge number of DNA changes. In cancer, the genome is shot to hell."

Researchers first discovered genes that could cause cancer in 1976, but we had indirect genetic hints earlier. For example, most substances known to be **carcinogens** (causing cancer) also proved to be **mutagens** (damaging DNA) when placed on cells growing in culture. Was the genetic change these chemicals promoted responsible for the cancer phenotype? A second line of evidence came from families in which colon or breast cancer was so prevalent that it could have been inherited as a Mendelian trait.

Inherited versus Sporadic Cancer

A cancer may result from faulty genes, but not follow Mendelian ratios or even "run in families." Three factors help explain the complexity of the role genes play in causing cancer:

1. Cancer may develop only after several genes mutate.

2. A gene may confer a cancer susceptibility that is only realized in the presence of an environmental trigger, such as exposure to cigarette smoke.

3. Cancer-causing mutations may be present in every cell of the body, or only in affected somatic cells.

A cancer is isolated, or sporadic, if the causative mutation occurs only in cells of the affected tissue. Such a **somatic mutation** might be a single, dominant mutation, or two recessive mutations. The cell harboring the mutation loses control of its cell cycle, divides continuously, and forms a tumor. Susceptibility to develop a sporadic cancer is *not* passed on to future

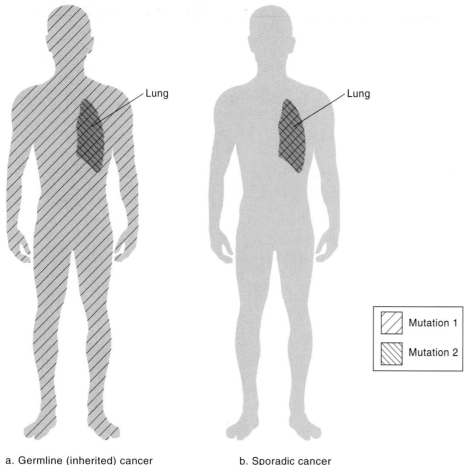

a. Germline (inherited) cancer   b. Sporadic cancer

Mutation 1
Mutation 2

figure 16.3

A germline cancer (also called inherited or familial) occurs when every cell has one cancer-susceptibility gene, and a second mutation occurs in the affected somatic tissue (a). This type of predisposition to cancer is transmitted as a Mendelian trait. A sporadic cancer (b) forms when two mutations occur in somatic cells.

generations because the gametes do not carry the mutant allele.

In contrast is a germline, or inherited, cancer susceptibility, which *is* passed to future generations. A person inherits a susceptibility gene that is present in every cell. This is called a **constitutional mutation,** because it is part of the individual's genetic makeup. Cancer develops when a second mutation occurs in somatic tissue. The cancer site in the body is the site of this second mutation (figure 16.3). Constitutional mutations may explain why some heavy smokers develop lung cancer, but many do not. The unlucky ones may have inherited a susceptibility allele. Years of bathing lung tissue in carcinogens eventually triggers a mutation in a lung cell, giving it a proliferative advantage. Without the susceptibility

gene, it would take two such somatic mutations to trigger the cancer.

Some familial cancers are so likely to occur that they appear in Mendelian ratios. This is the case for the DNA repair disorders discussed in chapter 8—Bloom syndrome, Fanconi anemia, ataxia telangiectasis, and xeroderma pigmentosum. The inherited DNA repair defect is so great that exposures to carcinogens in the environment are very likely to cause cancer. The tendency of sun exposure to cause skin cancer in a child with xeroderma pigmentosum is a good example of an environmental carcinogen triggering cancer in a highly susceptible individual.

Two types of genes that can cause cancer are oncogenes and tumor suppressor genes. **Oncogenes** activate genes that promote cell division, and **tumor suppressor**

genes inactivate or remove constraints on cell division. An oncogene is dominant and a tumor suppressor (sometimes called a recessive oncogene) is recessive. Oncogenes and tumor suppressors can contribute to causing the same cancer. We will look at these types of cancer genes later in the chapter.

Key Concepts

Cancer is a genetic disease, but it is not usually inherited as a Mendelian trait. Cancer is caused by a loss of cell division control. Implicated genes include those encoding growth factors, transcription factors, and telomerase.

Several mutations may contribute to development of a cancer. The genetic changes usually occur in somatic cells. Cancer may develop when an environmental trigger causes mutations in a somatic cell or when a somatic mutation compounds an inherited susceptibility. Oncogenes activate genes that promote cell division, and tumor suppressors remove constraints on cell division.

Characteristics of Cancer Cells

Cell division is a rigorously controlled process. Whether a cell divides or stops dividing and whether it expresses the sets of genes that make it specialize as a particular cell type depend upon biochemical signals from surrounding cells. A cancer cell simply stops "listening" to those signals. Mutations that affect any stage of extracellular message reception can catapult a cell toward unrestrained division.

Cancer cells can divide continuously if sufficient nutrients and space are available. This is vividly illustrated by the cervical cancer cells of a woman named Henrietta Lacks, who died in 1951. Her cells persist today as standard cultures in many research laboratories. So vigorously dividing are these "HeLa" cells that when they contaminate cultures of other cells growing in the laboratory because of human error, they soon comprise most of the cells in the culture.

Although cancer cells divide frequently, their mitosis rate is actually relative. Some

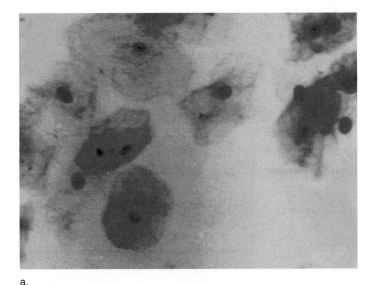
a.

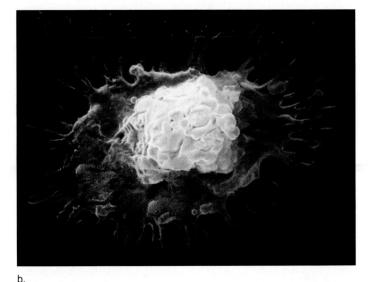
b.

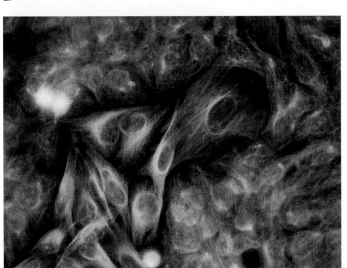
c.

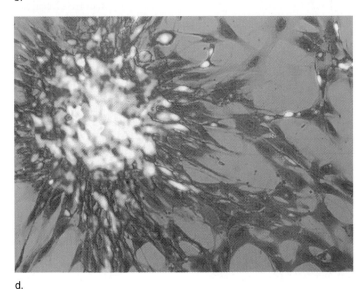
d.

figure 16.4

(a) Normal cells form sheets (×400). (b) Cancer cells become rounded and grow on top of each other (×3,000). (c) The orange cells are a melanoma (skin cancer) that is invading normal skin. Cancer cells, when stained for the presence of gene variants characteristic of cancer cells only, look very different from surrounding healthy tissue. (d) A malignant tumor spreads out, resembling a crab. The name *cancer* means crab.

cells normally divide frequently, and others rarely. Even the fastest-dividing cancer cells, which complete mitosis every 18 to 24 hours, do not divide as often as some normal cells of the human embryo do. It is more accurate to say that a cancer cell divides faster than the normal cell type it arose from, or that it divides at the normal rate but does not "know" when to stop dividing. A tumor may grow faster than surrounding tissue because a greater proportion of its cells are dividing.

Some cancers grow at an alarmingly fast rate. The smallest detectable fast-growing tumor is half a centimeter in diameter and can contain a billion cells. These cells divide at a rate that produces a million or so new cells in an hour. If 99 percent of the tumor's cells are destroyed, a million would still be left to proliferate. Other cancers develop very slowly and may not be noticed for several years. The rate of a tumor's growth is slower at first, because fewer cells divide. By the time the tumor is the size of a pea—when it is usually detectable—billions of cells are actively dividing.

When a cancer cell divides, both daughter cells are also cancerous, since they inherit the altered cell cycle control. Cancer is **heritable** because it is passed from parent cell to daughter cell. A cancer cell is also **transplantable.** If a cancer cell is injected into a healthy animal, the disease spreads as more cancerous cells divide from the original. A cancer cell looks different from a normal cell (figure 16.4). It is rounder because it is less adhesive to surrounding normal cells than usual and because the cell membrane is more fluid and allows different substances to cross it.

A cancer cell is also **dedifferentiated,** which means that it is less specialized than

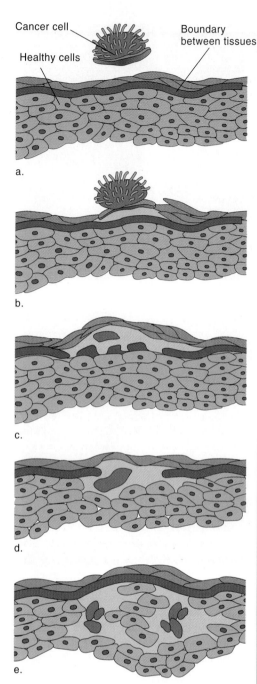

Cancer cell

Healthy cells

Boundary between tissues

a.

b.

c.

d.

e.

figure 16.5

A cancer's spread takes many steps. (a) A cancer cell adheres to normal cells that lie next to a basement membrane separating two sections of tissue. (b) The cancer cell secretes substances that cause the neighboring normal cells to move away, so that the cancer cell can now attach directly to the basement membrane. (c) Next, the cancer cell secretes enzymes that allow it to penetrate the basement membrane and (d) to invade the tissue in the adjacent compartment. (e) The cancer cell continues its migration and divides, starting a new tumor.

the normal cell type from which it arose. A skin cancer cell, for example, is rounder and softer than the flattened, scaly healthy skin cells above it in the epidermis. Cancer cell growth also differs from growth in normal cells. Whereas normal cells placed in a container divide to form a single layer, cancer cells pile up on one another. In an organism, this pileup would produce a tumor. Cancer cells growing all over one another are said to lack **contact inhibition**—they do not stop dividing once they crowd other cells.

Cancer cells have surface structures that enable them to squeeze into any space, a property called **invasiveness.** They anchor themselves to tissue boundaries, called **basement membranes,** where they secrete chemicals that cut paths through healthy tissue (figure 16.5). Unlike a benign (noncancerous) tumor, an invasive malignant tumor grows irregularly, sending tentacles in all directions (figure 16.4). *Cancer,* which means "crab" in Latin, comes from the resemblance of malignant tumors to crabs.

Eventually, unless treatment (drugs, surgery, or radiation) stops them, malignant cells reach the bloodstream or lymphatic vessels, which are conduits to other parts of the body. The traveling cancer cells secrete chemicals in their new locations that stimulate production of tiny blood vessels that bring blood to nourish them. A new way to treat cancer currently being tested halts this blood vessel formation.

Cancer cells may also secrete hormones that encourage their own growth. For example, pancreatic cancer cells secrete the hormone gastrin, which stimulates the tumor's growth. Pancreas cells normally do not produce gastrin. This suggests the frightening possibility that cancer cells can reach into the genome and activate whichever genes promote their growth.

Once cancer cells move to a new body part, the disease has spread, or **metastasized** (from the Greek for "beyond standing still"). After a cancer spreads, it becomes very difficult to treat, because the DNA of secondary tumor cells often mutates, many times causing chromosome aberrations. The metastasized cancer thus becomes a new genetic entity, often resistant to treatments that were effective against most of the original tumor. Table 16.1 summarizes characteristics of cancer cells.

table 16.1

Characteristics of Cancer Cells

Loss of cell cycle control

Heritability

Transplantability

Genetic mutability

Dedifferentiation

Loss of contact inhibition

Ability to induce local blood vessel formation (angiogenesis)

Invasiveness

Ability to spread (metastasis)

Key Concepts

Cancer occurs when cells divide faster or more times than normal. Cancer cells are heritable, transplantable, dedifferentiated, and lack contact inhibition, cutting through basement membranes and metastasizing.

Genes that Cause Cancer

We can view cancer as a normal process—mitosis—that is mistimed or misplaced. Genes are intimately involved in a cancer's genesis.

Oncogenes

Genes that normally control cell division are called **proto-oncogenes.** They are active where and when high rates of cell division are necessary, such as in a wound or in a rapidly growing embryo. When proto-oncogenes turn on at the wrong time or place, they function as oncogenes ("onco" means cancer) and cause cancer. This abnormal activation may be the result of a mutation. A single base change in a proto-oncogene causes bladder cancer, for example. Alternatively, a proto-oncogene may move near a gene that is highly expressed; then it, too, is rapidly or frequently transcribed.

Consider a human proto-oncogene that is normally activated in cells at the site of a wound. The activated oncogene stimulates production of growth factors that prompt mitosis to fill the damaged area in with new cells. When an oncogene is activated at a site other than a wound, it still hikes growth factor production and therefore stimulates mitosis. However, because the site of the action is not damaged tissue, the new cells form a tumor.

Some oncogenes encode transcription factors that are abnormally highly expressed. Recall from chapter 9 that transcription factors bind to specific genes and activate transcription. These activated genes contribute the cancer cell's characteristics.

Increased Expression in a New Location

A proto-oncogene can be transformed into its out-of-control oncogene counterpart when it is placed next to a different gene that boosts its expression. A virus infecting a cell, for example, may insert its genetic material next to a proto-oncogene. When the viral DNA begins to be rapidly transcribed, the proto-oncogene (now an oncogene) next to it is also rapidly transcribed. The heightened activity of the oncogene increases production of its protein product, which switches on the genes that promote inappropriate mitosis. This starts the cascade of cellular changes that leads to cancer.

Proto-oncogenes can also be activated when they are moved from their normal location next to a very active gene that is a normal part of the genome. This can happen when a chromosome is inverted or translocated. For example, a cancer of the parathyroid glands in the neck is associated with an inversion on chromosome 11, which places a proto-oncogene next to a DNA sequence that controls transcription of the parathyroid hormone gene. When the hormone is synthesized in this gland, the oncogene is expressed. The cells divide to form a tumor.

Paradoxically, the immune system contributes to cancer when a translocation or inversion places a proto-oncogene next to an antibody gene. Recall that antibody genes are normally moved into novel combinations when a B cell is stimulated (chapter 15), and they are very actively transcribed. Cancers associated with viral infections, such as liver cancer following

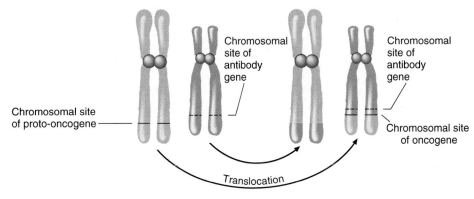

figure 16.6

The cause of Burkitt's lymphoma is translocation of a proto-oncogene on chromosome 8 to chromosome 14, next to a highly expressed antibody gene. Overexpression of the moved proto-oncogene, now an oncogene, starts the biochemical changes of cancer.

hepatitis, may be caused when proto-oncogenes mistakenly are activated along with antibody genes.

In Burkitt's lymphoma, a cancer common in Africa, a large tumor develops from lymph glands near the jaw. People with Burkitt's lymphoma are infected with the Epstein-Barr virus, which prompts specific chromosome movements in B cells to assemble antibodies against the virus. A translocation places a proto-oncogene on chromosome 8 next to an antibody gene on chromosome 14. The oncogene is overexpressed, and cell division rate increases. Tumor cells of Burkitt's lymphoma patients reveal the characteristic chromosome 8 to 14 translocation (figure 16.6).

Fusion Proteins with New Functions

Oncogenes are also activated when a proto-oncogene moves next to another gene, and the gene pair is transcribed and translated together, as if they form one gene. The double gene product, called a **fusion protein,** somehow lifts control of cell division.

The first cancer-causing fusion protein was found in patients with chronic myeloid leukemia. These patients nearly always have a small, unusual chromosome called the Philadelphia chromosome, which consists of the tip of chromosome 9 translocated to chromosome 22. Describing this cancer-chromosome link was quite a feat. At the time, 1960, cytogenetics was a relatively crude art. Reading 16.1 describes this groundbreaking work in cancer genetics.

An oncogene-induced fusion protein also causes acute promyelocytic leukemia. (Leukemias differ by the type of white blood cell affected.) A translocation between chromosome 15 and 17 brings together a gene coding for the retinoic acid receptor (a cell surface receptor) and an oncogene called *myl*. The fusion protein functions as a transcription factor, which is overexpressed to cause the cancer.

The nature of the fusion protein that causes acute promyelocytic leukemia explained an interesting clinical observation—some patients who receive retinoid (vitamin A-based) drugs enjoy spectacular recoveries. Their typically immature, dedifferentiated cancer cells, apparently stuck in an early stage of development where they divide frequently, suddenly differentiate, mature, and then die! Perhaps the fusion protein prevents affected white blood cells from getting enough retinoids to continue their specialization, locking them in an embryoniclike, rapidly dividing state. Supplying extra retinoids allows the cells to continue along their normal developmental pathway.

Tumor Suppressors

Unlike cancers caused by oncogene activation, some cancers result from loss of a gene that normally suppresses tumor formation. The normal state—tumor suppression—results when cells respond to growth-inhibiting signals. Whereas oncogene activation is usually associated with a point mutation, chromosomal translocation or

O n August 13, 1958, two men entered hospitals in Philadelphia with the same symptoms—weeks of unexplained fatigue. G. H., a thirty-three-year-old African American man, and E. K., a forty-one-year-old Caucasian man, each had very high white blood cell counts and were diagnosed with chronic myeloid leukemia (CML). Their blood had too many immature white blood cells, which were crowding out the healthy cells.

Before G. H. and E. K. died of their illnesses, they donated blood samples that fell into the hands of two young researchers at the University of Pennsylvania, assistant professor Peter Nowell and graduate student David Hungerford. Noticing that some of the white blood cells were dividing—a requirement to view chromosomes then—Nowell and Hungerford looked more closely. They knew that some cancer cells have unusual chromosomes. Would they find a specific problem in the cancerous white blood cells of the two men?

Nowell and Hungerford cultured the blood cells, arrested them in mitotic metaphase, and stained and photographed them. But in 1960, cytogenetics was in its infancy; the human chromosome number had been determined to be 46 just four years previously. Geneticists could not discern banded regions; they couldn't even tell similar-sized chromosomes apart. Nevertheless, Nowell and Hungerford studied many cells from G. H. and E. K. and found that each had a "minute chromosome," which they at first thought was a tiny Y chromosome. They published a paper in the *Journal of the National Cancer Institute*, reporting on G. H. and E. K., and seven months later in the journal *Science*, on seven others with CML and what would become known as the Philadelphia (Ph[1]) chromosome (figure 1).

Many scientists and physicians at first doubted that the Philadelphia chromosome

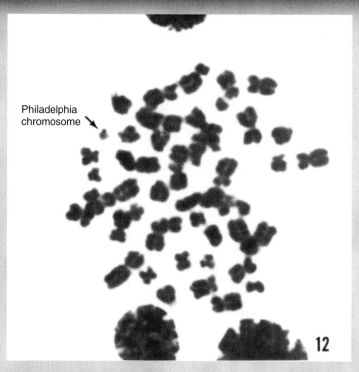

Philadelphia chromosome

12

figure 1

A tiny chromosome that appears consistently in the white blood cells of patients with chronic myeloid leukemia was named the Philadelphia chromosome, in honor of the city where researchers identified it in 1960. Note the poor quality of the chromosome preparation, compared to the intricately banded and DNA-probed chromosomes we view today.

could cause leukemia because the genetic link was a new idea. But as cases accumulated, the association strengthened. Then, with refinements in chromosome banding, important details emerged.

In 1972, Janet Rowley at the University of Chicago used new stains that distinguished AT-rich from GC-rich chromosome regions to tell that Ph[1] is a translocated chromosome: a piece from the tip of chromosome 9 is moved to chromosome 22. In 1983 and 1984, Dutch and U.S. researchers homed in on the two genes juxtaposed in the 9 to 22 translocation. These genes are called ABL (for Abelson oncogene) and BCR (for breakpoint cluster re-gion). When they come together, they form a fusion protein that somehow causes the cell to become cancerous.

Physicians can use the presence or absence of the chromosome abnormality to predict how patients will fare. Those with Ph[1] generally live 3 1/2 to 4 years before entering a "blast crisis," in which the immature white blood cells rapidly overtake other blood cell types. Patients in crisis survive only a few months. The few CML patients with normal chromosomes live only a year, total, from the time of diagnosis. However, interferon is used as a drug to treat CML and can lead to complete recovery.

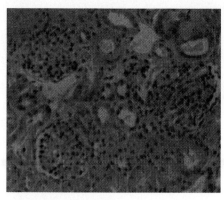

a.

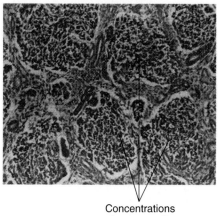

Concentrations
of cancer cells.

b.

figure 16.7

Sections from a normal (*a*) and cancerous kidney (*b*). When genes that halt cell division in the embryonic kidney are deleted, pockets of rapidly dividing, less specialized tissue persist in the kidney after birth. Three or more such genes may contribute to the development of Wilms' tumor.

inversion, and a gain of function, a tumor-suppressor gene mutation that causes cancer is typically a deletion. More rarely, a point mutation can cause loss of function of a tumor suppressor gene.

The childhood kidney cancer Wilms' tumor develops from loss of tumor suppression. When a gene that normally halts mitosis in the rapidly developing kidney tubules in the fetus is absent, a tumor results because mitosis does not cease on schedule. The child's kidney retains pockets of cells dividing as frequently as if they were still in the fetus, forming a tumor (figure 16.7).

Retinoblastoma (RB)

Alfred Knudson proposed the role of tumor-suppressing genes in cancer causation in 1971 as the intriguing story of a rare childhood eye tumor called retinoblastoma unfolded (Reading 16.2). Retinoblastoma has a long history. A 2000 B.C. Mayan stone depicts an affected child with an eye bulging out. In 1597, a Dutch anatomist provided the first clinical description of the eye cancer as a growth "the size of two fists." In 1886, researchers identified inherited cases. At that time, a child would survive the cancer only if the affected eye was removed—a drastic measure. Today, thanks to our understanding of how genes cause RB, children with an affected parent or sibling can be monitored from birth, so that noninvasive treatment can begin as soon as cancer cells appear. Full recovery is close to 100 percent.

About half of the 1 in 20,000 infants who develop RB inherit the disorder. They harbor one mutant allele for the RB gene in each of their cells. Cancer develops in any somatic cell where the second copy of the RB gene mutates. Therefore, inherited retinoblastoma requires two mutations or deletions, one germinal and one somatic. In sporadic (noninherited) cases, cells undergo two somatic mutations in the RB gene. Whether inherited or sporadic, RB usually starts in a cone cell of the retina, the part of the eye that provides color vision.

Many children with RB have deletions in the same region of the long arm of chromosome 13, which led researchers to a cancer-causing gene. In 1987, they found the gene altered in RB and identified its protein product, linking the cancer and control of the cell cycle. The 928-amino-acid-long protein normally binds transcription factors so that they cannot activate genes that carry out mitosis. When the RB gene is mutant or missing, the hold on the transcription factor is released, and cell division ensues.

The RB gene may be implicated in other cancers. For example, children who are successfully treated for retinoblastoma often develop bone cancer in their teens or bladder cancer in adulthood. Mutant RB genes have been found in patients with breast, lung, or prostate cancers, or acute myeloid leukemia, who never had the eye tumors. These other cancers may be expressions of the same genetic defect in different tissues.

p53 Causes Many Cancers

Another single gene that causes a variety of cancers is **p53**. (The unimaginative name comes from the fact that the gene product was initially known as "protein with molecular weight 53,000.") Like other tumor suppressors, p53 encodes a protein transcription factor. This factor intervenes in the cell cycle, stopping it at G_1. At this time, the cell must either repair DNA replication errors or, if it is irreparably damaged, cease dividing. If a cell loses a p53 gene, or if the gene mutates and no longer functions properly, the cell may become cancerous.

About 50 percent of all human cancers may involve an abnormal or missing p53 gene. The precise locations and types of mutations—a transition (purine to purine or pyrimidine to pyrimidine) or transversion (purine to pyrimidine or vice versa)—are different in different cancers. So far, cancers of the colon, breast, bladder, lung, liver, blood, brain, esophagus, and skin show distinct types of p53 mutations.

Unlike the cancer-causing genes discussed so far, which are usually associated with chromosomal rearrangements, the p53 gene seems especially prone to point mutation. The Technology Timeline on Cancer and p53 shows how researchers used the polymerase chain reaction (PCR) to posthumously identify a point mutation in p53 as the cause of former U.S. vice-president Hubert Humphrey's fatal bladder cancer.

Mutational analysis and epidemiological observations reveal that p53 may be the genetic mediator between environmental insults and the development of cancer (figure 16.8). Consider a type of liver cancer prevalent in populations in southern Africa

Retinoblastoma—The First Gene-Cancer Link

Our current understanding of tumor-suppressing genes began with the observations of Alfred Knudson, who developed the two-mutation hypothesis of cancer causation.

Knudson was interested in retinoblastoma (RB), a rare childhood eye cancer. Distinct tumors, representing individual original cancerous cells, develop in the eye (figure 1). Sometimes RB affects one eye, and sometimes both. Knudson examined the medical records of 48 children with RB admitted to M. D. Anderson Hospital in Houston between 1944 and 1969. He recorded the following information for each child:

1. Whether one eye or two were affected

2. How old the child was at the time of diagnosis

3. Whether any other relatives had RB

4. Sex

5. Number of tumors per eye

The fact that RB occurred in boys and girls told Knudson that any genetic control was autosomal. Pooling data from families with more than one case of RB revealed that approximately 50 percent of the children of an affected parent were also affected, suggesting dominant inheritance. Knudson also noted that in some families,

a child with two affected eyes would have an affected grandparent, but both parents had healthy eyes. A picture of autosomal dominant inheritance with incomplete penetrance began to emerge.

Knudson, however, proposed a different explanation. He hypothesized that an initial, inherited recessive mutation had to be followed by a second, somatic mutation in the eye to trigger tumor formation. Occasionally this second mutation would not occur, and this would explain the unaffected parents nestled between two affected generations.

Knudson's two-mutation hypothesis explained another observation gleaned from his search of the medical records. Children with tumors in both eyes become affected much earlier than children with tumors in only one eye—generally before the age of five. This would make sense if a hereditary, bilateral (two-eye) form of RB requires a germinal mutation followed by a somatic mutation, but a nonhereditary, unilateral (one-eye) form results from two somatic mutations in the same gene in the same cell. In other words, in the inherited form of RB, a child is already born halfway on the road to tumor development—one somatic mutation in the eye is all that is needed. The unilateral, noninherited form appears later in childhood because it takes longer for the required two somatic mutations to occur in the same cell.

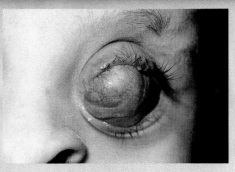

figure 1

In inherited retinoblastoma, all of the person's cells are heterozygous for a mutation in the RB gene. A second mutation, occurring in cone cells in the retina in the original unmutated allele, releases controls on mitosis, and a tumor develops.

Next, Knudson used a mathematical expression called a Poisson distribution to estimate the number of events required to account for a certain pattern of observations. He found that the average number of tumors per eye—three—was consistent with a two-causative-event mechanism, according to the equation.

Although it would be another 15 years before researchers identified the RB gene on chromosome 13, Knudson's insights paved the way for that particular discovery and for recognition of the widespread action of tumor suppressors in general.

and Qidong, China. These two groups have in common exposure to the hepatitis B virus and to a food contaminant called aflatoxin B1. Most of the people with the liver cancer have a mutation in the p53 gene, substituting a T for a G in the same codon. Could the food toxin, hepatitis virus, or both cause the mutation?

Similarly, in a type of lung cancer that develops in 1 in 8 heavy smokers, the same T to G base substitution occurs in the p53 gene in different patients. It also occurs in cells growing in culture exposed to benzo(a)pyrene, a component of cigarette smoke. The carcinogen 4-aminobiphenyl, found in black tobacco, mutates the p53

gene in a different way, causing a type of bladder cancer.

In the majority of p53-related cancers, mutations occur only in somatic cells. However, about 100 families worldwide suffer from a germline condition called the Li-Fraumeni family cancer syndrome. Those inheriting a mutation

Cancer and p53

The importance of using gene amplification to detect a cancer-causing mutation is not to clarify recent medical history, but to diagnose these cancers today at an earlier, more treatable stage. The Hubert Humphrey cancer timeline provides a peek at how cancer diagnosis will become increasingly molecular—and less invasive.

1967 Hubert Humphrey goes to physician, reporting blood in urine. Biopsy of bladder tissue is inconclusive; doctors disagree on whether tissue is malignant.

1973 Another biopsy diagnosed as "borderline malignancy."

1976 Infiltrating cancer diagnosed; bulk of tumor removed surgically.

1978 Humphrey dies of bladder cancer.

1994 PCR amplification of p53 gene in 1967 biopsy and 1976 surgical specimens reveal same single-base p53 mutation, not present in noncancerous tissue sampled at the same times.

Hubert H. Humphrey

in the p53 gene have a very high risk of developing cancer—50 percent by age 30, and 90 percent by age 70. A somatic mutation in the affected tissue is necessary for cancer to develop, as is true for inherited retinoblastoma.

Li-Fraumeni patients develop cancers of the breast, brain, blood, adrenal glands, or soft solid tissues, such as muscle or connective tissue. The cancers tend to arise earlier than they do in people who do not have the syndrome. Often the first sign is multiple tumors in one or several organs. National Cancer Institute researchers Fred Li and Joseph Fraumeni first described the syndrome in 1969, but it wasn't linked to the p53 gene until 1990. Now that the genetic cause of the syndrome is clear, family members can be tested before cancer symptoms appear, when treatment is more likely to succeed.

Table 16.2 lists some oncogenes and tumor-suppressor genes.

Key Concepts

Proto-oncogenes normally control the cell cycle. They can become oncogenes when they mutate, when they move next to a gene where they are highly expressed, or when they are transcribed and translated along with another gene, resulting in a fusion protein that triggers cancer.

Mutations in tumor-suppressing genes that cause cancer are deletions, usually causing loss of gene function. This loss enables a cell to ignore extracellular constraints on cell division. The mutation that causes retinoblastoma interferes with a protein's normal function of suppressing cell division. The RB and p53 genes both may cause a variety of cancer types, suggesting that genetically controlled lifting of tumor suppression may be a common factor in many cancers. The p53 gene is prone to specific point mutations in different cancer types. It may serve as a genetic mediator between environmental insults and cancer.

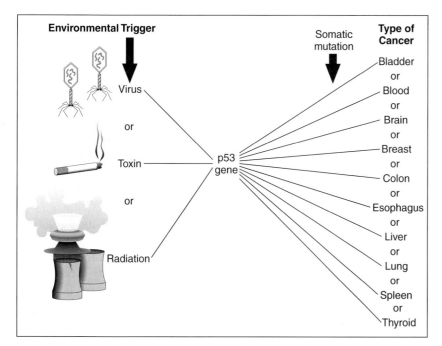

figure 16.8

The environment triggers genetic changes that lead to cancer. p53 may act as the genetic mediator.

table 16.2

Cancer Genes

Oncogenes	Cancer Location/Type	Mechanism
Gene		
myc genes	Blood, breast, lung, neurons, stomach	Alters transcription factor
PDGF	Brain	Alters growth factors or growth factor receptors
RET	Thyroid	Alters growth factors or growth factor receptors
erb-B	Brain, breast	Alters growth factors or growth factor receptors
HER-2/neu	Breast, ovarian, salivary glands	Alters growth factors or growth factor receptors
ras genes	Blood, lung, colon, ovary, pancreas	Affects signal transduction
Bcl-2	Blood	Releases brake on apoptosis
PRAD1	Breast, head and neck	Disrupts cell cycle protein (cyclin)
Tumor Suppressors		
MTS1	Many sites	Releases brake on cell cycle
RB	Eye, bone, breast, lung, bladder	Releases brake on cell cycle
WT1	Kidney	Releases brake on cell cycle
p53	Many sites	Disrupts p53 protein, which normally stops the cell cycle and promotes apoptosis
DPC4	Pancreas	Affects signal transduction
NF1	Peripheral nerves	Disrupts inhibition of wild type *ras,* which stimulates cell division
APC	Colon, stomach	Makes nearby DNA more susceptible to replication errors
BRCA1, BRCA2	Breast, ovary, prostate	Unknown
hMSH2, hMLH1, hPMS1, hPMS2	Colon, uterus, ovary	Disrupts DNA mismatch repair

A Series of Genetic Changes Causes Some Cancers

A two-step cancer, such as retinoblastoma, may be unusually simple. Some cancers are the culmination of a series of genetic changes. The requirement for mutations in more than one gene may explain why most cancers do not follow Mendel's laws, particularly when some of the genes are linked on the same chromosome.

Figuring out the sequence of genetic changes that lead to a particular cancer is like solving a mystery. To decipher the steps, researchers examine the genetic material of tumor cells from people in various stages of the same type of cancer. This approach is based on logic—the longer the tumor has existed, the more genetic changes have accumulated. A mutation present in all stages acts early in carcinogenesis, whereas a mutation seen only in the tumor cells of people near the end of the battle functions late in the process. By hypothesizing how each mutation contributes to cancer, researchers can identify potential new points of treatment intervention. Following is a closer look at two types of cancer that reflect a series of genetic changes.

A Rapidly Growing Brain Tumor

Astrocytomas are the most common types of brain tumors. They occur when cells called astrocytes divide uncontrollably, forming a tumor. (Astrocytes are a type of nervous system supportive cell, collectively called glia.) These tumors grow—and kill—quickly, unless they are removed at an early stage. The man whose brain is shown in figure 16.9 died just three months after reporting his first symptom to his physician—twitching in an eye.

During those three months, a series of single-gene and chromosomal-level changes occurred. An early change was loss of both p53 alleles. Researchers knew this was an early change on the road to cancer because they had seen it in many early-stage tumor cells, as well as in later ones.

By the time an astrocytoma has grown into a small tumor, another genetic change is apparent—loss of both alleles of several genes on chromosome 9. The missing genes encode interferons, so the loss probably disrupts immune protection against the developing cancer. Two other deleted genes are tumor suppressors.

At least two additional mutations speed the tumor's growth. First, an onco-gene on chromosome 7 is activated, over-expressing a gene that encodes a cell surface receptor for a growth factor. The cancer cells become dotted with too many growth factor receptors, receive too many messages to grow, and respond by racing through the cell cycle even faster. Finally, a drastic but still not understood change takes place—one or even both copies of chromosome 10 are lost. Researchers know that this is a final change, because they see it in all end-stage tumors, but not early ones.

Colon Cancer

Colon (large intestine) cancer does not usually occur in families with the frequency or pattern expected of a single-gene disorder. However, when family members with non-cancerous growths, called polyps, are considered along with those who have colon cancer, a familiar Mendelian pattern emerges. Five percent of cases are inherited. One in 5,000 people in the United States has precancerous colon polyps, a condition called familial adenomatous polyposis (FAP).

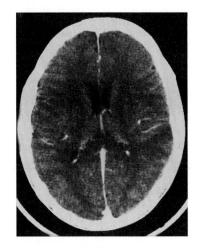

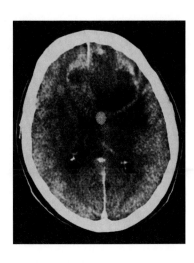

Loss or mutation of both p53 tumor suppressor alleles → Loss of chromosome 9 genes encoding interferons and tumor suppressors → Oncogene activation increases growth signals → Loss of chromosome 10, role unknown

Figure 16.9

A series of genetic changes transforms normal astrocytes, which support nerve cells in the brain, into a rapidly growing cancer.

FAP begins in early childhood with tiny polyps, often numbering in the hundreds, that progress over many years to colon cancer. Connecting FAP to the development of colon cancer enabled researchers to view the stepwise progression of a cancer. Several genes, including both oncogenes and tumor suppressors, take part.

The study of the hereditary nature of some colon cancers began in a genetics classroom at the University of Utah in Salt Lake City in the fall of 1947, when young professor Eldon Gardner stated that he thought cancer might be inherited. A student, Eugene Robertson, excitedly told the class that he knew of a family in which colon cancer affected a grandmother, her three children, and three grandchildren.

Intrigued, Gardner delved into the family's records and began interviewing relatives. He eventually found 51 family members and arranged for each to be examined with a colonoscope, a lit instrument passed into the rectum that views the wall of the colon. The colons of 6 of the 51 people were riddled with the gobletlike precancerous growths (figure 16.10), although they had no symptoms. Removal of their colons probably saved their lives.

In the years that followed, researchers identified other families with more than one case of colon polyps. Individuals with only polyps were diagnosed with FAP. If a person with colon polyps had cancer elsewhere, extra teeth, and pigment patches in the eye, the condition was called Gardner syndrome, named for the professor. The

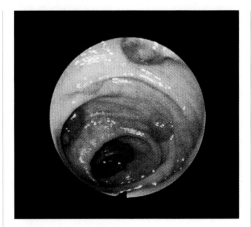

figure 16.10

The inner surface of this colon has a few polyps. Polyps can develop into cancer, so they must be removed.

chromosomal locus was identified in 1985, with the help of an unusual man.

At that time, a forty-two-year-old man entered the Roswell Park Cancer Institute in Buffalo, New York. He had several problems—no gallbladder, an incomplete liver, an abnormal kidney, mental retardation, and Gardner syndrome. To a geneticist, a seemingly unrelated combination of symptoms suggests a chromosomal abnormality affecting several genes. Sure enough, the man's karyotype revealed a small deletion in the long arm of chromosome 5. This was the first piece to the puzzle of colon cancer.

Since 1985, we have learned of other genes contributing to colon cancer, including p53. The genes act at different points,

culminating in cancer. A gene on chromosome 5q, called APC, may start the process. A point mutation that changes a T to an A in the APC gene results in a stretch of eight consecutive A's, which destabilizes replication enzymes. The result is a shift in the reading frame and a shortened protein. A plausible sequence of genetic events that causes FAP appears in figure 16.11, although other sequences are possible.

The immediate benefit of understanding how genes interact to gradually transform a patch of rapidly dividing tissue into an invasive cancer is that we can devise ways to catch the disease early enough to cure it. In the recent past, physicians had to perform an uncomfortable colonoscopy to diagnose colon cancer. Now, they can detect some of the genetic changes associated with colon cancer even earlier just by looking at cells in stool samples. The long-term benefit of knowing the genes, and of knowing the environmental triggers that start the process, is that we will be better prepared to carry out the battle against cancer that Richard Nixon called for in 1971.

Key Concepts

Some cancers may be the culmination of a series of mutations in several genes. We can decipher the sequence by determining which mutations are present in particular stages of a cancer.

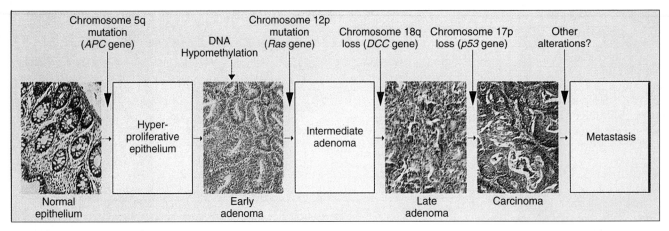

figure 16.11

Several genes contribute to familial adenomatous polyposis colon cancer. Cells lining the colon begin to divide more frequently when the APC gene on chromosome 5q undergoes a point mutation, which causes replication errors that disrupt the reading frame, shortening the protein product. The affected cell proliferates, forming a growth that progresses to an early precancerous stage when DNA loses protective chemical groups. Next, the *Ras* oncogene is activated. Loss of the p53 tumor suppressor gene produces cancer, and other genes may contribute to the cancer's spread. Researchers continue to fill in the gaps in the genetic orchestration of this cancer.

s u m m a r y

1. Cancer is a genetically dictated loss of cell cycle control.

2. Cancer may result from mutations in somatic cells only (sporadic), or from the combination of a **constitutional mutation** conferring cancer susceptibility plus a **somatic mutation** in the affected tissue (germline). Mutations in genes that encode or control transcription factors, growth factors, or telomerase may disrupt the cell cycle sufficiently to cause cancer.

3. A tumor cell divides more frequently or more times than cells surrounding it, has altered surface properties, loses the specializations of the cell type it arose from, and produces daughter cells like itself. A **malignant tumor** infiltrates nearby tissues and can **metastasize** by attaching to basement membranes and secreting enzymes that penetrate tissues and open a route to the bloodstream. From there, a cancer cell can travel and exit, establishing secondary tumors.

4. Cancer is often the result of a series of genetic changes involving activation of **proto-oncogenes** to **oncogenes,** and inactivation of **tumor-suppressing genes.**

5. Oncogenes are genes that normally promote controlled cell growth, but are overexpressed because of a point mutation, placement next to a highly expressed gene, or because they are transcribed and translated with another gene, producing a **fusion protein.**

6. A tumor suppressor is a gene that normally enables a cell to respond to factors that limit its division.

7. Oncogenes and tumor suppressors may cause cancer by altering the activities of transcription factors, which in turn, control expression of other genes. Environmental mutagens can activate oncogenes or disrupt the function of tumor suppressors, causing cancer.

8. A progressive series of genetic changes causes some cancers. Identifying the early changes can help suggest new treatments.

r e v i e w   q u e s t i o n s

1. How would mutations in genes that encode the following proteins lead to cancer?

   a. a transcription factor

   b. the p53 gene

   c. the retinoblastoma gene

   d. the *myl* oncogene

   e. a repair enzyme

   f. the APC protein

2. How can the same cancer be associated with deletions as well as translocations of genetic material?

3. What would be the value of knowing whether a person's cancer is sporadic or inherited?

4. List four characteristics of cancer cells.

5. Cite three reasons why cancer may not follow a Mendelian pattern, but nevertheless involves abnormal gene function.

6. What is inaccurate about the statement that "cancer cells are the fastest dividing cells in the body?"

7. Gilda Radner's ovarian cancer affected epithelial (lining cells) of the organ. This type of cancer has a poor outcome; it spreads rapidly because the affected cells are on the outside of the ovary, suspended in the abdominal cavity, and can contact other cells as the tumor grows. Ovarian cancer can also affect the more centrally located oocytes in the ovary; this type of ovarian cancer is often successfully treated. What other factors might make cancer in one cell type more deadly than cancer in another cell type in the same organ?

8. Three percent of all cancer cells have chromosome rearrangements. What other type of genetic change might be present in a cancer cell?

9. Eighty-five percent of lung cancer cases occur in heavy smokers. How can lung cancer still have a genetic origin?

10. List two differences between oncogenes and tumor suppressors.

applied questions

1. Breast cancer can arise in two ways. An individual can inherit a constitutional susceptibility gene, then undergo a second mutation in a breast cell, or undergo two mutations in a breast cell, one in each copy of a tumor suppressor gene. Cite another type of cancer, discussed in the chapter, that can arise in these two ways.

2. Several biotechnology companies offer tests to detect p53 alleles that confer cancer susceptibility. Cite a limitation of such a test.

3. Humans missing both p53 alleles are unknown. People with p53-related cancers either have a constitutional mutation and a somatic mutation in affected tissue, or two somatic mutations in the tissue. Experiments show that mice missing both copies of their p53 genes die as embryos, with massive brain abnormalities.

   a. Why don't we see people with two missing or mutant p53 alleles in all cells?

   b. Under what circumstances might a human with two mutant p53 alleles be conceived?

4. von Hippel-Lindau disease is an inherited cancer syndrome. The responsible gene lifts control over the transcription of certain genes, which, when overexpressed, cause cancers of the kidney, adrenal glands, or blood vessels. Would the von Hippel-Lindau gene be an oncogene or a tumor suppressor? Cite a reason for your answer.

5. A tumor is removed from a mouse and broken up into cells. Each cell is injected into a different mouse. Although all of the mice used in the experiment are genetically identical and raised in the same environment, the animals develop cancers with different rates of metastasis. Some mice die quickly, some linger, and others recover. What do these results indicate about the characteristics of the cells of the original tumor?

6. Mormon families are often used in genetic studies because they are large and keep meticulous genealogical records. Researchers at Johns Hopkins University School of Medicine are studying a few Mormon families in which prostate cancer seems to follow an autosomal dominant mode of inheritance. What should the researchers do next to identify genes that predispose these families to or cause prostate cancer?

7. Iron foundry workers in Finland and coke oven workers in Poland have high exposures to polycyclic aromatic hydrocarbons, and they tend to develop cancers caused by mutations in the p53 gene. What information would help determine whether the chemical exposure causes the mutation and whether the mutation causes the cancers?

8. A woman who finds a small lump in her breast goes to her physician, who takes a medical and family history. The woman mentions that her father died of brain cancer, a cousin had leukemia, and her older sister was just diagnosed with a soft tumor of the connective tissue. The doctor assures her that the family cancer history doesn't raise the risk that her breast lump is cancerous, because the other cancers were not in the breast. Is the doctor correct?

9. Hereditary nonpolyposis colon cancer is caused by any of four genes, located on chromosomes 2p, 3p, 2q, and 7q. The cancer results from a defect in mismatch DNA repair. How is it possible that this type of cancer can occur in four different ways?

suggested readings

Bodmer, Walter, Tim Bishop, and Peter Karran. March 1994. Genetic steps in colorectal cancer. *Nature Genetics,* vol. 6. Colon cancer is the culmination of many mutational steps.

Cavenee, Webster K., and Raymond L. White. March 1995. The genetic basis of cancer. *Scientific American.* Cancer often takes many genetic steps.

Cheresh, David A. April 1998. Death to a blood vessel, death to a tumor. *Nature Medicine,* vol. 4. Immune system biochemicals can be used as drugs to cut off a tumor's blood supply.

Collins, Francis. January 18, 1996. BRCA1— Lots of mutations, lots of dilemmas. *The New England Journal of Medicine,* vol. 334. Multiple alleles will greatly complicate screening for inherited breast cancer.

Culliton, Barbara J. May 5, 1994. Hubert Humphrey's bladder cancer. *Nature,* vol. 369. Years after the vice-president's death, PCR revealed a single base change in a single gene as the cause of the cancer.

Eeles, Rosalind A. et al. March 1998. Linkage analysis of chromosome 1q markers in 136 prostate cancer families. *The American Journal of Human Genetics,* vol. 62. An example of how researchers hunt for a specific gene.

Ford, D. et al. March 1998. Genetic heterogeneity and penetrance analysis of the BRCA1 and BRCA2 genes in breast cancer families. *The American Journal of Human Genetics,* vol. 62. Phenotypes associated with inherited breast cancer are complex.

Jaroff, Leon. April 1, 1996. The man's cancer. *Time.* Like many cancers, prostate cancer is more treatable if it is detected early.

Kolata, Gina. May 3, 1998. Two drugs eradicate tumors in mice. *The New York Times.* Two new drugs apparently cure cancer in mice—but will they do so in people?

Lewis, Ricki. September 1998. Telomerase tales. *BioScience.* Blocking telomerase may enable cancer cells to specialize.

Milner, Jo. September 1995. DNA damage, p53, and anticancer therapies. *Nature Medicine,* vol. 1. Half of all human cancers implicate a mutant p53 gene.

Plummer, Sarah J., and Graham Casey. February 1996. Are we any closer to genetic testing for common malignancies? *Nature Medicine,* vol. 2. Identifying the genes that cause cancer will make possible earlier detection.

Vogelstein, Bert, and Kenneth Kinzler. September 1997. A "trojan horse" mutation predisposing to colorectal cancer in 6% of Ashkenazi Jews. *Nature Genetics,* vol. 15. A mutation in the APC gene destabilizes replication, leading to cancer.

Wienberg, Robert A. September 1996. How cancer arises. *Scientific American.* Many genes cause cancer.

chapter
seventeen

Genetic Engineering

Humans have worn denim for many centuries; today, it is part of nearly every wardrobe. In modern times, agricultural workers have favored the fabric for its endurance, but in ancient times, denim was reserved for royalty. New techniques for producing indigo, the deep blue-violet dye used in denim, have made the fabric more widely available (fig. 1).

Natural sources of indigo include mollusks of genus *Murex* and fermented leaves of the European woad plant or Asian indigo plant. The 1883 discovery of indigo's chemical structure led to the invention of a synthetic process to produce the dye using coal-tar. That method has dominated the industry, but a technique based on genetic engineering may soon give it some competition.

Microbiologists discovered in 1983 that the common, well-studied bacterium *Escherichia coli* can produce indigo. In enzyme-catalyzed reactions, the bacterium converts glucose to the amino acid tryptophan, which then forms indole, a precursor to indigo. By learning the steps and offshoots of this biochemical pathway, researchers at a biotechnology company have engineered bacteria that suppress the alternative pathways for glucose, allowing them to synthesize much more tryptophan than they normally would. When given genes from another bacterial species, the bacteria take the biochemical pathway all the way to indigo.

The result: bacteria that produce the blue dye of denim jeans from glucose, a simple sugar! The genetic route to indigo production eliminates the need to use hazardous reagents in the synthetic process and does not release toxic by-products. It also does not deplete populations of indigo-producing organisms. Your next pair of jeans may come from genes!

figure 1

E. coli are genetically engineered to produce indigo, the dye used in denim.

Biotechnology

The middle-aged man arrives at the emergency room in the throes of a heart attack, and a doctor gives him an injection of tissue plasminogen activator (tPA). Within minutes, the tPA begins to break apart the blood clots blocking his heart's circulation. This lifesaving protein is naturally found in the human body in tiny amounts. The tPA drug this man receives, although identical to his own version of the biochemical, was manufactured in bacteria.

tPA and a growing list of other "biologic" drugs are all possible because of our knowledge of the chemistry of the gene. The quest to understand how DNA transmits hereditary information began in the 1950s and 1960s. In the 1970s and 1980s, knowledge of the molecular workings of the gene began to be put to practical use in human and veterinary health care, agriculture, food processing, and forensics. Today, altering genes is a part of many fields.

The use or alteration of cells or biological molecules for specific applications is broadly defined as **biotechnology.** The ancient art of fermenting fruit with yeast to produce wine is a biotechnology, as is the use of yeast to make dough rise in baking. Extracting biochemicals directly from organisms for various applications is also biotechnology. Fruit juices, for example, are processed using pectinase, an enzyme that breaks down solids. Lipases are used to manufacture cheeses. Proteases remove stains from dirty jeans, and cellulase makes them appear stonewashed. Reading 17.1 describes how bacteria are genetically altered to produce the indigo dye used in blue jeans.

The biotechnology popularly called **genetic engineering** refers to manipulations of genetic material. This includes altering the DNA of an organism to suppress or enhance the activities of its own genes and combining genetic material of different species, a technique used in **recombinant DNA technology** (on single cells) and **transgenic technology** (on multicellular organisms). Combining DNA from different species is possible because all life uses the same genetic code (figure 17.1). When recombinant bacteria—that is, those carrying "foreign" DNA—divide, they yield many copies, or clones, of that DNA and produce many copies of the protein the foreign DNA specifies.

Recombinant DNA technology was perfected first and was performed on bacteria and then on isolated cells. In the 1980s, genetic engineering of multicellular organisms followed, by altering DNA at the one-cell stage (a gamete or fertilized ovum). The transgenic organisms that develop from the original altered cell carry the genetic change in every cell.

a.

b.

figure 17.1

The genetic code is universal. Recombinant DNA and transgenic technologies are based on the fact that all organisms utilize the same DNA codons to specify the same amino acids. A striking illustration of the universality of the code appears in this transgenic tobacco plant (a) that contains genes from the firefly that specify the "glow" enzyme luciferase. When bathed in a chemical that allows the enzyme to be expressed, the plant glows (b).

Technology TIMELINE

Patenting Life

1790	U.S. patent act is enacted. A patentable invention must be new, useful, and not obvious.
1873	Louis Pasteur is awarded first patent on a life-form, for yeast used in industrial processes.
1930	New plant variants can be patented.
1980	First patent is awarded on a genetically engineered organism, a bacterium given four plasmids (DNA rings) that enable it to metabolize components of crude oil. The plasmids are naturally occurring, but do not all occur naturally in the manipulated bacteria.
1988	First patent is awarded for a transgenic organism, a mouse that manufactures human protein in its milk.
1992	Biotechnology company is awarded a broad patent covering all forms of transgenic cotton. Groups concerned that this will limit the rights of subsistence farmers contest the patent several times.
1996–present	Companies patent partial gene sequences and certain disease-causing genes.

The ability to combine genes from different types of organisms has led to intriguing legal questions—is a recombinant or transgenic organism an invention, deserving of patent protection? By definition, a patentable invention must be new, useful, and not obvious. The Technology Timeline on Patenting Life lists milestones in patenting life-forms. Researchers also patent specific DNA sequences, such as the wild type sequence of the BRCA1 gene, which causes breast cancer. Diagnostic tests can be developed from known gene sequences.

This chapter considers recombinant DNA technology, the transgenic technology it spawned, and gene targeting, which precisely inactivates or alters specific genes. Chapters 18 through 21 explore diverse applications of these biotechnologies.

Recombinant DNA Technology

In February 1975, 140 molecular biologists convened at Asilomar, a seaside conference center on California's Monterey Peninsula, to discuss the safety and implications of a new type of experiment. Investigators had found a simple way to combine the genes of two species and were initially concerned about experiments requiring the use of a cancer-causing virus. Researchers were also concerned about where the field was headed.

The scientists discussed placing restrictions on the sorts of organisms used in recombinant DNA research and explored what could be done to prevent escape of a recombinant organism from the laboratory. The guidelines drawn up at Asilomar outlined measures of "physical containment," such as using specialized hoods and airflow systems that would keep the recombinant organisms inside the laboratory, and "biological containment," such as weakening organisms so that they could not survive outside of the laboratory.

A decade after the Asilomar meeting, many members of the original group reconvened at the meeting site to assess progress in the field. Nearly all agreed on two points: recombinant DNA technology had proven to be safer than most had predicted, and the technology had spread from the research laboratory to industry far faster and in more diverse ways than anyone had imagined. Today, thousands of small companies are devoted to recombinant DNA work and other biotechnologies, and many major chemical and pharmaceutical firms have very active biotechnology programs.

Recombinant DNA-based products have been slow to reach the marketplace because of the high cost of research and the long time it takes to develop any new drug. By 1990, only a dozen drugs produced by recombinant DNA technology had been approved by the Food and Drug Administration (FDA), with 18 others under review. Today, several dozen such drugs are available, and many more are in the pipeline.

Recombinant DNA research initially focused on direct gene products—peptides and proteins with therapeutic actions, such as insulin, growth hormone, and clotting factors. However, the technology can target other biochemicals by affecting the genes that encode enzymes required to synthesize other substances, such as carbohydrates and lipids.

Constructing Recombinant DNA Molecules

Manufacturing recombinant DNA molecules requires using scissorlike biochemicals called **restriction enzymes** to cut a gene from its normal location, insert it into a circular piece of DNA, and then transfer the circle of DNA into cells of another species. Each of the hundreds of types of restriction enzymes cuts DNA at a specific base sequence. Cutting double-stranded DNA generates single-stranded ends that "stick" to each other through complementary base pairing (figure 17.2).

The natural function of restriction enzymes is to protect bacteria by cutting and thereby inactivating the DNA of infecting viruses. Protective methyl (CH_3) chemical groups shield the bacterium's own DNA from its restriction enzymes. Geneticists use restriction enzymes from bacteria to cut DNA at specific base sequences. A restriction enzyme that recognizes a long sequence—7 bases, for example—cuts DNA into a smaller number of larger fragments than a restriction enzyme that recognizes a short sequence, such as 4 bases. This is analogous to a word processing

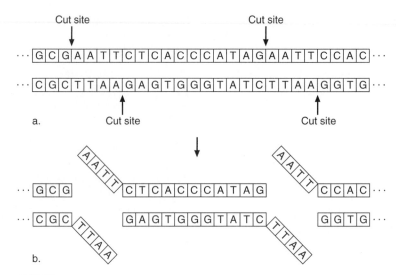

figure 17.2

A restriction enzyme makes "sticky ends" in DNA by cutting it at specific sequences. (a) The enzyme EcoR1 cuts the sequence GAATTC between G and the A. (b) This staggered cutting pattern produces "sticky ends" of sequence AATT. The ends attract through complementary base pairing.

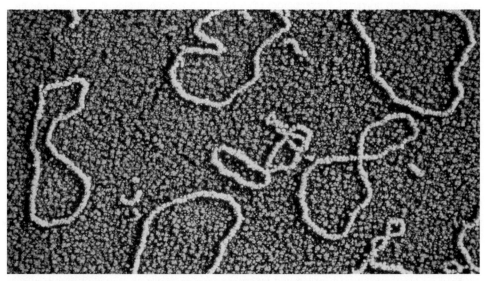

figure 17.3

Plasmids are small circles of DNA found naturally in the cells of some organisms. A plasmid can replicate itself as well as any other DNA inserted into it. For this reason, plasmids make excellent cloning vectors—structures that carry DNA from cells of one species into the cells of another.

search function that will find more sequences of the letters "the" than "their."

Another natural "tool" used in recombinant DNA technology is a **vector.** This structure, usually made of DNA, carries DNA from cells of one species into the cells of another. A vector can be any piece of DNA that an organism's DNA can attach to and then be transferred into the cell of another organism. A commonly used type

of vector is a **plasmid,** which is a small circle of double-stranded DNA found in some bacteria, yeasts, plant cells, and other types of organisms (figure 17.3).

Viruses that infect bacteria, called **bacteriophages,** provide another type of vector. Bacteriophages are manipulated so that they transport genetic material but do not cause disease. Disabled retroviruses (viruses that use RNA as their genetic material) are

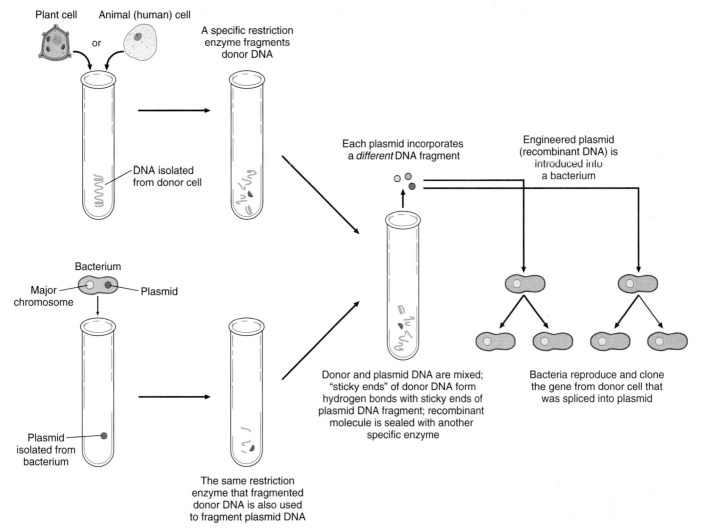

Plant cell   Animal (human) cell

or

A specific restriction enzyme fragments donor DNA

DNA isolated from donor cell

Bacterium
Major chromosome   Plasmid

Plasmid isolated from bacterium

The same restriction enzyme that fragmented donor DNA is also used to fragment plasmid DNA

Each plasmid incorporates a *different* DNA fragment

Engineered plasmid (recombinant DNA) is introduced into a bacterium

Donor and plasmid DNA are mixed; "sticky ends" of donor DNA form hydrogen bonds with sticky ends of plasmid DNA fragment; recombinant molecule is sealed with another specific enzyme

Bacteria reproduce and clone the gene from donor cell that was spliced into plasmid

figure 17.4

To construct a recombinant DNA molecule, DNA isolated from a donor cell and a plasmid are cut with the same restriction enzyme and mixed. Some of the sticky ends from the donor DNA hydrogen bond with the sticky ends of the plasmid DNA, forming recombinant DNA molecules. When such an engineered plasmid is introduced into a bacterium, it is mass produced as the bacterium divides.

used as vectors, too. Chapter 21 discusses larger vectors that can hold portions of human chromosomes.

The process of creating a recombinant DNA molecule begins when a restriction enzyme cuts DNA isolated from a donor cell (figure 17.4). An enzyme is used that cuts DNA at sequences known to bracket the gene of interest. The enzyme leaves single-stranded ends dangling from the cut DNA, each bearing a characteristic base sequence. Next, a plasmid is isolated and cut with the same restriction enzyme used to cut the donor DNA. Because the same restriction enzyme cuts both the donor DNA and the plasmid DNA, the same single-stranded base sequences extend from the

cut ends of each. When the plasmid and the donor DNA are mixed, the single-stranded "sticky ends" of some plasmids base pair with the sticky ends of the donor DNA. The result—a recombinant DNA molecule, such as a plasmid carrying the human insulin gene. The plasmid and its stowaway human gene can now be transferred into a cell from an individual of another species.

First, however, the recombinant molecules must be separated from molecules consisting of just donor DNA or just plasmid DNA. To do this, the experimenter designs the process so that the plasmid contains two genes that each enable a cell to grow in the presence of a different antibiotic

drug. When the piece of DNA to be cloned (mass-produced) inserts into the plasmid, it inactivates one of the antibiotic genes. A researcher can tell which cells have taken up the plasmid containing the foreign DNA by exposing cells to each antibiotic. Cells that grow in the presence of both antibiotics contain a plasmid that does not carry the foreign DNA. Bacteria lacking the plasmid altogether are killed by each antibiotic. Only bacteria that are killed by one antibiotic but grow in the presence of the other harbor the plasmid containing the foreign DNA.

When bacteria containing the recombinant plasmid divide, so does the plasmid. Within hours, the original bacterium gives rise to a culture of cells containing the recombinant plasmid. The enzymes, ribosomes, energy molecules, and factors necessary for protein synthesis present in the bacterial cells transcribe and translate the plasmid DNA and its stowaway human gene. The bacterial culture produces its human protein.

Bacteria, however, sometimes package recombinant proteins into structures called inclusion bodies or otherwise alter them. As a result, industries utilizing the technology must take measures to ensure that the desired product is collectable and pure. To do so, they compare recombinant DNA-based drugs to the same substances obtained by conventional means, such as chemical synthesis or extraction from organisms. Reading 17.2 discusses two recombinant DNA drugs—EPO and tPA.

Applications of Recombinant DNA Technology

Recombinant DNA technology provides a way to isolate individual genes from complex organisms and observe their functions on the molecular level. The first and most familiar application of the technology was to mass-produce protein-based drugs. Often such a genetically engineered drug is safer and less costly than drugs extracted directly from organisms. This is the case for human insulin, the first recombinant drug.

Before 1982, the insulin that 2 million people with diabetes in the United States inject daily came from pancreases removed from cattle in slaughterhouses. Cattle insulin is so similar to the human peptide, differing in only 2 of its 51 amino acids, that most people with diabetes can use it. However, about 1 in 20 patients is allergic to cow insulin because of the slight chemical difference. Until recombinant DNA technology was possible, the allergic patients had to use expensive combinations of insulin from a variety of other animals or from human cadavers.

Researchers cut the human insulin gene from its chromosome and inserted it into the DNA of *E. coli*, a common gut bacterium. When the *E. coli* reproduced, it replicated the human insulin gene along with its own genetic material. When the bacterial genes directed the synthesis of *E. coli* proteins, the transplanted human gene also directed the manufacture of its

table 17.1

Drugs Produced Using Recombinant DNA Technology

Drug	Use
Atrial natriuretic peptide	Dilates blood vessels, promotes urination
Colony stimulating factors	Help restore bone marrow after marrow transplant; restore blood cells following cancer chemotherapy
Deoxyribonuclease (DNase)	Thins pus in lungs of people with cystic fibrosis
Epidermal growth factor	Accelerates healing of wounds and burns; treats gastric ulcers
Erythropoietin (EPO)	Stimulates production of red blood cells in treatment of anemia caused by kidney failure
Factor VIII	Promotes blood clotting in treatment of hemophilia
Fertility hormones (follicle stimulating hormone, luteinizing hormone, human chorionic gonadotropin)	Treats infertility
Glucocerebrosidase	Treats Gaucher disease
Human growth hormone	Promotes growth of muscle and bone in people with very short stature due to hormone deficiency
Insulin	Allows cells to take up glucose in treatment of diabetes
Interferons	
Alpha	Treats genital warts, hairy cell leukemia, hepatitis C and B, Kaposi's sarcoma
Beta	Treats multiple sclerosis
Gamma	Treats chronic granulomatous disease (a blood disorder)
Interleukin-2	Treats kidney cancer
Lung surfactant protein	Helps alveoli in lungs to inflate in infants with respiratory distress syndrome
Renin inhibitor	Lowers blood pressure
Somatostatin	Decreases growth in muscle and bone in pituitary giants
Superoxide dismutase	Prevents further damage to heart muscle after heart attack
Tissue plasminogen activator	Dissolves blood clots in treatment of heart attacks, stroke, and pulmonary embolism

product, human insulin. Today, *E. coli* engineered to manufacture human insulin grow in vats at a major pharmaceutical company. A person with diabetes can now purchase genetically engineered human insulin at a local drugstore.

Human growth hormone is another drug produced with recombinant DNA technology. It is used to treat pituitary dwarfism in children; these children are very short due to absence or deficiency of growth hormone. A controversial use is to make short children grow taller. The hormone used to be collected from pituitary

glands of human cadavers. This source is costly because very little of the substance is found in each gland, and harvesting from cadavers can transmit serious viral infections of the central nervous system. In contrast, the hormone produced in genetically engineered *E. coli* is pure and plentiful. Still, it undergoes many tests before it is marketed to assure its potency, purity, and biological activity. Table 17.1 lists other drugs produced using recombinant DNA technology.

Products of recombinant DNA technology are also used in the food industry. The

Do We Need Recombinant DNA Drugs?

EPO

The invention of kidney hemodialysis in 1961 was a milestone in modern medicine, saving 120,000 lives per year in the United States by replacing kidney function. However, a side effect of dialysis, anemia, was so severe that dialysis patients required frequent blood transfusions. The reason for the anemia was that in addition to cleansing the blood, dialysis also depleted a small protein hormone manufactured in the kidneys, called erythropoietin (EPO).

Cells in the kidneys sense the oxygen level in the blood. If it is too low, the cells secrete EPO, which travels to the bone marrow and signals it to increase the production of oxygen-carrying red blood cells (figure 1). To counteract dialysis-induced anemia, then, it was necessary to boost the patients' EPO levels. In 1970, the U.S. government sponsored a search to find ways to produce large amounts of the pure substance. But how?

Levels of EPO in human plasma are too low to make pooling from donors feasible. A more likely potential source was people suffering from disorders such as aplastic anemia and hookworm infection, which cause them to secrete large amounts of EPO. The National Institutes of Health set up a program to extract EPO from the urine of South American farmers with hookworm infections. Government planes transported the EPO in diplomatic pouches! In 1976, the National Heart, Lung and Blood Institute began a grant program in search of ways to purify EPO. In 1977, supplies came in the form of 2,550 liters of urine from Japanese aplastic anemia patients.

Problems loomed for those trying to purify EPO from these sources. Was it ethical to obtain a scarce substance from the urine of sick, usually poor, people from one country to treat comparatively wealthy people from the United States? Then AIDS arose. Extracting any biochemical from human body fluids was simply not safe.

Recombinant DNA technology solved the EPO problem. Two companies engineered bacteria to produce the human

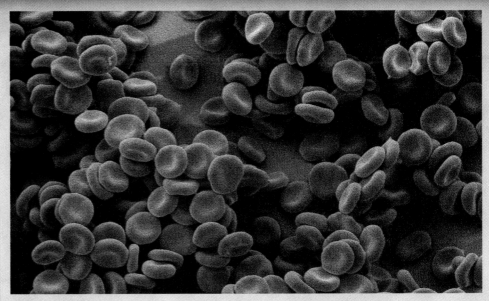

figure 1

These immature red blood cells are being mass produced in the bone marrow of a patient treated with erythropoietin.

protein; clinical trials were successful, and despite some quibbling between the manufacturers over patent rights, dialysis patients can now obtain pure, human EPO—at a cost of $10,000 per year.

Postscript: A large Scandinavian family has an inherited condition, benign erythrocytosis, that causes overproduction of EPO. The symptom? Great athletic skill. An Olympic skier in the family may owe his gold medal at least in part to his genes.

tPA

Using recombinant DNA technology to produce EPO was a milestone, because there was no other practical way to obtain this one-of-a-kind biomolecule. In the mid 1980s, another human biochemical, tissue plasminogen activator (tPA), was also widely heralded as a wonder drug available courtesy of genetic engineering. tPA is a "clot buster." If injected within four hours of a heart attack, it dramatically limits damage to the heart muscle by restoring blood flow. It is also used to treat stroke.

As was the case for EPO, several companies genetically engineered tPA, with the usual corporate infighting. Also like EPO, tPA is expensive—$2,200 per life-saving shot. The two drugs differ, however, in the crucial area of need. Unlike EPO, tPA is not the only clot-dissolving drug. Other available drugs are effective and much cheaper. One of them, streptokinase, is a bacterial protein that has been a standard of cardiac care for many years. Streptokinase costs $300 per injection.

At first, researchers predicted that tPA would prove to be a better clot buster because of its human origin. Many extensive clinical trials compared tPA and streptokinase. Surprisingly, tPA and streptokinase have turned out to be about equal in efficacy. Some physicians who were quick to deliver tPA are now rethinking the old standby streptokinase, reserving the more expensive tPA for patients who have already had streptokinase and could therefore have an allergic reaction to it.

The lesson learned from EPO and tPA is that the value of genetic engineering can not be judged in a scientific vacuum— economics, marketing, and plain common sense also enter the picture.

enzyme rennin, for example, is normally produced in calves' stomachs and is used in cheese making. The gene encoding the enzyme is inserted into plasmids and transferred to bacteria, which are mass-cultured to produce large quantities of pure rennin.

Sometimes a useful protein is rendered more accessible or plentiful by transferring its gene to a different host. This is the case for xylitol, a natural sweetener added to foods in place of sucrose because it doesn't promote tooth decay as much as sucrose does. A gene for an enzyme in the biosynthetic pathway for xylitol, found in the yeast *Pichia stipitis*, is expressed at a higher rate in the yeast *Saccharomyces cerevisiae*, which is a more common yeast the FDA describes as "generally recognized as safe." The second type of yeast turns into a mini-factory for xylitol.

Key Concepts

Biotechnology is the use or alteration of cells or biochemicals to provide a product or process. In recombinant DNA technology, a cell receives a vector that contains foreign DNA encoding a protein of interest. The cell then transcribes and translates the foreign gene. Genetic alteration of a gamete or fertilized ovum results in a transgenic organism. The universality of the genetic code and restriction enzymes, which cut DNA at specific sequences and create sticky ends, make these technologies possible.

Products of recombinant DNA technology are used in health care, food technology, agriculture, and forensics.

Transgenic Organisms

A transgenic animal develops from a genetically altered gamete or fertilized ovum. A transgenic plant can be derived from these sources, as well as from somatic cells. Different vectors and gene transfer techniques are sometimes used in plants because their cell walls, which are not present in animal cells are difficult to penetrate.

Transgenic technology permits rapid introduction of new traits. For example, a gene that confers an agriculturally useful characteristic—such as the ability to withstand a particular pesticide—is isolated from one species and inserted into a vector; then the recombinant vector is placed into single plant cells whose cell walls have been removed. A whole plant regenerated from the genetically engineered cell has the gene for the transferred trait in all of its cells.

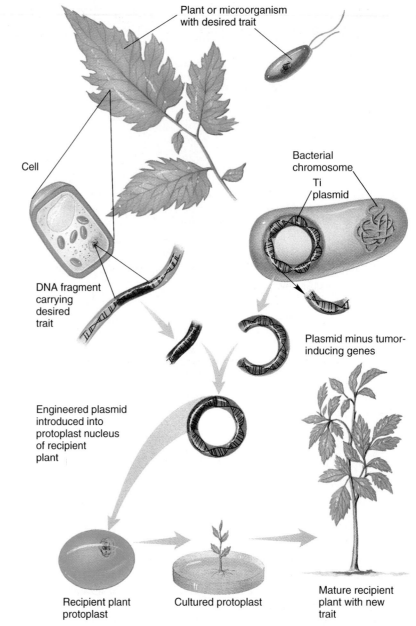

figure 17.5

Making a transgenic plant. A fragment of DNA carrying the desired gene—conferring resistance to a herbicide, for example—is isolated from its natural source and spliced into a Ti plasmid from which the tumor-inducing genes have been removed. The plasmid incorporating the foreign DNA is then allowed to invade a cell of the recipient plant, where it enters the nucleus and integrates into the plant's DNA. Finally, by means of cell culture, the cell is regenerated into a mature, transgenic plant that expresses the desired trait and passes it on to its progeny. A breeding step may be necessary to obtain plants homozygous for a recessive trait.

Delivering DNA

Frequently used plant vectors include the **Ti plasmid** (for "tumor-inducing"), which occurs naturally in the bacterium *Agrobacterium tumefaciens,* and viruses found in plant cells (figure 17.5). For example, a

table 17.2

Gene Transfer Techniques

Approach	How It Works
Virus	A human gene is inserted into a herpes virus, which infects a human cell, where it is expressed.
Retrovirus	An RNA virus carrying an RNA version of a human gene infects a somatic cell. The gene is reverse transcribed to DNA and inserts into a human chromosome. Here, it may produce a missing or abnormal protein.
Liposome transfer	A fatty bubble called a liposome carries a gene into a somatic cell. Here, the delivered gene may replace an abnormal one.
Chemical	Calcium phosphate or dextran sulfate opens transient holes in a cell membrane, admitting replacement DNA.
Electroporation	Electrical current opens transient holes in a cell's membrane, admitting replacement DNA.
Microinjection	A tiny needle injects DNA into a cell lacking that DNA sequence.
Particle bombardment	Metal pellets coated with DNA are shot with explosive force or air pressure into recipient cells.

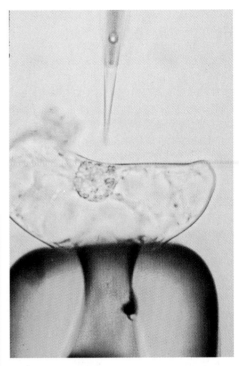

figure 17.6

One way to move foreign DNA into a plant cell nucleus is by direct injection with a microscopic glass needle. This approach is called "naked DNA."

gene from the bacterium *Bacillus thuringiensis* specifies a protein that destroys the stomach linings of insects. The gene is introduced into potato cells, and the cells are regenerated into plants that produce their own insecticide. The tobacco plant in figure 17.1 is transgenic for a firefly gene. (Many experiments use tobacco because it is easy to manipulate—not to manufacture cigarettes.)

Researchers have several ways to insert DNA into cells (table 17.2). Chemicals such as polyethylene glycol and calcium phosphate are used to open transient holes in cell membranes, allowing DNA to enter. **Liposomes** are fatty bubbles that can carry DNA into cells as cell membranes envelope them. In **electroporation,** a brief jolt of electricity opens transient holes in cell membranes that may permit entry of foreign DNA. DNA is also injected into cells using microscopic needles (figure 17.6).

Another way to introduce DNA into cells is **particle bombardment.** A gunlike device shoots tiny metal particles, usually gold or tungsten, coated with foreign DNA. When aimed at target cells, some of the projectiles enter. For example, gene guns shoot dividing cells in soybean seeds with an *E. coli* gene that stains cells expressing it a vibrant blue, allowing detection of the gene transfer.

Gene guns were pioneered on plant cells to blast through their tough cell walls, but also to effectively send DNA—at speeds up to 4,500 feet per second—into mitochondria, chloroplasts, bacteria, animal somatic cells, embryos, and eggs. A variation of the gene gun is to create a mist of two types of microscopic droplets, one consisting of DNA in solution and the other of microprojectiles. When the projectiles blast through a cell membrane, they open up a pathway for the DNA to follow.

Once foreign DNA is introduced into a target cell, it must enter the nucleus, replicate along with the cell's own DNA, and be transmitted when the cell divides. Finally, a mature individual must be regenerated from the altered cell. If the trait is dominant, the transgenic organism must express it in the appropriate tissues at the right time in development. Crosses between heterozygotes may be necessary to yield homozygotes that express the trait. Then the organisms must pass the characteristic on to the next generation. Therefore, generating a transgenic organism takes many steps.

Today, genetics journals abound with descriptions of transgenic organisms. Efforts to develop a sheep that secretes a human protein illustrate how difficult transgenic technology can be.

Transgenic Pioneers—Nancy, Ethel, and Herman

It was quite a quest to genetically engineer Nancy, a sheep who produces human alpha-1-antitrypsin (AAT) in her milk. AAT is a glycoprotein normally present in blood serum that helps microscopic air sacs in the lungs inflate and function properly. Lack of AAT causes an inherited form of emphysema in humans. The air sacs coalesce, impairing breathing. Donated blood doesn't yield enough AAT to treat the 20,000 people who have this ailment. But a herd of transgenic sheep, genetically altered to secrete AAT, can supply thousands of kilograms of the valuable substance in a single milking session.

To create a transgenic sheep, scientists give a ewe a drug to make her produce several mature oocytes at once, then artificially inseminate her with sheep sperm. Fertilized ova are washed out of her body and microinjected with copies of the human AAT gene attached to a sheep

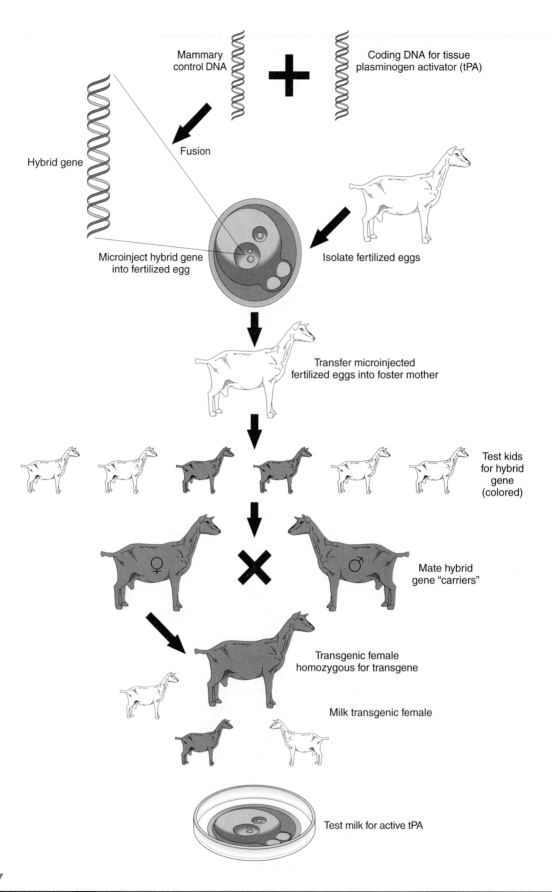

figure 17.7

Transgenic technology enables goats to secrete human drugs in their milk.

Used by permission of Genzyme Corporation and Tufts University School of Veterinary Medicine.

promoter (gene activating) sequence. The manipulated fertilized ova are then implanted into sheep surrogate mothers.

Transgenic technology is difficult to carry out. Very few human genes go where they are intended to go—that is, nestled in the host organism's genome at a place where they will be expressed. In the experiment that led to Nancy's birth, 152 surrogates implanted with the human AAT gene gave birth to 112 lambs. Of those, 1 male and 4 females had the transgene. Only one, a female, gave birth to a transgenic offspring. This was Nancy, whose milk contains pure, active, human alpha-1-antitrypsin—at a whopping yield of 35 grams per liter! Figure 17.7 outlines the steps in a similar process—transgenic "pharming" of a goat that secretes human tPA.

Ethel, the matriarch of a special flock in Scotland, is another pioneering transgenic sheep. She has a human gene for factor VIII, the protein required to clot the blood of people with hemophilia A. Another piece of DNA activates the gene in the sheep's milk, and the valuable protein need only be separated from the milk. A flock of transgenic sheep can provide enough clotting factor to supply the world's hemophilia A patients. This is very important, because today, more than 90 percent of people with hemophilia who obtained clotting factor from blood donations before 1985 have developed HIV infection, and many have died of AIDS.

Herman is the first transgenic dairy calf. He bears the human gene for lactoferrin, an iron-binding milk protein added to infant formula to prevent bacterial infections. Transgenic mice are similarly engineered to secrete human tPA, the heart drug, in their milk. Table 17.3 lists drugs that can be manufactured in transgenic animals.

Transgenic animals are also valuable research tools (table 17.4). One strain of transgenic mouse harbors the human BRCA1 gene that causes breast cancer, enabling researchers to study the very early development of this disease. When the gene for Huntington disease was identified in March 1993, culminating a ten-year search, the next step was to engineer a mouse with the human gene that causes this devastating neurological disorder.

table 17.3

Transgenic Pharming

Host	Product	Potential Use
Cows	Lactoferrin	Added to infant formula to bind iron and prevent bacterial infection
Goats	tPA	Breaks up blood clots
Pigs	Hemoglobin	Used as a blood substitute
Rabbit	Erythropoietin	Treats anemia from dialysis
Rat	Human growth hormone	Treats pituitary dwarfism
Sheep	Alpha-1-antitrypsin	Treats hereditary emphysema

table 17.4

Transgenic Mouse Models of Human Disease

Alzheimer disease	Insulin-dependent diabetes mellitus
Aniridia	Myotonic dystrophy
Atherosclerosis	Neuroblastoma
Beta thalassemia	Neurofibromatosis
Blindness	Obesity
Cartilage disorders	Rickets
Charcot-Marie-Tooth disease	Short fingers
Cystic fibrosis	Spinal and bulbar muscular atrophy
Duchenne muscular dystrophy	Spinocerebellar ataxia
Huntington disease	

Transgenic experimental organisms only approximate human disease. Differences in anatomy and physiology can make it difficult to draw conclusions applicable to the human condition from mice. For example, mice given human genes for cystic fibrosis and Duchenne muscular dystrophy do not exhibit the same spectrum of symptoms as affected children. Mice also develop cancer, and are cured ot it, much more easily than humans.

In a variation of using transgenic technology to model human disease, researchers grow normal human skin cells in culture and add a gene that turns them cancerous. The patch of lab-grown skin is then grafted onto immunodeficient mice. Researchers observe the changes that occur as the cancer develops.

Key Concepts

A transgenic organism is created by introducing foreign DNA into a single cell. The foreign DNA is then transmitted to each cell as the organism develops. Animals are transgenically altered to "pharm" useful human proteins in their milk and to provide models of human diseases.

Gene Targeting

Transgenic technology is not very precise because it does not direct the introduced DNA to a particular chromosomal locus.

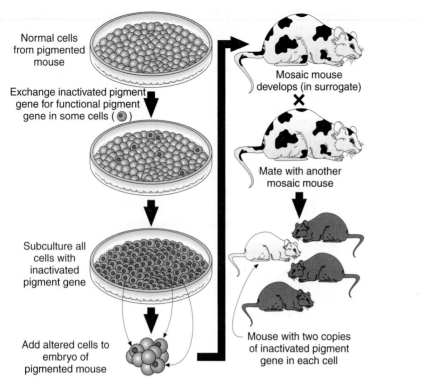

Normal cells from pigmented mouse

Exchange inactivated pigment gene for functional pigment gene in some cells ( )

Subculture all cells with inactivated pigment gene

Add altered cells to embryo of pigmented mouse

Mosaic mouse develops (in surrogate)

Mate with another mosaic mouse

Mouse with two copies of inactivated pigment gene in each cell

figure 17.8

Gene targeting. Inactivated pigment-encoding genes are inserted into mouse embryonic stem (ES) cells, where they trade places with functional pigment-encoding alleles. The engineered ES cells are cultured and injected into mouse early embryos. Mosaic mice develop, with some cells heterozygous for the inactivated allele. These mice are bred and, if all goes well, yield some offspring homozygous for the knocked-out allele. It's easy to tell which mouse this is in the pigment gene example, but gene targeting is particularly valuable for revealing unknown gene functions by inactivating targeted alleles.

The entry of the transgene can disrupt another gene's function, or the transgene can come under another gene's control sequence. Even if a transgene does insert into a chromosome and is expressed, the host's version of the same gene may overshadow the transgene's effect.

A more precise method of genetic engineering is **gene targeting,** in which the introduced gene exchanges places with its counterpart on a host cell's chromosome. Gene targeting uses a natural process called **homologous recombination.** In this process, a DNA sequence locates and displaces a similar or identical sequence in a chromosome. By introducing an inactivated gene in mice, researchers are able to "knock out" the gene it is swapped for and observe the effects of its absence, even in embryos and fetuses. This makes it possible to identify a gene's specific function, which helps researchers understand not

only inherited disease, but normal anatomy and physiology. Or, an altered gene can be swapped in.

Knocking Out Gene Function

Gene targeting entails genetic alteration plus complex developmental manipulations (figure 17.8). In mammals, gene targeting does not work on fertilized ova, so the intervention must occur later in development. Most gene targeting is done on mice because their embryonic cells are easiest to manipulate, but it is also possible to use the technique in the rhesus macaque, a type of monkey. Gene targeting can be done in humans, but this has not been carried beyond very early development and will probably never be used to generate new individuals.

To begin gene targeting, researchers use electroporation or microinjection to deliver a gene of interest into a cell from a

Table 17.5
Knockout Mouse Models of Human Disease

Ataxia telangiectasia
Fanconi anemia
Huntington disease
Immune deficiencies
Neurofibromatosis
Seizures
Tay-Sachs disease

mouse preembryo before it implants in the uterus. This cell is called an **embryonic stem (ES) cell.** ES cells are not specialized, which means that many of their genes have not yet been expressed.

An engineered ES cell is injected into a blastocyst (a ball of cells that does not yet show the layered structure of an embryo) from a different-colored mouse. The blastocyst is implanted into a surrogate mother mouse, where it continues development into an embryo that has some cells bearing the targeted gene. The newborn mouse is a chimera (mosaic), with patches of tissue whose cells bear the introduced gene. The mosaic mouse is then bred to a black mouse. Offspring that express the color encoded in the original engineered ES cell harbor the targeted gene, but in only one copy. The final step is to breed these heterozygotes to each other to obtain mice homozygous for the targeted gene.

Knockout Mice as Models

Gene targeting is very useful in developing animal models of genetic diseases (table 17.5). First, researchers identify the animal's version of a human disease-causing allele. Then they transfer the corresponding human mutant allele to mouse ES cells and follow the steps previously outlined to breed an animal homozygous for the inactivated gene. Typically, this animal is called a knockout mouse.

Knockout mice are valuable models of human disease because they provide a controllable test population. Consider severe combined immune deficiency (SCID) due to adenosine deaminase (ADA) deficiency, an immune disorder. The phenotypes in humans with this illness differ, depending upon a person's environment. A child raised in a bubble might be relatively healthy; a child out among others would suffer frequent infections. Also, people with this disorder are so rare, and often so ill, that it is difficult to learn much about the condition. This is where knockout SCID mice come in.

Mice with knocked out ADA genes can be raised under the same environmental conditions and bred to be genetically identical. Experiments using them, then, are highly controlled compared to observations of human patients. Knockout SCID mice can be exposed to particular infectious agents or undergo treatments such as gene therapies. The mice are quite ill. They only live a day or two after birth, exhibiting severe liver and small intestine degeneration, and their lungs never fully expand. Figure 17.9 compares a knockout mouse representing another human genetic disease, neurofibromatosis type I, to a non-knockout sibling.

Animals with knocked-out genes are also useful in studying polygenic disorders. For example, researchers are studying atherosclerosis by inactivating combinations of genes whose products oversee lipid metabolism. Similarly, scientists can study multiple genetic changes responsible for some cancers by targeting the genes in various combinations.

When Knockouts Are Normal

The ability to knock out gene function has led to many surprises—especially when animals with supposedly vital genes knocked out are perfectly healthy, or much healthier than expected. This is the case in mice lacking a gene encoding a type of collagen, a connective tissue protein. Scientists thought that type X collagen, in mice and humans, promoted normal growth and development of long bones. Mutations in collagen genes cause a variety of syndromes in humans, as Reading 10.2 discusses. Yet mice with

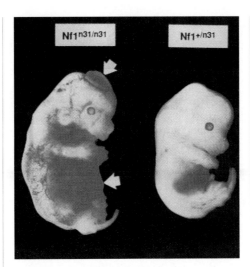

figure 17.9

For most dominant genetic diseases, homozygous mutants are not seen because defects are so severe that the individual dies as an embryo. Gene targeting can be valuable in creating knockout mouse models of such homozygotes. These mouse embryos are models for neurofibromatosis type I, which is remarkably similar to the autosomal dominant condition in humans. Heterozygotes in both species are prone to tumors. The mouse embryo on the left has two knocked-out genes that encode the protein, neurofibromin, whose absence causes the condition. It has a severely abnormal heart and dies in the middle of embryonic development. The mouse embryo on the right has one knocked-out gene. It has some tumors, but is not nearly as severely affected as its homozygous dominant sibling. In humans, a double dose of the mutant gene would cause a miscarriage. Neurofibromin in mice and humans shares 98 percent of the amino acid sequence.

knocked-out type X collagen genes have normal skeletons! How can this be?

A knockout mouse brimming with health forces researchers to rethink their assumptions about a gene's importance. Often these assumptions are based on knowing the gene product's function—such as contracting muscle or clotting blood. However, gene targeting experiments suggest that the importance of a gene's product must be considered in the context of the entire organism. Such a broader view of interact-

ing genes presents several possible explanations for healthy knockout mice:

1. Other genes encode the same or similar proteins as the knocked-out gene so that disabling one gene does not affect the phenotype.

2. An absent protein in a knockout does not alter the phenotype, though an abnormal protein might.

3. The knocked-out gene does not do what we thought, and it may even have no function at all.

4. The knocked-out gene functions under different circumstances than those the experiment observes. Type X collagen, rather than being necessary for growth and development of a newborn's skeleton, may be called into action to repair fractures. It would therefore appear to be unnecessary in embryonic and newborn mice.

Recombinant DNA, transgenic, and gene targeting technologies make genetic medicine possible. The next chapter explores the greatest challenge today's genetic researchers face—using genes to heal.

Key Concepts

In gene targeting, in mice, a gene of interest is inserted into an embryonic stem cell and recombines at the chromosomal site where it normally resides. The ES cell is then incorporated into a developing blastocyst from another individual, which is implanted into a surrogate. Animals with phenotypes indicating that they harbor cells with the targeted gene are bred to other animals to derive individuals who are heterozygous for the gene in every cell. Then, heterozygotes are mated to yield homozygotes for the targeted gene. Swapping an inactivated allele for a gene of interest produces a knockout mouse. These animals can model human disease, but they sometimes reveal that a gene's product is not as vital as we think.

1. **Biotechnology** is the alteration of cells or biochemicals to provide a useful product. It includes extracting natural products, altering an organism's genetic material, and combining DNA from different species.

2. **Recombinant DNA technology** is possible because of the universality of the genetic code. Recombinant DNA is used to mass-produce proteins in bacteria or other single cells. **Transgenic** organisms are multicellular and are altered at the single-cell or early embryonic stage. Recombinant DNA technology, begun hesitantly in 1975, has matured into a valuable method to mass-produce drugs and other useful proteins.

3. Constructing a recombinant DNA molecule begins when **restriction enzymes** cut the gene of interest and a **vector.** Because the foreign DNA and vector are cut at the same sequence, their ends attract by complementary base pairing. Some vectors incorporate foreign DNA. Selected recombinant plasmids are then introduced into host cells, where the foreign gene is propagated and expressed. A gene can be transferred to a host that does not normally manufacture the gene product, or to a host that allows greater expression of the gene.

4. Recombinant DNA on a multicellular level produces a transgenic organism. A single cell—a gamete in an animal or plant, or a somatic cell in a plant—is genetically altered. The organism develops, including the change in each cell and passing it to the next generation. We can introduce DNA into cells in many ways.

5. **Gene targeting** uses the natural attraction of a DNA sequence for its complementary sequence, called **homologous recombination,** to swap one gene for another. It is more precise than transgenic technology, which inserts a foreign gene but does not direct it to a specific chromosomal site. Gene targeting requires complex breeding schemes to achieve homozygous expression of the targeted gene. It is used to inactivate genes and then observe the effect on the organism. Knockout mice with inactivated genes can model human disease. Sometimes, knockout mice reveal that a gene product is not vital to survival.

review questions

1. Define each of the following terms:
   a. biotechnology
   b. recombinant DNA technology
   c. transgenic technology
   d. gene targeting
   e. homologous recombination

2. Describe the roles of each of the following tools in a biotechnology:
   a. restriction enzymes
   b. embryonic stem cells
   c. vectors

3. How do researchers use antibiotics to select cells containing recombinant DNA?

4. List the components of an experiment to produce recombinant human insulin in *E. coli* cells.

5. Why would recombinant DNA technology be impossible if the genetic code was not universal?

6. Why must manipulations to create a transgenic organism take place at the single-cell stage?

7. Describe three ways to insert foreign DNA into cells.

8. Why isn't transgenic technology as precise as gene targeting?

9. What do gene targeting and antisense technology have in common?

applied questions

1. Do you think that a genetically altered organism should be patentable?

2. What considerations should a pharmaceutical company take in deciding whether to produce a drug using recombinant DNA technology rather than extracting it directly from donated tissue?

3. You are a researcher charged with genetically altering cows to secrete human elastin in their milk. This is a connective tissue protein used in cosmetics. List the steps to accomplish the goal using transgenic technology and gene targeting. Which technique is easier to carry out? Which do you think is more likely to work?

4. Mouse models for cystic fibrosis have been developed by inserting a human transgene, and by gene targeting to inactivate the mouse counterpart of the alleles that cause the disorder. How do these methods differ? Which method do you think produces a more accurate model of human cystic fibrosis, and why?

5. Collagen is a large protein often used in cosmetics and skin care products. Would collagen be purer if extracted from human cadavers, or if manufactured in recombinant bacteria? Cite a reason for your answer.

6. Why were researchers at the Asilomar meeting concerned about the safety of recombinant DNA research? What measures did they suggest to make it as safe as possible?

7. Explain how recombinant DNA technology can help individuals with each of the following disorders:

a. diabetes

b. hemophilia

c. dwarfism due to a hormone deficiency

d. cystic fibrosis

8. A human oncogene called *ras* is inserted into mice, creating transgenic animals that develop a variety of tumors. Why are mouse cells able to transcribe and translate human genes?

9. A healthy knockout mouse cannot manufacture what was thought to be a vital enzyme. Suggest three possible explanations for this surprising finding.

10. In a mouse model of a human condition called "urge syndrome," in which the feeling of impending urination occurs frequently, researchers inactivate a gene encoding nitric oxide synthase, which produces nitric oxide (NO). NO is the neurotransmitter that controls muscle contraction in the bladder. What type of biotechnology does this describe?

suggested readings

Andersson, Karl-Erik. May 1997. A role for nitric oxide synthase in urinary "urge syndrome." *Nature Medicine,* vol. 3. An example of a knockout mouse that has a common human counterpart.

Davidson, Donald J. April 1995. Lung disease in the cystic fibrosis mouse exposed to bacterial pathogens. *Nature Genetics,* vol. 9. Mice transgenic for cystic fibrosis have some, but not all, of the symptoms seen in humans.

Jacks, Tyler, et al. July 1994. Tumor predisposition in mice heterozygous for a targeted mutation in NF1. *Nature Genetics,* vol. 7. Knockout mice can reveal defects in homozygous dominant mutants.

Laron, Zvi. February 15, 1996. Short stature due to genetic defects affecting growth hormone activity. *The New England Journal of Medicine,* vol. 334. Recombinant human growth hormone can add inches to children with growth hormone disorders.

Lewis, Ricki. September 29, 1997. Embryonic stem cells debut amid little media attention. *The Scientist.* E5-like human cells may enable researchers to grow human tissues and organs.

Lin, Michael, et al. August 1995. Heart and lung disease in engineered mice. *Nature Medicine,* vol. 1. Transgenic and knockout mice can be experimental stand-ins for humans.

Majzoub, Joseph A., and Louis J. Muglia. April 4, 1996. Knockout mice. *The New England Journal of Medicine,* vol. 334. Knockout mice reveal gene functions by eliminating their effects.

Marshall, Eliot. August 22, 1997. A bitter battle over insulin gene. *Science,* vol. 277. A legal dispute over experiments conducted during the early days of recombinant DNA technology continues today.

Nordlee, Julie A. March 14, 1996. Identification of a brazil-nut allergen in transgenic soybeans. *The New England Journal of Medicine,* vol. 334. Transgenic soybeans given a brazil-nut protein to improve the quality of their protein also gained a potent allergen.

Paigen, Kenneth. March 1995. A miracle enough: The power of mice. *Nature Medicine,* vol. 1. Mice—more like us than many of us realize—are getting genetic medicine off the ground.

Rosati, Rita, et al. October 1994. Normal long bone growth and development in type X collagen-null mice. *Nature Genetics,* vol. 8. Knockout mice that are unexpectedly healthy send scientists seeking new hypotheses to explain gene function.

Velander, William H., et al. January 1997. Transgenic livestock as drug factories. *Scientific American.* How a pig manufactures a human clotting factor.

chapter

eighteen

Gene and Protein Therapy

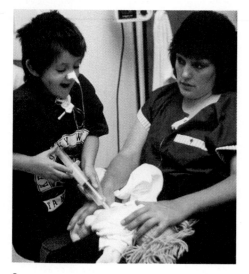
a.

b.

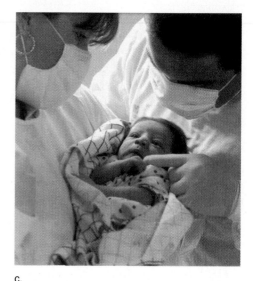
c.

figure 18.1

Children pioneering gene therapy. (a) Laura Cay Boren spent much of her life in hospitals until she received the enzyme that her body lacks, adenosine deaminase (ADA). Here, she pretends to inject her doll as her mother looks on. (b) Three years after receiving her own white blood cells, genetically altered to contain the ADA gene they lack, Ashanti DaSilva rides her bike—something she thought would never be possible. (c) Newborn Andrew Gobea received the ADA gene in stem cells taken from his umbilical cord. The percentage of T cells in his blood that carry the needed gene is steadily increasing. He is now a healthy grade-schooler.

The Evolution of a Cure

For the first few years of her life, Laura Cay Boren couldn't recall what it was to feel well (figure 18.1a). From her birth in July 1982, she fought infection after infection. Colds rapidly became pneumonia, landing her in the hospital. Routine vaccines caused severe abscesses. In February 1983, doctors identified Laura's problem—severe combined immune deficiency (SCID) due to adenosine deaminase (ADA) deficiency. She had inherited the autosomal recessive disorder from two carrier parents.

Lack of ADA blocks a biochemical pathway that breaks down the metabolic toxin deoxyinosine into uric acid, which is excreted. Without ADA, the substance that ADA normally acts upon builds up and destroys T cells. Without helper T cells to stimulate them, B cells cannot produce antibodies, and so both branches of the immune system fail. The child becomes extremely prone to infections and cancer, and despite medical treatment, usually does not live beyond a year in the outside environment.

The Duke University Medical Center, where she celebrated her first and second birthdays, became a second home to Laura.

In 1983 and again in 1984, she received bone marrow transplants from her father, which temporarily bolstered her immunity. Red blood cell transfusions also helped for a time. Still, Laura was spending more time in the hospital than out.

By the end of 1985, Laura was gravely ill. She had to be fed through a tube, and repeated infection had severely damaged her lungs. Laura's mother began to feel guilty for wishing that her child would die rather than suffer. Then a medical miracle happened.

Laura was chosen to be the first recipient of a new treatment. She had been second in line to a boy who was even more ill, but he died just before he was to be treated. In the spring of 1986, Laura received her first injection of PEG-ADA. This is the missing enzyme, ADA, taken from a cow and modified by adding polyethylene glycol (PEG) chains to it. PEG is the major ingredient in antifreeze.

Previous attempts at enzyme replacement therapy hadn't worked, because what remained of the immune system would rapidly destroy the injected, unaltered enzyme. Patients needed frequent doses, which provoked the immune system further, causing allergic reactions so severe that the treat-

ment had to stop. Laura's physicians hoped that adding PEG would keep ADA in the blood long enough to work.

Laura began responding to PEG-ADA almost immediately. Within hours her ADA level increased 20-fold. After 3 months, toxins were no longer in her blood, but her immunity was still suppressed. After 6 months, though, Laura's immune function neared normal for the first time ever—and stayed that way, with weekly doses of PEG-ADA. Her life changed drastically as she ventured beyond the hospital's germ-free rooms. By summer 1988, she could finally play with other children without fear of catching viral or bacterial illnesses. She began first grade in fall 1989, but had to repeat the year—not surprisingly, she had spent the year socializing!

PEG-ADA revolutionized treatment of this form of SCID, targeting the source of the disorder rather than trying to overcome the infections. But PEG-ADA was only the opening chapter of an ongoing story.

The second chapter began on September 14, 1990, at 12:52 P.M. Four-year-old Ashanti DaSilva sat up in bed at the National Institutes of Health in Bethesda, Maryland, and began receiving her own white blood cells intravenously (figure 18.1b). Earlier, doctors had removed the cells and patched them with normal ADA genes. Soon after, an eight-year-old, Cynthia Cutshall, received the same treatment. In the years following, both girls stayed relatively healthy. But this first gene therapy did not "heal" a sufficient percentage of the girls' cells. Both needed repeated treatments. One girl required continued PEG-ADA to remain healthy; the other, however, eventually showed the normal ADA gene in 25 percent of her T cells!

Even as Ashanti and Cynthia were being treated, researchers were onto the next step. Wouldn't the effect last longer if they could treat immature blood cells, the stem cells that continued to give rise to other cells? Stem cells reside in the bone marrow, where they account for only one in a million or so cells. The type of stem cell that produces T cells accounts for one in several billion marrow cells. It seemed dubious that scientists could ever harvest enough stem cells to try such a treatment.

However, researchers knew of another source of the valuable stem cells—umbilical cord blood. If fetuses who had inherited ADA deficiency could be identified and their parents agreed, then the appropriate stem cells could be separated from the cord blood at birth, given ADA genes, and reinfused into the newborn. The third chapter in the ADA deficiency saga was about to begin, with three babies in starring roles.

Crystal and Leonard Gobea had already lost a five-month-old baby to ADA deficiency when amniocentesis revealed their second fetus was affected. They and two other couples in the same situation were asked to participate in the experiment. The May 31, 1993, issue of *Time* magazine featured newborn Andrew Gobea (figure 18.1c). He and the other two participants received their own bolstered blood cells on the fourth day after birth, but they were also given PEG-ADA to prevent symptoms. The plan was to monitor the babies frequently to see if T cells carrying normal ADA genes would appear in the blood, as researchers expected.

The experiment was a success, although the altered T cells accumulate slowly. After a few months, in each child, about 1 in 10,000 T cells had the genetic alteration. But after a year, that number rose to 1 in 100! By the time each child was eighteen months of age, with the genetically

altered T cell population still rising, researchers halved the PEG-ADA dose. The babies remained healthy. By the summer of 1995, the three toddling two-year-olds each had about 3 in 100 T cells carrying the ADA gene. Gradually, the healthier, bolstered cells are replacing the ADA-deficient ones. Researchers hope that one day the children's ADA-producing T cells will be plentiful enough to discontinue the PEG-ADA treatment.

Key Concepts

ADA deficiency was the first disorder researchers treated with gene therapy. They began by replacing the missing enzyme, progressed to genetically altering mature white blood cells in ill children, and then targeted DNA in umbilical cord stem cells infused into newborns.

Types of Gene Therapy

The idea of fixing the symptoms of an inherited problem is not new; people with clotting disorders, for example, have received clotting factors for many years. Altering genes to treat an inherited disorder, however, can provide a longer-lasting effect.

Once we could change and transfer DNA molecules to cells that could express them, the questions turned to which genetic disorders to treat. Should we treat conditions that affect the greatest number of people, or those that would be easiest to treat? Many people feel that gene therapy should be perfected on the disorders we know the most about—those for which we know the affected gene, protein, and tissue. This is why early efforts focused on gene therapy for ADA deficiency, even though only a few youngsters have the disorder. As the human genome project identifies more genes, gene therapy efforts are targeting more common illnesses. For example, the technique of introducing corrective genes into umbilical cord stem cells is being used to treat leukemia.

Tables 18.1 and 18.2 list some general requirements and concerns for gene therapy.

table 18.1

Requirements for Approval of Clinical Trials for Gene Therapy

1. Knowledge of defect and how it causes symptoms
2. An animal model
3. Success in human cells growing in vitro
4. Either no alternate therapies, or a group of patients for whom existing therapies are not possible or have not worked
5. Safe experiments

table 18.2

Gene Therapy Concerns

1. Which cells should be treated?
2. What proportion of the targeted cell population must be corrected to alleviate or halt progression of symptoms?
3. Is overexpression of the therapeutic gene dangerous?
4. Is it dangerous if the engineered gene "escapes" and infiltrates other tissues?
5. How long will the affected cells function?
6. Will the immune system attack the introduced cells?

Treating the Phenotype— A Short-term Solution

Treating the symptoms of an inherited disease alleviates an individual's pain but does not alter the genetic misinformation that could pass to the next generation. Treating symptoms of genetic disease may actually increase the frequency of disease-causing alleles in a population by allowing individuals to have children who otherwise would not be healthy enough to do so.

We have been able to treat the phenotypes of some genetic disorders for several years. A child with cystic fibrosis sprinkles powdered cow digestive enzymes onto applesauce, which she eats

table 18.3
Newborn Screening

Disease	Incidence	Symptoms	Treatment	Cost per Treatment
Biotinidase deficiency	1/70,000 None in blacks or Asians	Convulsions, hair loss, hearing loss, vision loss, developmental abnormalities, coma, sometimes death	Most physical symptoms reversed by oral biotin	25–50¢
Maple syrup urine disease	1/250,000–300,000 More common in blacks and Asians	Lethargy, mental retardation, urine smells sweet, irritable, vomiting, coma, death by age 1 month	Diet very low in overproduced amino acids	50¢
Congenital adrenal hyperplasia	1/12,000 whites 1/15,000 Jews 1/680 Yupik eskimos	Masculinized female genitalia, dehydration, precocious puberty in males, accelerated growth, short stature, ambiguous sex characteristics	Hormone replacement, surgery	$1.50
Congenital hypothyroidism	1/3,600–5,000 whites Rare in blacks, more common in Hispanics	Mental retardation, growth failure, hearing loss, underactive thyroid, neurological impairment	Hormone replacement	$1.50
Galactosemia	1/60,000–80,000	Muscle weakness, cerebral palsy, seizures, mental retardation, cataracts, liver disease	Galactose-free diet	50¢
Homocystinuria	1/50,000–150,000	Blood clots, thin bones, mental retardation, seizures, muscle weakness, mental disturbances	Low-methionine, high-cysteine diet, drugs	50¢
Phenylketonuria (PKU)	1/10,000–25,000	Mental retardation	Low phenylalanine diet	$1.25
Sickle cell and other hemoglobinopathies	1/400 U.S. blacks	Joint pain, severe infection, leg ulcers, delayed maturation	Prophylactic antibiotics	$1.50

before each meal to replace the enzymes her clogged pancreas cannot secrete. A boy with hemophilia receives a clotting factor. Even wearing eyeglasses is a way of altering the expression of one's inheritance. Today, newborns are routinely screened for certain inborn errors of metabolism whose symptoms can be prevented or alleviated by correcting the phenotype, often by following a restrictive diet (table 18.3).

Somatic versus Germline Gene Therapy

Researchers distinguish two types of gene therapy, depending on whether it occurs in somatic tissue or in gametes or fertilized ova (figure 18.2).

Correcting only the somatic cells that a genetic condition affects is called **somatic gene therapy.** This form of the technology is nonheritable, which means that a recipient does not pass the genetic correction to offspring. For example, a bone marrow transplant is somatic gene therapy because it replaces only bone marrow cells, which are somatic. Clearing lungs congested from cystic fibrosis with a nasal spray containing functional CFTR genes is also somatic gene therapy; it doesn't alter the gametes (sperm or oocytes). Somatic gene therapy helps an individual, but not his or her descendants.

We must know a great deal about a disorder to develop a somatic gene therapy.

Which cells, in which tissues and organs, function abnormally, and when in development do they do so? Which biochemical is abnormal or missing? What DNA sequence must we add to correct the abnormality? How many cells must be altered to alleviate symptoms? Even when we have much of this information, designing a gene therapy is challenging. Some early gene therapy experiments have been disappointing because the correction isn't sufficient to overcome symptoms or because the immune system attacks the altered cells.

Germline gene therapy alters the DNA of a gamete or fertilized ovum. As a result, all cells of the individual that develop harbor the change. Unlike somatic gene therapy, germline gene therapy is

Somatic Gene Therapy

Brain

Kidney

Liver

Muscle

Germline Gene Therapy

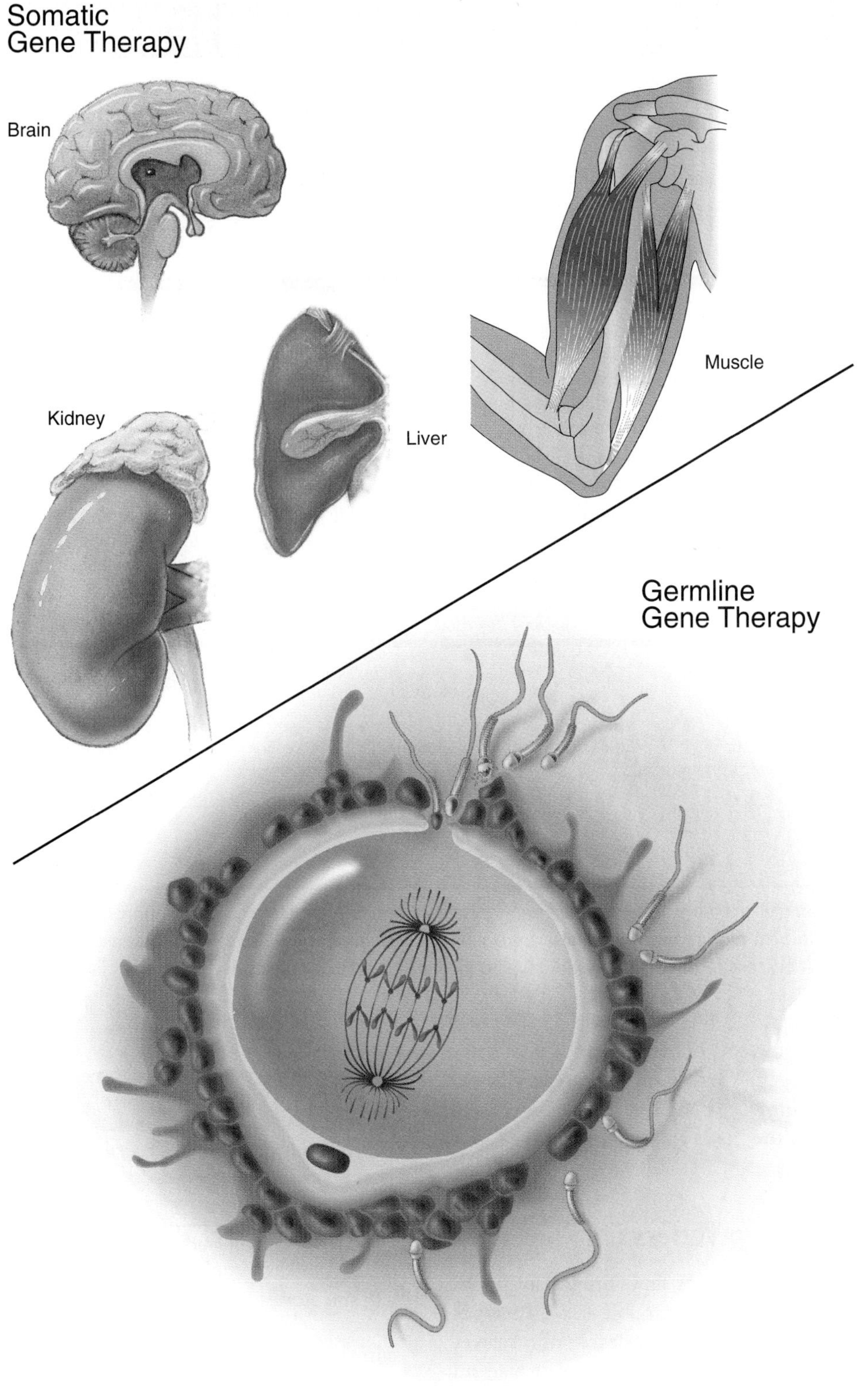

figure 18.2

Somatic (nonheritable) gene therapy targets somatic cells that comprise various tissues of the body. Germline (heritable) gene therapy targets sperm, oocytes, or fertilized ova, and intervenes early enough that all cells of the individual carry the genetic change.

heritable—it passes to offspring. Transgenic technology (discussed in chapters 17 and 19) is similar to germline gene therapy. The steps are the same; the goals are different. In many nations, governments have banned human germline gene therapy, or researchers have agreed not to attempt it.

Key Concepts

Protein-based therapies replace gene products, and gene therapies replace malfunctioning or absent genes. Somatic gene therapy targets somatic tissue and is therefore not heritable. Germline gene therapy targets gametes or fertilized ova and is heritable.

The Mechanics of Gene Therapy

The idea behind gene therapy is straightforward—introduce a piece of DNA into cells that do not function normally because they lack this DNA or have a mutant version of it. Finding ways to deliver genes to the appropriate cells and coaxing their continued expression requires creativity.

Gene Vectors

Researchers send foreign DNA into cells in several ways (table 17.2). Physical methods include electroporation, microinjection, and particle bombardment. Chemical methods include liposomes that enclose the gene cargo and lipid molecules that carry DNA across the cell membrane. The lipid carrier can penetrate the cell membrane that DNA alone cannot cross. However, lipid-based methods often fail to deliver a sufficient payload, and gene expression is transient.

Biological approaches to gene transfer utilize a vector. Recall that this is a piece of DNA used to introduce foreign DNA in a recombinant DNA or transgenic procedure. In gene therapy, the vector is a virus, nature's gene carrier, or parts of a virus.

Human gene therapy trials use several different types of viruses. Typically, researchers remove the parts of the virus that cause symptoms or alert the immune system and stitch in the corrective gene. Different viral vectors are useful for different experiments. A certain virus may transfer its cargo with great efficiency but carry only a short DNA sequence. Another virus might carry a large piece of DNA but send it to many cell types, causing side effects. Still another virus may not infect enough cells to alleviate symptoms. Some retroviruses have limited use because they infect only dividing cells. A type of retrovirus called a lentivirus, however, can infect dividing as well as nondividing cells. HIV is a lentivirus and, if disabled, may make an effective vector! Table 18.4 lists the characteristics of viral vectors used in gene therapy experiments.

Sometimes researchers attempt to send a virus where it would normally go. For example, the adenoviruses used to transport functioning CFTR genes to the airway passages of people with cystic fibrosis (CF) normally infect lung tissue. But by adding portions of other viruses, researchers can redirect a virus to infect a certain cell type. For example, adeno-associated virus (AAV) infects many cell types. But researchers can add a promoter (control region) from a certain gene of another virus, parvovirus B19. The added B19 gene restricts AAV's infectivity so it only enters specific bone marrow cells called erythroid progenitor cells. These cells give rise to immature red blood cells, which contain nuclei and produce proteins. After a short time in the circulation, the immature cells extrude their nuclei, becoming doughnut-shaped red blood cells.

Where does gene therapy come in? If AAV hooked to a parvovirus B19 promoter is also linked to a human gene that encodes a protein normally found in red blood cells, then the entire vector can treat an inherited disorder of blood. Sickle cell disease is a good example. A gene therapy being tested consists of a normal human beta

table 18.4

Vectors Used in Gene Therapy

Vector	Characteristics	Applications
Adeno-associated virus (AAV)	Integrates into specific chromosomal site Long-term expression Nontoxic Infects dividing and nondividing cells Carries small genes	Cystic fibrosis Sickle cell disease Thalassemias
Adenovirus (AV)	Large virus, carries large genes Transient expression Evokes immune response Infects dividing and nondividing cells, particularly in respiratory system	Cystic fibrosis Hereditary emphysema
Herpes	Long-term expression Infects nerve cells	Brain tumors
Retrovirus	Stable but imprecise integration Long-term expression Most types infect only dividing cells Nontoxic Most established in clinical experience	Gaucher disease HIV infection Several cancers

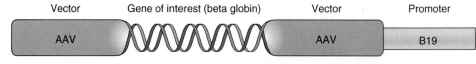

figure 18.3

A promoter from a parvovirus B19 gene directs adeno-associated virus (AAV) harboring a human beta globin gene to erythroid progenitor cells, which give rise to cells that mature into red blood cells. This vector is used in gene therapy to correct defects in red blood cells.

globin gene carried on AAV to erythroid progenitor cells (figure 18.3). Figure 18.4 depicts the basic ways to introduce DNA into cells.

Introducing Vectors

Gene therapy trials have progressively become more invasive. Table 18.5 lists types of gene therapy by their degree of invasiveness. The first gene therapy, performed on Ashanti and Cynthia, altered cells outside their bodies. The corrected cells were then infused into the girls. This approach is called **ex vivo gene therapy.**

In **in situ gene therapy,** the vector is injected into a very localized and accessible body part, such as a single melanoma skin cancer. In the most invasive approach, **in**

Table 18.5

Invasiveness of Gene Therapy

Type	Location
Ex vivo	Cells corrected outside body, then implanted
In situ	Vector introduced to localized and accessible body part
In vivo	Vector introduced into body

vivo gene therapy, the vector is introduced directly into the body. For example, in vivo gene therapy for CF is a nasal spray containing adenovirus carrying a wild type human CFTR gene.

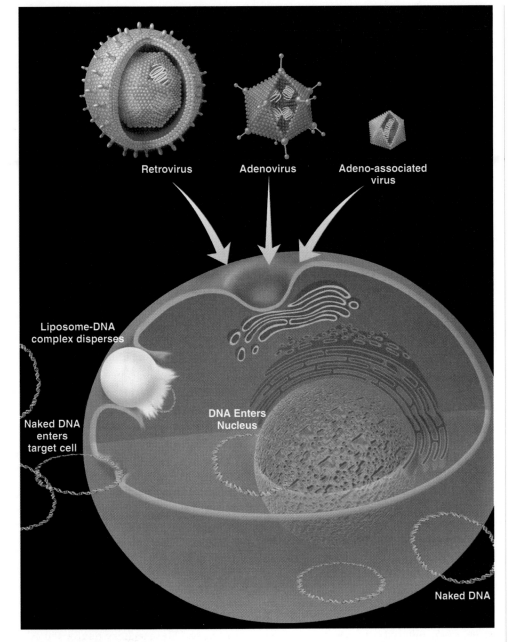

figure 18.4

DNA can be sent into cells in viruses, in liposomes, or alone ("naked"). The viruses are not drawn to scale—they are much smaller than a cell.

Key Concepts

Gene therapy introduces a corrective gene and stimulates its expression long enough to be therapeutic without causing side effects. Choosing an appropriate vector is key to targeting gene therapy. Ex vivo gene therapy removes cells from a patient, manipulates them, and returns them; in situ gene therapy delivers a gene directly to an accessible body part; in vivo gene therapy delivers the vector into the body.

Sites of Gene Therapy

Current gene therapy trials target several tissues. These include stem cells, endothelium, skin, muscle, liver, lungs, and nerve tissues.

Stem Cells

Stem cells are pluripotent—that is, they can give rise, by mitosis, to specialized daughter cells by restricting which genes these cells express. Stem cells in bone marrow can produce all of the many types of blood cells, and therefore they can be used for gene therapy for blood disorders.

Bone marrow transplants are more a form of cell therapy than gene therapy, because healthy cells from a donor replace a person's malfunctioning marrow cells. Figure 18.5 depicts a bone marrow transplant success story—a boy cured of sickle cell disease. Bone marrow stem cells can also receive corrective genes and then be infused into a patient.

Because a bone marrow transplant recipient's own marrow is destroyed prior to treatment, he or she is highly prone to infection for several months. This contributes to the 20 percent mortality rate. Alternate sources of stem cells, such as umbilical cord blood or fetal cells, may be safer to use.

Fetal stem cells are valuable for several reasons. They are not yet capable of eliciting an immune response, they divide, and they are easier to obtain than tissues in an adult. The source of fetal hematopoietic (blood-forming) stem cells is not actually the fetus, but an extraembryonic membrane, the yolk sac, which contains groups of cells called blood islands (figure 18.6). The cells that make up the blood islands are called progenitors because they give rise to specialized cells. Cells on the edges of the islands develop into blood vessel wall cells (endothelium). Cells near the center of the blood islands form stem cells, which later migrate to the fetus's liver and then "seed" the bone marrow.

The two types of progenitor cells in the fetal yolk sac could have many uses in gene therapy. The cells on the edges of the blood islands could be altered and then implanted into blood vessels in a child or adult, enabling the vessels to secrete needed proteins. The cells destined to become bone marrow stem cells could be used to

figure 18.5

Seye Arise was born with sickle cell disease. At a year of age, his hands and feet swelled due to blocked circulation, and he needed frequent transfusions to dilute his sickled red blood cells with normal ones. At age four, he began limping from a stroke. Because strokes can be lethal, Seye's parents allowed him to undergo an experimental bone marrow transplant, with brother Moyo donating the marrow. Four months later, Seye ran and played for the first time. He and 16 of 22 children in the study were completely cured.

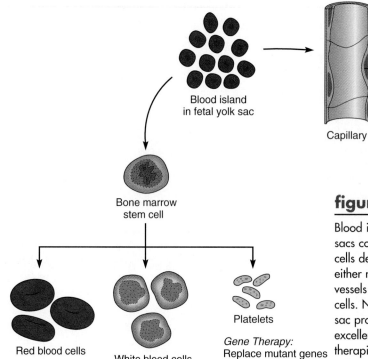

figure 18.6

Blood islands in fetal yolk sacs consist of progenitor cells destined to develop into either microscopic blood vessels (capillaries) or blood cells. Normal or altered yolk sac progenitor cells are excellent candidates for gene therapies targeted to blood cells or vessels.

treat a variety of blood and immune system disorders, such as inherited anemias, immune deficiencies, and blood cancers.

Ex vivo gene therapy for sickle cell disease may be possible on the cells that directly give rise to lymphocytes (T and B cells). In one experiment, researchers took prelymphocytes from patients and added naked DNA consisting of a short double-stranded piece (oligonucleotide) of RNA and DNA. In some cells, this oligonucleotide replaced the mutant beta globin gene, which corrected the defect. The more of the oligonucleotide added, the more cells were treated. The next step will be to reinfuse these cells into patients to see if it alleviates symptoms or prevents painful sickling crises. Reading 18.1 explores yet another type of gene therapy used to treat sickle cell disease.

Endothelium—Gateways to the Bloodstream

A tissue that is very amenable to nonheritable gene therapy is **endothelium.** Endothelial cells attach to one another, forming sheets that curve to form capillaries. Genetically altered endothelium can secrete a needed substance right into the bloodstream; in a person with diabetes, for example, altered endothelium might secrete insulin. Implants combine genetically engineered endothelium "seeds" with collagen and biochemicals that stimulate blood vessel growth.

Skin

Skin cells grow well in the laboratory. A patch of skin the size of a letter on this page, when cultured for 3 weeks, grows as large as a bathmat. The skin can then be lifted out of the dish and grafted onto the donor, with no tissue rejection.

A human gene, such as the one encoding human growth hormone, can be inserted (on a vector) into human skin cells growing in culture. When grafted onto mice from a strain that does not reject foreign tissue, the grafts grow into normal appearing mouse epidermis, but they secrete human growth hormone! Skin grafts genetically engineered to secrete drugs may provide a new drug delivery route for humans.

Muscle

Muscle tissue is a good target for gene therapy for several reasons. It comprises about one-half of the body's mass, is easily accessible, and is near a blood supply. Much effort focuses on developing a gene therapy for Duchenne muscular dystrophy. Recall that in DMD, absence of dystrophin collapses the group of glycoproteins that link the cytoskeleton of a muscle cell to the extracellular matrix. Unable to withstand the force of contraction (figure 2.13), the cells collapse and die and are ultimately replaced with fat and connective tissue.

The dystrophin gene presented a great challenge to developing gene therapy because of its huge size—more than 3 million bases! Researchers have used AV, AAV, and liposomes to inject a shortened version of the gene into the muscles of mice called *mdx,* which have a DMD-like illness. In another approach, researchers add a synthetic oligonucleotide (a short nucleic acid) that is the antisense sequence to part of dystrophin mRNA. The oligonucleotide swaps into the mRNA and replaces the faulty area, restoring the reading frame and enabling treated cells to temporarily produce dystrophin. In yet another approach, researchers coax cells to overproduce a different muscle protein, called **utrophin,** which is normally located at the junctions between nerve and muscle cells. In *mdx* mice, the excess utrophin substitutes for dystrophin, and muscle function improves.

An alternative to injecting genes into muscle cells is to alter immature muscle cells, called **myoblasts.** Because these cells can divide, retroviruses can introduce genes into them. Myoblasts are easy to culture and readily accept foreign genes. They secrete large amounts of protein and can be implanted into muscles in the body. Here, myoblasts may supply missing dystrophin. Or, they can be used to secrete other vital proteins into the bloodstream by becoming part of the muscular layer of blood vessel walls. Boys with DMD are being experimentally treated with implants of dystrophin-secreting myoblasts from their fathers, with mixed results. The challenge with somatic gene therapy of DMD is that the missing protein must be supplied to many muscles to have an effect.

The Liver

The liver is an important candidate for gene therapy because it has many functions and can regenerate. That is, an implant of corrected cells can take over liver function.

The first liver gene therapy experiments in humans target heart disease. Normal hepatocytes (liver cells) have low density lipoprotein (LDL) receptors on their surfaces. These receptors bind cholesterol in the bloodstream and bring it into the cell. When liver cells lack LDL receptors, cholesterol accumulates on artery interiors. Heterozygotes for familial hypercholesterolemia (FH) have half the normal number of LDL receptors on liver cells and have very high serum cholesterol levels. They suffer heart attacks in early or mid-adulthood.

Genetically altering liver cells to produce more LDL receptors could reverse the effects of FH. A twenty-nine-year-old woman heterozygous for FH recently underwent such a procedure with encouraging results. Surgeons removed 15 percent of her liver, isolated hepatocytes, and infected the cells with retrovirus vectors bearing normal LDL receptor genes. The patient received the altered cells through a major liver vein. Eighteen months later, the grafted liver cells bore more LDL receptors! The woman's serum cholesterol levels also improved.

Gene therapy to add LDL receptors to liver cells would be lifesaving for the one-in-a-million individuals who are homozygous for the mutant FH allele. These people die in childhood of massive heart attacks. Presently, treatment consists of administering cholesterol-lowering drugs and periodically cleansing the blood.

Another liver disease that may be treatable with gene therapy is hereditary tyrosinemia, an enzyme deficiency that causes liver failure in infancy. In a mouse model, a retrovirus is used to introduce the wild type gene encoding the liver enzyme. When just 1,000 patched cells are added to the liver, the cells proliferate faster than the impaired liver cells. Gradually, the corrected cells comprise more of the liver, and symptoms abate. In a human, gene therapy would have to "fix" about 5 percent of the liver's 10 trillion cells to be effective.

The Lungs

The respiratory tract is a good target for gene therapy because its lining cells may be reached directly by an aerosol spray, eliminating the need to remove, treat, and reimplant cells. Several experimental treatments for cystic fibrosis are aerosols that replace the defective gene. For example, a modified adenovirus that causes the common cold is genetically altered to not cause symptoms and to contain a functional CFTR gene. Once inhaled, respiratory lining cells take up the altered vector and produce the protein that is missing or abnormal in cystic fibrosis.

Liposomes are also used to deliver CFTR genes. Retroviruses aren't useful because the target cells lining the respiratory passages do not divide frequently. The challenge in gene therapy for CF is to deliver the correct DNA to enough cells and have them produce normal CFTR protein long enough to alleviate symptoms.

Another respiratory target of gene therapy is the gene encoding the enzyme **alpha-1-antitrypsin** (AAT). This enzyme is normally synthesized in the liver and in white blood cells, which carry it to the lungs. Here, AAT prevents white blood cells from releasing too much of another enzyme, **elastase,** which destroys infecting bacteria. In hereditary emphysema, AAT is absent or abnormal, lifting control on elastase levels. The enzyme eats away at delicate lung inner surfaces.

Only 2 percent of emphysema cases are inherited. Prolonged cigarette smoking causes many of the remainder. Chemical irritants in smoke attract white blood cells to the irritated lungs but alter AAT so it cannot protect against the ravages of excess elastase. Gene therapies currently in development will deliver the AAT gene to lung connective tissue cells of people with hereditary emphysema, either on a retrovirus or in liposomes.

Nerve Tissue

Many common illnesses and injuries affect the nervous system, including seizures, strokes, spinal cord injuries, and degenerative disorders such as Alzheimer disease, Parkinson disease, Huntington disease, and amyotrophic lateral sclerosis. Gene therapy of nervous tissue therefore isn't restricted to inherited disease. If a protein is known that could be used to correct an abnormal situation, then cell implants or gene delivery can possibly heal.

So far, herpes viruses, which naturally enter neurons, are the best routes to nervous system gene therapy. Retroviruses are not useful because neurons do not divide, although they can be used on the supportive glia cells that do divide. Naked DNA cannot enter neurons easily, and liposomes enter, but not as well as do herpes viruses.

As with other conditions, gene therapy of nervous tissue starts with identifying an involved protein and choosing a vector. In an experiment to treat spinal cord injuries in rats, for example, some of the animals' skin cells were removed and genetically altered to produced a growth factor. When introduced as part of a herpes virus vector near the damaged neurons in the rats' brains, affected cells produced the growth factor, which stimulated limited cell growth. The rats began to walk, and the effect lasted a few months.

To treat the movement disorder Parkinson disease, gene therapy attempts to restore the ability of cells in a part of the brain called the substantia nigra to manufacture the neurotransmitter dopamine. Because dopamine is not a protein, the therapy uses a herpes virus to enable neurons to produce tyrosine hydroxylase, which is an enzyme necessary to synthesize dopamine. In rats, such correction increased levels of the enzyme and the neurotransmitter. Symptom severity diminished.

N early a half century after Linus Pauling discovered that abnormal hemoglobin causes sickle cell disease, the National Heart, Lung and Blood Institute announced the first available treatment—a drug called hydroxyurea. The road to that treatment was an interesting meeting of cell biology, chemistry, and biophysics.

"Like Having Your Hand Caught in a Car Door"

At the molecular level, sickle cell disease is a chain reaction, beginning with a missense mutation in the beta globin gene that replaces a glutamic acid with valine at the sixth amino acid position (figures 10.3 and 10.4). The valine protrudes from the otherwise globular molecule, causing it to latch onto other beta globin molecules. After a few seconds, the abnormal beta globins stick to each other and rapidly form sheets that bend the red blood cell. The red blood cell's membrane changes and exposes receptors that glue it to blood vessel linings.

The sickle-shaped, sticky cells lodge in the small passageways of the circulatory system—but only when the blood is low in oxygen. (Globin molecules have slightly different shapes, depending upon the presence of oxygen.) The blocked circulation causes the acute pain of a sickle cell crisis. This is an apt term—one boy described the pain as similar to having your hand crushed in a car door.

Sickled red blood cells live only 20 days, compared to the normal 120-day life span, and as they die, anemia develops. The spleen works overtime to handle the onslaught of dying cells, abandoning its immune functions. Infections grow more troublesome. Newborn screening detects babies who have inherited sickle cell disease, and doctors administer prophylactic antibiotics from then on to prevent infections. Blood transfusions and pain medication can help during crises. Hydroxyurea can prevent flare-ups but also increases the risk of developing leukemia.

A Clue from Fetuses

The road to using hydroxyurea began with an observation: people who had a blood abnormality called "hereditary persistence of fetal hemoglobin" (HPFH) were healthy or had very mild anemia. Adult hemoglobin consists of two alpha chains and two beta chains, each encoded by a separate gene. Fetal hemoglobin, adapted to the different oxygen requirements before birth, consists of two alpha chains and two delta chains. After six months of age, beta chains gradually replace the delta chains. The beta and delta globin genes lie beside each other on chromosome 11.

The fact that people with HPFH are healthy proved that fetal hemoglobin does no harm in an adult. Could "turning on" fetal hemoglobin cure a disorder of the beta chains—such as sickle cell disease?

Biochemists knew that, in adults, the inactive delta genes are normally shrouded in methyl groups (a carbon atom bonded to three hydrogen atoms). A drug that removes the methyl groups might expose the delta genes. If these genes were transcribed and translated, they might produce delta globins that could replace the abnormal beta globins.

Drug Trials

In 1982, researchers found that a drug called 5-azacytidine indeed removed the methyl groups and raised the proportion of fetal hemoglobin. But this drug causes cancer, and therefore couldn't be used for the many years necessary to treat sickle cell disease.

The next piece in the puzzle was the discovery that 5-azacytidine not only removes methyl groups, but is also toxic to (or "stresses") red blood cells. Which effect actually caused production of fetal hemoglobin? Researchers found that an existing, safer drug, hydroxyurea, also stresses the cells that give rise to red blood cells. Could it be used to turn on fetal globin genes?

From 1984 till 1992, experiments in monkeys, healthy humans, and sickle cell disease patients showed that hydroxyurea raises fetal hemoglobin levels. A trial began on 299 adults to see if this effect improved symptoms—half of the group received the

Even though neurons can take up and express foreign genes, they are not ideal targets for gene therapy because they normally do not divide. Using other cell types can overcome this limitation. Consider a gene treatment for mice injured in the part of the brain that degenerates in Alzheimer disease. Fibroblasts given a gene for nerve growth factor were implanted at the wound site. They secreted the growth factor, and nearby neurons grew and secreted the neurotransmitter. This type of treatment may also help treat Huntington disease and clinical depression.

Key Concepts

Gene therapy applies to many different sites in the body. Altered stem cells can treat blood disorders. Skin cells can be genetically altered in culture, expanded, then grafted onto animals, where they secrete foreign gene products. Altered endothelium, implanted in blood vessels, could secrete proteins into the bloodstream. Muscle deficiencies may be treated by direct DNA application or by implanting donated healthy or corrected myoblasts. Liver cells given LDL receptors can take up excess cholesterol in the bloodstream. Disabled cold viruses can carry genes into lung cells. Nerve cells can be exposed to altered herpes viruses or affected by altering other cell types near them.

drug, half received a placebo. By 1995, re-searchers called off the study. The partici-pants receiving the drug were doing so much better than the others that it was un-ethical to deny the placebo group treat-ment. The patients receiving hydroxyurea had far fewer crises and needed fewer transfusions. However, researchers are still studying the risks this drug may present if taken for many years.

A Curious Mechanism

The way hydroxyurea works shows how bi-ology, chemistry, and physics converge. First, the drug increases the proportion of delta (fetal) globin molecules. Some of the delta globins bind to mutant beta globins, preventing them from forming the sheets that bend red blood cells, blocking circula-tion (figure 1). This also prolongs the time it takes for the mutant beta globin chains to join, simply because gamma chains are now in the mix. The time is long enough for a red blood cell to return to the lungs. When the cell picks up oxygen, sickling cannot occur. By slowing the sickling process, hy-droxyurea corrects a devastating phenotype.

Teaming hydroxyurea with the kidney hormone erythropoietin (EPO) might work even better because EPO stimulates bone marrow to produce more red blood cells. Other compounds are also being tested for their ability to reactivate dor-mant fetal globin genes.

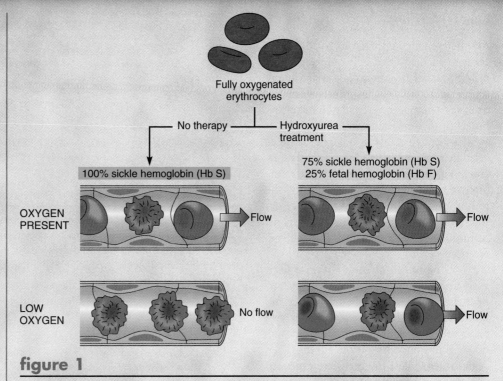

figure 1

Hydroxyurea stimulates production of fetal hemoglobin (Hb F), which dilutes sickled hemoglobin (Hb S). With less polymerized hemoglobin, the red cells do not bend out of shape as much and can reach the lungs. Oxygen restores the cells' shapes, averting a sickling crisis.

Gene Therapy Against Cancer

About half of current gene therapy trials target cancer. Molecular surgery and ma-nipulation of the immune response are two promising strategies.

Molecular Surgery— Targeting Brain Tumors

Viruses may treat a type of brain tumor called a glioma, which affects the glial cells that support and interact with neurons. Unlike neurons, glia can divide. Cancer-ous glia divide very fast, usually causing death within a year. Based on the differ-ence between the dividing capacities of neurons and glia, researchers reasoned that an agent directed against only divid-ing cells might halt the cancer. One candi-date was a "suicide" gene from the herpes simplex virus. In the presence of a certain drug, activation of the gene causes the cell containing it to die. Would cancer cells infected with the virus that harbors this gene perish?

The herpes gene therapy system has several components (figure 18.7). Mouse fibroblasts are infected with a retrovirus vector that contains the herpes gene encod-ing an enzyme, thymidine kinase. Any cell that produces thymidine kinase is suscepti-ble to the anti-herpes drug ganciclovir. Be-cause a retrovirus can only infect dividing cells, it should not harm nondividing, healthy brain neurons.

The booby-trapped mouse fibroblasts are injected into the brain tumor in very ill patients (a hole is drilled in the skull). There, the implanted cells produce the viruses, which infect neighboring tumor cells, which then produce thymidine kinase. When the patient takes ganciclovir, the drug is changed into a toxin that kills the cell and nearby cells. A few people have greatly improved.

Cancer Vaccines

Another genetic approach to battling cancer is to enable tumor cells to produce immune system biochemicals or to mark tumor cells so that the immune system recognizes them more easily. These approaches are called cancer vaccines.

In ex vivo trials, a patient's cancer cells are removed, altered in a way that attracts an immune response, then reimplanted into the patient. Specifically, the tumor cells are altered to overproduce cytokines (such as interleukins, interferons, or tumor necrosis factor) or HLA cell surface molecules.

Melanoma, an often-fatal skin cancer, is amenable to both ex vivo and in situ treatment, because it is on the body's surface and therefore accessible. In one group of ex vivo experiments, melanoma cells are removed, given genes encoding interleukins, then reimplanted, where the genes are expressed and evoke an immune response.

In in situ experiments, researchers inject liposomes bearing genes encoding HLA proteins directly into tumors. Figure 18.8 describes this approach for an HLA protein called HLA-B7. This protein, when displayed on tumor cell surfaces, stimulates the immune system to respond to the tumor as if it was foreign tissue.

Key Concepts

Gene therapies used to fight cancer include molecular "surgery" and cancer vaccines. A herpes simplex gene for thymidine kinase, carried into glioma cells on a retrovirus, can selectively target cancer cells, when the patient takes an anti-herpes drug. Tumors can be altered to synthesize immune system biochemicals or to bear surface markers that evoke an immune system response.

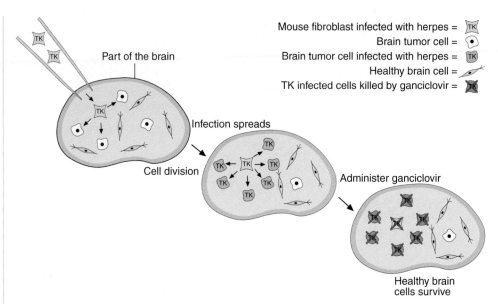

Mouse fibroblast infected with herpes = [TK]
Brain tumor cell = ⊙
Brain tumor cell infected with herpes = [TK]
Healthy brain cell = ⤙
TK infected cells killed by ganciclovir = ✖

figure 18.7

A herpes virus attacks cancer. When mouse fibroblasts harboring a thymidine kinase gene from the herpes simplex virus, in a retrovirus vector, are implanted near the site of a brain tumor, the engineered viruses infect the rapidly dividing tumor cells. When the patient takes the antiviral drug ganciclovir, the cells producing thymidine kinase are selectively killed, providing a gene-based cancer treatment from within.

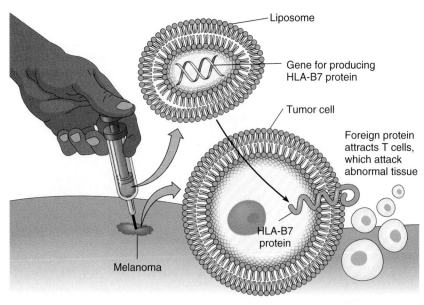

figure 18.8

A gene that encodes a cell surface protein that attracts the immune system's tumor-killing T cells is injected directly into a melanoma tumor.

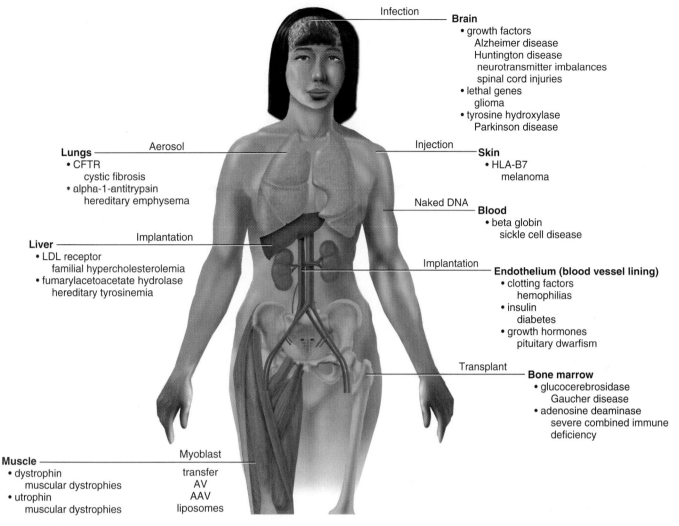

figure 18.9

Gene therapy sites. Beneath the label for each site are listed the targeted protein (•) and then the disease.

Perspective: A Slow Start, But Great Promise

When the age of gene therapy dawned in the 1990s, expectations were high—and for good reason. Work in the 1980s had clearly shown abundant, pure, human biochemicals, useful as drugs, could come from recombinant single cells and from transgenic organisms. It was merely a matter of time, researchers speculated, until genetic altering of somatic tissue would routinely treat a variety of ills.

In reality, gene therapy progress has been slow. Boys with DMD who receive myoblasts with healthy dystrophin genes do not walk again. People with cystic fibrosis who sniff viruses bearing the CFTR gene do not enjoy vastly improved lung function. Genetic correction for babies with SCID given normal ADA genes in umbilical cord stem cells take years, with only partial correction achieved.

Perhaps we expected too much too soon. The fact is, at a molecular and cellu-

lar level, gene therapy *is* working. The patients with muscular dystrophy, cystic fibrosis, and SCID have cells that have accepted and expressed therapeutic genes. The challenge now is to find just the right vector to deliver a sustained, targeted, genetic correction without alerting the immune system.

As figure 18.9 indicates, we are well on the way toward making gene therapy an important part of medical practice.

summary

1. Researchers can correct some mutant phenotypes by replacing deficient or abnormal proteins or the genes that encode them. **Somatic gene therapy** affects somatic tissue and is not passed to offspring. **Germline gene therapy** affects gametes or fertilized ova, affects all cells of an individual, and is transmitted to future generations.

2. Gene therapy uses technology to obtain tissue, deliver new genes, implant the tissue, and encourage production of a needed substance at appropriate times and in therapeutic (not toxic) amounts.

3. Several types of viral vectors are used in gene therapy. **Ex vivo gene therapy** is applied to cells outside the body that are then reimplanted or reinfused into the patient. **In situ gene therapy** occurs directly on accessible body parts. **In vivo gene therapy** is applied in the body.

4. Stem cells are important targets of gene therapy because they are pluripotent and divide. Fetal yolk sacs, umbilical cord blood, and bone marrow are sources of stem cells.

5. Genetically altered skin and endothelium secrete biochemicals into the bloodstream. Researchers can implant healthy or genetically altered **myoblasts** into dystrophic muscle or deliver therapeutic genes directly to muscle. Liver cells given genes for LDL receptors admit more cholesterol, lowering serum cholesterol levels. Aerosols deliver disabled cold viruses carrying needed genes to the lungs. Herpes viruses are used in nervous system gene therapy to treat inherited degenerative diseases and injuries.

6. Gene therapy against cancer consists of a herpes virus gene that renders cells that express it susceptible to an antiviral drug. Cancer vaccines give tumor cells the ability to synthesize cytokines or HLA proteins, which then attract an immune response.

review questions

1. Explain the differences between ex vivo, in situ, and in vivo gene therapy. Give an example of each.

2. Would somatic gene therapy or germline gene therapy have the potential to affect evolution? Cite a reason for your answer.

3. Figure 16.3 illustrates the difference between cancer-causing somatic and constitutional mutations. How is this distinction similar to that between somatic and germline gene therapy?

4. What factors would a researcher consider in selecting a viral vector for gene therapy?

5. Do eyeglasses correct one's phenotype or genotype?

6. Describe what is happening in the following (real life) clinical trials for gene therapies designed to treat cancer. Identify the vector, the gene, and how the therapy might correct the phenotype.

   a. A retrovirus carrying the interleukin-2 gene is delivered to the lungs of people with lung cancer.

   b. Lipids are used to deliver HLA genes to people with malignant melanoma.

   c. A wild type p53 gene is delivered on an adenovirus vector to treat liver cancer.

   d. A herpes simplex thymidine kinase gene inserted into a retrovirus is used to treat head and neck cancer.

7. What are two challenges in providing gene therapy for Duchenne muscular dystrophy?

applied questions

1. Why is Andrew Gobea's gene therapy for ADA deficiency expected to be longer lasting than the treatment that Ashanti DeSilva and Cynthia Cutshall received?

2. Hereditary emphysema, SCID, and familial hypercholesterolemia are all very rare inherited conditions. Why are they used as models for developing gene therapies if so few people are affected?

3. Genes can be transferred into the cells that form hair follicles. Would gene therapy to treat baldness most likely be ex vivo, in situ, or in vivo? Cite a reason for your answer.

4. Suggest three specific ways to use protein or gene therapy to treat sickle cell disease.

5. Gene therapies to treat cystic fibrosis and Duchenne muscular dystrophy using an adenovirus vector have produced disappointing results because the patient's immune system attacks the adenovirus on repeated exposure. Suggest a way to circumvent this problem.

6. A drug called butyrate is a possible treatment for sickle cell disease because it delays the switch from gamma globin (and fetal hemoglobin) to beta globin (and adult hemoglobin), and may even turn the fetal genes back on in a child. How would this drug prevent symptoms from developing?

suggested readings

The June 1997 issue of *Scientific American* has several articles on gene therapy.

Anderson, W. French. April 30, 1998. Human gene therapy. *Nature,* vol. 392 supplement. An update on routes to human gene therapy.

Blau, Helen, and Paul Khavari. June 1997. Gene therapy: progress, problems, prospects. *Nature Medicine,* vol. 3. Development of gene therapy has been slow, but steady.

Caplen, Natasha J., and Eric Alton. April 15, 1996. Gene therapy for cystic fibrosis. *Chemistry and Industry.* The challenge in gene therapy for CF is to correct enough cells to see an effect.

Cole-Strauss, A. September 6, 1996. Correction of the mutation responsible for sickle cell anemia by an RNA-DNA oligonucleotide. *Science,* vol. 273. Healing oligonucleotides can restore function to mutant beta globin genes.

Dickson, George. April 15, 1996. Gene therapy of Duchenne muscular dystrophy. *Chemistry and Industry.* Many approaches are being tried to treat DMD.

Friedmann, Ted. February 1995. Standing in the way of gene therapy. *Nature Medicine,* vol. 2. Our immune systems are hampering gene therapy efforts.

Goldberg, Jeff. April 1998. A head full of hope. *Discover.* A personal account of drastic gene therapy.

Lewis, Ricki. March 1993. Genes to the rescue. *The World and I.* Adeno-associated virus, given a parvovirus gene, can alter the cells that give rise to red blood cells, providing a way to synthesize therapeutics right in the bloodstream.

Lewis, Ricki. April 3, 1995. End of century marks dawn of clinical trial era for cancer vaccines. *The Scientist.* Gene therapy that alerts the immune system to a cancer is also called a cancer vaccine.

Lewis, Ricki. April 1, 1995. Gene transfer methods evolve as technology moves potential products toward the market. *Genetic Engineering News.* Choosing and designing the vector is the key to effectively targeted gene therapy.

Lewis, Ricki. April 15, 1998. Suicide gene therapy kills human cancer in lab mice. *Genetic Engineering News.* A herpes virus helps destroy tumor cells.

Miller, A. D. March 1997. Putting muscle to work for gene therapy. *Nature Medicine,* vol. 3. AAV can be used to directly introduce doctored DNA into muscle cells.

Pardoll, Drew M. May 1998. Cancer vaccines. *Nature Medicine,* vol. 4. Vaccine supplement. The immune system can be boosted to fight cancer recurrence.

Platt, Orah S. April 1995. Sickle cell paths converge on hydroxyurea. *Nature Medicine,* vol. 1. Turning on fetal genes tempers this inherited disorder.

Sly, William S., and Carole Vogler. July 1997. Gene therapy for lysosomal storage disease; A no-brainer? *Nature Medicine,* vol 3. A mouse model is helping researchers develop gene therapy for Sly disease (see chapter 2, Applied Question 5).

Verma, Inder M., and Nikunj Somia. September 18, 1997. Gene therapy—promises, problems and prospects. *Nature,* vol. 389. Progress in gene therapy has been slow, but steady.

Vile, Richard G. April 15, 1996. Gene therapy for treating cancer—hope or hype? *Chemistry and Industry.* Genes are being used to stop cancer.

chapter nineteen

Agricultural and Environmental Biotechnology

Mustard from plant engineered to contain more heart-healthy oils

French fries from altered potatoes with more starch to absorb less oil in cooking

Wheat and sesame seeds from herbicide-resistant crops

Pickle from cucumber that produces its own insecticide

Ketchup from high-solids, slow-ripening tomato

Beef from extra-lean cows

Cheese made with milk from cows given recombinant bovine growth hormone

figure 19.1

Someday, much of our food may come from genetically altered organisms.

Not Your Average Salad Bar

At a recent biotechnology conference, attendees were treated to an unusual meal. A salad of peas, carrots, and peppers was exceptionally tasty, courtesy of genetic manipulation that promotes sweetness. Nongreasy french fries came from potatoes altered to contain more starch, and thereby to absorb less cooking oil. Flounder fillets came from fish that reach market size a year before their nongenetically altered counterparts. The flour in the biscuits came from soybeans that made their own insecticide. The tomato sauce on the pasta, made from a high-solids tomato, was a bit bland, prompting one discriminating diner to comment, "It needs some genetically engineered Tabasco sauce." Science can't do everything!

One needn't attend a biotechnology conference to sample genetically engineered foods. Many crop plants are genetically altered to withstand pesticides or low temperatuares. Milk on many supermarket shelves comes from cows that received bovine growth hormone manufactured in recombinant bacteria, boosting their milk yields 10 percent.

As the new century dawns, more and more foods will likely come from organisms that have received genes to create highly specific phenotypes suited to human uses (figure 19.1). Agricultural biotechnology will also impact on such varied industries as food processing, pharmaceuticals, forestry, and fabrics. Table 19.1 lists some desirable characteristics that can be genetically introduced into plants, and table 19.2 lists some new types of foods available from plant biotechnology. However, these products will have to be proved safe and be accepted by consumers.

Economic, Ecological, and Evolutionary Concerns

Agricultural biotechnology—altering DNA, organelles, or cells of organisms that we use for a variety of purposes—can be controversial, because we can't always predict the consequences of our manipulations. Producing foods that are more healthful and easier to market may seem beneficial, particularly in the potential to feed populations suffering from food shortages. However, the opposite may occur.

Consider canola oil, a product of the rapeseed plant. A transgenic rapeseed plant given a gene from the California bay tree gains an enzyme that alters the lengths of some of its fatty acids, producing substances called lauric oils that are

table 19.1

Genetically Engineered Traits in Crop Plants

Resistance to insects, insecticides, and herbicides

Slowed ripening

Larger fruits

Improved sweetness

Faster or more uniform growth

Additional nutrients

Easier processing

Pharmaceutical production

Insecticide production

Ability to fix nitrogen, decreasing fertilizer requirements

used to manufacture soap and shampoos. We traditionally extract lauric oils from coconuts and palms imported from southeast Asia. Genetically rerouting domestic rapeseed plants to produce the valuable oils diverts funds that would otherwise go to poor southeastern Asian farmers.

Ecological concerns compound economic considerations. Some biologists fear that the genes that give crop plants the characteristics we want could be transferred to wild and weedy relatives. For example,

table 19.2

Agricultural Biotechnology Products

On the Market or Being Tested	Advantage
Canola with high-laurate oil	Can be grown domestically; less costly than importing palm and coconut oils
Carrot bites and sticks	Improved taste
Delayed ripening tomato	Extended shelf life
Herbicide-resistant cotton	Makes possible use of previously toxic herbicide
Minipeppers	Improved flavor, few seeds
Recombinant bovine growth hormone	Increased milk production in cows

On the Market by 2001	
Bananas resistant to fungal infection	Extended shelf life
Delayed-ripening bananas and pineapples	Extended shelf life
Elongated sweet pepper	Improved flavor, easier to slice
Engineered cotton fiber	Easier fabric manufacturing
Engineered paper pulp trees	Paper component (lignin) easier to process
High-starch potatoes	Absorbs less oil on frying
Insecticide-resistant cotton	Makes possible use of previously toxic insecticide
Pest-resistant corn	Can grow in presence of European corn borer
Seedless minimelons	Single serving size
Sweet peas and peppers	Retain sweetness longer
Salmon with growth hormone genes added	Growth rate doubled, faster to market
Weather-hardy strawberries	Survive freezing and thawing

figure 19.2

Bollgard cotton is transgenic. It produces a bacterial (*Bacillus thuringiensis*) protein that destroys the digestive systems of pests such as the bollworm and budworm.

Monsanto (St. Louis)

herbicide-resistant rapeseed could pass the resistance gene to birdscrape mustard or wild mustard, which are troublesome weeds. Another ecological concern is that creating plants that can grow in the presence of toxic herbicides and insecticides will encourage use of these chemicals.

On a broader scale, altering the genetic makeup of a species for human benefit is playing with evolution. Introducing an organism with a selective advantage depletes natural genetic diversity as the altered individuals come to predominate in populations. For example, transgenic carp that grow 40 percent faster than normal because they have a growth hormone gene from rainbow trout will outcompete slower-growing fish and lead the population toward genetic uniformity. This is a setup for disaster. Should an environmental change render the alteration a liability, entire populations could perish.

Using biotechnology to increase the use of insecticides and herbicides can also encourage persistence of pests that are resistant to the chemicals. This has happened with insect-killing proteins that come from spores of the bacterium *Bacillus thuringiensis,* called Bt toxins. Farmers have used the protein as an insecticide for 30 years by drying out bacterial spores and spreading the material on crops. Different varieties and combinations of Bt toxins target flies, beetles, and moths, but they do not harm other animals. Normally, sunlight degrades the insecticide within days. The use of this insecticide has been so pervasive that in some places, resistant insects are already beginning to take over pest populations.

Today, use of Bt toxins as insecticides is even more widespread, because transgenic crops produce them. In 1997, about 20 percent of the U.S. corn crop, totaling 14 million acres, consisted of transgenic

corn that makes the bacterial pesticide (figure 19.2). Alfalfa, canola, soy, wheat and sorghum also manufacture Bt toxins. Because these crops will almost certainly ease persistence of resistant insects, farmers are also growing nonengineered crops. This maintains some nonresistant insects, which mate with the resistant ones and keeps entire pest populations from becoming resistant to this long-used insecticide.

Traditional Breeding versus Biotechnology

Biotechnology of multicellular organisms requires several steps, with interventions at the molecular, cellular, organismal, and eventually ecological levels. Chapter 17 addressed the methods used to genetically alter cells. Then, a mature individual is regenerated from the altered cells. Breeding experiments may then be necessary to obtain individuals with the desired trait. If the trait is recessive, heterozygotes are bred to produce a homozygous recessive individual.

The organisms are then observed in conditions like those in the natural environment, such as greenhouses for plants, soil microenvironments or bioreactors for bacteria, and tanks or pens for animals. Figure 19.3 outlines the general steps for plants. Because the other chapters concentrate on human and other animal biotechnologies, we will concentrate here on plant biotechnology.

figure 19.3

The steps of plant biotechnology. Note that different biotechnologies can alter, silence, or replace a gene.

Gene transfer

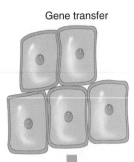

Gene inactivation (gene targeting, antisense)

or

Tissue explant

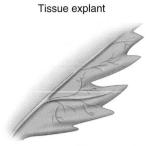

or

Plant regeneration

Plant reproduces and transmits trait of interest

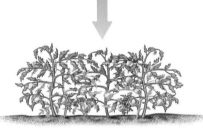

Propogation in greenhouse

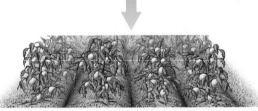

Grow from seed in field under normal conditions

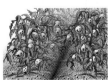

Pests

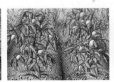

Pesticides Herbicides

Temperature extremes

Salinity extremes

pH extremes

Drought

A longer-term goal of agricultural biotechnology is to discover desirable combinations of traits. Although most biotechnologies manipulate one inherited trait at a time, traditional breeding shows that valuable characteristics are often a combination of traits. Consider viticulture—wine making. Viticulturists have meticulously bred the combination of traits that make a flavorful wine grape over the centuries. Wine producers are understandably wary of biotechnology's ability to rapidly and drastically alter grapes! Nevertheless, researchers have already developed transgenic buds of the grapes used to manufacture cabernet sauvignon and chardonnay wines.

The steps in traditional plant breeding and biotechnology are similar. First, researchers identify and breed, or engineer, an interesting trait into a plant whose other characteristics comprise a valuable package. For example, larger fruit size might be desirable in a plant that can already withstand temperature extremes and resist pests. The new variety is then tested in various habitats and seasons to determine the best growth conditions. Finally, seeds are distributed to growers.

Traditional plant breeding introduces new varieties by a sexual route. The male gamete (sperm nucleus) that pollen produces carries a set of genes that may differ from the set in the female gamete (egg cell) of the ovule, even if both types of sex cells derive from the same plant. Because each gamete contributes a different combination of the parent plant's traits, offspring from a single cross are not genetically uniform—some plants may be taller, more robust, or may produce smaller seeds than others. Such genetic diversity is a direct consequence of meiosis and illustrates Mendel's laws.

In contrast, most biotechnologies do not begin with sperm and egg, which have a half set of genetic instructions each, but with somatic (body) cells, which form nonsexual parts of the plant such as leaves and stems. Cells taken from embryos are another source of somatic tissue. Somatic cells contain a complete set of genetic instructions. Plants regenerated from somatic cells of the same plant do not have the unpredictable mixture of traits that plants derived from sexual reproduction do, because the somatic cells are usually

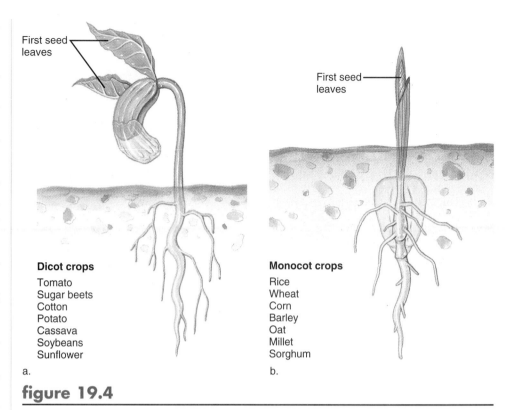

First seed leaves

First seed leaves

Dicot crops
Tomato
Sugar beets
Cotton
Potato
Cassava
Soybeans
Sunflower

a.

Monocot crops
Rice
Wheat
Corn
Barley
Oat
Millet
Sorghum

b.

figure 19.4

(*a*) A dicot, such as this bean plant, has two seed leaves. (*b*) A monocot, such as this corn plant, has one seed leaf.

genetic replicas, or clones, of each other. Biotechnology, then, offers a degree of precision and can assure consistency in crop quality from season to season. However, biotechnological approaches are usually much more expensive than using conventional seeds.

Biotechnology can alter plant structure or function at the level of the gene, the organelle, or the cell.

Transgenic Technology in Plants

Bacteria are often the source of genes transferred to plants because they can confer useful traits such as built-in resistance to disease, insecticides, herbicides, and environmental extremes. The donor DNA, as well as the vector DNA that transports it into the plant cell, are cut with the same restriction enzyme so that they can attach to each other at the ends to form a recombinant molecule, as chapter 17 describes. The vector and its cargo gene are then placed into the plant cell.

Gene Transfer in Dicots and Monocots

Plant cells seem to have preferences about how they take up DNA. Dicots are plants that produce two seed (also called first) leaves, and they include cucumbers, squashes, and beans (figure 19.4a). Ti plasmids are used to introduce genes into dicots (see figure 17.5).

Examples abound of dicots with new traits, thanks to Ti plasmids. Sugar beets are rendered herbicide-resistant. This is an important trait because 37 percent of the world's sugar supply relies on this difficult-to-grow crop. Tomatoes are altered to display a protein on their cell surfaces that "fools" the tomato spotted wilt virus so that it does not infect them, in a manner similar to the way a vaccine works.

In contrast to a dicot, which lives and forms a lump of unspecialized tissue at the site of Ti plasmid infection, a monocot (a plant with one seed leaf, as in figure 19.4b) dies when a Ti plasmid infects it. Researchers must transfer genes into monocots in other ways. This is important because the monocots include the cereals (rice, corn, wheat, and others), which feed half the world's people. Gene transfer techniques such as electroporation, microinjection, and particle acceleration (table 17.2) made genetic engineering of monocots feasible for rice in 1988, for corn in 1990, for wheat in 1992, and for sorghum in 1994.

Applications of Transgenic Plants

Transgenic plants can be used in a variety of ways.

Nutrition

By altering protein-encoding genes or the genes that specify enzymes that control production of lipids or carbohydrates, researchers can tailor the nutritional value of a food. For example, changing the number and types of genes for gluten proteins alters the quality of dough that can be made from a particular strain of wheat. Figure 19.5 shows the dramatic effects of placing a gene conferring herbicide resistance into soybeans. Table 19.3 lists some applications of recombinant DNA technology or transgenic technology in crop plants.

Pharmaceutical Production

Transgenic plants, particularly seeds, can also serve as drug factories by harboring genes encoding proteins with therapeutic value, such as cytokines (immune system biochemicals) and blood clotting factors. Seeds are useful because they are abundant, easy to store, resistant to environmental extremes, and are alive. Soybeans are especially efficient miniprotein factories, because they are 40 to 45 percent protein. Corn is also a candidate for pharmaceutical production. Protein comprises only 10 to 12 percent of a corn kernel, but a single plant yields many kernels.

Vaccines

A new type of vaccine is a vegetable. The vaccine is a transgenic plant that produces part of an antigen that triggers an immune response from lymphocytes associated with

figure 19.5

The soybeans on the left contain a viral gene that enables them to grow in the presence of glyphosate, a commercial herbicide. Exposure to the herbicide severely stunts growth of the unaltered plants on the right.

the human digestive tract. A potato-based vaccine, for example, protects against diarrhea caused by *E. coli*. Another vegetable vaccine consists of potatoes that protect against hepatitis. Vaccines taken in cereals or other plant-based foods would be extremely useful in developing nations, where conventional vaccines and clean, disposable syringes are often in short supply.

Textiles

Cotton plants transgenic for Bt toxins resist bollworm and budworm infections. The plants require little or no nonbiological insecticide, and yields are usually higher than with traditional crops.

Cotton can be improved in other ways. For example, two genes from a bacterium, *Alcaligenes eutrophus,* work with a cotton gene to produce poly-hydroxybutyrate (PHB), a plastic! A gene gun sends bacterial genes into cotton plant embryos. Plastic granules form within the cellulose strands, so they are not noticeable in cotton fabric. This naturally plasticized cot-

ton retains heat longer than unaltered cotton fibers and may be very useful in making outdoor clothing.

Paper and Wood Products

Development of transgenic trees has lagged somewhat behind other applications, mostly because the generation time of a tree is so long, and regenerating plants from altered cells is difficult. However, several poplar species are emerging as valuable model systems for experimenting with transgenic trees. Researchers can evaluate new phenotypes on trees too young to reproduce, or incorporate sterility genes into experimental trees to control or contain the spread of novel traits.

Several types of genetic manipulations can ease paper processing. For example, part of the process is to remove lignin, which comprises 15 to 35 percent of the dry weight of wood. Identifying genes that minimize lignin production and adding them to commercially valuable trees can lower the cost of removing it.

table 19.3

Recombinant DNA Solutions to Agricultural Challenges

Challenge	Possible Solution
Crops are damaged by frost	Spray crops with bacteria genetically altered to lack surface proteins that promote ice crystallization. Bacteria can also be manipulated to encourage ice crystallization, used to increase snow buildup in winter sports facilities.
Crops are damaged by herbicides and pesticides	Isolate genes from an organism not affected by the chemical and engineer the gene into the crop plant.
Crops need costly nitrogen fertilizer because atmospheric nitrogen is not biologically usable	Short term: genetically engineer nitrogen-fixing *Rhizobium* bacteria to overproduce enzymes that convert atmospheric nitrogen to a biologically usable form in root nodules of legumes. Alter *Rhizobium* to colonize a wider variety of plants. Long term: transfer *Rhizobium* nitrogen-fixation genes into plant cells and regenerate transgenic plants.
A plant food is low in a particular amino acid	Transfer gene from another species that controls production of a protein rich in the amino acid normally lacking in the crop plant.
A crop plant is killed by a virus	Genetically alter crop plant to manufacture a protein on its cell surface normally found on the virus's surface. Plant becomes immune to virus.
Public concern about the safety of synthetic pesticides	Engineer *Bacillus thuringiensis* to overproduce its natural pesticide, which destroys insects' stomach linings. Transfer *B. thuringiensis* bioinsecticide gene to crop plant.
Fruits and vegetables ripen quickly once picked	Suppress or slow production of ripening enzymes.

Transgenic technology is becoming important in protecting trees from pests. Using either *B. thuringiensis* or a gene gun, larch, white spruce, pioneer elm, and American sweetgum trees have been rendered resistant to attack by gypsy moth and forest tent caterpillars. Poplar trees transgenic for a gene from rice resist attack by the beetle *Chrysomella tremulae,* a major pest. The rice gene enables the trees to manufacture a polypeptide that blocks production of the insects' digestive enzymes. To protect chestnut trees from the chestnut blight fungus *Cryphonectria parasitica,* researchers identified an RNA virus that infects the fungus and greatly lowers its virulence. The cloned virus, added to chestnut trees, enters fungal cells, making the infection less severe.

Poplars can be manipulated to reduce "stress"—the buildup of oxygen free-radicals—by overproducing the enzyme glutathione reductase. Such oxygen stress impairs photosynthesis by damaging chlorophyll, cell membranes, and key enzymes. Plant growth slows, signs of aging accelerate, and susceptibilities to infection increase. Making excess glutathione reductase enables the tree to regenerate glutathione, which helps break down hydrogen peroxide made from superoxide free radicals.

Key Concepts

Biotechnology adds or modifies traits in organisms that provide products. These efforts can have economic, ecological, and evolutionary repercussions. Transgenic plants are generated by introducing foreign DNA into a cell and regenerating a plant from that cell. The plant must express the foreign gene appropriately and transmit it to future generations. Methods of gene transfer include the Ti plasmid in dicots and other methods in monocots. Transgenic traits provide protection and the ability to produce novel substances with diverse applications.

Altering Plants at the Cellular Level

Several techniques that alter, transfer, or combine organelles and cells produce interesting new plant variants (table 19.4). Somatic cells from plants can give rise to regenerated mature plants, unlike the situation in animals; that is, a carrot plant can grow from a carrot leaf cell, though a new person couldn't grow from a skin cell, at least not using current technology.

Protoplast Fusion

A natural impediment to manipulating plant cells is the tough cell wall that surrounds each one. Stripping off this barrier leaves a **protoplast** (figure 19.6), the denuded cell within, which is much more easily manipulated. Protoplasts fused from two different types of plants can yield interesting new hybrids.

Not all altered plant cells yield results useful to humans. Consider the "pomato" plant, which grows from a tomato protoplast fused with a potato protoplast. The regenerated plant produces both types of vegetables in the proper part of the plant, but they are stunted, with tiny seeds. Interesting and potentially useful as this hybrid is, it cannot be propagated. A plant derived from a parsley protoplast fused with a carrot protoplast also produces the desirable parts—carrot roots and parsley leaves—but with seeds that are too small. At least the pomato and carrot/parsley hybrid aren't as useless as a fusion of radish and cabbage protoplasts. The

table 19.4

Cell-based Plant Biotechnologies

Technique	How It Works	Advantage
Artificial seeds	An embryo grown in cell culture from a somatic cell is combined with nutrients and hormones and encased in a gel-like substance	Gives a crop uniform growth and other physical characteristics
Chlybridization	A chloroplast (a plant organelle that converts solar energy into chemical energy) is introduced into a cell in a liposome (a fatty bubble)	Endows cell with increased ability to harness energy
Clonal propagation	Cells are cultured and grown into genetically identical plants	Creates uniform crops that are easier to harvest Speeds growth
Cybridization	Two cells are fused, and the nucleus of one is destroyed by radiation	Yields a cell with a desired combination of organelles
Mibridization	A mitochondrion is introduced into a cell in a liposome	Enhances energy-producing capacity of cell and introduces mitochondrial genes
Mutant selection	Cells in culture are exposed to a toxin; resistant surviving cells are used to start a crop	Creates crops resistant to herbicides, frost, disease
Protoplast fusion	Two cells from different species have their cell walls removed and are fused; a hybrid plant is regenerated	Introduces a plant with a new combination of traits
Somaclonal variation	A mutant somatic cell that is part of a callus grows into a plant with a new trait	Provides an abundant source of new variants

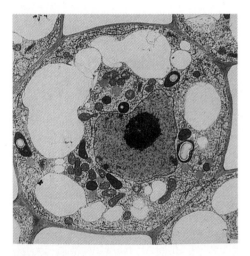

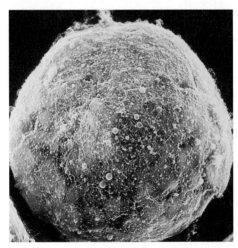

a.   b.

figure 19.6

(a) A plant cell's rigid cell wall gives it a characteristic cuboidal shape. (b) Removing the cell wall leaves a protoplast, which is easier to manipulate.

Callus Culture

Some plant manipulations use undifferentiated plant cells growing in culture. A fascinating thing happens when protoplasts or tiny pieces of plant tissue, called **explants,** are nurtured in a dish with nutrients and plant hormones. After a few days, the cells lose their special characteristics and form a white lump called a **callus.** The lump grows for a few weeks as its cells divide. Then certain cells of the callus grow into either a tiny plantlet with shoots and roots, or a tiny embryo. An embryo grown from callus is called a **somatic embryo** because it derives from somatic, rather than sexual, tissue. Callus growth is apparently unique to plants. In humans, it would be the equivalent of taking a cultured skin cell, multiplying it into a blob of unspecialized tissue, and then sprouting tiny humans or human embryos!

Most of the time, embryos or plantlets grown from a single callus are genetically identical. Sometimes, however, the embryos or plantlets differ because genes in certain of the callus cells mutate. This is an example of somatic mutation, and plants with novel phenotypes are called

not-very-tasty plant grows radish leaves and cabbage roots!

Fusing protoplasts to create new plant hybrids works better when the cells come from related species. For example, when a protoplast from a potato plant normally killed by the herbicide triazine is fused with a protoplast from the wild black nightshade, a relative that is naturally resistant to the herbicide, the resulting potato hybrid grows well in soil treated with triazine to control weeds.

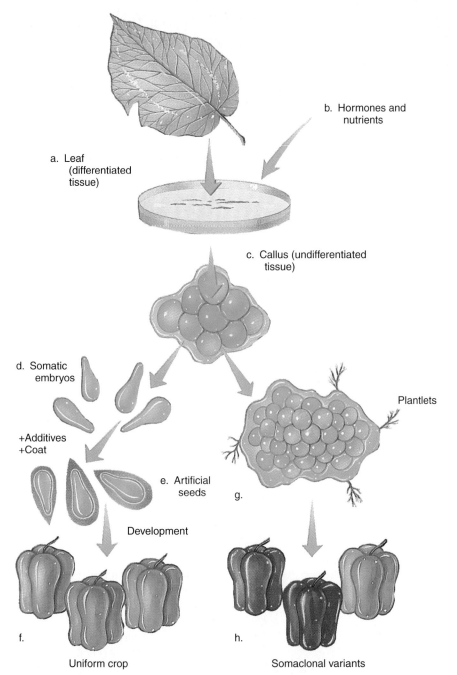

a. Leaf (differentiated tissue)

b. Hormones and nutrients

c. Callus (undifferentiated tissue)

d. Somatic embryos

+Additives +Coat

e. Artificial seeds

g.

Plantlets

Development

f.

Uniform crop

h.

Somaclonal variants

figure 19.7

A callus yields embryos or plantlets. Whether they are genetically identical or somaclonal variants depends upon the culture conditions. Wrapping identical somatic embryos in a gelatinous coat, with nutrients, hormones, and maybe even insecticide, forms artificial seeds, but they are very costly. Plantlets that differ from each other provide interesting new variants, such as stringless celery, crunchier carrots, and buttery popcorn.

somaclonal variants. Biotechnologists can, to some extent, control whether growths from a callus are identical by altering the nutrients and hormones in the culture (figure 19.7). Controlling callus growth is important because agriculture sometimes benefits from a uniform crop, and at other times, seeks new varieties. Corn of the same height, for example, is easier to pick, and tomatoes of uniform water content are easier to boil into commercially prepared sauce than highly variable crops.

Biotechnology Provides Different Routes to Solving a Problem

In the past, farmers were frustrated when herbicides controlled weeds but also killed the crop plants they were meant to protect. The traditional way to render a crop herbicide resistant was to find a weed resistant to the herbicide and related to the crop plant. The hardy weed and its domesticated relative were then crossbred until a variant arose that retained the desired qualities of each parent plant—resistance to the herbicide, plus the characteristics that made the plant a valuable crop. In the past, if an herbicide-resistant crop could not be bred, then the herbicide was simply not used for that plant.

Today, instead of changing herbicides to fit crops (called the "spray and pray" approach), biotechnologists alter crops to fit herbicides. In a technique called **mutant selection,** cells that grow in the presence of the herbicide are isolated and used to regenerate resistant plants (figure 19.8). A callus grown in the presence of the herbicide would yield resistant embryos or plantlets.

Transgenic technology can also be used to design an herbicide-resistant crop. The first step is to identify the biochemical reaction that the herbicide affects in the crop plants. Then, a gene is identified, from any organism, that might enable the plant to prevent or undo whatever damage the herbicide causes. The herbicide-resistant cotton that Reading 19.1 describes illustrates how a protective gene can be incorporated into a crop's genetic makeup.

Key Concepts

It is easier to manipulate plant cells if the cell walls are removed, leaving protoplasts. Fusing protoplasts from different types of plants can produce novel variants. An explant grows into an undifferentiated callus, which may yield plantlets or somatic embryos. Culture conditions can be altered to produce genetically identical plantlets or somatic embryos or somaclonal variants. Mutant selection and transgenic technology can fashion plants with agriculturally useful traits.

Better Tomatoes

Winter tomatoes are typically hard, barely orange orbs that bear little resemblance to the succulent, red fruits of summer. Armed with knowledge of the biochemical basis of ripening, plant biotechnologists have fashioned tomatoes that bring summer richness to grocery bins all year long.

The first genetically altered tomato uses a gene stitched into one of its chromosomes in reverse (figure 19.11). This gene blocks synthesis of a ripening enzyme called poly-galacturonase. The backwards gene encodes mRNA that is an antisense version of the mRNA that normally instructs the cell to make poly-galacturonase. Without the enzyme, which breaks down pectin in the cell wall to cause fruit softening, tomatoes stay on the vine longer, retaining their flavor and firmness—year-round.

Other variations target enzymes responsible for production of ethylene, a plant hormone that hastens ripening. Somaclonal variation has yielded tomatoes in a variety of hues. Biotechnologists are working on tomatoes with increased pectin content for easing tomato paste production, tomatoes with more antioxidants, and tomatoes with controllable ripening rates.

Healthier Squash

We usually associate vaccines with human health care, but crop plants require infection protection too. The Freedom II looks like any yellow crooknecked squash, but on a microscopic level, each cell of this transgenic plant bears antigens that normally come from two squash pathogens—the watermelon mosaic virus and the zucchini yellow mosaic virus.

Freedom II transgenic squash do not succumb to these two viruses, which can decimate from 20 to 80 percent of a crop. A farmer planting these squash can increase yield up to fivefold. On the negative side, some geneticists fear that introducing portions of viruses into plants could plant the seeds for the evolution of new and perhaps more infectious viruses.

Freedom II is the first plant genetically altered to resist disease. However, researchers don't know how it works—to the best of our knowledge, squash lack immune systems.

Herbicide-Resistant Cotton

Not all crop plants produce foods—the U.S. cotton market exceeds $4 billion annually, making our demand for cotton just slightly less than our demand for tomatoes. Farmers use the herbicide bromoxynil to control populations of ragweed, cockleburs, and morning glory that are common weeds among a wide variety of crops. Cotton, however, wasn't among the treated crops because the herbicide kills it. Enter biotechnology. Researchers developed transgenic cotton that harbors a gene from a soil bacterium. This gene encodes an enzyme called nitrilase, which enables cotton to grow in the presence of bromoxynil.

figure 19.8

Mutant selection yields herbicide-resistant corn. The corn plants on the left descended from mutant plants that survived treatment with the herbicide imidazolinone. The herbicide destroyed the nonmutant plants on the right.

table 19.5

Information Sought in Field Tests

1. Can the genetically altered organism survive in the environment outside the laboratory?
2. Can the organism reproduce, and if so, how quickly?
3. Does the genetically altered organism have a selective advantage over species already living in the field environment? Do they compete for resources?
4. Can the transferred gene move to other species?
5. Does the genetically altered organism move beyond the test site? If so, does it move on its own, or by attaching to another organism?

figure 19.9

Researchers conducting the first field tests of genetically engineered microbes wore spacesuits and protective gear. Today, after many successful field tests, these scientists use far less protective equipment.

Release of Genetically Engineered Organisms to the Environment

The first recombinant and transgenic organisms were not meant to exist outside the laboratory. For example, the first recombinant bacteria contained "suicide genes" that turned on, killing the cells, if they escaped the laboratory. Greenhouses contain transgenic plants, and animal facilities separate herds of transgenic goats and sheep from their unaltered brethren.

Borrowing from the biological containment measures used on those first recombinant bacteria, scientists contain fast-growing transgenic fish not only with nets, screens, and electric fences, but with chromosome alterations that render the fish unable to reproduce, should they escape. To do this, normally diploid fish are made triploid—they have three sets of chromosomes. The fish manufacture unbalanced gametes that have two copies of some chromosomes, rather than the normal one. Fertilized ova cannot survive.

Field Tests

Fast-growing fish escapees would be the result of an accident. Some products of agricultural biotechnology, however, are meant to eventually live beyond the confines of a laboratory. At some point, these products must be tested in the field. Table 19.5 lists some of the questions field tests try to answer.

The first field tests of genetically altered organisms sparked public panic (figure 19.9). In 1987, people living near fields where potato and strawberry seedlings were sprayed with "ice-minus" bacteria repeatedly sabotaged the experiments. Their overreaction was especially inappropriate because the bacteria were actually *missing* a gene they normally carried. In the years since, genetically altered plants have not proven to be, as one researcher put it, the "giant rutabagas that ate New Jersey." Today, thousands of field tests of transgenic plants take place each year. Still, some researchers conduct an intermediate type of test, called a microcosm experiment, between the laboratory and the field to assess the environmental readiness of genetically altered bacteria and viruses.

Microcosm Experiments

A microcosm is a recreation of a portion of an ecosystem in a laboratory. To study genetically altered soil-borne bacteria, for example, researchers work with a cylinder of soil about the dimensions of a small drum. Such parameters as pH (acidity or alkalinity), moisture, antibiotic compounds present, temperature, oxygen content, nutrient content, and other organisms present are adjusted to mimic conditions in a natural ecosystem. The test bacteria or viruses are added to the microcosm and the resulting changes monitored. If presence of the microbe adversely affects any component of the microcosm, researchers can avoid a potentially dangerous field test.

A microcosm experiment produced results that prompted researchers to halt field testing of a bacterium genetically altered to be able to convert rotting vegetation to ethanol, an alcohol that is the starting material for many industrial processes. In a microcosm, the altered bacteria not only made ethanol, but they also destroyed fungi that grow on the roots of several types of plants, including many crops. Researchers noticed plants in the microcosm dying. Had these bacteria gone directly from the laboratory to the field, results on native plants would have been disastrous.

Genetically altered bacteria or viruses that pass microcosm and/or field tests can be very useful. A genetically altered virus proved particularly helpful in the 1994 rabies epidemic. Researchers transferred a gene from the rabies virus into *Vaccinia* virus, which was for many years used as a smallpox vaccine. The rabies gene converts *Vaccinia* virus into a rabies vaccine. Fish meal inoculated with the viral vaccine was left in forests as bait, effectively vaccinating many raccoons, the primary source of infection in cats and dogs.

Bioremediation

In **bioremediation,** bacteria or plants with natural or engineered abilities to detoxify certain pollutants are intentionally released or grown in a particular area as a biotechnological approach to cleaning the environment. Natural selection has sculpted such organisms, perhaps as adaptations that render them unpalatable to predators.

One type of tree that grows in a tropical rain forest on an island near Australia accumulates so much nickel from soil that slashing its bark releases a bright green latex ooze. Up to 20 percent of the tree's dry weight may be nickel! Similarly, a microbe called *Citrobacter* absorbs the nuclear wastes plutonium and uranium from contaminated soils. Bioremediation can clean up organic wastes, too. A common pond weed called parrot feather, for example, detoxifies the pollutant trinitrotoluene. Because an enzyme catalyzes the detoxification reaction, biotechnologists hope to borrow its gene and perhaps transfer it to other species.

Detoxifying genes from one microorganism can be transferred to another. Consider a gene from the bacterium *Pseudomonas mendocina,* which specifies the synthesis of toluene monooxygenase. This enzyme degrades trichloroethylene (TCE), an industrial degreaser and solvent found in many polluted areas.

Toluene monooxygenase lowers TCE contamination levels from 20 parts per million to 2 parts per billion—but not without a problem. *Pseudomonas mendocina,* the natural host, requires a constant supply of toluene (another solvent) to activate the enzyme that digests TCE. In the common bacterium *E. coli,* though, the enzyme degrades TCE without toluene. *E. coli* given the *Pseudomonas* toluene monooxygenase gene effectively degrades TCE, leaving behind harmless chemicals and cellular debris.

Bioremediation is helpful in environmental disasters. Ten weeks after a tanker drenched Alaska's once clean Prince William Sound in 11 million gallons of oil, U.S. Environmental Protection Agency workers spread nitrogen and phosphorus fertilizer on 750 areas along the seventy-four miles of oil-slicked shore. The fertilizer stimulated growth of bacteria that consume organic toxins in the oil, specifically polycyclic aromatic hydrocarbons. The pollutants disappeared, and the beaches whitened, five times faster in the treated areas. Similarly, *Pseudomonas* bacteria with a taste for chlorine are used to detoxify polychlorinated biphenyl compounds in Hudson river sediments.

Conserving Genetic Resources

Genes are the raw material of any biotechnology, providing instructions in the language of biochemistry on how to use organisms' great variety of traits. Utilizing natural plant products and microbial processes is an ancient art; identifying, isolating, and perhaps transferring and amplifying genes is a modern science that separates and directs a particular biochemical talent. Yet it is ironic that as genetic technology advances, habitats containing the most diverse species and sources of genes are vanishing. Researchers are thus making efforts to preserve natural genetic diversity in cell and seed banks.

Cell and Seed Banks

Cell and seed banks preserve genetic material from the present to fight future en-

figure 19.10

Pollen, frozen in small plastic ampules, is stored at the cryogenic gene bank at the University of California at Irvine.

dangerment and extinction. The San Diego Zoo maintains a zoo of frozen mammalian connective tissue cells from 2,350 species. The International Rice Research Institute in the Philippines cold stores seeds of more than 70,000 rice variants; the International Potato Institute in Lima, Peru, stores more than 13,000 varieties of potato cells; and the Kansas Agricultural Experimental Station banks wheat cells. Pollen and seeds from 250 endangered species of flowering plants occupy a plant gene bank at the University of California at Irvine (figure 19.10). A technique called vitrification is used to dehydrate seeds before freezing them. This procedure prevents the formation of crystals that can damage tissues.

The world now has more than 700 seed banks, which store more than 2.5 million plant species or variants, many of them wild versions of crops. Some of these banks have been storing seeds for more than 50 years; others started storing seeds following decimation of 70 percent of the U.S. corn corp in 1970 from the Southern corn leaf blight fungus. A male sterility gene that had been widely bred into the crop was closely linked to a gene rendering susceptibility to the fungus. This disaster

Wild, colorless tomatoes

Typical cultivated tomatoes

Cultivated tomatoes given quantitative trait loci, conferring deeper color from wild variant

a.   b.   c.

figure 19.11

Wild species and variants often have unexpressed, yet valuable, inherited characteristics. RFLP maps can identify such useful genes.

vividly demonstrated the danger of relying on a genetically uniform crop. Introducing disease-resistance genes from wild strains restored the crop.

Many modern crop plants are the result of population bottlenecks dictated by intentional selection of traits tailored to human desires. Researchers are attempting to breed more robust crops by using the tools of molecular biology to identify useful genes in wild strains and applying traditional breeding methods to add these genes to cultivated varieties (cultivars). Seed banks are crucial sources of existing, but largely untapped, genetic diversity.

Complex Traits Revisited

Single genes determine most of the disease- and herbicide-resistance traits discussed so far. Other agriculturally valuable characteristics, such as yield, fruit size, and color, more often result from the actions of several genes, called **quantitative trait loci.** RFLP analysis has enabled researchers to identify the genes that lie behind polygenic traits. This is called QTL analysis, and it has revealed two surprises:

1. Not all quantitative loci that contribute to a continuously varying trait do so equally. Some genes have greater effects than others.

2. The phenotype of a plant does not necessarily reveal all of its genetic potential. For example, a plant with small fruits might have some genes that would specify large fruits, if present in a plant with different alleles of other genes. This seems counterintuitive—it is a little like two parents who are very poor in math having a child who is a math genius.

RFLP maps of wild plant genomes are enabling researchers to base breeding decisions on genotype rather than phenotype, which uncovers qualities not necessarily obvious in a parent plant's appearance. This is a new approach for agriculture, and it has already worked in rice and tomatoes.

In tomatoes, a substance called lycopene imparts the red color to the fruit. Domesticated tomatoes have an extra gene at the end of the biosynthetic pathway for lycopene that makes them darker than wild tomatoes. However, wild plants have more active alleles for the enzymes that function earlier in the lycopene pathway. When wild plants, shown by QTL analysis to have these alleles, are bred to domestic plants, the resulting fruits are redder than ever! Similarly, a wild tomato plant with tiny fruits, when bred to domestic plants, produces very large tomatoes (figure 19.11).

In rice, researchers crossed a wild Malaysian species (*Oryza rufipogon*) with an Asian domesticated species (*Oryza sativa*) and grew 300 plants. Sixty of the plants had yields greater than the parent cultivar, indicating that the wild species, thought to be useless, indeed harbored some agriculturally valuable genes. These new types of tomatoes and rice have encouraged researchers to reconsider the great value of seed banks.

Reading 19.2 focuses on genetic manipulation of marine organisms.

Key Concepts

After organisms are genetically altered, they must be tested in microcosms and then in the field to see how they affect natural ecosystems. Bioremediation is the intentional release of organisms that detoxify heavy metals and organic wastes in the environment. Enzyme-catalyzed biochemical reactions carry out the detoxification. These reactions may be a natural part of an organism's biochemistry or may be added transgenically or using recombinant DNA technology. Cell and seed banks are helping preserve genetic diversity and provide a source of gene variants not obvious in phenotypes of wild species.

We know little about the genetics of sea life compared to plant life, but biotechnology is also targeting these organisms. Valuable traits in marine organisms include disease resistance, better flesh texture, faster growth, and broader habitat requirements. Aquaculture is the "farming" of sea life. Following are some examples of how biotechnology is becoming part of aquaculture.

Horseshoe Crab Immunity

Limulus polyphemus, better known as the horseshoe crab, is called a "living fossil" because it has existed, virtually unchanged as far as we can tell, for more than 150 million years. One reason for the animal's longevity is that it has remarkable immunity against bacteria and other infectious microorganisms. When bacteria attempt to infect the crab, its copper-blue blood produces a protein that wedges into the bacterial cell wall, bursting the invading cell. Researchers have cloned this gene in a plasmid and are now attempting to introduce it into talapia salmon, and other fishes, hoping to provide disease resistance.

Prolific Shrimp

Researchers have isolated a protein hormone that increases the rate and clutch number of live larvae that female shrimp release into water. It is normally manufactured in a gland near the animal's jaw. Adding the hormone to culture tanks vastly increases shrimp production Once the gene is isolated, it can be introduced into the shrimp so that they naturally have more offspring.

Super Salmon

On a fish farm on Prince Edward Island, salmon grow at four times their normal

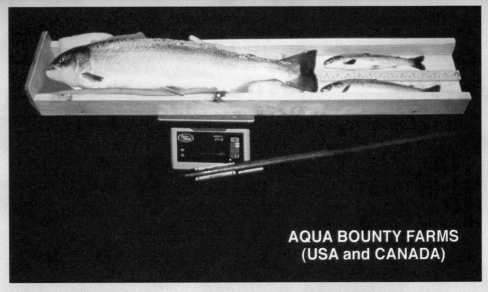

AQUA BOUNTY FARMS (USA and CANADA)

figure 1

Salmon grow faster and larger when a flounder antifreeze gene is attached to their growth hormone gene, because the hormone is produced in winter.

rate and grow to ten times their normal weight (figure 1). The reason—a gene from Arctic flounder that produces an antifreeze protein. The pituitary glands of salmon normally cease production of growth hormone (GH) in the winter, although the liver continues to make it. When the flounder antifreeze gene is stitched into the salmon GH gene, pituitary output of the hormone, and growth, continues, even in the cold. The same technique is being applied to char, turbot, halibut, and trout.

Seaweed

A smorgasbord of biotechnologies is applied to red and brown marine algae. These "seaweeds" are the source of such food additives as agar and carageenan, and a type called *Porphyra* provides "nori," used to make sushi. Transgenic seaweeds and protoplast fusions are producing new types of carageenan with unique gelling properties. Mutant selection has yielded faster-growing seaweed variants. Protoplast fusion has provided new types of *Porphyra* that can tolerate summer heat, improving crop yields.

Fighting Fungi

Bacteria on lobster and squid eggs naturally manufacture proteins that destroy fungi. Researchers are deciphering the biosynthetic pathways for these proteins and will be able to add appropriate genes to species that we use for food to provide built-in protection against fungal infection—courtesy of bacteria.

1. Biotechnology can produce organisms with agriculturally useful traits, but factors beyond the genetic manipulations are important. Genetically altered organisms placed outside the laboratory can affect the balance of species in an ecosystem.

2. Biotechnology differs from traditional plant breeding in that it is asexual, more precise, faster, and considers one trait at a time.

3. Transgenic dicots are created using Ti plasmids as gene vectors. Physical techniques are necessary to add genes to monocots.

4. Traits that can be introduced into crops include herbicide and insecticide resistance, altered flavor, increased uniformity, additional nutrients, and the ability to fix nitrogen. Transgenic seeds can produce drugs and vaccines. Transgenic trees may ease paper and pulp production.

5. **Protoplasts** are plant cells minus cell walls. Fusing protoplasts from two types of plants can create useful variants.

6. Cultured protoplasts or explants can yield a **callus,** which produces plantlets or **somatic embryos.** These may be genetically identical or **somaclonal variants,** depending upon culture conditions.

7. Different biotechnologies can address the same problem. **Mutant selection** and transgenic technology can both generate herbicide-resistant plants.

8. Physical and biological containment methods keep genetically altered organisms under controlled conditions. Organisms intended to be released to the environment are sometimes tested first in microcosms, and then in the field, to determine their survival, fertility, and interactions with other organisms.

9. **Bioremediation** uses an organism's natural or engineered metabolic reactions to detoxify pollutants.

10. Cell and seed banks help preserve the genetic diversity of endangered species. **Quantitative trait loci** analysis can reveal hidden genes of agricultural value in wild plant species.

review questions

1. Give an example of how agricultural biotechnology can affect
   a. economics.
   b. ecology.
   c. evolution.

2. Explain how a plant can be genetically altered to function as a vaccine to immunize people against an infectious disease.

3. Under what circumstances might it be dangerous to genetically alter a crop plant to resist a herbicide?

4. How can releasing a genetically altered organism to a natural ecosystem influence natural selection?

5. How can biotechnology help preserve the genetic diversity of organisms living in threatened environments?

6. How does a somatic embryo differ from a normal embryo?

7. Why is it helpful to remove a plant's cell wall before attempting a genetic manipulation?

8. How are modern biotechnologies such as cell culture and recombinant DNA technology similar to and different from traditional plant breeding?

9. List the steps necessary to make plants altered at the cell or DNA level useful agricultural varieties.

10. Why do plants that are derived sexually from the same parent plant differ from each other, whereas plants derived from somatic tissue from the same plant are identical?

11. Cite one reason why plants are easier to alter by biotechnology than animals are, and one reason why plants are harder to manipulate.

12. Growing identical plants is essential in the ornamental flower industry. Suggest a biotechnology that could meet this requirement.

13. What does somaclonal variation in plants have in common with some cancers in humans? Return to chapter 16 for your answer.

14. What are two reasons that creating transgenic trees is challenging?

applied questions

1. Suggest three ways to develop a crop plant that is resistant to a particular herbicide.

2. A food manufacturer wishes to develop popcorn that glows in the dark. Devise a way to do this.

3. Genetic engineering includes (1) adding genetic function to form a transgenic organism and (2) removing genetic function using gene targeting (chapter 17), antisense technology (chapter 9), or a naturally occurring deletion such as bacteria that prevent frost damage. Do you think that adding a genetic function is more dangerous than deleting or silencing a function? Why or why not?

suggested readings

Arakawa, T. and W. H. R. Langridge. May 1998. Plants are not just passive creatures! *Nature Medicine,* vol. 4. Vaccines can be delivered in transgenic plants.

Arntzen, Charles J. May 1998. Pharmaceutical foodstuffs—oral immunization with transgenic plants. *Nature Medicine,* vaccine supplement, vol. 4. Arntzen tested transgenic potatoes that, when eaten, protect against an *E. coli* toxin.

Brown, Kathryn Sergeant. October 1995. The green clean: Plants are useful in bioremediation. *BioScience,* vol. 45.

Coghlan, Andy. November 23, 1996. Weaving genes to make a warmer fibre. *New Scientist.* Transgenic cotton manufactures plastic within its cellulose fibers.

Hall, Stephen S. September 1987. One potato patch that is making genetic history. *Smithsonian.* The first release of a genetically altered bacterium onto plants was traumatic for residents of the town that included the testing site. Today we take such tests for granted.

Hileman, Bette. August 21, 1995. Views differ sharply over benefits and risks of agricultural biotechnology. *Chemical and Engineering News,* vol. 73. Agricultural biotechnology is a multidimensional area.

Jacob, Miriam. September 1, 1997. Biotechnology and aquaculture driving development of enhanced marine foods. *Genetic Engineering News.* Swapping genes between species increases supplies of seafood.

Krimsky, Sheldon, et al. October 1995. Standardized microcosms in microbial risk assessment. *BioScience,* vol. 45. A microcosm is a good intermediate test between the laboratory and the field.

Nestle, Marion. March 14, 1996. Allergies to transgenic foods—questions of policy. *The New England Journal of Medicine,* vol. 334. Transferring genes between species may also mean transferring allergens.

Niebling, Kenneth. July 1995. Agricultural biotechnology companies set their sights on multibillion dollar markets. *Genetic Engineering News.* Agricultural biotechnology has not been as financially successful as pharmaceuticals, but it will catch up, market analysts predict.

Nordlee, Julie A. March 14, 1996. Identification of a brazil-nut allergen in transgenic soybeans. *The New England Journal of Medicine,* vol. 334. Adding a brazil-nut gene to soybeans also transferred an allergen.

Pennisi, Elizabeth. April 3, 1998. Transferred gene helps plants weather cold snaps. *Science,* vol. 280. Protection against frost damage to crops is a huge business.

Podila, Gopi, and David Karnosky. December 16, 1996. Fibre farms of the future: genetically engineered trees. *Chemistry and Industry.* Transgenic trees resist pests.

Redenbaugh, Keith, et al. 1992. *Safety assessment of genetically engineered fruits and vegetables: A case study of the FlavrSavr tomato.* Boca Raton, Fla.: CRC Press. An in-depth report on the invention of a genetically altered tomato with improved shelf life.

Tanksley, Steven D., and Susan R. McCouch. August 22, 1997. Seed banks and molecular maps: unlocking genetic potential from the wild. *Science,* vol. 277. With plants, what you see is not always what you get, in terms of genetics.

Thayer, Ann. April 28, 1997. Betting the transgenic farm. *Chemical and Engineering News.* Each year, more transgenic crops are planted.

chapter twenty

Reproductive Technologies

New Ways to Make Babies

A woman carrying her own grandchildren through pregnancy; a sixty-two-year-old woman carrying another woman's fertilized ovum to term; a couple's repeated try to conceive, over a long period, using several different technologies. Reproductive techniques that sounded like science fiction a few years ago are science at work today.

A Grandmother and Mother at the Same Time

When forty-two-year-old Arlette Schweitzer gave birth to twins Chelsea and Chad at St. Luke's Midland Hospital in Aberdeen, South Dakota, the event made national headlines. A woman in her forties having twins isn't so odd these days, but Arlette's twins were rather unusual—they were her genetic grandchildren, but also her gestational children.

Arlette had given birth to Christa two decades earlier. Christa had healthy ovaries and oocytes, but she lacked a uterus, and therefore could not carry children.

After Christa was happily married, she desperately wanted children; her mother stepped in to help. Christa's oocytes and her husband Kevin's sperm were mixed in a laboratory dish, where they joined to form fertilized ova. After a few cell divisions, preimplantation embryos were placed into Arlette's uterus. Arlette's hormonal cycle had been manipulated with drugs to make the uterine lining receptive to pregnancy. Christa and Kevin's unusual route to parenthood was a resounding success because the technology worked and because the people involved shared the same goal.

Midlife Motherhood

Rosanna Della Corte became a mother at age sixty-two (figure 20.1), after her teenage son died in an accident. An oocyte a younger woman had donated was fertilized with sperm from Rosanna's husband Mauro, in a laboratory dish. The fertilized ovum divided twice. Meanwhile, hormone treatments thickened Rosanna's uterine lining. Her body nurtured the preimplantation embryo that would develop into baby Riccardo.

The Cortes' success shows that it is not the condition of the uterine lining in an older woman that makes conceiving,

figure 20.1

After undergoing hormone treatments, Rosanna Della Corte became pregnant at age sixty-two with a donated oocyte fertilized by her husband Mauro's sperm in a laboratory dish. Her pregnancy proved that the uterine lining of an older woman can support a fetus to term if she receives the appropriate hormones.

carrying, and delivering a healthy baby difficult. Rather, the age of the oocyte is what limits pregnancy in older women. (Soon after Riccardo's birth, a sixty-three-year-old woman had a child!)

A Five-Year Wait

The experience of Pamela and Jonathon Loew is more typical than that of Arlette Schweitzer or the Cortes. For five years, the Loews underwent a long list of techniques trying to conceive, culminating in Alexandra's birth.

The Loew's quest began with ruling out various causes of the inability to conceive. Pamela received hormone therapy, then a physician placed Jonathon's sperm near her cervix eight times. One time, this resulted in pregnancy, but it was ectopic—the preimplantation embryo lodged in one of her fallopian tubes and had to be removed to save Pamela's life.

Next, antigens were removed from the surfaces of Jonathon's sperm to prevent Pamela's immune system from attacking. The "washed" sperm were placed in her fallopian tube, close to the uterus, along with oocytes from Pamela's ovary. If all went well, the gametes would meet and merge. The first time the Loew's used this

procedure, it didn't work. The second time, it resulted in Alexandra.

Our increased knowledge of how the genetic material from two individuals comes together has spawned several **assisted reproductive technologies** that can help people who are having difficulty becoming parents. These procedures replace the source of a male or female gamete, aid fertilization, or provide a uterus. Yet assisted reproductive technologies are controversial. Some people argue that in an overpopulated world, where many children are orphaned or mistreated, these technologies are unnecessary.

Infertility

Infertility is the inability to conceive a child after a year of frequent intercourse without the use of contraceptives. On a more personal level, infertility is a seemingly endless monthly cycle of raised hopes and crushing despair. As a woman ages, the incidence of pregnancy-related problems rises, including chromosomal anomalies, fetal deaths, premature births, and low-birth-weight babies. For most conditions, the man's age does not raise the risk.

Physicians specializing in infertility treatment can identify a physical cause for

table 20.1
Causes of Infertility

Men

Problem	Possible Causes	Treatment
Low sperm count	Hormone imbalance, varicose vein in scrotum, possibly environmental pollutants	Hormone therapy, surgery, avoiding excessive heat
	Drugs (cocaine, marijuana, lead, arsenic, some steroids and antibiotics)	
	Y chromosome gene deletions	
Immobile sperm	Abnormal sperm shape	None
	Infection	Antibiotics
	Malfunctioning prostate	Hormones
Antibodies against sperm	Problem in immune system	Drugs

Women

Problem	Possible Causes	Treatment
Ovulation problems	Pituitary or ovarian tumor	Surgery
	Underactive thyroid	Drugs
Antisperm secretions	Unknown	Acid or alkaline douche, estrogen therapy
Blocked fallopian tubes	Infection caused by IUD or abortion or by sexually transmitted disease	Laparotomy, oocyte removed from ovary and placed in uterus
Endometriosis	Delayed parenthood until the thirties	Hormones, laparotomy

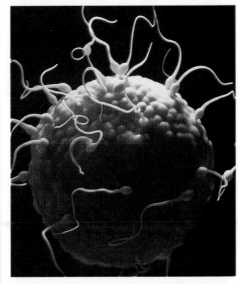

a.

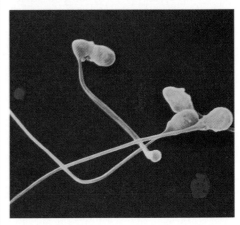

b.

figure 20.2

(a) Healthy sperm in action. (b) A misshapen sperm cannot fertilize an oocyte.

infertility in 90 percent of all cases. Of these, 30 percent of the time the problem is primarily in the male, and 60 percent of the time it is primarily in the female. The statistics are somewhat unclear, because in 20 percent of the 90 percent, both partners have a medical condition that could contribute to infertility. A common combination, for example, is a woman with an irregular menstrual cycle and a man with a low sperm count.

One in six couples has difficulty in conceiving or giving birth to children. Table 20.1 summarizes causes of infertility.

Male Infertility

Infertility in the male is easier to detect but sometimes harder to treat than female infertility. One in 25 men are infertile. Some men have difficulty fathering a child because they produce fewer than the average 120 million sperm cells per milliliter of ejaculate. If low sperm count is due to a hormonal imbalance, administering the appropriate hormones may boost sperm output. Sometimes a man's immune system produces antibodies that cover the sperm and prevent them from binding to oocytes. Male infertility can also be due to a varicose vein in the scrotum. This enlarged vein draws too much heat near to developing sperm, and they cannot mature. A scrotal varicose vein can be surgically removed.

Until recently, no cause could be identified for 30 to 40 percent of cases of male infertility. Researchers then discovered that many of these men have small deletions of the Y chromosome that remove the only copies of key genes whose products control spermatogenesis. Clues to this cause of male infertility came from men who cannot make any sperm, and who also have very large Y chromosome deletions. If a deletion is very small, the man may make some sperm.

For many men with low sperm counts, fatherhood is just a matter of time. If an ejaculate contains at least 60 million sperm cells, fertilization is likely eventually. To speed conception, a man with a low sperm count can donate several semen samples over a period of weeks at a fertility clinic. The samples are kept in cold storage, then pooled. Some of the seminal fluid is withdrawn to leave a sperm cell concentrate, which is then placed in the woman's reproductive tract. It isn't very romantic, but it is highly effective at achieving pregnancy.

Sperm quality is even more important than quantity. Sperm cells that are unable to move—a common problem—cannot reach an oocyte. If the lack of motility is due to a physical defect, such as sperm tails that are misshapen or missing, or bumps near the sperm head, there is no treatment (figure 20.2). If the cause is hormonal,

Scrutinizing Sperm

Both the quality and quantity of sperm are essential factors in the ability of a man to father a child. If a sperm head is misshapen, if a sperm cannot swim properly, or if a man simply has too few sperm cells, completing the arduous journey to approach the well-protected oocyte may be an insurmountable task.

Until recently, sperm analysis was rather subjective, based on viewing the cells under a microscope. Now, computer-aided sperm analysis—CASA, for short—is standardizing and expanding criteria for normalcy in human male seminal fluid and the sperm cells it contains.

To obtain a sperm analysis, a man abstains from intercourse for 2 to 3 days, then provides a sperm sample, which must be analyzed within the hour. The man must also provide information about his reproductive history and possible toxic exposures. The sperm sample is placed on a slide under a microscope, and then technology intervenes. A video camera sends an image to a VCR, which projects a live or digitized image, and to a computer, where sperm trajectories can be traced and displayed on the monitor or printed out. Figures 1 and 2 show a CASA of normal sperm, depicting how the swimming pattern alters along their journey.

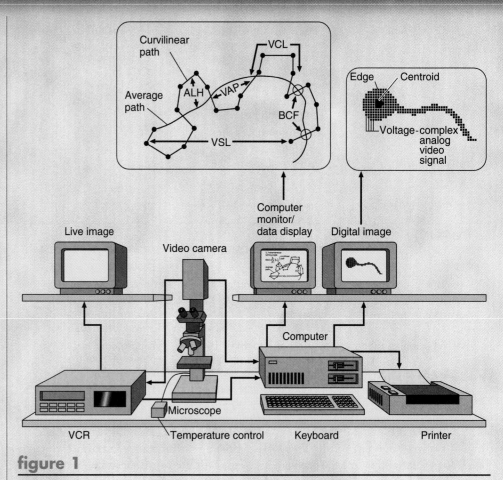

figure 1

Computer analysis has improved the objectivity and accuracy of describing sperm in terms of abundance, shape, and motility.

however, replacing the absent hormones can sometimes restore sperm motility. Immature sperm cells can be removed from a man's testes and injected into an oocyte, an approach discussed later in the chapter. Computers are used to track sperm shape and movements (Reading 20.1).

Several studies have shown that, worldwide, human sperm counts have in recent years fallen by 2 percent a year and that the proportion of sperm that cannot swim has increased by 1 percent annually. Researchers do not yet know if these trends have affected fertility. The changes in human sperm parallel increasing estrogen-like environmental pollutants.

Female Infertility

Female infertility can be caused by abnormalities in any part of the reproductive system. Many women with infertility have irregular menstrual cycles, making it difficult to pinpoint when conception is most likely. In an average menstrual cycle of 28 days, ovulation usually occurs around the 14th day after menstruation begins, and this is when a woman is most likely to con-

ceive. For a woman with regular menstrual cycles who is under thirty years old and not using birth control, pregnancy is likely to happen within three or four months. A woman with irregular menstrual periods can use an ovulation predictor test that detects a peak in the level of a certain hormone that precedes ovulation by a few hours, or keep a record of her body temperature each morning using a special thermometer with very fine subdivisions. Basal body temperature rises slightly within a day before ovulation. This method often does not help much because

figure 2

A computer tracks sperm movements. In semen, sperm swim in a straight line (*a*), but as biochemicals in a woman's reproductive tract activate them, their trajectories widen (*b*). The sperm in (*c*) narrow their trajectories in the mucus of a woman's cervix, and the sperm in (*d*) are attempting to penetrate the structures surrounding an oocyte.

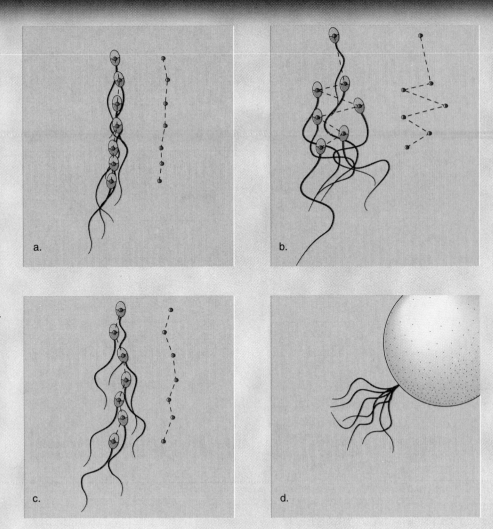

Hundreds of CASA systems are now in use, mostly at fertility clinics. The devices are also helpful in analyzing sperm as "bio-markers" of toxin exposure. For example, one study compared the sperm of men who work in the dry-cleaning industry and are exposed to the solvent perchloroethylene (believed to damage sperm) to the sperm of men who work in the laundry industry and share many of the same exposures, except to this one chemical. CASA showed a difference in sperm motility that was directly related to level of exposure, as measured by exhalation of the chemical. This result supported the reproductive evidence—although the men in both groups had the same numbers of children, it took far longer for the dry cleaners and their partners to achieve pregnancy than it did for the launderers and their partners.

sperm can fertilize oocytes if they have been in the woman's body for up to 5 days before ovulation, but can fertilize for only a short time after ovulation.

The hormonal imbalance that usually underlies irregular ovulation can have various causes—a tumor in the ovary or in the pituitary gland in the brain that hormonally controls the reproductive system, an underactive thyroid gland, or use of steroid-based drugs such as cortisone. Sometimes a woman produces too much prolactin, the hormone that normally promotes milk production and

suppresses ovulation in new mothers. If prolactin is abundant in a nonpregnant woman, she will not ovulate and therefore cannot conceive.

Fertility drugs can stimulate ovulation, but they can also cause women to "super-ovulate," producing more than one oocyte each month. A commonly used drug, clomiphene, is sometimes too successful; it raises the chance of having twins from 1 to 2 percent to 4 to 6 percent. If a woman's ovaries are completely inactive or absent (due to a birth defect or surgery), she can become pregnant only if she uses a donor

oocyte. Ovary transplants have succeeded only between identical twins.

A common cause of female infertility is blocked fallopian tubes, where fertilization usually occurs. Blockage can prevent sperm from reaching the oocyte, or entrap a fertilized ovum, keeping it from descending into the uterus (figure 20.3) and resulting in an **ectopic pregnancy.** Fallopian tubes can be blocked due to a birth defect or, more likely, from an infection such as pelvic inflammatory disease. A woman may not know she has blocked fallopian tubes until she has difficulty conceiving and

figure 20.3

Sites of reproductive problems in the human female.

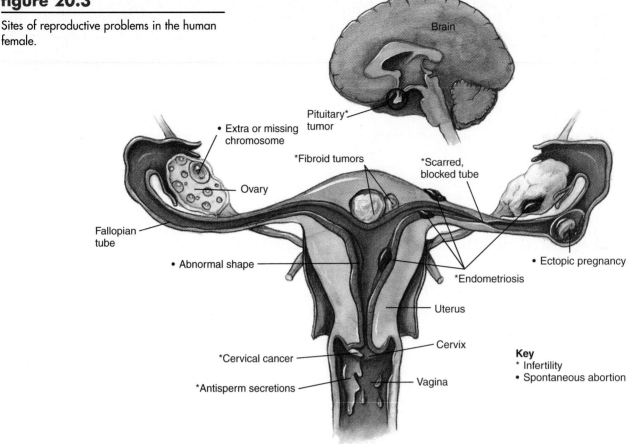

medical tests uncover the problem. Surgery can sometimes open blocked tubes.

Excess tissue growing in the uterine lining may make it inhospitable to an embryo. This tissue can include benign tumors, called **fibroids,** or a condition called **endometriosis,** in which tissue builds up in the uterus and sometimes outside of it, too. In response to the hormonal cues to menstruate, the tissue bleeds, causing painful cramps. Endometriosis can make conception difficult, but curiously, once a woman with endometriosis has been pregnant, the cramps and bleeding usually subside. An indirect cause of infertility is abnormalities related to the use of a drug. A woman whose mother took a drug called diethylstilbestrol (DES) while pregnant with her can have an abnormally shaped uterus that cannot maintain pregnancy.

Sometimes a woman has no structural abnormalities, but secretions in the vagina and cervix may be hostile to sperm. If cervical mucus is unusually thick or sticky, as can happen during infection, sperm become entrapped and cannot move far enough to encounter an oocyte. Sometimes vaginal secretions are so acidic or alkaline that they weaken or kill sperm. Secretion problems can be treated with low doses of the hormone estrogen or by douching daily with an acidic solution such as acetic acid (vinegar) or an alkaline solution, such as bicarbonate. These solutions alter the pH of the vagina so that it is more receptive to sperm cells. Too little mucus is treated with low daily doses of oral estrogen. Another problem that sometimes arises is that mucus in a woman's body may harbor antibodies that attack sperm. Infertility may also result if the oocyte fails to release sperm-attracting biochemicals.

One reason that female infertility increases with age is that older women are more likely to produce oocytes with an abnormal chromosome number, which often causes spontaneous abortion. Losing very early embryos may appear to be infertility because the bleeding accompanying the aborted embryo resembles a heavy menstrual flow. The higher incidence of meiotic errors in older women may occur because their oocytes have been exposed longer to harmful chemicals, viruses, and radiation.

Infertility Tests

A number of medical tests can identify the cause or causes of infertility. The man is checked first, because it is easier, less costly, and it is certainly less painful to obtain sperm than oocytes. Sperm are checked for number (sperm count), motility, and morphology (shape). An ejaculate containing up to 40 percent unusual forms is still considered normal, but many more than this can impair fertility. A urologist performs sperm tests. Table 20.2 lists normal values for a sperm analysis.

If a male cause of infertility is not apparent, the next step is for the woman to consult a gynecologist. This medical specialist checks to see that the structures of the woman's reproductive system are present and functioning, using some of the tests described in table 20.3.

Some cases of infertility have no clear explanation. Psychological factors may be at play, or it may be that inability to conceive results from consistently poor timing. Sometimes an "infertile" couple adopts a child, only to conceive one of their own shortly thereafter; at other times, the couple's infertility is a lifelong mystery.

Key Concepts

Male infertility is due to a low sperm count or sperm that cannot swim or are abnormal in structure. Female infertility can be due to an irregular menstrual cycle (traced to a tumor in the ovary or the pituitary gland, an underactive thyroid, or excess prolactin) or blocked fallopian tubes (resulting from an infection or a birth defect). Fibroid tumors, endometriosis, or a misshapen uterus may prevent implantation of a fertilized ovum, and secretions in the vagina and cervix may inactivate or immobilize sperm. Oocytes may fail to release a sperm-attracting biochemical. Early pregnancy losses due to aneuploidy may be mistaken for infertility; this is more common among older women. A variety of medical tests can pinpoint the cause of infertility, but sometimes find no cause.

table 20.2

Semen Analysis

Characteristic	Normal Value
Volume	1.5–5.0 milliliters/ejaculate
Sperm density	120 million cells/milliliter
Percent motile	> 40%
Motile sperm density	> 8 million/milliliter
Average velocity	> 20 micrometers/second
Motility	> 8 micrometers/second
Percent abnormal morphology	< 40%
White blood cells	> 5 million/milliliter

table 20.3

Tests to Assess Female Infertility

Test	What It Checks
Hormone levels	Whether ovulation occurs
Ultrasound	Placement and appearance of reproductive organs and structures
Postcoital test	Whether cervical mucus is thin enough to allow sperm through soon after unprotected intercourse
Endometrial biopsy	Whether a small piece of uterine lining sampled and viewed under microscope indicates that the uterus can support an embryo
Hysterosalpingogram	Whether dye injected into fallopian tube and followed with scanner can move through tube or is blocked
Laparoscopy/Laparotomy	Whether scar tissue blocks tubes (small, lit optical device inserted near navel detects scar tissue that could be missed in ultrasound; if so, scar tissue removed through incision made for laparoscopy)

Assisted Reproductive Technologies

Until recently, there was only one way to make a baby—sexual intercourse shortly before or at the time of ovulation. However, a growing number of couples with fertility problems are turning to alternative ways to achieve pregnancy, many of which were perfected in nonhuman animals. The Technology Timeline on reproductive technologies depicts the chronology for these assisted reproductive technologies.

Donated Sperm— Artificial Insemination

The oldest assisted reproductive technology is **artificial insemination,** in which a doctor places donated sperm into a woman's reproductive tract. Her partner may be infertile or carry a gene for an inherited illness that the couple wishes to avoid passing to their child, or a woman may undergo artificial insemination if she desires to be a single parent without having sex. More than 250,000 babies have been born worldwide as a result of this procedure.

The first artificial inseminations in humans were done in the 1890s. For many years, physicians donated sperm, and this became a way for male medical students to earn a few extra dollars. By 1953, sperm could be frozen and stored. Today, donated sperm is frozen and stored in sperm banks, which provide the cells to obstetricians who perform artificial inseminations.

A couple who chooses artificial insemination can select sperm from a catalog that lists the personal characteristics of donors, such as blood type, hair and eye color, skin

Technology TIMELINE

Landmarks in Reproductive Technology

	In Animals	In Humans
1782	Use of artificial insemination in dogs	
1799		Pregnancy reported from artificial insemination
1890s	Birth from embryo transplantation in rabbits	Artificial insemination by donor
1949	Use of cryoprotectant to successfully freeze and thaw animal sperm	
1951	First calf born after embryo transplantation	
1952	Live calf born after insemination with frozen sperm	
1953		First reported pregnancy after insemination with frozen sperm
1959	Live rabbit offspring produced from in vitro ("test tube") fertilization (IVF)	
1972	Live offspring from frozen mouse embryos	
1976		First reported commercial surrogate motherhood arrangement in the United States
1978	Transplantation of ovaries from one cow to another	Baby born after IVF in United Kingdom
1980		Baby born after IVF in Australia
1981	Calf born after IVF	Baby born after IVF in United States
1982	Sexing of embryos in rabbits	
	Cattle embryos split to produce genetically identical twins	
1983		Embryo transfer after uterine lavage
1984		Baby born in Australia from frozen and thawed embryo
1985		Baby born after gamete intrafallopian transfer (GIFT)
		First reported gestational surrogacy arrangement in the United States
1986		Baby born in the United States from frozen and thawed embryo
1989		First preimplantation genetic diagnosis
1992		First pregnancies from sperm injected into oocytes
1994		Sixty-two-year-old woman gives birth from donated oocyte
1996	Sheep cloned from embryo cells	
1997	Sheep cloned from adult cells	
1998		Baby born 7 years after his twin.

Source: Data from Office of Technology Assessment, *Infertility: Medical and Social Choices,* U.S. Congress, Government Printing Office, Washington, D.C., May 1988.

color, build, and even educational level and interests. This can, of course, be silly, because not all of these traits are inherited.

Problems can arise in artificial insemination, as they can in any pregnancy. One woman used the same sperm donor twice, and twice conceived and gave birth to a child with the same rare inborn error of metabolism. Several engaged couples in Chicago discovered that they were half-siblings, thanks to artificial insemination.

In the future, male infertility may be treatable with a transplant. Researchers have restored fertility to male mice with transplants of spermatogonia (the stem cells that give rise to mature sperm) from fertile mice.

A male's role in reproductive technologies is simple compared to a woman's role. This is because a man can be a genetic parent, contributing half of his genetic self in his sperm, but a woman can be both a genetic parent (donating the oocyte) and a gestational parent (donating the uterus). Problems can result when a second female assists in either the conception and/or gestation of a child. Table 20.4 highlights some cases of assisted reproductive disasters.

table 20.4

Assisted Reproductive Disasters

1. A physician in California used his own sperm to artificially inseminate 15 patients and told them that he had used sperm from anonymous donors.

2. A plane crash killed the wealthy parents of two preimplantation embryos stored at −320°F (−195°C) in a hospital in Melbourne, Australia. Adult children of the couple were asked to share their estate with two 8-celled siblings-to-be.

3. Several couples in Chicago planning to marry discovered that they were half-siblings. Their mothers had been artificially inseminated with sperm from the same donor.

4. Two Rhode Island couples are suing a fertility clinic for misplacing several preimplantation embryos.

5. Several couples in California are suing a fertility clinic for implanting their oocytes or preimplantation embryos in other women without consent from the donors. One woman is requesting partial custody of the resulting children if her oocytes were taken and full custody if her preimplantation embryos were used, even though the children are of school age and she has never met them.

6. A man sued his ex-wife for possession of their frozen fertilized ova. He won, and donated them for research. She had wanted to be pregnant.

7. Jaycee Buzzanca once had five parents and now has none. In 1995, she was conceived using a sperm donor, an egg donor, and a surrogate mother, to be turned over at birth to John and Luanne Buzzanca. But John left his wife and refused to pay child support, and a judge agreed with him, calling Luanne a "temporary custodial person," rather than a mother. The other three parents did not want the child. Luanne eventually adopted Jaycee.

A Donated Uterus— Surrogate Motherhood

If a man produces healthy sperm but his partner's uterus is absent or cannot maintain a pregnancy, a **surrogate mother** may help by being artificially inseminated with the man's sperm. When the child is born, the surrogate mother gives the baby to the couple. In this variation of the technology, the surrogate is both the genetic and the gestational mother. Attorneys usually arrange surrogate relationships. The surrogate mother signs a statement signifying her intent to give up the baby, and she is paid for her nine-month job.

The problem with surrogate motherhood is that a woman may not be able to predict her responses to pregnancy and childbirth in the cold setting of a lawyer's office. When a surrogate mother changes her mind about giving up the baby, the results are wrenching for all. A prominent, early case involved a young woman named Mary Beth Whitehead, who carried the child of a married man for a fee and then changed her mind about relinquishing the baby. Whitehead's ties to "Baby M," as the infant was known while her three parents battled over custody, were perhaps stronger because she was both the genetic and the gestational mother.

Another type of surrogate mother lends only her uterus, receiving a fertilized ovum conceived from a man and a woman who has healthy ovaries but lacks a functional uterus. The gestational-only surrogate mother turns the child over to the donors of the genetic material. This arrangement works as long as all parties agree, as was the case for Arlette Schweitzer, who gladly lent her uterus to house her grandchildren-to-be. However, gestational surrogacy can also go drastically awry. Consider what happened to Anna Johnson, Mark and Crispina Calvert, and the child whom the Calverts conceived and Johnson carried.

Crispina Calvert had had her uterus removed, but her ovaries and oocytes were healthy. The Calverts contracted with Anna Johnson, a young, single nurse in financial need, to be a gestational surrogate and carry their fertilized ovum to term for $10,000. Johnson agreed—at first. Near the end of the pregnancy, Johnson had misgivings and asked the court to name her the natural mother and to grant her visitation rights to the child. The question in this case addressed the very essence of motherhood—was Crispina Calvert the mother of baby Christopher, or was Anna Johnson? Christopher wouldn't have been conceived without Calvert's oocyte, but he wouldn't have developed without a uterus, which Johnson provided.

The California court ruled in favor of genetics. Judge Richard N. Parslow, Jr., told the courtroom:

> **Anna Johnson is the gestational carrier of the child, a host in a sense . . . she and the child are genetic hereditary strangers . . . Anna's relationship to the child is analogous to that of a foster parent providing care, protection and nurture during the period of time that the natural mother, Crispina Calvert, was unable to care for the child. (Annas, 1992; see Suggested Readings at end of chapter)**

The judge based his ruling on evidence of the important role genes play in establishing one's characteristics compared to the role of the environment; the valid contract; and what he thought would be in the best interests of the child. A court of appeals unanimously affirmed the ruling.

Not everyone agrees with the court's decision. Many a woman who has felt a fetus within her grow and experienced childbirth would argue that her role qualifies her for motherhood more than donating a cell. The American College of Obstetricians and Gynecologists states that gestation, not genetics, defines motherhood. The American Academy of Pediatrics defines a surrogate mother as "a woman who carries a pregnancy for another woman," avoiding the genetic-gestation distinction, but recommends that "surrogate parenting arrangements be considered a tentative, preconception adoption agreement in which the surrogate mother is the sole decision maker until after she gives birth to the infant. After birth, applicable local adoption rules and practices should be followed." With such divergent views, we will certainly hear more about surrogate motherhood.

In Vitro Fertilization

In **in vitro fertilization** (IVF), which means "fertilization in glass," sperm and oocyte meet and join in a laboratory dish. Then, the preimplantation embryo is placed in the oocyte donor's uterus (or another woman's uterus), and, if all goes well, it will implant

figure 20.4

Louise Joy Brown was conceived when her father's sperm cell met her mother's oocyte in a laboratory dish. Here she stands among some younger "test-tube babies."

into the lining. Louise Joy Brown, the first "test-tube baby," was born in 1978 (figure 20.4). Thousands of children have been born by this route since her birth.

A woman might undergo IVF if her ovaries and uterus work but her fallopian tubes are blocked. To begin, the woman takes a superovulation drug that causes her ovaries to release more than one "ripe" oocyte at a time. Using a laparoscope, a physician removes several of the largest oocytes and transfers them to a laboratory dish. Chemicals that mimic those in the female reproductive tract are added, and sperm donated by her partner are applied to the oocytes. If the sperm cannot readily penetrate the oocyte, they may be sucked up into a tiny syringe and microinjected into the female cell. This is called **intracytoplasmic sperm injection (ICSI),** and it is more effective than IVF alone.

ICSI is very helpful for men who have low sperm counts or high percentages of abnormal sperm. The procedure even works with immature sperm, making fatherhood possible for men who cannot ejaculate, such as men who have suffered spinal cord injuries (figure 20.5).

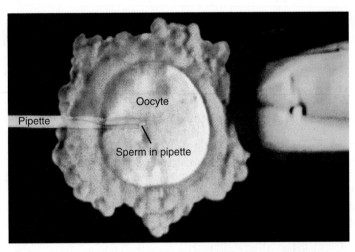

figure 20.5

Intracytoplasmic sperm injection (ICSI) enables some infertile men, men with spinal cord injuries, or certain illnesses to become fathers. A single sperm cell is injected into the cytoplasm of an oocyte.

A day or so after sperm wash over the oocytes in the laboratory dish, or are injected into them, some of the preimplantation embryos—balls of 8 or 16 cells—are transferred to the woman's uterus. If the hormone human chorionic gonadotropin appears in her blood a few days later, and its level rises, she is pregnant.

IVF costs from $5,000 to $10,000 per attempt. The success rate is at best only 14 percent and is often much lower. By contrast, two-thirds of preimplantation embryos begun in the normal way, in the woman's body, implant.

To increase the odds that IVF will lead to a birth, several preimplantation embryos are transferred. This can result in multiple births, as Michele and Ray L'Esperance learned in 1988 when their attempt to have one baby via IVF resulted in five (figure 20.6)! Today, with increased success for IVF, fewer preimplantation embryos are transferred. When too many implant, some may have to be removed so that two or three have room to develop. Extra preimplantation embryos are usually donated to an infertile couple, or frozen for later use by the genetic parents.

Measures to improve the chance of IVF culminating in a birth include the following:

1. Blocking certain of a woman's hormones during the superovulation stage, which produces more mature oocytes that are more likely to be fertilized and develop.

2. Transferring preimplantation embryos slightly later in development.

3. Culturing fertilized ova and early preimplantation embryos with other cells that normally surround the oocyte in the ovary. These "helper" cells may provide extra growth factors.

4. Developing tests to tell which preimplantation embryos are most likely to successfully implant in the uterus. Such tests might check metabolism or chromosomes. One developmental biologist who has performed hundreds of IVF procedures claims that he can predict which preimplantation embryos will "take" just by their appearance!

Figure 20.7 takes a whimsical look at a birth certificate that recognizes several assisted reproductive technologies.

Gamete Intrafallopian Transfer

As the world marveled at the miracle of Louise Joy Brown and other "test-tube" babies, disillusioned couples were learning that IVF is costly, time-consuming, aggravating, and rarely works. IVF may frequently fail because of the artificial environment for fertilization. A procedure called GIFT, which stands for **gamete intrafallopian transfer,** improves the setting. Fertilization is assisted in GIFT, but it

figure 20.6

IVF worked well for Michele and Ray L'Esperance. In 1988, Michele underwent IVF because her diseased fallopian tubes had been removed. Five fertilized ova implanted in her uterus completed development, and now they are Erica, Alexandria, Veronica, Danielle, and Raymond. Usually today, only two or three fertilized ova or preimplantation embryos are implanted. But in late 1997, an Iowa couple had septuplets. They had been unwilling to undergo "selective reduction" to reduce the number of babies when IVF worked too well.

occurs in the woman's body rather than in glassware. Certain religions approve of GIFT, but not IVF, because GIFT preserves more natural reproductive function.

In GIFT, a woman takes a super-ovulation drug for a week, and then several of her largest oocytes are removed. The man submits a sperm sample, from which the most active cells are separated. The collected oocytes and sperm are deposited together in the woman's fallopian tube, at a site past any obstruction so that fertilization can occur. GIFT is about 26 percent successful, and costs about half as much as IVF.

A variation of GIFT is ZIFT, for **zygote intrafallopian transfer.** In this procedure, an in vitro fertilized ovum is introduced into the woman's fallopian tube. Allowing the fertilized ovum to make its own way to the uterus seems to increase the chance of implantation. ZIFT is 23 percent successful.

Oocyte Banking and Donation

Can female gametes be stored, as sperm are? If so, a woman wishing to have children later in life, when fertility is naturally

---

CERTIFICATE OF LIFE

Commonwealth of California, Department of Health's Vital Records

Subject:	Baby Boy, Miller
Date of conception:	November 15, 2018, 12:15 P.M.
Place:	Comprehensive Fertility Institute, Beverly Hills, CA
Number of parents:	Three, including surrogate mother—mother donated egg, father sperm
Method of conception:	In vitro fertilization followed by embryo transfer. Mother's body had rejected her artificial fallopian tube. After 8 days on Pergonal, mother produced two eggs. Both were removed during routine laparoscopy and screened for possible defects. Eggs united with father's sperm. After 48 hours in incubator, embryos were removed from growth medium and placed in surrogate's womb. Only one embryo attached itself to uterine wall.
Prenatal care:	Ultrasound at 3 months. Fetal surgery performed at 5 months.
Date/time of birth:	Jason Lawrence Miller born July 20, 2019, 4:15 A.M.
Father:	Jason L. Miller, Sr.
Mothers:	Amy Wong (natural); Maribeth Rivers (surrogate)
Birth method:	Newly lifed in Morningstar Birthing Center, division of Humana Corporation. Natural delivery after 5-hour labor. Labor pains controlled through acupuncture. Therapeutic touch used for last hour of labor. Child's father, adopted sister, and natural mother attended the delivery.
Weight/length:	10 pounds; 25 inches
Eye color:	Green
Projected life span:	82 years

figure 20.7

A look ahead.

Reprinted with the permission of Simon & Schuster, Inc. from *July 20, 2019: Life in the 21st Century* by Arthur C. Clarke. Copyright © 1986 by B. V. Serendib and Omni Publications International, Ltd.

lower, could set aside oocytes earlier. Storing healthy oocytes would also be valuable for women who must undergo a medical treatment that damages oocytes, such as cancer chemotherapy; who work with toxins; or who have entered premature menopause.

Oocytes are frozen in liquid nitrogen at –30 to –40 degrees Celsius, when they are at metaphase of the second meiotic division. At this time, the chromosomes are aligned along the spindle, which is sensitive to temperature extremes. If the spindle comes apart as the cell freezes, the oocyte may lose a chromosome, which would devastate development. Another problem with freezing oocytes is retention of a polar body, leading to a diploid oocyte. Can you see how this would hamper development?

Alternative approaches try to overcome the difficulty of freezing oocytes. Researchers are developing ways to nurture in the laboratory one-millimeter-square sections from ovaries that are packed with oocytes. So far, laboratory culture of oocytes appears to require a high level of oxygen and a complex combination of biochemicals.

Most donated oocytes are taken from younger women. Often these women are undergoing IVF and have "extra" harvested oocytes. The donation of an oocyte is a very generous gift. The donor must receive several daily shots of a superovulation drug, have her blood checked each morning for 3 weeks, then have laparoscopic surgery to collect her oocytes. The potential father's sperm and donor's oocytes are placed in the recipient's uterus (figure 20.8), or fertilization occurs in the laboratory, and an 8- or 16-celled preimplantation embryo is transferred to the woman's uterus.

Women with a variety of problems can benefit from oocyte donation. These include a woman who has begun menopause early; has had her ovaries removed to treat cancer; or is at high risk of transmitting an inherited illness. This last scenario might be a woman who herself has inherited an autosomal dominant condition, is a carrier of a sex-linked condition, or is a carrier of an autosomal recessive illness that her partner also carries.

figure 20.8

Anthony Miceli was born from Vicki Miceli's uterus, but he was conceived when Larry Miceli's sperm fertilized an oocyte donated by Bonny De Irueste, Vicki's sister (in pink). Says Bonny, "I'm his aunt, that's it." Not all reproductive technologies have such joyous outcomes.

The first baby to result from oocyte donation was born in 1984. The success rate ranges from 20 to 50 percent, and the procedure costs at least $10,000.

Because oocytes are harder to obtain than sperm, availability of oocyte donation technology has lagged far behind that of sperm banks, the male version of gamete donation. However, oocyte banking is catching up. One IVF facility that has run a donor egg program since 1988 has a patient brochure that describes 120 oocyte donors of various ethnic backgrounds. It is very much like a catalog of sperm donors. The egg donors range in age from twenty-one to thirty-four and have undergone extensive medical and genetic tests. Recipients may be up to fifty-five years of age.

Embryo adoption is a variation on oocyte donation. A woman with malfunctioning ovaries but a healthy uterus carries an embryo that results when her partner's sperm artificially inseminates a woman who produces healthy oocytes. If the woman conceives, the preimplantation embryo is gently "lavaged" or flushed out of her uterus a week after the insemination and inserted through the cervix and into the uterus of the woman with malfunctioning ovaries. The child is genetically that of the man and the woman who carries it for the first week, but is born from the woman who cannot produce healthy oocytes.

Preimplantation Genetic Screening

Prenatal diagnostic tests such as amniocentesis, chorionic villus sampling, and fetal cell sorting can be used in pregnancies achieved with assisted reproductive technologies. A technique called **preimplantation genetic diagnosis** detects genetic and chromosomal abnormalities before a pregnancy starts. The couple can thereby select a preimplantation embryo free of a certain detectable genetic condition (figure 20.9).

Preimplantation genetic diagnosis is possible because 1 cell can be removed for testing from an 8-cell preimplantation embryo, and the remaining 7 cells, if transferred to a uterus, can complete development, apparently none the worse for the early intervention. Before the 7 cells are implanted into the woman, the single cell is karyotyped, or its DNA amplified and probed for particular genes that the parents carry. Only those partial preimplantation embryos free of the family's genetic legacy are implanted and continue developing.

The first children who had preimplantation genetic diagnosis were born in 1989. In these cases, probes for DNA sequences found only on the Y chromosome were used to select female preimplantation embryos, who would develop into girls and not be affected by the devastating X-linked conditions their mothers carry. The conditions avoided included Lesch-Nyhan syndrome (profound mental retardation with self-mutilative behavior),

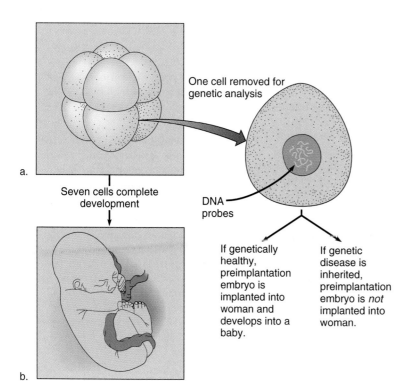

a.

One cell removed for genetic analysis

Seven cells complete development

DNA probes

b.

If genetically healthy, preimplantation embryo is implanted into woman and develops into a baby.

If genetic disease is inherited, preimplantation embryo is *not* implanted into woman.

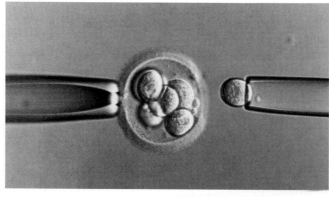

c.

figure 20.9

Preimplantation genetic diagnosis probes disease-causing genes or chromosome aberrations in an 8-celled preimplantation embryo. A single cell is separated from the ball of cells and tested to see if it contains a disease-causing gene combination or chromosome imbalance (*a*). If it doesn't, the remaining seven cells are implanted into the oocyte donor to complete development (*b*). The preimplantation embryo in (*c*) is held still by suction applied on the left. On the right, a pipette draws up a single blastomere. Fertilization took place 45 hours previously, in vitro.

another form of mental retardation, and adrenoleukodystrophy, in which seizures and nervous system deterioration are followed by sudden death in early childhood.

In March 1992, Chloe O'Brien was born. She was a healthy little girl whose parents, who were carriers of cystic fibrosis, had had her checked as an 8-cell preimplantation embryo to see if she had escaped inheriting the disease. Chloe's brother was seriously ill with the disorder, and the parents wanted to avoid having another affected child.

Preimplantation genetic diagnosis offers an alternative to terminating a pregnancy in much later stages following prenatal diagnosis. However, the technology is expensive (at least $10,000 for the IVF procedure, DNA amplification, and use of genetic probes) and technically difficult. Progress in improving the technology in the United States has slowed because government funds cannot be used on research that uses preimplantation embryos. Still, several facilities in the U.S., and also in Europe, offer the procedure as part of IVF under some circumstances. Table 20.5 lists conditions that preimplantaion genetic diagnosis has detected.

table 20.5

Disorders That Preimplantation Genetic Diagnosis Has Detected

alpha 1 antitrypsin deficiency	Huntington disease
Charcot-Marie-Tooth disease	Lesch-Nyhan syndrome
cystic fibrosis	Marfan syndrome
Duchenne muscular dystrophy	retinitis pigmentosa
Down syndrome	Tay-Sachs disease
fragile X syndrome	Turner syndrome
hemophilia A	

Key Concepts

In artificial insemination, donor sperm is placed in a woman's reproductive tract. A genetic and gestational surrogate mother is artificially inseminated, becomes pregnant, then gives the baby to the father and his partner. A gestational surrogate mother gestates a baby conceived in vitro with gametes from a man and a woman who cannot carry a fetus. In IVF, a sperm and oocyte unite outside the body, and the resulting preimplantation embryo is transferred to the uterus. Preimplantation embryos can also be frozen and used later. In GIFT, sperm and oocytes are placed in a fallopian tube at a site past the blockage that has kept the woman from conceiving. In ZIFT, a preimplantation embryo conceived in vitro is placed in a fallopian tube. Oocytes can be donated. In embryo adoption, an artificially inseminated woman has a preimplantation embryo washed out of her uterus and transferred to a woman who lacks oocytes. Cells can be removed from early preimplantation embryos and screened for genetic and chromosomal abnormalities.

summary

1. **Infertility** is the inability to conceive a child after a year of unprotected intercourse.

2. Causes of infertility in the male include a low sperm count, a malfunctioning immune system, a varicose vein in the scrotum, structural sperm defects, drug exposure, and abnormal hormone levels.

3. Female infertility can be caused by absent or irregular ovulation, blocked fallopian tubes, an inhospitable or malshaped uterus, antisperm secretions, or lack of sperm-attractant biochemicals. Early pregnancy loss due to aneuploidy is more common in older women and may appear to be infertility.

4. **Assisted reproductive technologies** help people to have children. In **artificial insemination,** sperm is obtained from a donor and introduced into a woman's reproductive tract in a clinical setting.

A gestational and genetic **surrogate mother** provides her oocyte, which is artificially inseminated by a man whose mate cannot conceive or carry a fetus. The surrogate also provides her uterus for nine months. A gestational surrogate mother receives an **in vitro fertilized** ovum, which belongs genetically to the couple who ask her to carry it. In IVF, oocytes and sperm meet in a laboratory dish, fertilized ova divide a few times, and the resulting preimplantation embryos are placed in the woman's body, circumventing blocked tubes or an inability of the sperm to penetrate the oocyte.

5. Embryos can be frozen and thawed and then complete development when placed in a woman's uterus. **GIFT** introduces oocytes and sperm into a fallopian tube past a blockage; fertilization occurs in the

woman's body. **ZIFT** places a preimplantation embryo in a fallopian tube.

6. Oocytes can be frozen and stored. In **embryo adoption,** a woman is artificially inseminated. A week later, the preimplantation embryo is washed out of her uterus and introduced into the reproductive tract of the woman whose partner donated the sperm.

7. Preimplantation embryos can develop normally if a cell is removed at the 8-cell stage. Cells removed from preimplantation embryos can be examined for abnormal chromosomes, or DNA can be amplified and probed to detect certain genetic diseases. This is called **preimplantation genetic diagnosis.**

review questions

1. Which assisted reproductive technologies might help the following couples? (More than one answer may fit some situations.)

   a. A woman born without a uterus manufactures healthy oocytes.

   b. A man's cancer treatments greatly damage his sperm.

   c. A woman undergoes a genetic test that reveals she will develop Huntington disease. She wants to have a child, but not pass on this presently untreatable illness.

   d. Two women wish to have and raise a child together.

   e. A man and woman are each carriers of sickle cell disease. They do not want to have an affected child, but they also do not want to terminate a pregnancy.

   f. A woman's fallopian tubes are scarred and blocked, so an oocyte cannot reach the uterus.

2. Why are men typically tested for infertility before women?

3. A man reads his medical chart and discovers that the results of his sperm analysis indicate that 22 percent of his sperm are shaped abnormally. He wonders why the physician said he had normal fertility if so many sperm are abnormally shaped. Has the doctor made an error?

4. Cite a situation in which both man and woman contribute to an infertility problem.

5. How does ZIFT differ from GIFT? How does it differ from IVF?

6. A Tennessee lower court, in ruling on the fate of seven frozen preimplantation embryos in a divorce case, called them "children in vitro." In what sense is this label incorrect?

7. Explain how preimplantation genetic diagnosis is similar to and different from CVS and amniocentesis.

8. A child born following artificial insemination needs a bone marrow transplant. Is the sperm donor or the father (the man whose wife was artificially

inseminated) more likely to have compatible bone marrow?

9. At the same time that 62- and 63-year-old women gave birth, actors Tony Randall and Anthony Quinn became fathers at ages 77 and 78—and didn't receive nearly as much criticism as did the women. Do you think this is an unfair double standard, or is it based on valid biological information?

10. Many people spend thousands of dollars pursuing pregnancy. What might be an alternative solution to their quest for parenthood?

11. What are some of the causes of infertility among older women?

12. How do each of the following reproductive technologies deviate from the normal biological process?

   a. in vitro fertilization

   b. GIFT

   c. embryo adoption

   d. gestational surrogacy

   e. artificial insemination

applied questions

1. An Oregon man anonymously donated sperm that were used to conceive a child. The man later claimed, and won, rights to visit his child. Is this situation for the man more analogous to a genetic and gestational surrogate mother, or an oocyte donor who wishes to see the child she helped to bring into existence?

2. Big Tom is a bull with valuable genetic traits. His sperm is used to conceive 1,000 calves. Mist, a dairy cow with exceptional milk output, is given a superovulation drug, and many oocytes are removed from her ovaries. Once fertilized, the oocytes are implanted into surrogate mothers, and with their help, Mist becomes the genetic mother of 100 calves—far more than she could give birth to naturally.

   What two reproductive technologies performed on humans are based on these two agricultural examples?

3. State who the genetic parents are and who the gestational mother is in each of the following scenarios:

   a. A man was exposed to herbicides during the Vietnam war and abused drugs for several years before and after that. Now he wants to become a father, but he is concerned that his past exposures to toxins have damaged his sperm. His wife is artificially inseminated with sperm from the husband's brother, who led a calmer life.

   b. A twenty-six-year-old woman has her uterus removed because of cancer. However, her ovaries are intact and her oocytes are healthy. She takes drugs to superovulate, has oocytes removed, and these are fertilized in vitro with her husband's sperm. Two fertilized ova are implanted into the uterus of the woman's best friend.

   c. Max and Tina had a child by IVF in 1986. At that time, they had frozen three extra preimplantation embryos. Two are thawed years later and implanted into the uterus of Tina's sister, Karen. Karen's uterus is healthy, but she has ovarian cysts that often prevent her from ovulating.

   d. Forty-year-old Christensen von Wormer wanted children, but not a mate. He donated sperm, and an Indiana mother of one was artificially inseminated with them for a fee. On September 5, 1990, von Wormer held his newborn daughter, Kelsey, for the first time.

   e. Two men who live together want to raise a child together as a family. They go to a fertility clinic, have their sperm collected and mixed, and used to artificially inseminate a friend, who turns the baby over to them.

4. Delaying childbirth until a woman is over age thirty-five is associated with certain physical risks, yet an older woman is more mature and financially secure. Many women delay childbirth so that they can establish careers. Can you suggest societal changes, perhaps using a reproductive technology, that would allow women to more easily have both children and careers?

5. An IVF attempt yields 12 more preimplantation embryos than the couple who conceived them can use. What could they do with the extras?

6. What do you think children born of a reproductive technology should be told about their origins?

7. Wealthy couples could hire poor women as surrogates or oocyte donors simply because the adoptive mother does not want to be pregnant. Would you object to this practice? Why or why not?

8. Do you think guidelines can be established for handling cases where surrogate mothers change their minds and wish to keep the babies they give birth to, or should the courts handle these situations on a case-by-case basis?

9. A forty-year-old woman was born without ovaries but has a healthy uterus. She became pregnant by receiving a preimplantation embryo conceived in vitro using her husband's sperm and her sister's oocyte. She preferred using her sister's gametes because then the child would be more biologically related to her than if the oocyte donor had been a nonrelative. How closely is the child related to the adoptive mother genetically, compared to a child born from a natural pregnancy? How genetically related would they be if the sister is the woman's identical twin?

suggested readings

Annas, George J. February 6, 1992. Using genes to define motherhood—the California solution. *The New England Journal of Medicine*, vol. 326, no. 6. Not everyone agrees that genes alone define parenthood.

Chattingius, Sven, M.D., Michele R. Forman, Ph.D., Heinz W. Berendes, M.D., M. H. S., and Leena Isotalo, M.D. August 19, 1992. Delayed childbearing and risk of adverse perinatal outcome. *The Journal of the American Medical Association*, vol. 268, no. 7. Older women face an increased risk of pregnancy complications.

DeKretser, David M., and Henry G. Burger. February 20, 1997. The Y chromosome and spermatogenesis. *The New England Journal of Medicine*, vol. 336. Some cases of male infertility are caused by deletions in the Y chromosome.

Edwards, Robert, and Patrick Steptoe. 1980. *A Matter of Life*. New York: William Morrow. The story of Louise Joy Brown—the first "test tube baby."

Howards, S. S. February 2, 1995. Current concepts: Treatment of male infertility. *The New England Journal of Medicine*, vol. 332. A comprehensive and timely review of treatments for male infertility.

Lemonick, Michael D. March 18, 1996. What's wrong with our sperm? *Time.* Are pollutants dropping human sperm counts?

Lewis, Ricki. July 1996. Special delivery sperm. *Photonics Spectra.* Two lasers are used through a microscope to fertilize an oocyte—one traps a sperm cell, and the other drills a hole in the zona pellucida surrounding the oocyte.

Moran, Nuala. September 1995. Manmade chemicals and reproductive health. *Nature Medicine,* vol. 1. Human sperm counts are falling on a global scale. Why?

Palermo, Gianpiero, et al. December 18, 1996. Evolution of pregnancies and initial follow-up of newborns delivered after intracytoplasmic sperm injection. *The Journal of the American Medical Association,* vol. 276. ICSI.

Simpson, Joe Leigh, and Sandra Ann Carson. September 24, 1992. Preimplantation genetic diagnosis. *The New England Journal of Medicine,* vol. 327, no. 13. Will preimplantation genetic diagnosis be widely used?

Van Steirteghem, A. January 15, 1998. Outcome of assisted reproductive technologies. *The New England Journal of Medicine,* vol. 338. Was an infant who was part male, part female, that way because of in vitro fertilization?

chapter twenty one

The Human Genome Project

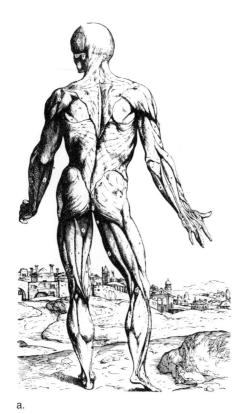

```
GAAGCATCGAAGTTAGGAGGATCTGGTAATTTCACACAC
ATTTGGCCTCATAGAGTTAGTACAGATAAACATGGGTTTA
TCCAACATTGGAAATCACATACTGATGAGAGTACAAATTG
TCATCACAAATAGATGTTTCAACAGGATAGATAAAGCACT
GTAACAAGTATACCTTAGACTAAGTCCCAGAGGCAAAGG
CATCTTACGGTACAGGTTCCGCTAAACTATCCACAGGAC
ACGACAAGAGTGAGACTCTGCAGTCACGCATCCTTATGG
ATATATCAAATATAGTCACTCAGCTCTGGGCTCATGCTC
CCTGAGGATAGTGTCAGCGAATACATAGGTGTATTGTGA
CTTTCAGGGCTACTGGTCACCACCTCTCTGAAAGTGTGT
GCCAGCCATTCAGTCATTTGCCCCTACCTTGGCTAGTTA
CTGAAAGACACGTCACACTAACCTCAGCTTATACCCAAG
CCACCTCACTCCAGCCTGAGAACCTATAATATTGTGCTTG
ACTTTGACCTTATCAAACAGGAGGCACAGCGTGATGACA
CCGCGGCAAGAGCCAGCATGAGTACTTGCACACAAAGC
TTCTCATCTTTCTCCTCCTGTAGTGTTTTCCTAAGGGGTT
```

a.

b.

figure 21.1

Two views of humanity—the anatomical view circa 1543 (a), and a look at human genetic blueprints (b).

Why Sequence Genomes?

Nighttime bedwetting is an age-old problem, noted as long ago as 1500 B.C. Treatments have ranged from drinking the broth from boiled hens combs, to blocking the urethra at night, to punishment and ridicule. What a relief it was when genetic researchers identified a gene that causes inherited nocturnal enuresis—nighttime bedwetting. Many affected individuals, and their concerned parents, now know that their problem is not social, but genetic.

Localization of the bedwetting gene to a specific chromosomal site is but one of many discoveries spawned from the on-going human genome project (HGP), the deciphering of the sequence of the 3 billion DNA nucleotide bases that form our biochemical blueprints. The HGP is an entirely new way of looking at what it is to be human (figure 21.1).

Results of the human genome project will have repercussions on the practice of medicine for years to come. The project is revealing, on a weekly basis, the genetic underpinnings of many human conditions. Such gene discoveries lead first to development of new diagnostic tests, and then to

table 21.1

Genome Sequencing Projects

Species	Approximate Genome Size (millions of base pairs)
Bacteria	
Mycoplasm genitalium	0.58
Borrelia burgdorferi (causes Lyme disease)	1.3
Helicobacter pylori (causes ulcers)	1.7
Haemophilus influenzae (causes meningitis)	1.8
Bacillus subtilis	4.2
Escherichia coli	4.6
Yeast (*Saccharomyces cerevisiae*) (bread yeast)	12.1
Roundworm (*Caenorhabditis elegans*)	100
Mustard weed (*Arabidopsis thaliana*)	100
Fruit fly (*Drosophila melanogaster*)	165
Mouse (*Mus musculus*)	3,000
Corn (*Zea mays*)	3,000
Human (*Homo sapiens*)	3,000

treatments. Sequencing the genomes of other species (table 21.1) addresses broader questions about the evolutionary relatedness of different species. Reading 21.1 focuses on a genome project for *Canis lupus familiaris,* the dog. Genome projects are underway for diverse species, including sheep, cows, zebrafish, worms, slime molds, and microorganisms. Figure 21.2 summarizes the types of knowledge the

Gregor Mendel and Pepper (figure 1) are two very special canines. The owners of University of California at Berkeley geneticist Jasper Rine, Gregor and Pepper head a dog dynasty serving as a canine genome project. Rine and his colleagues are teaming conventional breeding with molecular genetics to identify the DNA sequences that make Gregor, a border collie, so different in appearance and behavior from Pepper, a Newfoundland.

Dogs are ideal subjects for genetic analysis because the differences among modern breeds represent a small number of genes, which we should be able to isolate. Plus, breeds are very uniform genetically. We have artificially selected the 129 canine breeds only over the past 250 years, from a handful of ancient founder breeds. These include the Maltese from 28,000 years ago; the mastiff that accompanied Julius Caesar when he invaded England in 55 B.C.; and the Pekinese, which lived in the Tang dynasty of eighth-century China.

Gregor and Pepper's pups are helping researchers pinpoint the genes responsible for their distinctive traits. Gregor, the border collie, displays his breed's herding instinct, rounding up everything from sheep to tennis balls. Herding dogs exhibit an unblinking stare, or "eye," and a crouched, flat stance, or "clapping"; they do not bark. The "eye" and "clapping" are usually enough to keep their charges grouped together, although tennis balls are not as responsive as sheep! Gregor weighs 37 pounds and is multicolored.

Pepper, the "Newfie," weighs 99 pounds and is jet black. Her oily coat, slightly webbed toes, and powerful muscles make her an excellent swimmer. She'll happily plunge into water and haul a struggling human to safety, displaying her innate water rescue skills. So inborn is the

figure 1

Geneticist Jasper Rine began his canine genome project by mating male border collie Gregor Mendel with female Newfoundland Pepper. Gregor Mendel and Pepper are on the right, with some of their descendants nearby.

Newfie's love of water that pups often stumble into their water dishes!

What happens when a border collie and Newfie mate? Gregor and Pepper's seven pups are of intermediate weight, are mostly black, love water, and stare, though not quite as intensely as papa Gregor. As in Mendel's pea experiments, the next step was to mate the F_1 generation, Gregor and Pepper's pups, to each other—something that could hardly be done with humans. For each F_2 dog, the researchers are recording specific traits characteristic of their grandparents' breeds, and are also tracking microsatellites (short repetitive DNA sequences) scattered among the 78 dog chromosomes. If a particular chromosomal region appears exclusively in animals with a specific trait, this will signal where researchers should look further for a causative gene.

The several canine genome projects in progress will have a number of applications. Identifying the genes that cause breed-specific health problems (see Reading 14.1, table 1) will enable breeders to select out these traits. Researchers will be able to study inherited disorders that dogs and people share, such as certain clotting disorders, Duchenne muscular dystrophy, prostate cancer, severe combined immune deficiency, and inborn errors of metabolism. On a broader scale, identifying behavior genes in canines may eventually help explain behaviors in other animals.

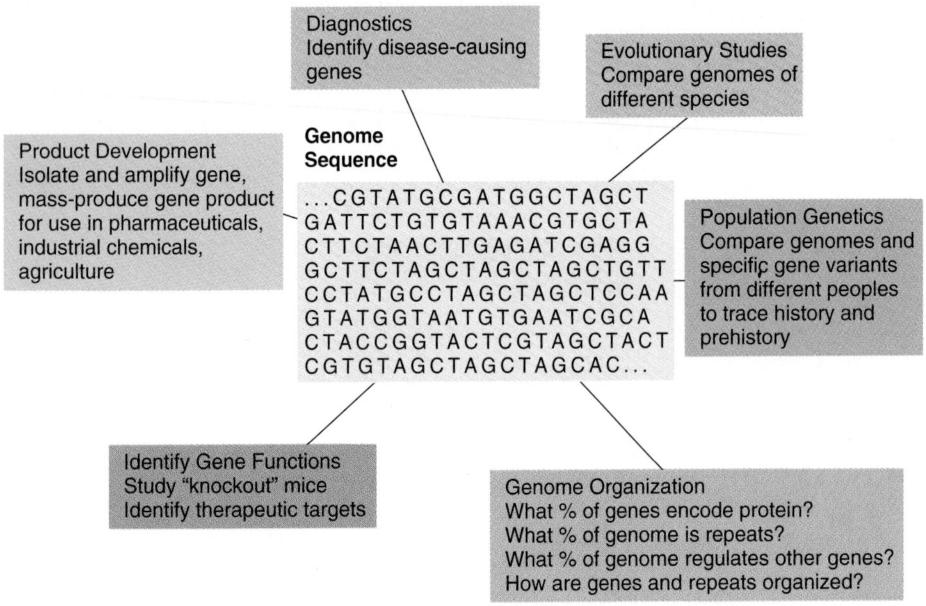

figure 21.2

Uses for genome project information.

Diagnostics
Identify disease-causing genes

Evolutionary Studies
Compare genomes of different species

Product Development
Isolate and amplify gene, mass-produce gene product for use in pharmaceuticals, industrial chemicals, agriculture

Genome Sequence

...CGTATGCGATGGCTAGCT
GATTCTGTGTAAACGTGCTA
CTTCTAACTTGAGATCGAGG
GCTTCTAGCTAGCTAGCTGTT
CCTATGCCTAGCTAGCTCCAA
GTATGGTAATGTGAATCGCA
CTACCGGTACTCGTAGCTACT
CGTGTAGCTAGCTAGCAC...

Population Genetics
Compare genomes and specific gene variants from different peoples to trace history and prehistory

Identify Gene Functions
Study "knockout" mice
Identify therapeutic targets

Genome Organization
What % of genes encode protein?
What % of genome is repeats?
What % of genome regulates other genes?
How are genes and repeats organized?

genome project will provide and how we might utilize the information.

A genome-level approach introduces new ways to identify disease-causing genes. One technique, called **representational difference analysis,** compares two genomes and highlights the differences between them. This approach is useful, for example, in identifying the genes that distinguish a person's cancerous cells from healthy ones, revealing cancer-causing mutations. Another technique, **genomic mismatch scanning,** works in the opposite way, detecting DNA sequences that are the same in two genomes. This approach is used on inbred populations that have a high prevalence of a specific inherited disorder. Comparing the genomes of different individuals with the same disorder helps highlight the disease-causing genes by identifying DNA sequences that the people all have, but that unaffected individuals do not.

Key Concepts

The information obtained from the human genome project will provide new medical tools and reveal evolutionary relationships. Comparing genomes can reveal disease-causing mutations.

Roots of the Human Genome Project

Headlines often depict the HGP as a 1990s phenomenon. The project is actually a continuation of genetic research performed throughout the twentieth century.

An Overview of the Project

The task of deciphering the human genome is often compared to deciphering a thousand telephone directories that are each a thousand pages long. Just as you wouldn't look up an item in a phone book by reading the entire document from the beginning, but would search for key words located near the entry of interest, the HGP has proceeded in a series of steps to make the huge amount of information more accessible. Such steps as creating linkage maps and studying cytogenetic abnormalities to localize genes predate the genome project. Today's gene searches still often begin with these classical tools to localize genes, then turn to molecular-level techniques to obtain small pieces of DNA that contain genes of interest.

Once genes are localized to parts of a specific chromosome, sequencing technologies describe the gene, base by base. Finally, sequences are compared—between

table 21.2

Steps in Genome Analysis

1. Obtain chromosome maps with landmarks (gene loci or known sequences, such as restriction enzyme cut sites).
2. Obtain chromosome pieces.
3. Sequence the pieces.
4. Overlap the sequences and extend the known sequence.
5. Compare sequences.

genes, individuals, or species. Genome comparison and analysis is called **informatics;** the entire process of sequencing genomes and learning their organization is called **genomics.** An emerging area, called functional genomics, considers how genes interact and how they affect an organism as a whole. Table 21.2 lists the general steps in analyzing genomes, and table 21.3 lists techniques discussed in previous chapters.

The Human Genome Project Timetable

The idea to sequence the human genome came in 1986 from Renato Dulbecco, a noted virologist who thought the information would reveal how cancer arises. That summer, enthusiastic geneticists convened at Cold Spring Harbor on New York's Long Island, and soon, worldwide planning began. The project officially started in 1990, under the auspices of the U.S. Department of Energy and the National Institutes of Health. The focus at first was to develop tools and technologies to divide the genome into pieces small enough to sequence, and to improve the efficiency of sequencing techniques.

By 1995, researchers concurred that the time had come to shift from gene mapping to sequencing. It was a little like going from marking states on a map of the United States to filling in individual streets. The original goal for completion was the year 2005; improved technology invented along the way has moved it to 2001.

Genome mapping techniques used at the start of the project first cut the genome

table 21.3
Genome Analysis Tools

Technique	Chapter
Linkage maps based on recombination frequencies	5
Computerized databases for gene identity and mutation analysis	9
DNA probes	11
Fluorescence in situ hybridization (FISH)	11
DNA fingerprinting	12
Electrophoresis and Southern blotting	12
RFLP analysis (how mutations alter restriction sites)	12
Restriction maps	12

into overlapping pieces of about 40,000 bases. (This is also known as 40 kilobases; a **kilobase** equals 1,000 bases.) These pieces were then randomly cut, or "shotgunned," into small fragments. Because researchers could shotgun several genomes in a single experiment, many of the resulting fragments overlapped. Researchers would then painstakingly determine the sequences of those smaller pieces—a process that is now automated (Reading 21.2). Software programs align the sequenced, small pieces by their regions of overlap, and using the larger pieces as guidelines, reconstruct the entire sequence.

In 1995, researchers developed software that could rapidly locate the overlaps among many small pieces of DNA and assemble them into a continuous sequence. This eliminated the step of cutting a large chromosome segment into 40-kilobase pieces. Using this software, researchers obtained the first complete genome sequence for an organism—in under a year. The organism with this distinction is *Haemophilus influenzae,* a bacterium that in the wild can cause meningitis and ear infections. The researchers cut the bacterium's 1,830,137 bases into 24,000 fragments, sequenced the fragments, and then software assembled them. Although the human genome is 1,500 times the size of the genome of *H. influenzae,* researchers expect the approach to work for humans, too.

Another shortcut, using gene fragments called **expressed sequence tags** (ESTs), allows researchers to identify the parts of the genome most likely to include disease-causing genes. Expressed sequence tags are short pieces of genes that encode protein. Only about 5 percent of the genome encodes protein. DNA sequences that do not encode protein may specify RNA only, control other DNA sequences, or be highly repetitive. Despite all the progress, we do not know the function of most of our genome.

To obtain ESTs, researchers extract mRNA from a cell. The mRNA molecules represent the genes expressed in that particular cell. These include the "housekeeping" genes that provide basic cellular functions, as well as genes that confer specialized activities such as contractility or secretion. The mRNAs are mixed with reverse transcriptase and free DNA nucleotides. Recall that reverse transcriptase can join DNA nucleotides to form a strand complementary in sequence to an RNA strand. The resulting DNA molecule is called a **complementary DNA,** or a cDNA for short. Researchers can choose from tens of thousands of ESTs and use them as DNA probes to localize (map) protein-encoding genes.

Key Concepts

Gene searches often begin with linkage or cytogenetic data, then move to molecular localization and sequencing. Expressed sequence tags represent protein-encoding genes and are often given priority in genetic research because they may affect health.

A Genome Project Progress Report

The genome project has yielded results as it progresses. Here is a brief look at some of the interim information the project has revealed.

What Is a Gene?

It may seem odd to pose this question at the end of a genetics textbook—odder still that researchers pioneering genome analysis should pose such a seemingly fundamental question. Yet the act of deciphering the genome base by base has shown that the classical idea of gene structure as "beads on a string" is an oversimplification.

Before we knew what DNA is and does, biologists defined a gene as a unit of genetic function that maps to a particular chromosome and, when mutated, alters the phenotype. Once we knew the molecular nature of the gene, the definition evolved to be a DNA sequence that is transcribed into RNA and encodes protein, plus its control sequences. We know now that neither definition suffices.

DNA sequencing has revealed many complexities concerning the relationship between gene structure and function. For example, knowing the sequence of a gene makes it possible to identify mutations that do not alter the phenotype or even the protein product. Sequencing shows that some stretches of DNA are part of more than one gene, because they are part of exons that appear in different transcripts. Introns, too, are more complex that we had thought. A DNA sequence that is an intron on one strand of the DNA double helix may, on the other strand, encode one or even several genes.

Genome projects that are closer to completion than the human project have proven humbling, by indicating that we actually know the functions of very few genes. In the *C. elegans* (roundworm) genome, for example, about half of the thousands of known genes do not correspond to known genes in other organisms—we have no idea what they do. It is becoming clear that when the human genome is unveiled, rather than knowing our genetic makeup intimately, we will learn how much we still do not know.

Two Routes to DNA Sequencing

The Sanger Method

Modern DNA sequencing instruments utilize a basic technique Frederick Sanger developed in 1977. The overall goal is to generate a series of DNA fragments of identical sequence that are complementary to the sequence of interest. These fragments differ in length from each other by one end base:

```
      sequence of interest:  T A C G C A G T A C
 complementary sequence:  A T G C G T C A T G
        series of fragments:  T G C G T C A T G
                                    G C G T C A T G
                                       C G T C A T G
                                          G T C A T G
                                             T C A T G
                                                C A T G
                                                   A T G
                                                      T G
                                                         G
```

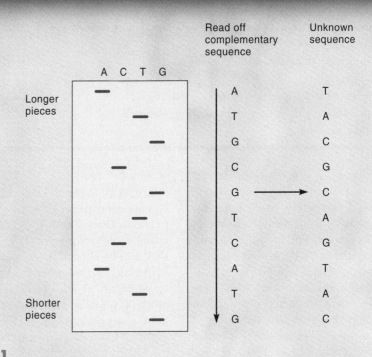

figure 1

In the Sanger method of DNA sequencing, complementary copies of an unknown DNA sequence are terminated early because of the incorporation of dideoxynucleotides. A researcher deduces the sequence by labeling the end bases and placing the fragments in size order.

Note that the entire complementary sequence appears in the sequence of end bases of each fragment. If the gene of interest can be cut into a collection of such pieces, and the end bases distinguished with a radioactive or fluorescent label, then polyacrylamide gel electrophoresis (figure 12.6) can be used to separate the fragments by size. Once the areas of overlap are aligned, reading the labeled end bases in size order reveals the sequence.

Sanger invented a way to generate the gene pieces. In a test tube, he included the unknown sequence and all of the biochemicals needed to replicate it, including supplies of the four nucleotide bases. Some of each of the four types of bases were chemically modified to contain two oxygen atoms instead of one—in the language of chemistry, they were dideoxyribonucleotides rather than deoxyribonucleotides. The "dideoxy" bases also incorporated a radioactive label. DNA synthesis halts when DNA polymerase encounters a "dideoxy" base, leaving only a piece of the newly replicated strand.

Sanger repeated the experiment four times, each time using a dideoxy version of A, T, C, then G. The four experiments were run in four lanes of a gel (figure 1). Today, fluorescent labels are used, one for each of the four base types, allowing a single experiment to reveal the sequence. The data appear as a sequential readout of the wavelengths of the fluorescence from the labels.

How Many Genes Comprise the Human Genome?

In 1990, researchers estimated the number of genes in the human genome at about 100,000. As they have deciphered major portions of chromosomes, most researchers have lowered that number to between 60,000 and 70,000. However, estimates have ranged anywhere from 14,000 to 129,000.

The reason for these widely differing estimates is that genes that encode proteins are squeezed together in some regions of the genome, yet dispersed among highly repeated sequences in other regions. One stretch of a million base pairs may house 43 protein-encoding genes, another as few as 13 genes. It is a little like trying to esti-

Sequencing on a Microchip

The best automated gene sequencers claim output of up to 7,200 bases per hour. A new technique, **sequencing-by-hybridization,** promises to sequence 32,000 bases an hour. The method utilizes a small glass square on which short DNA fragments of known sequence are immobilized. The DNA-studded glass square is called a DNA microchip or a DNA microarray. In one version, the 4,096 possible 6-base combinations (hexamers) of DNA are placed onto a 1-centimeter-by-1-centimeter microchip. Copies of an unknown DNA segment incorporating a fluorescent label are then also placed on the microchip. The copies stick (hybridize) to immobilized hexamers whose sequences are complementary to the DNA segment's sequences. Under laser light, the bound hexamers fluoresce. Because the researcher (or computer) knows which hexamers occupy which positions on the microchip, a scan of the chip reveals which 6-base sequences comprise the unknown sequence. Then, software aligns the identified hexamers by their overlaps. This reconstructs the complement of the entire unknown sequence. Figure 2 depicts a simplified version of sequencing-by-hybridization.

The idea for a DNA chip began as a whimsical suggestion at a biotechnology company that genes be placed on chips like transistors are. When one researcher took the suggestion seriously, the DNA chip was born. The devices will continue to be used to sequence genomes and then

1. Unknown DNA sequence _ _ _ _ _ _ _ _ _ _ _ _ _

2. Hybridize complementary, fluorescently labeled copies to microchip:

```
CTTGATCGATCCATATCGAAGCATA
GATCTACGTGCATTCGATGCCTATC
GTCCATGTACGTACGTTAGCGATCG
GACTAGCCTCTAGCCGTATAACGT
CTACCGTTTTACGTGCCCATTCTCG
AAGCCCGATATGCATTTCATCGACC
CGCTTATTCCCCTACGAAAAAAGTA
CCCCCGAGAGATCGAGCTACGTTG
GTAGTAATGCTTTTTACCCGGGCTA
AATTATCGAGTACCCTAAGTTAGCA
```

Fluorescence pattern

3. Align fluorescing fragments at overlaps:

```
CCGTAT
    TATCGA
        CGATCC
```

4. Derive sequence from overlaps:

```
CCGTATCGATCC
```

5. Derive complementary sequence = unknown:

```
GGCATAGCTAGG
```

figure 2

In sequencing-by-hybridization, a labeled DNA segment of unknown sequence complementary base pairs to short, known DNA sequences immobilized on a small glass microchip. Identifying the small, bound sequences, overlapping them, and then reading off their sequences, reveals the unknown DNA sequence.

to compare genomes of individuals to detect polymorphisms. The technology will also make possible many genetic tests. These will include tests to screen a particular gene—such as BRCA1 or p53—for many mutations, as well as panels of hundreds or even thousands of genes implicated in disease. Physicians will be able to tailor chips to individual patients, examining those genes that are more likely to be mutant based on ethnic background, pedigree, or symptoms.

mate the population of the United States by extrapolating from two areas: New York City and tiny Oxford, Ohio.

Based on studies of ESTs, genome mappers estimate that one protein-encoding gene occurs about every 40,000 to 50,000 bases. Since a protein is generally a few hundred amino acids long, and a gene therefore has three times that many nucleotide bases, it's clear that much of the genome does not encode protein. Again, we have a lot yet to discover!

How Are Genes Functionally Distributed?

A genome-level view reveals how genes are allocated to different functions. Figure 21.3 shows a macroscopic way of summarizing

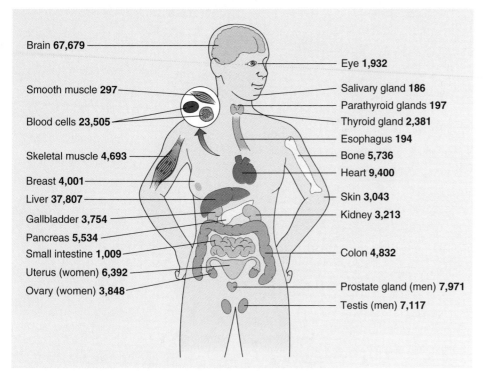

Brain **67,679**
Smooth muscle **297**
Blood cells **23,505**
Skeletal muscle **4,693**
Breast **4,001**
Liver **37,807**
Gallbladder **3,754**
Pancreas **5,534**
Small intestine **1,009**
Uterus (women) **6,392**
Ovary (women) **3,848**

Eye **1,932**
Salivary gland **186**
Parathyroid glands **197**
Thyroid gland **2,381**
Esophagus **194**
Bone **5,736**
Heart **9,400**
Skin **3,043**
Kidney **3,213**
Colon **4,832**
Prostate gland (men) **7,971**
Testis (men) **7,117**

figure 21.3

Now that the genome project is nearing completion, researchers can try to sort out all the information. One way to consider genome data is to chart where genes are active.

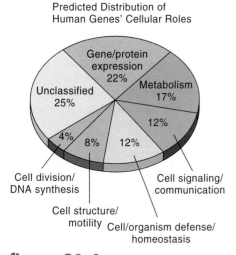

Predicted Distribution of Human Genes' Cellular Roles

Gene/protein expression 22%
Metabolism 17%
Unclassified 25%
12%
4% 8% 12%
Cell division/ DNA synthesis
Cell structure/ motility
Cell/organism defense/ homeostasis
Cell signaling/ communication

figure 21.4

We can also categorize genes according to their roles at the molecular and cellular levels.

genes identified by their ESTs—a genetic "atlas" of sites of gene action. Not surprisingly, the brain, the most complex organ, tops the list. Figure 21.4 is a microscopic view of gene function at the molecular and cellular levels. Of course, these estimates may change as discoveries mount.

Huntington Disease Research Illustrates the Evolution of Genome Technology

Progress made since the early 1980s in understanding Huntington disease (HD) illustrates the birth and development of genome technology. Even today, gene analysis often begins with families, as was the case for HD.

Recall that HD is an autosomal dominant neurodegenerative disorder, with adult-onset symptoms of worsening gait, constant uncontrollable movement, and personality changes. Death usually comes 10 to 15 years after the initial diagnosis. The HD gene resides near the tip of the short arm of chromosome 4 and encodes a brain protein, huntingtin. Affected individuals have an expanded trinucleotide repeat (figure 10.13).

Beginnings in a Venezuelan Village

The search for the HD gene took a decade, predating the HGP by several years. It started in a remote village on the shores of Lake Maracaibo, Venezuela. Seven generations ago, in the 1800s, a local woman married a visiting Portuguese sailor who, as the folklore goes, habitually walked as if intoxicated. Like most couples in the poor fishing village, the woman and sailor had many children. Some grew up to walk in the same peculiar way as their father had.

Of the couple's nearly 5,000 descendants, 250 living today have HD. Another 727 have at least one affected parent, and 39 individuals have two affected parents. It is very unusual to see people who have inherited two dominant disease-causing alleles, because we would expect them to be very severely affected. However, HD homozygotes have the same phenotype as heterozygotes. Researchers interpret this to mean that the mutant gene product introduces a new function rather than destroys a normal function.

The large and extended Venezuelan family with HD presented a natural experiment to geneticists, and they began by drafting a huge pedigree. Molecular studies followed. If researchers could identify a DNA sequence found only in affected family members, then that DNA would likely contain the mutant gene that causes HD. The family was large enough that researchers just might be able to pinpoint a single causative sequence.

Finding the HD Marker

In 1981, Columbia University psychologist Nancy Wexler, herself the child of a person with HD, began yearly visits to

Lake Maracaibo. The people lived in huts perched on stilts, as their ancestors did. They looked forward to Wexler's visits and would permit her to take skin biopsies and blood samples in exchange for blue jeans and M&M candies.

Meanwhile, James Gusella and his colleagues at Massachusetts General Hospital were sampling tissue from an Iowa family of 41, 22 of whom had HD. The researchers extracted DNA from the samples, cut it with restriction enzymes, and began the enormous task of testing random DNA probes to see if any always bound to the DNA of sick individuals but never to that of healthy adults. This would identify a **restriction fragment length polymorphism** (RFLP—a site where a restriction enzyme cuts) unique to people with the disease, showing where among the 23 chromosome pairs the gene lies. Then the team started testing pieces of the Venezuelan DNA. With several hundred DNA probes, they expected the testing to take years.

A third research group, led by P. Michael Conneally at Indiana University, applied the probe data to pedigrees of the Venezuelan and Iowa families, looking for a pattern. Population, transmission, and molecular genetics were coming together in the search.

One warm May night in 1983, the Indianapolis computer crunching the RFLP information found a match. By sheer luck, the twelfth probe studied, called G8, worked. Within both the Venezuelan and Iowa families, a distinctly sized piece of DNA that occurs in just one place in the genome—called G8—hybridized only to the DNA of people who had HD (figure 21.5). This piece of DNA, containing an RFLP, is called a **genetic marker.** It marks the presence of a closely linked disease-causing gene. In essence, inheriting the marker means a high probability of also inheriting the mutant gene. The marker sequence must be on the same homolog as the disease-causing gene.

A genetic marker cannot indicate a linked gene's presence with 100 percent accuracy, because crossovers can break the linkage. If a crossover event moves the marker or disease-causing gene to the other homolog, the marker can no longer predict HD. However, the closer the marker is to the gene, the less likely a

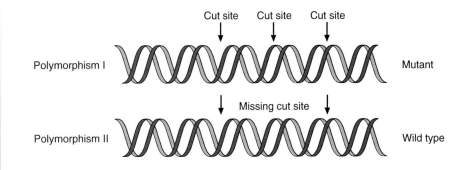

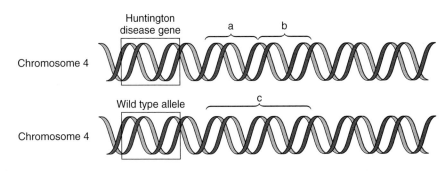

figure 21.5

An RFLP serves as a marker for Huntington disease. (*a*) For a marker to be informative, the person being tested must by heterozygous for the RFLP—that is, the DNA sequence at a particular point must differ on the two homologs. (*b*) The RFLP must also be on the same homolog as the disease-causing gene. In a family with this gene arrangement, cutting an individual's DNA with the appropriate restriction enzyme yields pieces *a* and *b* if the person has inherited the disease. Now a direct gene test is possible for HD, but genetic markers continue to be a useful first step in understanding many other inherited illnesses.

crossover is to separate them. Often an RFLP that is extremely close to a gene of interest is inherited along with the gene nearly all the time. This very tight linkage is called **linkage disequilibrium.** Using markers on either side of a disease-causing gene can increase the accuracy of predicting the gene's presence, since two chance crossovers would be very unlikely.

Computers tally how often genes and markers are inherited together. The "tightness" of linkage between a marker and the gene of interest is described with a **LOD score,** which stands for "logarithm of the odds." A LOD score indicates the likelihood that particular crossover frequency data indicate linkage.

A LOD score of 3 or greater signifies linkage. It means that the observed data are 1,000 (10^3) times more likely to have

occurred if the two DNA sequences (a disease-causing allele and its marker) are linked than if they reside on different chromosomes and just happen to often be inherited together by chance. It is somewhat like deciding whether two coins tossed together 1,000 times always come up both heads or both tails by chance, or because they are attached side by side in that position, as linked genes are. If the coins land with the same side up in all 1,000 trials, it indicates they are very likely attached.

Even though a marker is not the gene of interest, it makes possible a molecular-level diagnosis—even before symptoms appear. A marker test requires DNA samples from several family members to follow linkage of the marker to the disease-causing gene.

Localizing a Gene

A marker tells researchers where a gene of interest likely lies on a specific section of a specific chromosome arm. For some disorders, cytogenetic abnormalities that appear in affected individuals provide this initial clue. For example, researchers knew to look at a particular region on the short arm of chromosome 5 for a gene causing a type of melanoma, because patients had deletions and translocations affecting this area. Once researchers identify a marker or cytogenetic abnormality, they can isolate DNA probes that bind to the chromosomal region (figure 21.6).

Finding a disease-causing gene once a genetic marker or cytogenetic clue is in hand is a technological tour de force. The search begins by scanning a collection of probes specific for the chromosome of interest. Figure 21.6*b* describes a technique called **flow cytometry** used to obtain large amounts of a single human chromosome. This helps narrow the gene search. Researchers can then shatter the DNA of the specific chromosome and use it to make probes to further study its sequence. Often researchers maintain DNA probes as pieces of recombinant DNA that grow in bacteria. This method of storage is called a **DNA library.**

To extend the known DNA sequence, researchers locate a DNA probe that slightly overlaps the genetic marker or cytogenetic abnormality that serves as a toe-hold on the chromosome. Then they find a probe overlapping this probe, and so on, in an approach called "chromosome walking." Other techniques loop out sections of uninteresting DNA, allowing a chromosome "jump." Finally, a computer aligns the probes by overlaps, creating a contiguous or **contig map.** By sequencing the probes and assembling their sequences according to overlaps, the computer deciphers the entire sequence. Figure 21.7 uses a sentence analogy to describe how geneticists build a contig map.

Identifying a Gene

After gene mapping and sequencing comes the "informatics" part of gene discovery—searching a long sequence of DNA for clues, almost like punctuation, that indicate the

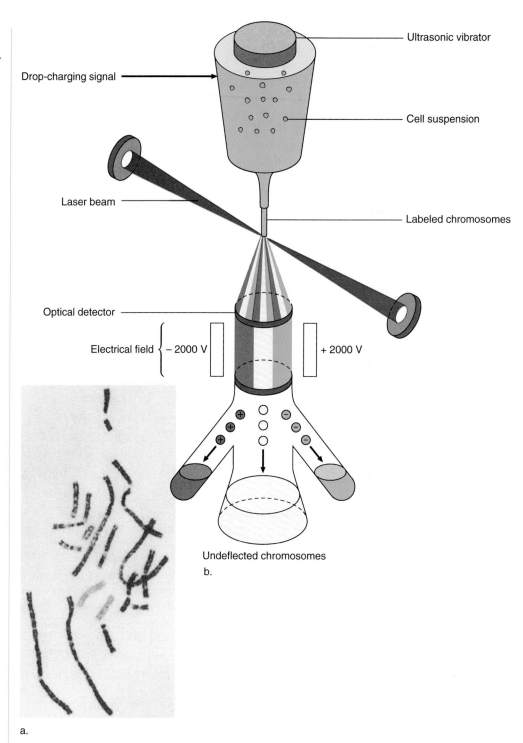

figure 21.6

Isolating chromosomes. (*a*) Somatic cell hybridization generates cells with only one or a few human chromosomes. When rodent and human cells are fused, human chromosomes are lost as the cell divides. This cell has a human X chromosome and chromosome 3, which appear lighter than the other, rodent chromosomes. If a DNA probe corresponding to a specific human gene binds only to somatic cell hybrids that contain human chromosome 3, then researchers know that the probe identifies a gene on that chromosome. (*b*) In flow cytometry, a device called a fluorescence-activated cell sorter recognizes distinctive fluorescent label patterns of particular chromosomes as they shoot through a jet of water. A computer assigns a positive or negative charge to the fluorescence pattern of a chromosome of interest, and an electric field deflects large numbers of the chromosome into a receptacle.

```
                        FEELING WE'RE NOT
        TOTO, I HAVE A FEE
                              ELING WE'RE NOT IN KANSAS ANYMORE
                   A FEELING
             AVE A FEELING WE'RE NOT IN KANSAS A
                   ING WE'R
                            'RE NOT IN KANSAS ANYMORE
              ELING WE'RE NOT IN KANS
        I HAVE A FEELING WE
               FEELING WE'R
                       NG WE'RE NOT IN KANSAS ANYMO
        TOTO, I HAVE A FEELING WE'RE NOT IN KANSAS ANYMORE
```

figure 21.7

Chromosome walking and aligning overlapping sequences to build a contig map is comparable to reconstructing a whole sentence from overlapping fragments.

locations of protein-encoding genes. One such clue is a stretch of repeats of CG, called CpG islands. In mammals, CGCGCG . . . often marks the beginning of a protein-encoding gene.

The HD gene contig map spanned half a million bases, an area that encodes about one hundred genes. At first, all were candidates for the HD causative gene. How would researchers figure out which of the candidate genes causes HD? At this point, researchers need a clue, which often comes from the nature of the illness. In cystic fibrosis, for example, a gene in the narrowed region whose product controls the passage of chloride ions into and out of cells emerged as a likely candidate, because abnormalities in that particular gene would explain the disease's signs and symptoms.

The key clue in the HD quest came from David Housman at the Massachusetts Institute of Technology, who had discovered the triplet repeats that cause myotonic dystrophy (figure 10.12). In early 1992, Housman suggested that similar expansions might cause HD, because both disorders affect the brain's control over nerves and muscles.

Looking for a triplet repeat was a long shot. But on February 24, 1993, the researchers found it—a stretch of DNA, about 210,000 base pairs long, that was even longer in people with HD. Gusella named the long-sought gene a rather unremarkable IT15; IT stands for "interesting transcript." Other types of experiments began to describe the protein product, named huntingtin.

First, researchers compared the DNA sequence to gene sequences from other species, using a national database called GenBank, which is part of the National Library of Medicine. Finding counterparts (homologs) to an unfamiliar human gene sequence in other species provides powerful evidence that the gene has been evolutionarily conserved and is therefore important. This was the case for the IT15 gene sequence, which has homologs in yeast, fruit flies, and mice. The gene that causes HD is ancient and important, but at this writing, its exact role is unknown.

Another type of experiment that helps describe a newly discovered gene determines which tissues express the gene (table 21.4). To do this, researchers use a **cDNA library,** which is a collection of cDNAs from a particular tissue type. (Recall that the cDNAs from a cell reflect the mRNAs there.) If a candidate gene sequence hybridizes to a cDNA in a particular library, researchers know that is the tissue where the gene functions. Not surprisingly, the HD candidate gene IT15 hybridized to a brain library. It was no longer a candidate—it was the gene.

Discovering the HD gene made marker tests for the disease obsolete. Now any person can be tested for the expanded gene without taking blood samples from several family members. On the research front, neurobiologists are using the HD gene to identify people who have inherited the disease before symptoms arise, then viewing the course of the illness in the brain through imaging techniques.

The search for the HD gene, well underway when the genome project began, pioneered many of the techniques that genome researchers use today. The Technology Timeline in Chapter 10 chronicles these events. Table 21.5 summarizes the techniques for mapping and sequencing genomes.

table 21.4

Identifying a Candidate Gene

Evidence for a Candidate Gene

CpG islands

Evolutionary conservation

Expression in appropriate tissues

Confirmation of a Candidate Gene

Sequencing and protein determination fit phenotype

Mutations correlate with presence of disease

Key Concepts

The search for the HD gene began with pedigrees from two large affected families. A DNA probe that hybridized to DNA of affected individuals in both families revealed an RFLP that is a marker for the disease-causing gene when inherited on the same homolog. A LOD score represents the statistical likelihood that a gene and a marker are inherited together because they are tightly linked. The HD marker provided a presymptomatic diagnostic test.

Researchers overlap DNA probes beginning with a marker or cytogenetic guidepost, then create a contig map. The probes are sequenced, and the total sequence is reconstructed from the probe overlaps.

The quest to find the HD gene illustrates many genome research techniques. Researchers identified a genetic marker closely linked to the HD gene in extended families, then used overlapping probes to "walk" down the tip of chromosome four. They recognized the HD gene out of about 100 genes in the chromosomal region because of its alteration in patients, expression in the brain, and high degree of evolutionary conservation.

table 21.5

Techniques for Studying Genomes

Technique	Description and Use
cDNA library	A gene library of cDNAs made from mRNAs from a specific cell type, reflecting gene expression in that tissue
Chromosome walking to construct a contig map	A method that overlaps DNA probes to extend a known DNA sequence and reconstruct a larger sequence
Expressed sequence tags	Pieces of cDNAs that help researchers locate protein-encoding genes
Flow cytometry	Shooting fluorescently labeled single chromosomes past a laser and an optical detector that deflects and collects large numbers of the same chromosome type
Gene library	Pieces of human DNA propagated as recombinant DNA molecules in bacteria
Genome mismatch scanning	A method of comparing several genomes that identifies genes they have in common
Representational difference analysis	A method of comparing two genomes that reveals genes that are different in each
Sanger method of DNA sequencing	A technique for generating complementary copies of a gene that differ from each other by one labeled end base, then reading the sequence by arranging the pieces in size order
Sequencing-by-hybridization	A technique for sequencing DNA by complementary binding an unknown sequence to known DNA pieces immobilized on a small glass microchip
Somatic cell hybridization	Creating rodent-human hybrid cells that retain only one human chromosome, used to localize DNA probes to specific chromosomes

Preventing Genetic Discrimination

Until recently, if the phrase "family history of Huntington disease" appeared anywhere in your medical record, you probably could not obtain adequate health insurance. You might not have been hired for certain jobs if the employer knew of your family history. Unfortunately, while gene discoveries provide beneficial medical tools such as diagnostic tests and new treatments, they also provide targets for discrimination. Because of the potential misuse of HGP information, part of the project's annual budget is earmarked to explore ethical, legal, and social implications of the results.

In many nations, laws are in place or are being developed to prevent discrimination in obtaining health insurance for those who take genetic tests. Still, many people refuse genetic testing, or pay for it themselves and do not use their real names, to be certain that the test results cannot be used to stigmatize them. Organizations that represent people with particular inherited illnesses are very vocal about insurers not discriminating against the "healthy ill"—those people with presymptomatic diagnoses. But the insurance issue is multifaceted. Some people argue that it wouldn't be fair to protect someone whose brain tumor is known to be caused by a faulty gene from high insurance rates, but not someone with a brain tumor not known to have a genetic cause. From yet another perspective, insurers fear that people will learn that they have inherited certain conditions or disease risks that are not yet clinically detectable (meaning that the people could pass a physical exam to purchase insurance) and not disclose the genetic test information to the insurance company, so that they will receive a large payout when they become ill. Clearly, many issues remain unresolved concerning access to genetic information.

The problem of genetic discrimination may eventually solve itself. As our genes are sequenced, we all will be found to harbor a disease-causing or disease-susceptibility allele—or two or even three.

Key Concepts

The results of the HGP will provide an unprecedented ability to predict which individuals are at high risk to develop certain illnesses. Steps are being taken to prevent discrimination based on test results.

Epilogue

Since the dawn of humanity, people have probably noted inherited traits among themselves, from height and body build, to hair and eye color, to special abilities, behavioral quirks, and illnesses. Genetics provides the variety that makes life interesting. The science of genetics began as the recognition that certain characteristics and medical problems tended to run in families, recurring with predictable frequencies. Today, genetics is rapidly becoming a medical field in its own right, and in the future it will impact our lives in many ways.

You will likely encounter many of the genetic technologies discussed in this book at some time in your life. You might

- serve on a jury asked to evaluate DNA fingerprint evidence.

- be tested to see whether you are a carrier of cystic fibrosis, or have an inherited susceptibility to a certain type of cancer.

- receive a chromosome report on your child-to-be.

- eat a genetically altered fruit or vegetable.

- take medication that is a human protein manufactured in bacteria given a human gene, or in transgenic sheep or cattle.

- buy flowers whose color pattern reflects pigment genes silenced by gene targeting or antisense technology.

- adopt a pet that is especially healthy because disease-causing genes have been artificially selected against.

- wear jeans dyed with a pigment made in recombinant bacteria.

- use paper from genetically engineered trees.

- eat a fish four times its normal size, thanks to added growth hormone genes.

The list of genetics applications is long and ever-expanding. I hope this book has offered you glimpses of the future and prepared you to deal personally with the avalanche of genetic information that will arrive with the new century. Let me know your thoughts!

Ricki Lewis
rickilewis@nasw.org

s u m m a r y

1. The human genome project is a global effort to decipher the sequence of the three billion DNA bases that comprise human chromosomes. The information the project reveals will have diverse applications.

2. New methods of gene analysis scan entire genomes to detect sequence similarities and differences.

3. The HGP began as researchers mapped RFLPs and sites of cytogenetic abnormalities and is continuing as they sequence and overlap short DNA sequences to extend known sequences.

4. The HGP officially began in 1990. Initial goals were to speed sequencing and to divide the genome into workable pieces. **Expressed sequence tags,** which are **cDNA** pieces of genes that indicate protein-encoding genes, identify parts of the genome most likely to contain disease-causing genes.

5. In Sanger's method of DNA sequencing, an unknown sequence is replicated repeatedly but exposed to dideoxynucleotides that cause early chain termination. The sequence is inferred by labeling the end bases of the pieces and aligning the fragments in size order. **Sequencing-by-hybridization** screens an unknown sequence against labeled, short sequences immobilized in known positions on a glass microchip. The alignment of the bound short sequences reveals the unknown DNA sequence.

6. Gene organization is more complex than the earlier beads-on-a-string description indicates, with regions of overlap. Defining a gene by its observable phenotype omits some genes. Exons may be spliced in different patterns, and an exon on one strand may function as an intron on the complementary strand.

7. The total number of human genes is 60,000 to 70,000. Gene density varies in different parts of the genome. ESTs reveal that one protein-encoding gene typically occurs every 40,000 to 50,000 bases, indicating that much DNA does not encode protein. Many human genes function in the brain.

8. The discovery of the HD gene pioneered many genome technologies. A gene hunt involves population, transmission, and molecular genetics.

9. A **genetic marker** is a part of a chromosome that includes a polymorphism that adds or deletes a restriction site and is closely linked to a gene of interest. Researchers use a series of overlapping probes, binding at the site of a marker or a cytogenetic abnormality, to identify the disease-causing gene.

10. Researchers identify a candidate gene for a particular illness by considering whether it encodes protein, is highly conserved, is expressed in appropriate tissues, and is altered in people who have the illness.

11. The HGP raises new ethical and legal questions and includes efforts to prevent genetic discrimination.

r e v i e w   q u e s t i o n s

1. How would each of the following phenomena complicate finding an RFLP marker for a disease-causing gene?

   a. incomplete penetrance

   b. genetic heterogeneity

   c. a phenocopy

2. List five applications of human genome information.

3. How do gene searches involve population, transmission, and molecular genetics?

4. How is the canine genome project described in Reading 21.1 similar to the quest for the HD gene?

5. Genome researchers use many colorful terms to describe their activities. What do each of the following expressions mean?

   a. shotgunning

   b. chromosome walking

   c. informatics

   d. genomics

   e. CpG islands

6. How are representational difference analysis and genomic mismatch scanning similar and different?

7. Why does a cDNA reflect gene expression?

8. List two ways that genome organization is more complex than the arrangement of beads on a string.

9. Why must an RFLP be on the same homolog as the disease-causing gene to function as a genetic marker? What might be the consequence if it is not?

10. List three ways that researchers narrow the list of candidate genes for a certain disease-causing gene.

applied questions

1. Researchers have identified genetic markers for a gene that causes inherited nighttime bedwetting. What should their next steps be in finding the causative gene?

2. One newly identified human gene has counterparts (homologs) in bacteria, yeast, roundworms, mustard weed, fruit flies, mice, and chimpanzees. A second gene has homologs in fruit flies, mice, and chimpanzees. What does this information reveal about the functions of these two human genes with respect to each other?

3. How many kilobases of DNA comprise the genome of *Haemophilis influenzae*? How large was each fragment that researchers sequenced in this bacterium?

4. What does a LOD score of 5 mean?

5. Children's snap beads come in many colors, and each bead has a protrusion at one end and a hole on the other that fits the protrusion. Devise an experiment using four colors of these snap beads to model Sanger's method of DNA sequencing.

6. A tumor suppressor gene that, when abnormal or absent, causes hereditary nonpolyposis colon cancer is homologous to a gene in yeast that repairs DNA. Apply this information to develop a hypothesis that explains how the cancer develops.

7. *Haemophilus influenzae* has 1,743 genes, *Saccharomyces cerevisiae* (yeast) has 6,000, *Caenorhabditis elegans* (roundworm) has 15,000 genes, and humans have about 70,000 genes. Using the information in table 21.1, determine which species has the greatest density of protein-encoding genes and which has the lowest density.

8. Restriction enzymes break a sequence of bases into the following pieces:

   T T A A T A T C G

   C G T T A A T A T C G C T A G

   G C T T C G T T

   A A T A T C G C T A G C T G C A

   T A A T A T C G C T A G C T G C A

   C T T C G T

   T A G C T G C A

   G T T A A T A T C G C T A G C T G C A

   How long is the original sequence? Reconstruct it.

9. Best disease is an autosomal dominant form of blindness that develops very gradually in adulthood. Reading and driving are no longer possible by age sixty. Researchers examined a large family with Best disease and found a genetic marker common to all 29 affected relatives that was not found among the unaffected family members. The marker and gene behind Best disease are located on chromosome 11. A gene already known to map to the same region, ROM-1, codes for a protein found only in the retina that is known to be abnormal in some forms of blindness.

   Using any of the techniques described in this chapter, devise an experimental approach to test whether ROM-1 is a candidate gene for Best disease.

suggested readings

Beardsley, Tim. March 1996. Vital data. *Scientific American.* Who should have access to genome information?

Boguski, Mark S. September 7, 1995. Hunting for genes in computer databases. *The New England Journal of Medicine,* vol. 333. Comparing a newly discovered gene sequence to those in huge databases is the fun part of genome work.

Lee, Adrian. March 19, 1998. The *Helicobacter pylori* genome—new insights into pathogenesis and therapeutics. *The New England Journal of Medicine,* vol. 338. Probing an organism's genome can reveal how it functions.

Lewis, Ricki. January 15, 1998. Genetic testing guidelines released. *Genetic Engineering News.* The ELSI program is trying to prevent genetic discrimination.

Lewis, Ricki. January 5, 1998. Comparative genomics reveals the interrelatedness of life. *The Scientist.* Probing genomes shows that species are more alike than different.

Ostrander, Elaine, and Edward Giniger. September 1997. Semper fidelis: what man's best friend can teach us about human biology and disease. *The American Journal of Human Genetics,* vol. 61. Dogs develop many disorders that humans do.

Pokorski, Robert J. January 1997. Insurance underwriting in the genetic era. *The American Journal of Human Genetics,* vol. 61. The insurance industry will have to keep up with genetic testing.

Quigley, Harry A. April 19, 1998. The search for glaucoma genes—implications for pathogenesis and disease detection. *The New England Journal of Medicine,* vol. 338. A good illustration of how genetic analysis of a disorder that is not usually inherited can help many people.

Rosenthal, Nadia. March 2, 1995. Fine structure of a gene—DNA sequencing. *The New England Journal of Medicine,* vol. 332. How to sequence DNA.

Rothenberg, Karen. March 21, 1997. Genetic information and the workplace: legislative approaches and policy challenges. *Science,* vol. 275. Laws are being developed now to prepare society for the coming explosion of genetic information.

Sedlak, Bonnie Joy. February 1, 1998. Functional genomics. *Genetic Engineering News.* Identifying and mapping genes is only the opening chapter of truly understanding genetics.

Stipp, David. March 31, 1997. Gene chip breakthrough. *Fortune.* DNA chips will detect many mutant genes.

Wade, Nicholas. April 8, 1997. Meeting of computers and biology: the DNA chip. *The New York Times.* Genetic disease detection occurs on a tiny glass square.

Wexler, Alice. 1995. *Mapping Fate.* New York: Times Books, Random House. An account of the discovery of the HD gene.

Answers to End-of-Chapter Questions

Chapter 1 Overview of Human Genetics

Answers to Review Questions

1. a. A dominant allele determines phenotype in one copy. A recessive allele determines phenotype in two copies.

   b. Genotype is the allele constitution in an individual for a particular gene. Phenotype is the physical expression of an allele combination.

   c. A gene is a sequence of DNA encoding a protein. A chromosome is a rod in the nucleus that consists of a continuous molecule of DNA and associated proteins.

   d. An autosome carries genes that do not determine sex. A sex chromosome carries a gene or genes that determine sex.

   e. DNA is a double-stranded nucleic acid that includes deoxyribose and the nitrogenous bases adenine, guanine, cytosine, and thymine. DNA carries the genetic information. RNA is a single-stranded nucleic acid that includes ribose and the nitrogenous bases adenine, guanine, cytosine, and uracil. RNA carries out gene expression. Protein is a polymer (chain) of amino acids.

2. A DNA sequence of a gene encodes the amino acid sequence of a protein, whose function provides a trait.

3. Genetics in the news: discoveries of disease-causing genes; DNA fingerprinting evidence in criminal trials; new drugs from recombinant DNA technology; people hesitant to take new genetic tests; labeling of genetically altered fruits and vegetables; gene therapy clinical trials; cloning of animals; genetically engineered bioweapons; high-nicotine tobacco.

4. A genetic condition recurs with a predictable probability within a family. An inherited illness can be "diagnosed" before symptoms appear.

5. Mode of inheritance refers to whether a trait is dominant or recessive and whether a gene is transmitted on an autosome or a sex chromosome. Modes of inheritance are sex-linked recessive, autosomal recessive, sex-linked dominant, and autosomal dominant. Knowing mode of inheritance is important in determining risk of transmitting a trait.

6. At the molecular level, a gene can mutate, which can alter the final protein product and possibly cell function, which can greatly affect body function. A mutation can appear in other family members and be passed to offspring. The mutant allele can be present in the population at large, but the allele may be more common to a particular group that marries among themselves. Any genetic disease can be used as an example.

7. A permanent wave and contact lenses change the phenotype (appearance), but not the genotype (specific alleles), because the person's children are not born with curly hair or wearing contact lenses.

8. Genetic counselors inform families of recurrence risks for specific inherited illnesses by applying the laws of inheritance to that family's health history.

9. It is possible to predict that a genetic disease will develop because the genotype is present from conception; the phenotype may develop later.

10. Examples might include height, weight, and skin color.

11. A gene can affect how the body metabolizes a drug or reacts to a toxin.

Answers to Applied Questions

1. Two brothers with sickle cell disease can have different experiences because of the effects of other genes that they do not have in common (unless they are identical twins).

2. Benefits of presymptomatic genetic testing are that people can make informed decisions about the future and have diagnostic tests early, when treatment may be more effective. The risks are that people who are presymptomatically diagnosed may imagine symptoms before they actually occur, become depressed, or suffer discrimination by employers or insurance companies.

3. DNA fingerprinting typically compares only a few DNA sequences. The accused father and son may have the same alleles for the sequences examined.

4. People fear genetics because DNA may seem mysterious and because altering DNA can affect future generations.

5. The answers to these questions are personal but may be based on utility. That is, what can an individual gain by knowing that a particular disease lies in the future?

6. Insurance companies and employers could refuse to insure or hire people perceived to be at high risk because of their genotype. Several laws attempt to prevent this.

7. Allergies, autoimmune disorders, and infections involve the immune system. Because many immune system biochemicals are proteins, genes control immune function.

Chapter 2 Cells

Answers to Review Questions

1. Specialized cells express different subsets of all the genes that are present in all cell types, except for red blood cells.

2. a. A prokaryotic cell is usually small and lacks a nucleus and other organelles. A eukaryotic cell contains membrane-bound organelles, including a nucleus, that compartmentalize biochemical reactions.

   b. During interphase, cellular components are replicated. During mitosis, the cell divides, distributing its contents into two daughter cells.

   c. Mitosis increases cell number. Apoptosis eliminates cells.

   d. Rough ER is a labyrinth of membranous tubules, studded with ribosomes that synthesize proteins. Smooth ER is the site of lipid synthesis.

e. Microtubules are tubules of tubulin, and microfilaments are rods of actin. Both form the cytoskeleton.

f. A cell has a membrane and complex structures within cytoplasm. A virus is a nucleic acid in a protein coat. A prion is a proteinaceous infectious particle.

3. Compartmentalization separates biochemicals that could harm certain cell constituents. It also organizes the cell so it can function more efficiently.

4. Because enzymes are proteins, genes encode them.

5. Proteins are encoded in DNA sequences and are synthesized in the cytoplasm on rough ER. In the smooth ER, lipids are added. Lipids and proteins bud off in vesicles and move to the Golgi body, picking up sugars and starches. From here, the secretion moves to the cell surface and buds off in vesicles or moves through the cell membrane.

6. In signal transduction and secretion, a cell interacts with its environment. Signal transduction brings information into the cell, and secretion carries materials out.

7. The nucleus

8. a. Mitochondria extract energy from nutrients to fuel cellular activities.

b. Lysosomes are sacs of enzymes that break down debris.

c. Peroxisomes break down certain lipids and rare biochemicals, synthesize bile acids, and detoxify compounds that result from excess oxygen exposure.

d. Smooth ER is the site of lipid synthesis.

e. Rough ER is the site of protein synthesis.

f. The Golgi body is the site of carbohydrate addition to proteins to form secretions.

9. The CFTR protein forms a chloride channel in cell membranes.

Lactase enables a person to digest the milk sugar lactose.

Protein receptors admit cholesterol to liver cells.

Biotinidase controls the rate that the body uses the vitamin biotin.

Lysosomal enzymes break down debris in lysosomes.

Peroxisomal enzymes break down lipids, synthesize bile acids, and detoxify poisons.

Tubulin, actin, spectrin, and ankyrins are part of the cytoskeleton.

CAMS (selectins, integrins, and adhesion receptor proteins) provide cell adhesion.

Cyclins and kinases control the cell cycle.

10. Apoptosis is programmed cell death and is a normal part of development. Necrosis is a response to injury.

11. Hormones and growth factors affect the cell from the outside. They are produced and released from glands and travel to their target cells in the bloodstream. Cyclins and kinases act from within the cell on genes.

12. In normal cells, telomeres shorten to a point that halts cell division.

13. A virus is a nucleic acid wrapped in a protein coat. A cell is more complex and contains all the structural and biochemical components necessary to function and reproduce independently. A virus requires a host cell and its DNA to replicate.

Answers to Applied Questions

1. a. Lack of cell adhesion can speed the migration of cancer cells.

b. Impaired signal transduction can block a message to cease dividing.

c. Blocking apoptosis can cause excess mitosis and an abnormal growth.

d. Lack of cell cycle control can lead to too many mitoses.

e. If telomerase is abnormal, a cell might not cease to divide when it normally would.

2. a. Abnormal chloride channels in cell membranes of lung-lining cells and pancreas.

b. Lack of a transport protein in peroxisomes leads to buildup of long-chain fatty acids.

c. Abnormal ankyrin collapses the cytoskeletal attachment to the cell membrane, causing red blood cells to balloon out.

d. Abnormal growth factors and signal transduction lead to nerve overgrowth beneath the skin.

e. Lack of CAMs impairs wound healing.

3. Lysosomes cannot break down glycogen to simple sugars. The large carbohydrates accumulate, swelling lysosomes and impairing heart muscle.

4. The muscle weakness gene resides in mitochondria, which only females transmit.

5. Lysosomes and the nucleus

6. The protein abnormal in Wiskott-Aldrich syndrome can affect several components of the cytoskeleton and signal transduction pathways, causing different symptoms.

7. Different types of muscular dystrophy affect dystrophin or the glycoproteins that are near it in the cell membrane.

Chapter 3 Human Development

Answers to Review Questions

1. a. 2

b. 2

c. 1

d. 2

e. 1

f. 1

2. Male: sperm are manufactured in seminiferous tubules packed into the testes, and mature sperm are stored in the epididymis. The epididymis is continuous with the vas deferens, which carries sperm to the urethra, which sends them out through the penis. The prostate gland and the seminal vesicles secrete into the vas deferens, and the bulbourethral glands secrete into the urethra, forming seminal fluid.

Female: Oocytes develop within the ovaries and are released into the fallopian tubes. The fallopian tubes carry them to the uterus, which narrows at its base to form the cervix, which opens to the vagina.

3. 2^{39}. This is an underestimate because it does not account for crossing over.

4. Mitosis divides somatic cells into two daughter cells with the same number of chromosomes as the diploid parent cell. Meiosis forms gametes, in which the four daughter cells have half the number of chromosomes of the parent cell. Genetic recombination occurs in meiosis.

5. Both produce gametes, but oogenesis takes years, and spermatogenesis takes months.

6. In female gamete maturation, most of the cytoplasm concentrates in one huge cell. In male gamete maturation, four similarly shaped sperm derive from an original cell undergoing meiosis.

Answers to Applied Questions

1. a. F
   b. D
   c. I
   d. A
   e. E, F
   f. C
   g. H
   h. E, F
   i. G
   j. G
   k. E

2. Haplotypes can reveal if people without symptoms have the haplotype associated with the condition. These people are nonpenetrant.

3. a. 1/2
   b. 1/2
   c. 0
   d. 0

4. 1/4

5. The Bombay phenotype accounts for the young woman's type O blood. She is *hh*.

6. a. This alters the phenotype.
   b. Bombay phenotype

Chapter 6 Matters of Sex

Answers to Review Questions

1. Sex is expressed at the chromosomal level as inheriting XX or XY; at the gonadal level by developing ovaries or testes; at the phenotypic level by developing male or female internal and external structures; and at the gender identity level by feelings.

2. a. Female
   b. Female
   c. Female

3. Sustentacular cells secrete anti-Müllerian hormone, which stops development of female reproductive structures. Interstitial cells secrete testosterone, which promotes development of male reproductive structures.

4. Absence of the SRY gene product causes the Müllerian ducts to develop into ovaries. The ovaries produce female hormones, which

influence the development of external and internal reproductive structures.

5. Feelings of very young children; twin studies in which identical twins are more likely to both be homosexual than are fraternal twins; fruit fly behavior; genes on the X chromosome that segregate with homosexuality

6. Coat color in cats is sex-linked. In females, one X chromosome in each cell is inactivated, and the pattern of a calico cat's coat depends on which cells express which coat-color allele. A male cat, with only one coat-color allele, would have to inherit an extra X chromosome to be tortoiseshell or calico.

7. Inactivation of the gene in some cells but not others results in a patchy phenotype.

8. Each cell in a female's body contains only one active X chromosome, which makes females genetically equivalent (in terms of sex-linked genes) to males.

9. A sex-linked trait appears usually in males and may affect structures or functions not distinct to one sex. A sex-limited trait affects a structure or function distinct to one sex. A sex-influenced trait is inherited as a recessive in one sex and dominant in the other.

10. Mouse zygotes with two female pronuclei or two male pronuclei are abnormal. In humans, two male and one female genome in the same embryo yields a placenta, while two female and one male genome yields a normal embryo with an abnormal placenta. Hydatidiform moles (placental tissue with no embryo) consist of cells with two male genomes; a teratoma contains cells with two female genomes.

11. If methylation silences a gene in one sex, it could account for genomic imprinting.

Answers to Applied Questions

1. Evidence demonstrating a biological role in homosexuality argues against the idea that it is an abnormal behavior, a crime, or against religion.

2. a. Because the phenotype is not severe
   b. 1 in 2 (50%), because she is a carrier
   c. 1 in 1 (100%)

3. a. Carriers are individuals I4, II3, III2, III5.
   b. 1/2
   c. 1/2
   d. Women would have to inherit kinky hair disease from an affected father and a carrier mother; affected males would not live long enough to have children.

4. a. 1/2
   b. 1/2
   c. 1/2

5. a. 1/2
   b. 0
   c. Lesch-Nyhan syndrome is inherited from a carrier mother, who has a normal copy of the gene to protect her.

6. 1/2

7. 1/4

8.

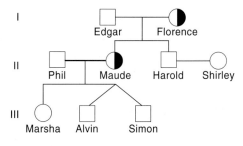

Chapter 7 Complex Traits

Answers to Review Questions

1. a. Obesity
   b. Hypertension
   c. Heart disease
   d. Alcoholism
   e. Obesity
   f. Neurotransmitter imbalance, leading to behavioral disorder

2. Estimating risk recurrence of a multifactorial disorder depends upon empiric data. In Mendelian inheritance, estimating risk depends on the mode of inheritance.

3. Restrict dietary lipids.

4. Exposure to an anesthetic drug is required to induce symptoms.

5. The change in height is too great and fast to reflect genetics alone. Nutrition has improved in the population and may have contributed to the observed increase in height.

6. A child shares 1/4 of genes with a grandparent, who is a second-degree relative.

7. Adoptees and their adopted families could have a common ancestor and not be aware of it. The environment shared by adoptees and

adoptive families is not necessarily different from that shared between a child and biological parents.

8. If the mothers and fathers are identical twins

9. Leptin is a satiety factor, and lipoprotein lipase breaks down fats in blood vessels. Inability to recognize leptin can lead to overeating and obesity. Malfunctioning lipoprotein lipase can cause fat cells to grow too large.

10. Concordance data and elevated recurrence risk within families suggest that narcolepsy with cataplexy is inherited.

Answers to Applied Questions

1. No

2. NTDs are complex traits, and, therefore, the empiric risk increases with each affected birth. Albinism is a Mendelian trait, so risk is the same for each offspring.

3. She can avoid consuming alcohol.

4. When studying behavior, some reliance on people's reports of their feelings may be unavoidable. Statistics may be based on inaccurate assumptions. Following genetic markers to study behavior may compensate for the shortcomings of other methods.

5. Seasonality of births of people with schizophrenia suggests the role of a virus, because viral infections are more common in the winter months.

6. Research can isolate a chromosomal region where the DNA sequence is common to people with Wolfram syndrome, and eventually discover and describe the causative gene. The specific nature of the corresponding protein product may explain how a half normal gene dose causes the behavioral problems of relatives.

7. Information on inherited predisposition to alcoholism could be used to help individuals avoid becoming alcoholic. It could be abused by restricting employment and insurance opportunities and other rights of individuals identified to be at risk.

8. Bipolar affective disorder

Chapter 8 DNA Structure and Replication

Answers to Review Questions

1. DNA is replicated so that it is not used up in directing the cell to manufacture protein.

2. 1. E
2. C
3. D
4. B
5. A

3. The nucleotide base sequence encodes information.

4. One end of a strand of nucleotides has a phosphate group attached to the 5′ carbon of deoxyribose. The other end has a hydroxyl group attached to the 3′ carbon. Phosphodiester bonds (which bind the sugar-phosphate backbone) form between the 3′ OH of the nucleotide chain and the 5′ phosphate of an incoming nucleotide. Thus, the chain grows in the 5′ to 3′ direction. The two strands are antiparallel—one strand is 5′ → 3′, and the other is 3′ → 5′.

5. Helicases, RNA polymerase, DNA polymerase, ligase, photolyases

6. a. A G C T C T T A G A G C T A A
b. G G C A T A T C G G C C A T G
c T A G C C T A G C G A T G A C

7. Histone protein, nucleosome, chromatin

Answers to Applied Questions

1. The sugar-phosphate backbone of replicating DNA cannot attach.

2. DNA repair enzymes added to suntan lotion could prevent formation of pyrimidine dimers in skin cells by ultraviolet radiation in sunlight.

3. 20 cycles × 2 minutes/cycle = 40 minutes

4. If both conditions are autosomal recessive, and each person has a defect in a different DNA repair enzyme, then the mutations are in different genes, and the risk to a child of theirs is not 25%.

5. Lacking DNA polymerase makes life impossible, because cells cannot divide.

6. PCR can directly detect HIV RNA, rather than a sign that the human body is responding to the presence of the virus.

7. Parental and newly replicated DNA misaligns in areas where the sequence is repetitive, resulting in different length microsatellite sequences.

Chapter 9 Gene Function

Answers to Review Questions

1. a. H bonds between A and T, and G and C join the strands of the double helix.

b. In DNA replication, a new strand is synthesized semiconservatively, with new bases inserted opposite their complementary bases to form a new strand.

c. An mRNA is transcribed by aligning RNA nucleotides against their complements in one strand of the DNA.

d. The sequence preceding the protein-encoding sequence of the mRNA base pairs with rRNA in the ribosome.

e. A tRNA binds to mRNA by base pairing between the three bases of its anticodon and the three mRNA bases of a codon.

f. The characteristic cloverleaf of tRNA is a consequence of H bonding between complementary bases.

2. The central dogma does not account for the flow of genetic information from RNA to DNA in retroviruses. Also, RNA is involved in DNA replication and gene expression to a greater extent and in more ways than depicted in the central dogma.

3. a. Proteins with an incorrect sequence of amino acids may not function.

b. If the initial amino acid is released, additional amino acids cannot add on.

c. If rRNA cannot bind to the ribosome, then mRNAs cannot be translated into protein.

d. If ribosomes cannot move, then a protein would not grow beyond two amino acids in length.

e. If a tRNA picks up the wrong amino acid, the protein's amino acid sequence will be abnormal.

4. Transcription is the DNA-directed synthesis of a strand of mRNA by the enzyme RNA polymerase. Translation is the synthesis of proteins by ribosomes, which read the triplet code in the mRNA and translate the code into a chain of amino acids.

5. RNA contains ribose and uracil and is single stranded. DNA contains deoxyribose and thymine and is double stranded. DNA preserves and transmits genetic information; RNA expresses genetic information.

6. DNA replication occurs in the nucleus of eukaryotes. Prokaryotes have no nucleus, so replication occurs in the cytoplasm. The same is true of transcription. Translation occurs in the cytoplasm of all cell types. In eukaryotes, some ribosomes are attached to the ER.

7. Transcription controls cell specialization by turning different sets of genes on and off in different cell types.

8. Retroviruses have an RNA genome and reverse transcriptase, which synthesizes DNA from RNA. The human genome is DNA, and RNA polymerase transcribes mRNA from DNA.

9. In transcription initiation, the DNA double helix unwinds locally, transcription factors bind near the promoter, and RNA polymerase binds to the promoter.

10. mRNA is the intermediate between DNA and protein, carrying the genetic information to ribosomes. tRNA connects mRNA and amino acids and transfers amino acids to ribosomes for incorporation into protein. rRNA associates with proteins to form ribosomes.

11. Posttranscriptional changes to RNA include adding a cap and poly A tail and removing introns.

12. Ribosomes consist of several types of proteins and rRNAs in two subunits of unequal size.

13. Discovery of introns was surprising because genes were thought to be contiguous, and discovery of ribozymes was surprising because only proteins were thought to function as enzymes.

14. An overlapping code constrains protein structure because certain amino acids would always be followed by the same amino acids in every protein.

15. Transcription and translation are economical because tRNAs and ribosomes are recycled.

16. Proinsulin is shortened to insulin after translation. RNA editing shortens apolipoprotein B posttranscriptionally.

17. The amino acid sequence determines a protein's conformation by causing attractions and repulsions between different parts of the molecule.

18. Proteins make up part of the structure of ribosomes, and enzymes are involved in protein synthesis. To create a mature mRNA for translation, snurps (small RNAs and proteins) excise introns in pre-mRNAs. Ribozymes assist in peptide bond formation.

19. A two-nucleotide genetic code would specify only 16 types of amino acids. There are 20 amino acids in biological proteins.

Answers to Applied Questions

1. a. A A U G U G A A C G A A C U C U C A G

   b. U G A A C C C G A U A C G A G U A A T

   c. C C G A C G U U A U C G G C A U C U A

   d. C C U U A U G C A G A U C G A U C G U

2. a. C G A T A G A C A G T A T T T T C T C C T

   b. C A C C G C A T A A G A A A A G G C C C A T C C

   c. C T C C C T T A A G A A A G A G T T C G T T C A

   d. T C C T T T T G G G G A G A A T A A T A T C T A

3. U U C G C U A A A G A C U G U

4. Many answers are possible, using combinations of his (CAU or CAC), ala (CGU, GCC, GCA, GCG), arg (CGU, CGC, CGA, CGG), ser (AGU, AGC, AGA, AGG), leu (CUU, CUC, CUA, CUG), val (GUC, GUG) and cys (UGU, UGC).

5. Several answers are possible because of the redundancy of the genetic code. One answer is C A T A C C T T T G G G A A A T G G.

6. There is only one genetic code.

7. Use ACA with any triplet other than CAA and see whether threonine or histidine occurs. Whichever occurs, ACA encodes.

8. The CF gene product is a protein that lets chloride ions out of cells. If the protein is misshapen, chloride ions become trapped, drawing water in, which dries out secretions, causing symptoms of CF.

9. Crick added 1, 2, or 3 contiguous bases to a gene whose sequence he knew, and noted that adding only 3 nucleotides restored the reading frame.

Chapter 10 Gene Mutation

Answers to Review Questions

1. A spontaneous mutation can arise if a DNA base is in its rare tautomeric form at the precise instant when the replication fork arrives. A wrong base is inserted opposite the rare one.

2. Mutational hot spots are direct repeats or symmetrical regions of DNA.

3. Site-directed mutagenesis causes a mutation at a particular place.

4. Mutations in the third codon position are often silent. Mutations in the second position may replace an amino acid with a similarly shaped one. Sixty-one codons specify 20 amino acids.

5. a. A degenerate codon

   b. A mutation that replaces an amino acid with a structurally similar one

   c. A mutation that replaces an amino acid in a part of the protein not essential for its function

   d. A mutation in an intron

6. A conditional mutation is expressed only under certain conditions, such as increased temperature or exposure to particular drugs or chemicals.

7. A germinal mutation occurs in a gamete or a fertilized ovum. Therefore, it affects all the cells of an individual and is more serious than a somatic mutation, which affects only some tissues and is not transmitted to future generations.

8. The gene for collagen is particularly prone to mutation because it is very symmetrical.

9. Frameshift, deletion, duplication, insertion, transposable element

10. Retention of an intron and expanding triplet repeats can provide a new function for a gene, which may cause disease.

11. A jumping gene can disrupt gene function by altering the reading frame or shutting off transcription.

12. A new recessive mutation will not become obvious until two heterozygotes produce a homozygous recessive individual with a phenotype.

13. The gene is expanding.

14. Gaucher mutations include an insertion of one DNA base, which disrupts the reading frame, and a fusion gene that forms between part of the functional gene and part of a pseudogene.

Answers to Applied Questions

1. The second boy's second mutation, further in the gene, restores the reading frame so that part of the dystrophin protein has a normal structure, providing some function.

2. asn to lys: AAU to AAA AAC to AAG

    ile to thr: AUU to ACU AUC to ACC AUA to ACA

3. Nonsense

4. arg to his: CGU to CAU CGC to CAC

5. GAU to GUU or GAC to GUC

6. The mutation in this person must have occurred in a cell in a very early embryo. The mutation is therefore in only some cells.

7. Victoria could have undergone a spontaneous mutation.

8. Mutations in these 13 exons may be lethal or not have an effect.

9. Nonsense

10. Several different genes can cause familial Alzheimer disease. It would not be cost-effective to test everyone for several genes.

Chapter 11 Cytogenetics

Answers to Review Questions

1. a. Homologs do not separate in meiosis I or II, leading to a gamete with an extra or missing chromosome.

    b. DNA replicates but is not apportioned into daughter cells, forming a diploid gamete.

    c. Increased tendency for nondisjunction in the chromosome 21 pair

    d. Crossing over in the male yields unbalanced gametes, which can fertilize oocytes, but too much or too little genetic material halts development.

    e. A gamete including just one translocated chromosome will have too much of part of the chromosome and too little of other parts. Excess chromosome 21 material causes Down syndrome.

2. Patches of octaploid cells in liver tissue may arise as a result of abnormal mitosis in a few liver cells early in development.

3. a. An XXX individual has no symptoms, but she may conceive sons with Klinefelter syndrome by producing XX oocytes.

    b. A female with XO Turner syndrome has wide-set nipples, flaps of skin on the neck, and no secondary sexual development.

    c. This is a female with trisomy 21 or translocation Down syndrome. Phenotype includes short, sparse, straight hair, wide-set eyes with epicanthal folds, a broad nose, protruding tongue, mental retardation, and increased risk of a heart defect, suppressed immunity, and leukemia.

    d. A male with XXY Klinefelter syndrome is tall and thin, may be mentally subnormal, and has no secondary sexual development.

4. Basketball players may have an extra Y chromosome that makes them tall.

5. Triploids are very severely abnormal. Trisomy 21 is the least severe trisomy and involves the smallest chromosome. Klinefelter syndrome symptoms are worse if there is more than one extra X chromosome.

6. A balanced translocation causes duplications or deletions when a gamete contains one translocated chromosome, plus has extra or is missing genes from one of the chromosomes involved in the translocation. A paracentric or pericentric inversion can cause duplications or deletions if a crossover occurs between the inverted chromosome and its homolog. Isochromosomes result from centromere splitting in the wrong plane, duplicating one chromosome arm but deleting the other.

7. Chromosomes would not contort during meiosis because their genes are aligned.

8. a. High-resolution chromosome banding: Cells in culture are synchronized in early mitosis, then the chromosomes are spread and stained.

    b. FISH: Fluorescently labeled DNA probes bind homologous regions on chromosomes.

    c. Amniocentesis: Fetal cells and fluid are removed from around a fetus. Cells are cultured and their chromosomes stained or exposed to DNA probes, then karyotyped.

    d. Chorionic villus sampling: Chromosomes in chorionic villus cells are directly karyotyped.

    e. Fetal cell sorting: A fluorescence-activated cell sorter separates fetal from maternal cells, and fetal chromosomes are karyotyped.

    f. Maternal serum markers: Abnormal levels of proteins such as AFP and hCG in a pregnant woman's blood indicate increased risk of certain disorders.

Answers to Applied Questions

1. Down syndrome caused by aneuploidy produces an extra chromosome 21 in each cell. In mosaic Down syndrome, the extra chromosome is only in some cells. In translocation Down syndrome, unbalanced gametes lead to an individual with extra chromosome 21 material in each cell.

2. An XY sperm fertilizing a normal egg would produce Klinefelter syndrome.

3. Hospital mental patients might have had abnormal sex chromosome constitutions.

4. a. A translocation carrier can produce an unbalanced gamete that lacks chromosome 22 material.

    b. The microdeletion may be more extensive than the deleted region in the translocation individuals.

    c. Translocation family members might be infertile or have offspring with birth defects.

5. One of the Watkins probably has a balanced translocation, because there is more than one Down syndrome case. The two spontaneous abortions were the result of unbalanced gametes. Their problems are likely to repeat with a predictable and high frequency because the translocated chromosome is in half of the carrier parent's gametes. In contrast, the Phelps child with Down syndrome is more likely the result of nondisjunction, which is unlikely to repeat. The Phelps child has trisomy Down syndrome; the Watkins child may have only a partial extra copy of chromosome 21.

6. a. Reciprocal translocation

    b. She doesn't have extra or missing genes.

    c. She might have a child with translocation Down syndrome.

7. At the second mitotic division, replicated chromosomes failed to separate, yielding one of four cells with an extra two sets of chromosomes.

Chapter 12 When Gene Frequencies Stay Constant

Answers to Review Questions

1. A gene pool refers to a population.

2. Evolution is not occurring.

3. All organisms on earth use the same genetic code.

4. The possibility of two unrelated Caucasians without a family history of CF having an affected child is $1/4 \times 1/23 \times 1/23 = 1/2116$. If one person knows he or she is a carrier, the risk is $1/4 \times 1/23 = 1/92$.

5. RFLP analysis breaks DNA into pieces and then uses DNA probes to pull out certain sequences. PCR replicates part of a chromosome between two known sequences.

6. DNA fragments generated by restriction enzyme digestion are separated according to size by polyacrylamide gel electrophoresis.

7. Natural selection does not act on STRs.

8. Population databases are necessary to interpret DNA fingerprints because alleles occur with different frequencies in different populations.

9. For females, use the standard formula. For males, gene frequency equals phenotypic frequency.

Answers to Applied Questions

1. $0.1 \times 0.1 = 0.01 =$ chance both are carriers. If both are carriers, $0.25 \times 0.01 = 0.0025 = 0.25\%$ chance the child will be affected.

2. a. $q^2 = 1/190 = 0.005$. Square root of $0.005 = 0.071 =$ frequency of mutant allele q

   b. Frequency of wild type allele $= p = 1 - 0.071 = 0.929$

   c. Carriers $= 2pq = 2 \times 0.071 \times 0.929 = 0.132$

   d. Nonrandom mating

3. $q^2 = 1/8000 = 0.000125 \quad q = 0.011$ $p = 1 - 0.011 = 0.989$ carrier frequency $= 2pq = 2 \times 0.011 \times 0.989 = 0.022$

4. $4/177 = 0.0225 = 2.25\%$ are carriers.

5. F_1 (students) genotypes: 6 TT 4 Tt 10 tt

P$_1$ (parents) genotypes:

   of 6 TT students = 9 TT 2 Tt 1 tt

   of 4 Tt students = 2 TT 4 Tt 2 tt

   of 10 tt students = 8 Tt 12 tt

F_1 allele frequencies: $T = p = 1/2Tt + TT = 1/2$ (4) $+ 6 = 8/20$ students $= .4$

$\quad t = q = .6$

P$_1$ allele frequencies: $T = p = 1/2Tt + TT = 1/2$ (14) $+ 11 = 18/40$ parents $= .45$

$\quad t = q = .55$

The gene is evolving because the allele frequencies change between generations.

6. $15/2000 \times 23/2000 \times 62/2000 \times 7/2000 = 0.0075 \times 0.0115 \times 0.031 \times 0.0035 = 9.345$ billion

Chapter 13 Changing Gene Frequencies

Answers to Review Questions

1. a. Agriculture

   b. Cities, as groups of immigrants arrive and mix in

   c. Cousins having children together

   d. Unusual gene frequencies among the Dunkers

   e. Endangered species, survivors of massacres or natural disasters and their descendants

   f. Introducing a disease into a population

2. a. Highly virulent TB bacteria are selected against because they kill hosts quickly. Resistant hosts are selected for because they survive infection and live to reproduce. In this way, TB evolved from an acute systemic infection into a chronic lung infection. In the 1980s, antibiotic-resistant TB strains led to reemergence of the disease.

   b. Bacteria that become resistant to antibiotics by mutation or by acquiring resistance factors from other bacteria selectively survive in the presence of antibiotics.

   c. CF is especially prevalent in ancient populations where individuals had a mutation and did not leave the settlement or marry outside it.

3. Increasing homozygosity increases the chance that homozygous recessives will arise who may be too unhealthy to reproduce. The population may decline.

4. Misuse of antibiotics provides a selective pressure that benefits and maintains populations of drug-resistant bacteria.

5. Recessive alleles persist in heterozygotes.

6. Sickle cell disease protects against malaria.

7. An infectious disease may reemerge if some people refuse vaccination, if the causative agent mutates so that it is transmitted more readily, or if a strain emerges that resists treatment.

8. Historical records, geographical information, and linguistics

9. Decreased variation in mitochondrial and Y chromosome DNA sequences indicates a population bottleneck.

10. In the Dunker population, the frequencies of blood type genotype are quite different from those of the surrounding U.S. population and the ancestral population in Europe.

11. The most common CF allele is more common in France (70%) than in Finland (45%).

12. Homozygotes for a mutant allele are too ill to reproduce, or they may die before they reach childbearing age.

13. African Americans are more closely related to Europeans than Japanese, and to Wolofs than Nigerians.

Answers to Applied Questions

1. a. The settlers in North America who were ancestors of these Native Americans did not include a person with type B blood, or if they did, he or she did not leave descendants with type B blood.

   b. All modern Afrikaners with porphyria variegata descend from the same person in whom the disorder originated.

   c. One person, who had the dental disorder, contributed disproportionately to future generations.

   d. The high frequency of heart defects, polydactyly, and dwarfism in the Amish is due to mating only among themselves.

   e. Genetic diversity plummeted among cheetahs due to a population bottleneck.

   f. Mongrel dogs have more heterozygous loci compared to purebred animals, masking expression of deleterious recessive alleles.

   g. The Pingelapese people have a very high incidence of blindness due to a population bottleneck following a devastating typhoon.

2. a. Founder effect

   b. Geographical barriers and natural selection, acting over time, make two populations have different variants of inherited characteristics.

   c. Nonrandom mating

   d. Natural selection

3. Treating PKU has increased the proportion of mutant alleles in the population because without treatment, affected individuals would not have been able to reproduce.

4. a. Having one copy of the second CF allele increases the risk of developing asthma.

   b. Percent of people with wild type CF alleles who have asthma

5. A consanguineous relationship between individual III2 and III3 has produced a child with two copies of the same mutant recessive allele, inherited from a common ancestor.

6. a. Balanced polymorphism

   b. Founder effect

   c. Migration

7. Balanced polymorphism

Chapter 14 Human Origins and Evolution

Answers to Review Questions

1. Hominoids are ancestral to apes and humans, whereas hominids are ancestral to humans only. Therefore, hominoids are more ancient.

2. The child would be human. Five thousand years isn't long enough for a species to differ much from today.

3. Gene sequences are more specific because different codons can encode the same amino acids.

4. Mutation rates are not the same across genomes. Genes mutate at different rates.

5. One gene encodes one polypeptide; therefore, comparing the evolution of a gene tracks a tiny part of the biology of the organism. DNA hybridization assesses relationships among many genes, and thus means more. Also, much of the genome does not encode protein.

6. A chromosome band may contain many genes; therefore, comparing them is not specific.

7. Some proteins are nearly identical in sequence between humans and chimps, indicating that deviations from the sequence are selected against. Other proteins can still function if some amino acids are substituted, and, therefore, these differences would not be selected against, and their genes would vary within a species.

8. Knowledge of a DNA, RNA, or polypeptide sequence and the mutation rate is necessary to construct an evolutionary tree diagram. An assumption is that mutation rate is constant. A limitation is that only one biochemical is considered and not large-scale characteristics such as behavior and anatomy.

9. Sterilizing people with mental retardation; encouraging poor people to limit family size; avoiding marriage to a person who carries a disease-causing allele

Answers to Applied Questions

1. a. A small duplication occurred in human chromosome 11 to give rise to the Betazoid karyotype. The Klingon and Romulan karyotypes could have arisen from fusion of human chromosomes 15 and 17.

   b. The Betazoids are our closest relatives because of greater similarity in chromosome bands and chromosome arrangement. Cytochrome c sequences and intron pattern in the collagen gene are identical between humans and Betazoids.

   c. They are not distinct species because they can interbreed.

   d. c

2. Negative eugenics:

   sterilizing people who are mentally retarded; restricting certain groups from immigrating; encouraging people with inherited disease or carriers not to reproduce

   Positive eugenics:

   a sperm bank where Nobel prizewinners make deposits; people seeking very smart people as mates; governments paying people with the best jobs and the most education to have larger families

3. People in Third World nations might be alarmed by white-coated strangers wielding hypodermic needles, seeking blood samples. A compromise would be to collect hair instead of blood and use PCR to amplify the genes. Another compromise is to offer vaccines in exchange for tissue samples.

4. The action was eugenic in that nonwhite students were indirectly selected against. It was not eugenic in that, superficially, all applicants were evaluated using the same criteria.

Chapter 15 Genetics of Immunity

Answers to Review Questions

1. Specificity, diversity, memory

2. Blood type is determined by specific glycoprotein antigens on red blood cell surfaces. Incompatibility results when a person's immune system manufactures antibodies that attack red blood cells bearing antigens of other blood types.

3. Different combinations of a limited number of components generate diversity.

4. Humoral: plasma B cells, memory B cells, antibodies

   Cellular: helper T cells, cytotoxic T cells, macrophages, cytokines

5. Macrophages are scavengers and display foreign antigens. Mast cells cause allergy symptoms

6. Allergens stimulate production of IgE antibodies that bind mast cells, causing them to release allergy mediators. In an autoimmune disorder, antibodies attack the body's cells and tissues.

7. Memory cells alert the immune system of the first exposure and ensure that a secondary immune response occurs on subsequent exposure to the Coxsackie virus.

8. Closely matching HLA types between tissue donors and recipients; administering immunosuppressive drugs before and after transplantation; stripping antigens from donor tissues

9. More people can register as organ donors. Cell implants can be developed so that one organ can go to several individuals. Tissue engineering can produce semisynthetic organs and tissues.

10. a. Transplanted bone marrow cells (the graft) recognize cells in the recipient (the host) as foreign. The donor's cells attack the host's cells.

    b. ADA deficiency may result in severe combined immune deficiency, in which a lack of ADA poisons T cells, which then cannot activate B cells.

c. An autoimmune condition in which autoantibodies attack cells that line joints

d. In AIDS, HIV infects helper T cells and reproduces, eventually killing enough T cells to overcome cellular immunity. Secondary invaders also infect during this HIV-induced immunosuppression.

e. An inappropriate immune response to grass antigens (allergens) induces production of IgE that causes mast cells to release histamines, causing allergy symptoms.

11. T cells control B cell function.

12. Memory and plasma B cells respond specifically to one antigen following a cytokine cue from a T cell. Plasma B cells secrete antigen-specific antibodies and are in the circulation for only a few days. Memory B cells remain, providing a fast response the next time the antigen is encountered.

13. In the body, a polyclonal antibody response attacks an invader at several points simultaneously, hastening recovery. MAbs are useful as a diagnostic tool because of their specificity.

Answers to Applied Questions

1. O negative blood lacks ABO cell surface antigens and the Rh antigens, so it is less likely to evoke a rejection reaction than other types of blood.

2. Autoimmune

3. To people on transplant lists who are not rich, famous, or influential, giving an organ to a celebrity who had little hope of recovery was very upsetting.

4. a. Allograft

b. Isograft

c. Xenograft

d. Autograft

5. Robin would have better immunity because her immune system was challenged more when it was developing during childhood.

6. Strip the pig cells of antigens, or genetically engineer the pig to have human cell surface antigens.

7. No. Many people can have the same HLA profile.

8. There will not be an Rh incompatibility because the female would have to be Rh⁻ for this to occur.

9. Colony stimulating factor

10. Some people may object to the fact that the little girl would not exist if her sister did not need compatible bone marrow.

11. During fetal development, expose a fetus to different tissue types so T cells catalog those cells as self.

12. The bonobo's cells would bear antigens specific to a particular human.

Chapter 16 Genetics of Cancer

Answers to Review Questions

1. a. An overexpressed transcription factor could function as an oncogene, causing too frequent cell division.

b. Mutations in the p53 gene lift tumor suppression, allowing too many cell divisions.

c. Mutations in the retinoblastoma gene lift tumor suppression.

d. The *myl* oncogene allows too frequent cell division.

2. Cancer is a consequence of disruption of the cell cycle. Deletion of a tumor suppressor gene and translocation of an oncogene next to a highly active gene would have the same effect of uncontrolled division.

3. Only an inherited cancer susceptibility can pass to future generations.

4. Cancer cells divide continuously and indefinitely; they are heritable, transplantable, dedifferentiated, and lack contact inhibition.

5. One inherits a susceptibility to cancer, not the cancer itself. Cancer may affect only somatic tissue. Many mutations may be necessary for cancer to develop.

6. Cancer cells divide faster than cells from which they derive. Some normal cells divide faster than cancer cells.

7. The rate of division of a cell type from which a cancerous tumor arises could affect how rapidly the cancer grows and spreads. How close the cell is to the blood supply affects rate of metastasis.

8. A cancer cell could have a point mutation.

9. A person with a particular p53 mutation can develop lung cancer even if he or she does not smoke.

10. Oncogenes are dominant; tumor suppressors are recessive. Oncogenes are activated by increased gene expression; tumor suppressors cause cancer when they are inactivated or removed.

Answers to Applied Questions

1. Retinoblastoma

2. Before a p53 test can be developed, we need to identify other factors, including effects of other genes and the environment, that contribute to developing cancer.

3. a. Missing both p53 alleles is lethal.

b. A person with two mutant p53 alleles could be conceived if both parents have one mutant allele.

4. It is an oncogene because it caused overexpression of a transcription factor.

5. The cells from the original tumor are not genetically identical.

6. The researchers should look for genetic markers that seem to segregate with the cancer and for chromosomal abnormalities in people with the cancer.

7. Are certain p53 mutations more prevalent among exposed workers, compared to people not exposed to PAHs? If so, the PAHs may cause the mutation.

8. The woman could have a familial cancer syndrome.

9. Four enzymes are involved in this particular DNA repair pathway.

Chapter 17 Genetic Engineering

Answers to Review Questions

1. a. Biotechnology—specific uses of altered cells or biochemicals

b. Recombinant DNA technology— inserting foreign genes into bacteria or other single cells, where they are expressed

c. Transgenic technology—a genetic alteration of a gamete or fertilized ovum, perpetuating the change in every cell of the individual that develops

d. Gene targeting—introducing a gene that exchanges places with its counterpart in a chromosome

e. Homologous recombination—a gene introduced into a cell exchanging places with a gene on a chromosome

2. a. Restriction enzymes cut DNA at specific sequences. They can be used to create DNA fragments for constructing recombinant DNA molecules.

b. In gene targeting, genes of interest are added to embryonic stem cells where they exchange places with a homologous gene. The engineered embryos grow into transgenic animals with a particular gene knocked out.

c. Vectors carry DNA sequences into cells.

3. Antibiotics are used to set up a system where only cells that have taken up foreign DNA can survive.

4. Human insulin DNA cut with a restriction enzyme; vector DNA cut with the same restriction enzyme; *E. coli;* DNA ligase; selection mechanism (such as antibiotic)

5. Bacteria couldn't manufacture the products of human genes if the genetic code was not universal.

6. In order for all cells of a transgenic animal to express the transgene, it must be introduced at the single-cell stage so that it is present in every cell.

7. Foreign DNA can be inserted in a virus, carried across cell membranes in liposomes, microinjected, electroporated, or sent in with particle bombardment

8. Transgenic technology is not very precise because the introduced DNA is not directed to a particular chromosomal locus, as it is in gene targeting.

9. Gene targeting and antisense technology each can be used to silence genes.

Answers to Applied Questions

1. An invention can be patented if it is novel, nonobvious, and useful. Perhaps genetically altered organisms should be patented only if they are useful.

2. Factors to consider: cost, efficacy, safety, and if the recombinant drug can help people who cannot use other forms of the drug.

3. Transgenic: isolate human elastin gene, deliver it to a cow fertilized ovum, implant fertilized ovum in surrogate, mate animals of the next generation that are heterozygous for the human gene, test milk of homozygotes for human elastin. Use other genes to distinguish different genotypes.

Gene targeting: assume cows make elastin. Isolate human elastin gene, deliver human gene to ES cells of cows, identify ES cells with human gene and culture them, inject cells into early mouse embryos, breed mosaic mice and select those that secrete human elastin in their milk.

The transgenic approach is less precise, but simpler, because the fertilized ovum yields an individual with the change in every cell. There is no mosaic stage.

4. Gene targeting shows the result of no CFTR protein. A transgenic model shows effects of an abnormal CFTR protein. Gene targeting would model the most extreme expression of CF in humans.

5. Collagen, or any protein, is purer if made using recombinant DNA technology because there are no viruses, which could be present in cadavers.

6. At Asilomar, researchers were initially concerned that recombinant DNA work might produce unnatural organisms that might escape labs and cause disease. They set up biological and physical containment measures.

7. Recombinant DNA technology can produce the proteins that are abnormal in these conditions—insulin, a clotting factor, human growth hormone, and CFTR.

8. Mice can express human genes because they use the same genetic code.

9. Another gene specifies the same enzyme; another gene specifies a different enzyme with the same or a similar function; the enzyme isn't vital.

10. Gene targeting

Chapter 18 Gene and Protein Therapy

Answers to Review Questions

1. Ex vivo gene therapy alters cells outside the body, then injects or implants them. SCID is treated this way. In situ gene therapy is a localized procedure on accessible tissue, such as treating melanoma. In vivo gene therapy occurs inside the body, such as a nasal spray to deliver the CFTR gene to a person with cystic fibrosis.

2. Germline gene therapy can affect evolution because the changes are heritable.

3. Somatic cancers and somatic gene therapy target somatic cells. A cancer-causing constitutional mutation and germline gene therapy affect gametes or fertilized ova and are therefore passed to all cells.

4. Researchers should consider the amount of DNA the virus can carry, the types of cells the virus normally infects, how stable the incorporated vector is in the human genome, if toxic effects are associated with use of the virus, and whether or not the virus stimulates a strong immune response.

5. Phenotype

6. a. A retrovirus vector carries interleukin-2 genes into lung cancer cells to encourage a strong immune response directed against the cancer cells.

b. Lipids carry HLA genes directly into melanoma cells. The HLA gene products, displayed on cell surfaces, stimulate the immune system to respond to the tumor as if it were foreign tissue.

c. An adenovirus vector carries wild type p53 genes into cells that lack a functional copy. The p53 tumor suppressor protein the gene expresses halts cancer cell division.

d. A retrovirus vector carries thymidine kinase genes from a herpes virus into cancer cells, making those cells susceptible to an antiherpes drug.

7. Fitting the huge dystrophin gene into a vector and getting gene expression in enough muscle cells to affect symptoms

Answers to Applied Questions

1. Andrew's therapy affects stem cells, which persist far longer than the mature cells treated in the two girls.

2. Understanding how a rare illness occurs and can be treated can help us develop treatments for other disorders with similar symptoms.

3. In situ, because only the scalp need be treated

4. A viral vector (AAV) to add globin genes to red blood cell precursor cells; a bone marrow transplant; hydroxyurea to stimulate production of fetal hemoglobin

5. Snip out part of AV that evokes an immune response.

6. Increasing fetal hemoglobin would dilute the amount of sickled hemoglobin, and more red blood cells could reach the lungs and get oxygen fast enough to prevent sickling.

Chapter 19 Agricultural and Environmental Biotechnology

Answers to Review Questions

1. a. A new agricultural variant from biotechnology can replace a native species in the marketplace, adding new competition.

   b. New variants from biotechnology can invade niches, depleting native populations.

   c. Artificial selection (breeding) can change gene frequencies by setting up matings to perpetuate certain traits or select against others.

2. Plants can be genetically altered to have a molecule from a pathogen that will elicit a primary immune response. Eating the plant would then take the place of a vaccine.

3. Nearby weeds could also become herbicide resistant.

4. If the genetic alteration offers a selective advantage to the altered organism, it will replace natural species in the environment.

5. Seed and germplasm banks can preserve species near extinction.

6. A somatic embryo is an embryo grown from a callus rather than from sexual tissues.

7. It is difficult to penetrate a cell wall.

8. Identify an interesting trait. In breeding, new varieties are introduced by mating plants. The offspring are not genetically uniform. A biotechnological approach would begin with somatic cells into which the gene of interest is introduced. The resulting somatic cells are clones, unless they undergo somaclonal variation.

9. Alter a cell. Grow a mature plant, and test to see if it has the desired trait, is fertile, and can transmit the trait. Grow the plant variety in a greenhouse. Conduct field tests under varying conditions.

10. Sexually derived plants have different combinations of parental genes. Plants derived from somatic tissue carry identical genes and are clones.

11. Plants are easier to manipulate because they can be regenerated from somatic tissue. They are harder to manipulate because cell walls protect them.

12. Callus culture

13. Somaclonal variation and human cancers are mutations in somatic tissue.

14. Genetic alteration of trees is challenging because of the long generation time and the difficulty of regenerating plants from altered cells.

Answers to Applied Questions

1. Techniques to develop an herbicide-resistant crop include transgenic technology, protoplast fusion, and mutant selection.

2. Create corn transgenic for a bioluminescence gene from a firefly or jellyfish.

3. Adding a function is more dangerous because it is less predictable.

Chapter 20 Reproductive Technologies

Answers to Review Questions

1. a. Surrogate mother

   b. Artificial insemination

   c. Oocyte donation, preimplantation genetic diagnosis

   d. Artificial insemination

   e. Preimplantation genetic diagnosis or artificial insemination

   f. IVF, ZIFT, or GIFT

2. It is easier, less costly, and less painful to detect infertility in men than in women.

3. A man can have up to 40% abnormally shaped sperm and still be considered fertile.

4. A man with a low sperm count and a woman with an irregular menstrual cycle

5. ZIFT and GIFT occur in the fallopian tube, whereas IVF takes place in the uterus. ZIFT and IVF transfer a zygote, whereas GIFT transfers gametes. In IVF, fertilization occurs outside the body.

6. They are "embryos in vitro" because a uterus is required for the embryos to develop—and there is no guarantee that this will happen.

7. Preimplantation genetic diagnosis is similar to amniocentesis and CVS in that it allows prenatal detection of disease-causing genes. It is different in that it takes place much earlier in gestation.

8. The genetic father (sperm donor) would be more likely to have compatible bone marrow with the child.

9. An older man fathering a child does not have to alter his physiology the way a postmenopausal woman must to conceive.

10. Adoption

11. Endometriosis, scarred fallopian tubes, irregular ovulation, nondisjunction

12. a. Fertilization occurs outside of the body.

    b. Oocytes and sperm are collected and placed in the fallopian tubes.

    c. Conception occurs in a woman other than the one who gives birth.

    d. Conception occurs outside the body, and a woman other than the genetic mother carries the fetus.

    e. Conception does not occur as a result of sexual intercourse, but in a Petri dish.

Answers to Applied Questions

1. Oocyte donor

2. Big Tom illustrates artificial insemination. Mist illustrates surrogate motherhood.

3. a. The genetic parents are the sperm donor and the woman, who is also the gestational mother.

   b. The genetic parents are the woman whose uterus is gone and her husband. The gestational mother is the woman's friend.

   c. The genetic parents are Max and Tina; the gestational mother is Karen.

   d. The genetic parents are von Wormer and the Indiana woman, who was also the gestational mother.

   e. The genetic and gestational mother is the woman who is the friend of the men. The genetic father can be determined if DNA fingerprints of the child are compared to those of the sperm donors.

4. Younger women can freeze oocytes or early embryos, to be fertilized or implanted years later.

5. Extra preimplantation embryos can be donated to infertile couples.

6. People will vary in when they think children born from assisted reproductive technologies should be told of their origins.

7. Paying for reproductive services because one is lazy is not the same as seeking assistance because one has a fertility problem.

8. Perhaps a combination of legislation and case-by-case considerations should be used in surrogate mother cases.

9. The child is one-half as related genetically to the adoptive mother as she would have been naturally because the adoptive mother and her sister (the biological mother) share half their genes. The child would be genetically related to the same degree to the adoptive mother if both mothers were identical twins.

Chapter 21 The Human Genome Project

Answers to Review Questions

1. a. For a marker study, one needs to find a DNA sequence that is always present in affected individuals. If a gene of interest is incompletely penetrant, some people who inherit the mutant gene will not have a phenotype and, therefore, would not be identified, destroying the association between the gene and its marker.

b. If a disorder is genetically heterogeneic, a person could have the phenotype of interest, but not the genotype.

c. A phenocopy is not inherited. An infection might be mistaken for a genetic disorder.

2. Studies on human evolution, population genetics, and genome organization; identification of gene function; new drugs and diagnostics; predictive genetic testing; forensics

3. At the population level, researchers must know how common specific alleles are in specific populations. At the transmission level, researchers need to know the mode of inheritance. At the molecular level, researchers must decipher the DNA sequence.

4. Researchers are looking for chromosomal regions that appear only in the animals with a specific trait to identify causative genes, just as

researchers did with human populations where HD was prevalent.

5. a. Cutting large pieces of DNA into smaller pieces, which are sequenced and ordered according to overlapping regions

b. Using overlapping DNA probes to extend a known DNA sequence and reconstruct a larger sequence

c. Comparing sequences between genes, individuals, or species

d. Sequencing genomes and learning their organization

e. Regions in DNA with repeats of CG

6. Representational difference analysis and genomic mismatch scanning are both genome-level techniques, but the former identifies differences between two genomes, and the latter identifies genes that two genomes have in common.

7. Complementary DNA (cDNA) is synthesized from mRNA, which comes only from expressed genes.

8. Genomes include many repeated sequences. Exons can combine in different ways so that the same DNA sequence can be part of more than one gene.

9. When a marker is on the same homolog as a disease-causing gene, inheritance of the marker means that the deleterious allele was also inherited. If the marker is on the other homolog, the marker and the disease-causing allele could be inherited separately, and the marker no longer indicates presence of the disease-causing gene.

10. A candidate gene should be expressed in tissues appropriate for the phenotype, mutations should correlate to disease, and the protein should explain the phenotype.

Answers to Applied Questions

1. Next, researchers should get markers closer to the gene of interest and look for

affected individuals who have chromosome abnormalities. They should then identify protein-encoding genes in the region. They can then make cDNAs from mRNAs in affected tissues and see which of the candidate genes are expressed in those tissues. Which proteins explain the phenotype? Which mutations are seen in affected individuals?

2. The gene that has counterparts in more species is more ancient and, therefore, must control a very important function.

3. 1,800 kb comprise the genome of *H. influenzae*. Each fragment was 75 bases long.

4. Odds are 10,000 to 1 against an event occurring by chance.

5. Build a long necklace of beads, say 16, using the four colors. Then make copies of the sequence, each missing one additional base from the same end, to generate a set of necklaces of 16, 15, 14, etc., bases. The sequence is the end base of each piece.

6. This cancer may develop as a result of impaired DNA repair.

7. *H. influenzae* has the greatest density, and humans have the least density. Calculations:

H. influenzae: 1,743 genes/1,800,000 bases in genome = 0.00097

yeast: 6,000 genes/12,500,000 bases in genome = 0.0048

C. elegans: 15,000 genes/100,000,000 bases in genome = 0.00015

humans: 70,000 genes/3,000,000 bases in genome = 0.000023

8. G C T T C G T T A A T A T C G C T A G C T G C A

9. To see if ROM-1 is a candidate gene for Best disease, look at relatives with markers and symptoms to see if they have mutations in this gene.

glossary

acrocentric chromosome   A chromosome in which the centromere is located close to one end, pinching off a very short piece.

acrosome   A protrusion at the front end of a sperm cell containing enzymes that help cut through the oocyte's membrane.

adenine   One of two purine nitrogenous bases in DNA and RNA.

allantois   A membrane surrounding the fetus that gives rise to umbilical blood vessels.

allele   An alternate form of a gene.

allograft   A transplant in which donor and recipient are members of the same species.

alpha-1-antitrypsin (ATT)   An enzyme that controls levels of elastase in the lungs, protecting lung tissue. Lack of ATT causes hereditary emphysema.

alu sequences   Repeated sequences of 300 bases that occur throughout the human genome.

amino acid   A small organic molecule that is a protein building block. Contiguous triplets of DNA nucleotide bases encode the 20 types of amino acids that polymerize to form biological proteins.

amniocentesis   A prenatal diagnostic procedure in which a physician inserts a needle into the uterus to remove a small sample of amniotic fluid, which contains fetal cells and biochemicals. A chromosome chart is constructed from cultured fetal cells, and tests for certain inborn errors of metabolism are conducted on fetal biochemicals. Amniocentesis is usually performed during the 15th week of pregnancy.

amniotic cavity   A space between the inner cell mass and the outer cells anchored to the uterine lining.

anaphase   The stage of mitosis when the centromeres of replicated chromosomes part.

aneuploid   A cell with one or more extra or missing chromosomes.

angiotensinogen   A protein elevated in the blood of people with hypertension.

antibody   A multisubunit protein, produced by B cells, that binds a specific foreign antigen at one end, alerting other components of the immune system or directly destroying the antigen.

anticodon   A three-base sequence on one loop of a transfer RNA molecule that is complementary to an mRNA codon, and therefore brings together the appropriate amino acid and its mRNA instructions.

antigen binding site   The region of an antibody molecule that includes the idiotype, where foreign antigens bind.

antigen-presenting cell   A cell displaying a foreign antigen.

antigen processing   A macrophage's display of a foreign antigen on its surface, next to an HLA self antigen. This alerts the immune system.

anti-Müllerian hormone   A hormone that sustentacular cells in the fetal testes secrete, preventing female reproductive structures from developing.

antiparallel   The head-to-tail arrangement of the two entwined chains of the DNA double helix.

antisense technology   Using a piece of RNA that is complementary in sequence to a sense RNA to stop expression of a particular gene.

apolipoprotein   The protein portion of a lipoprotein; controls lipid transport and utilization and plays a role in cardiovascular health.

apoptosis   A form of cell death that is a normal part of growth and development.

Archaea   A recently discovered third type of cell that shares certain characteristics with prokaryotes and eukaryotes, but also has distinctive features.

artificial insemination   Placing a donor's sperm into a woman's reproductive tract. This is done in a medical setting to assist a couple to conceive when the man is infertile.

artificial selection   Selective breeding; choosing particular individuals to reproduce together, based on the perceived value of their inherited characteristics.

assisted reproductive technologies   Procedures that replace a gamete or the uterus to help people with fertility problems have children.

autoantibodies   Antibodies that attack the body's own cells.

autograft   A transplant of tissue from one part of a person's body to another.

autoimmunity   An immune attack against one's own body.

autosomal dominant   The inheritance pattern of a dominant allele on an autosome. The phenotype can affect males and females and does not skip generations.

autosomal recessive   The inheritance pattern of a recessive allele on an autosome. The phenotype can affect males and females and can skip generations.

autosome   A non-sex-determining chromosome. A human has 22 pairs of autosomes.

b

bacteriophage   A virus that infects bacterial cells. Bacteriophages are used as vectors to introduce foreign DNA into cells.

balanced polymorphism   Maintenance of a harmful recessive allele in a population because the heterozygote has a survival or reproductive advantage.

Barr body   A dark-staining, inactivated X chromosome in a cell.

basement membranes   Boundaries between tissues. Cancer cells anchor here and secrete biochemicals that ease their spread from one tissue section to another.

B cells   A type of lymphocyte that secretes antibody proteins in response to nonself antigens displayed on other immune system cells.

bioremediation   Use of an organism's natural or engineered metabolic abilities to remove toxins from the environment.

biotechnology   The alteration of cells or biochemicals with a specific application, including monoclonal antibody technology, genetic engineering (recombinant DNA technology, transgenic technology, and gene targeting), and cell culture.

blastocyst   A hollow ball of cells descended from a fertilized ovum.

blastomere   A cell in a blastocyst.

bulbourethral glands   Glands joined to the male urethra that contribute mucus to the seminal fluid, easing sperm release.

#

callus   A lump of undifferentiated plant somatic tissue growing in culture.

cancer   A group of disorders resulting from loss of cell cycle control.

capacitation   Activation of sperm in a woman's body.

carbohydrate   A type of macromolecule; sugars and starches.

carcinogen   A substance that induces cancerous changes in a cell.

cDNA library   A collection of cDNAs that represent the mRNAs in a particular cell type and therefore define gene expression in that cell type.

cell   The fundamental unit of life.

cell cycle   A cycle of events describing a cell's preparation for division and division itself.

cell membrane   A structure consisting of a lipid bilayer with embedded proteins, glycoproteins, and glycolipids that forms a selective barrier around a cell.

cellular adhesion molecules (CAMs)   Proteins that carry out cell-cell interactions by enabling cells to physically contact each other.

cellular immune response   T cells releasing cytokines to stimulate and coordinate an immune response.

centrioles   Structures consisting of microtubules oriented at right angles to each other near the nucleus that begin to form the spindle during mitosis.

centromere   The largest constriction in a chromosome, located at a specific site in each chromosome type.

cervix   The opening between the vagina and the uterus.

chaperone proteins   Proteins that stabilize partially folded portions of a polypeptide chain as it forms.

chord distance   A physical depiction of the degree of relationship between populations based on allele frequencies.

chorionic villi   Fingerlike growths that extend from an embryo where it implants in the uterine wall.

chorionic villus sampling   A prenatal diagnosis technique that analyzes chromosomes in chorionic villus cells, which, like the fetus, descend from the fertilized ovum.

chromatid   A single, very long DNA molecule and its associated proteins forming half of a replicated chromosome.

chromatin   DNA and its associated histone proteins.

chromosomal mosaic   An individual in whom some cells have a particular chromosomal anomaly, and others do not.

chromosome   A structure within a cell's nucleus that carries genes. A chromosome consists of a continuous molecule of DNA and proteins wrapped around it.

cleavage   A series of rapid mitotic cell divisions after fertilization.

clines   Allele frequencies that differ greatly in different communities.

clitoris   A 2-centimeter-long structure in the female genitalia that is very sensitive to touch.

cluster-of-differentiation antigen   A T cell antigen that alerts the immune system by recognizing foreign antigens displayed on macrophages. CD4 antigens are HIV targets.

coding strand   The side of the DNA double helix that is transcribed into RNA.

codominant   A heterozygote in which both alleles are fully expressed.

codon   A continuous triplet of mRNA that specifies a particular amino acid.

coefficient of relationship (r)   A value that indicates the genetic closeness (percentage of genes shared) between two individuals.

colony stimulating factors   A class of cytokines that stimulate bone marrow to produce lymphocytes.

complement   A set of biochemicals that destroy microbes and attack transplanted tissue.

complementary base pairs   The pairs of DNA bases that bond together; adenine hydrogen bonds to thymine and guanine to cytosine in the DNA double helix.

complementary DNA (cDNA)   A DNA molecule that is the complement of an mRNA, copied using reverse transcriptase.

completely dominant   An allele that masks the expression of another allele.

completely penetrant   A disorder or trait in which every individual inheriting the genotype displays symptoms or characteristics.

complex traits Traits that do not follow Mendel's law, but have an inherited component.

concordance A measure indicating the degree to which a trait is inherited, calculated by determining the percentage of twin pairs in which both members express a particular trait. High concordance among monozygotic (identical) twins indicates a considerable genetic component.

conditional mutation A genotype that is expressed only under certain environmental conditions.

conformation The three-dimensional shape of a molecule.

consanguinity "Same blood"; term for blood relatives having children together.

constant regions The lower portions of an antibody amino acid chain, which are similar in different species.

constitutional mutation A mutation that occurs in every cell in an individual, indicating that it was inherited. Also called a germline or familial mutation.

contig map A representation of part of a chromosome obtained by overlapping bound DNA probes.

critical period The time during prenatal development when a structure is sensitive to damage from an abnormal gene or an environmental intervention.

crossing over An event during prophase I when homologs exchange parts, adding to genetic variability.

cytogenetics A discipline that matches phenotypes to detectable chromosomal abnormalities.

cytokine A biochemical that a T cell secretes that controls immune function.

cytoplasm Cellular contents other than organelles.

cytosine One of the two pyrimidine nitrogenous bases in DNA and RNA.

cytoskeleton A framework composed of protein tubules and rods that supports the cell and gives it a distinctive form.

cytotoxic T cells Lymphocytes that attack nonself cells by binding them and releasing chemicals that attack the cell.

dedifferentiated A cell less specialized than the cell it descends from, such as a cancer cell.

degenerate codons Different codons specifying the same amino acid.

dehydrotestosterone (DHT) A hormone, derived from testosterone, that stimulates the development of male external reproductive structures.

deletion A missing sequence of DNA or part of a chromosome.

density-dependent inhibition The tendency of a cell to cease dividing once it touches another cell.

density shift experiment Experiment in which bacterial cultures labeled with radioactive isotopes are centrifuged to separate those that have incorporated the "heavier" isotopes into their DNA. This allows researchers to study DNA replication.

deoxyribonucleic acid (DNA) The genetic material. The biochemical that forms genes.

deoxyribose The 5-carbon sugar in a DNA nucleotide.

dihybrid cross A cross of individuals who are heterozygous for two traits.

diploid cell A cell containing two sets of chromosomes.

dizygotic twins Twins that originate as two different fertilized ova and that are thus not identical. (Commonly known as fraternal twins.)

DNA *See* **deoxyribonucleic acid.**

DNA hybridization A technique using complementary base pairing to estimate how similar the genomes of two species are. The more closely related the two species are, the more hybridization occurs between their genomes.

DNA library A collection of human genes maintained in recombinant bacteria.

DNA polymerase An enzyme that participates in DNA replication by inserting new DNA bases and correcting mismatched base pairs.

DNA probe A labeled short sequence of DNA that corresponds to a specific gene. When applied to a biological sample, the probe complementary base pairs with its corresponding sequence, and the label reveals its locus.

DNA replication Construction of a new DNA double helix using the information in parental strands as a template.

dominant A gene variant expressed when present in even one copy.

duplication An extra copy of a gene or DNA sequence, usually caused by misaligned pairing in meiosis; a chromosome containing repeats of part of its genetic material.

ecogenetics Gene-based differences in response to environmental factors.

ectoderm The outermost primary germ layer.

ectopic pregnancy An embryo that grows outside of the uterus, usually in a fallopian tube.

elastase An enzyme that destroys bacteria infecting the lungs, but that can also damage the lungs. Elastase levels are elevated in hereditary emphysema.

electroporation Using a brief jolt of electricity to open transient holes in a cell membrane, allowing foreign DNA to enter.

embryo A prenatal human between the third and eighth weeks of development. The cells in an embryo can be distinguished from each other, but all basic structures are not yet present.

embryo adoption A procedure in which a fertile woman is artificially inseminated by a man whose partner cannot produce healthy oocytes, but who has a healthy uterus. A week later, the preimplantation embryo is flushed from the fertile woman's body and transferred to the other woman's uterus.

embryonic induction A process in which one group of cells causes an adjacent group of embryonic cells to specialize.

embryonic stem (ES) cell A cell from a preimplantation embryo that is manipulated in gene targeting.

empiric risk Probability that a trait will recur based upon its incidence in a particular population.

endoderm The innermost primary germ layer.

endometriosis Abnormal buildup of uterine tissue in and on the uterus, causing cramps and impairing fertility.

endoplasmic reticulum (ER) A labyrinth of membranous tubules on which proteins, lipids, and sugars are synthesized.

endothelium Tissue that forms capillaries and linings of larger blood vessels. Genetically altering endothelium allows drug delivery directly into the bloodstream.

enzyme A type of protein that speeds the rate of a specific biochemical reaction so that it is fast enough to be compatible with life.

epididymis A tightly coiled tube in the male reproductive tract where sperm cells mature and are stored.

epistasis One gene masking expression of another.

equational division The second meiotic division, producing four cells from two.

euchromatin Chromosomes that do not stain and contain regions of active genes.

eugenics The control of individual reproductive choices to achieve a societal goal.

eukaryotic cell A complex cell containing organelles, including a nucleus.

euploid (cell) A somatic cell with the normal number of chromosomes for that species. The human euploid chromosome number is 23 pairs.

evolutionary conservation Similarity in sequence of a gene or protein between species.

excision repair Enzyme-catalyzed removal of pyrimidine dimers in DNA, which corrects errors in DNA replication.

exon The DNA base sequences of a gene that encode amino acids. Exons are interspersed with noncoding regions called introns.

expanding triplet repeat A type of mutation in which a gene grows with each generation.

explant A small piece of plant tissue used to start a culture.

expressed sequence tags (ESTs) Short pieces of cDNAs that genome researchers use to locate and isolate protein-encoding genes.

ex vivo gene therapy Genetic alteration of cells removed from a patient, then reinfused or implanted back into the patient.

F₁ The first filial generation in a pedigree; the children.

F₂ The second filial generation in a pedigree; the grandchildren.

fallopian tubes Tubes leading from the ovaries to the uterus.

fertilized ovum An oocyte that a sperm has penetrated.

fetal cell sorting A process that separates rare fetal cells from a pregnant woman's blood.

fibroids Noncancerous tumors in the uterus.

flow cytometry A technique used to obtain large amounts of a single chromosome type.

fluorescence in situ hybridization (FISH) A technique that binds a DNA probe and an attached fluorescent molecule to its complementary sequence on a chromosome.

follicle cells Nourishing cells surrounding a developing oocyte.

foreign antigen A molecule that stimulates an immune system response.

founder effect A type of genetic drift in human populations in which a few members leave to found a new settlement, perpetuating a subset of the alleles in the original population.

frameshift mutation A mutation that alters a gene's reading frame.

fusion gene A gene that is transcribed and translated, but that consists of two genes that have fused when one moved next to the other.

fusion protein A protein that consists of the products of two genes. It is transcribed and translated continuously because the two source genes have fused.

gamete A sex cell.

gamete intrafallopian transfer (GIFT) An infertility treatment in which sperm and oocytes are placed in a woman's fallopian tube, assisting fertilization in a natural setting.

gap 1(G₁) phase The stage of interphase when proteins, carbohydrates, and lipids are synthesized in preparation for impending mitosis.

gap 2(G₂) phase The stage of interphase when additional proteins are synthesized in preparation for impending mitosis.

gastrula A three-layered embryo.

gene A sequence of DNA that instructs a cell to produce a particular protein.

gene flow Movement of alleles between populations.

gene frequency The percentage of alleles of a certain type in a population.

gene pool All the genes in a population.

gene targeting A form of genetic engineering in which an introduced gene exchanges places with its counterparts on a host cell's chromosome by homologous recombination.

genetic code The correspondence between specific DNA base sequences and the amino acids they specify.

genetic counseling A medical specialty in which a counselor calculates the risk of recurrence of inherited disorders in families, using pedigree charts and applying the laws of inheritance.

genetic drift Changes in gene frequencies when small groups of individuals are separated from or leave a larger population.

genetic engineering Manipulations of genetic material. A broad term encompassing several biotechnologies.

genetic heterogeneity One phenotype that can be caused by any of several genes.

genetic load The collection of deleterious recessive alleles in a population.

genetic marker A piece of DNA, containing a detectable polymorphism, that is closely linked to and therefore almost always inherited with a disease-causing gene.

genetics The study of inherited variation.

genome All the genetic material in the cells of a particular type of organism.

genomic imprinting A process in which the phenotype differs depending upon which parent transmits a particular allele.

genomic mismatch scanning Comparing genomes from individuals and identifying genes they have in common.

genotype The allele combinations in an individual that cause a particular trait or disorder.

genotypic ratio The ratio of genotype classes expected in the progeny of a particular cross.

germinal mutation A mutation that occurs in every cell in an individual and that was therefore inherited from a parent.

germline gene therapy Genetic alterations of gametes or fertilized ova, which perpetuate the change throughout the organism and transmit it to future generations.

Golgi body An organelle, consisting of flattened, membranous sacs, where secretion components are packaged.

gonads Paired structures in the reproductive system where sperm or oocytes are manufactured.

graft-versus-host disease Symptoms that occur when transplanted bone marrow attacks the recipient's body.

growth factor A protein that stimulates mitosis.

guanine One of the two purine nitrogenous bases in DNA and RNA.

haploid (cell) A cell containing one set of chromosomes (half the number of chromosomes of a somatic cell).

haplotype A series of known DNA sequences linked on a chromosome.

Hardy-Weinberg equilibrium An idealized state in which gene frequencies in a population do not change from generation to generation.

heavy chain Either of the two longer amino acid chains of the four that comprise an antibody subunit.

helicase A type of enzyme that unwinds and holds apart strands of replicating DNA.

helper T cells Lymphocytes that recognize foreign antigens on macrophages, activate B cells and cytotoxic T cells, and secrete cytokines.

hemizygous The sex that has half as many sex-linked genes as the other sex; a human male.

heritability An estimate of the proportion of phenotypic variation in a group due to genes, equal to double the difference of the percent variation between the groups.

heritable Passed from parent to progeny cell.

heterochromatin Dark-staining genetic material that is inactive but that maintains the chromosome's structural integrity.

heterogametic sex The sex with two different sex chromosomes; a human male.

heteroplasmy The phenomenon of mitochondria within the same cell having different alleles of a particular gene.

heterozygous Having two different alleles of a gene.

highly conserved Genes or proteins whose sequences are very similar in different species.

high-resolution chromosome banding A technique that stains chromosomes in early mitosis, revealing many bands.

histone A protein around which DNA entwines.

homeobox A 60-base sequence of DNA found in many species' genes that controls body formation.

hominoid An animal ancestral to apes and humans only.

homologous pairs Chromosomes with the same gene sequence.

homologous recombination A naturally occurring process in which a piece of DNA exchanges places with its counterpart on a chromosome.

homozygous Having two identical alleles of a gene.

hormone A biochemical secreted in one part of the body that travels in the bloodstream to another part, where it exerts an effect.

human chorionic gonadotropin (hCG) The hormone that prevents menstruation and indicates that a woman is pregnant.

human genome project A global effort to determine all the DNA sequences constituting the human genome.

human leukocyte antigen (HLA) complex Five very polymorphic genes closely linked on the short arm of chromosome 6 that encode cell surface proteins important in immune system function.

humoral immune response Process in which B cells secrete antibodies into the bloodstream.

hyperacute rejection reaction The immune system's very rapid destruction of a transplant from another species.

i

ideogram A diagram of a chromosome showing bands and locations of known genes. An ideogram combines cytogenetic and molecular information.

idiotype The part of an antibody's antigen binding site that fits itself around a particular foreign antigen.

inborn error of metabolism An inherited disorder resulting from a malfunctioning or absent enzyme.

inbreeding Conception of offspring whose parents are blood relatives.

incomplete dominance A heterozygote intermediate in phenotype between either homozygote.

incompletely penetrant A disorder or trait in which not every individual inheriting the genotype displays symptoms or characteristics.

independent assortment The random arrangement of homologous chromosome pairs, in terms of maternal or paternal origin, down the center of a cell in metaphase I. The consequence is that inheritance of a gene on one chromosome does not influence inheritance of a gene on a different chromosome.

infertility The inability to conceive a child after a year of unprotected intercourse.

initiation complex Aggregation of the components of the protein synthetic apparatus formed before mRNA is translated.

initiation site The site where DNA replication begins on a chromosome.

inner cell mass A clump of cells on the inside of the blastocyst that will continue developing into an embryo.

interferons A class of cytokines that fight viral infections and cancers.

interleukins A class of cytokines that control lymphocyte differentiation and growth.

interphase The stage of the cell cycle during which a cell is not dividing.

interstitial cells Cells in the fetal testes that secrete testosterone, causing the development of male internal reproductive structures.

introns Base sequences within a gene that are transcribed but are excised from the mRNA before translation into protein. Introns are interspersed with protein-encoding exons.

invasiveness The ability of cancer cells to squeeze into tight places.

in vitro fertilization (IVF) Placing oocytes and sperm in a laboratory dish with appropriate biochemicals so that fertilization occurs, then after a few cell divisions, transferring the preimplantation embryos to a woman's uterus.

in vivo gene therapy Direct genetic manipulation of cells in the body.

isochromosome A chromosome with identical arms, forming when the centromere splits in the wrong plane.

isograft A transplant in which the donor and recipient are identical twins.

k

karyotype A chart that displays chromosome pairs in size order.

kilobase One thousand DNA nucleotide bases.

l

law of segregation The distribution of alleles of a gene into separate gametes during meiosis. This is Mendel's first law.

leader sequence A short sequence at the start of an mRNA molecule that binds a ribosome.

leptin A protein that signals the brain that fat stores are adequate.

lethal allele An allele that causes early death, even before birth.

ligase An enzyme that catalyzes the formation of covalent bonds in the sugar phosphate backbone of DNA.

light chain Either of the two shorter polypeptide chains of the four that comprise an antibody subunit.

linkage The relationship between genes on the same chromosome.

linkage disequilibrium Extremely tight linkage between two genetic loci, typically a marker and a disease-causing allele.

linkage maps Maps that show how genes are ordered on chromosomes, determined from crossover frequencies between pairs of genes.

lipid   A type of macromolecule; a fat or an oil.

lipoprotein lipase   An enzyme that breaks down fat along the linings of small-diameter blood vessels.

liposomes   Fatty bubbles that can enclose and transport DNA into cells.

LOD score   A statistical measurement that indicates whether DNA sequences are usually inherited together due to linkage or chance.

lymphocytes   Types of white blood cells that provide immunity; they include B cells and T cells.

lysosome   A saclike organelle containing enzymes that degrade debris.

m

macroevolution   Genetic change sufficient to form a new species.

macromolecule   A very large molecule, such as a carbohydrate, lipid, protein, or nucleic acid.

macrophage   A large, wandering scavenger cell that alerts the immune system by binding foreign antigens.

malignant tumor   A cancerous tumor; a tumor that grows and infiltrates surrounding tissue.

manifesting heterozygote   A female carrier of a sex-linked recessive gene who expresses the phenotype because the wild type allele is inactivated in some affected tissues.

map unit   The relative distance between linked genes, determined from crossover frequencies.

mast cells   Circulating cells that have IgE receptors. They release allergy mediators when IgE binds to receptors on their surfaces. This causes allergy symptoms.

maternal inheritance   Transmission of a trait that a mitochondrial gene encodes. The trait is passed only by females but affects offspring of both sexes.

meiosis   A type of cell division that halves the usual number of chromosomes to form haploid gametes.

melanin   A pigment molecule.

memory cells   Descendants of activated B cells that participate in a secondary immune response.

Mendelian trait   A trait that a single gene specifies.

mesoderm   The middle primary germ layer.

messenger RNA (mRNA)   A molecule of ribonucleic acid complementary in sequence to the sense strand of a gene. Messenger RNA carries the information that specifies a particular protein product.

metacentric chromosome   A chromosome with the centromere located approximately in the center.

metaphase   The stage of mitosis when chromosomes align along the center of the cell.

metastasis   Spread of cancer from its site of origin to other parts of the body.

microevolution   Change of allele frequency in a population.

microfilament   A solid rod of actin protein that forms part of the cytoskeleton.

microsatellite   A short DNA sequence that repeats on a chromosome. Normally, microsatellites are the same size in an individual.

microtubule   A hollow structure of (tubulin) protein that forms part of the cytoskeleton.

mismatch repair   Proofreading of DNA for misalignment of short, repeated segments (microsatellites).

missense   A single base change mutation that alters an amino acid in the gene product.

mitochondrial Eve   A theoretical "first woman" traced through mitochondrial DNA sequence similarities among modern people.

mitochondrion   An organelle consisting of a double membrane that houses enzymes that catalyze reactions that extract energy from nutrients.

mitosis   Division of somatic (nonsex) cells.

mode of inheritance   The pattern in which a gene variant passes from generation to generation, determined by whether it is dominant or recessive and is part of an autosome or a sex chromosome.

molecular clock   A tool for estimating the time elapsed since two species diverged from a shared ancestor, based on DNA or protein sequence differences and mutation rate.

molecular evolution   Changes in protein and DNA sequences over time. We use this information to estimate how recently species diverged from a common ancestor.

molecular genetics   The study of inheritance at the biochemical level, focusing on DNA and proteins.

monoclonal antibody (MAb)   A single antibody type, produced from a B cell fused to a cancer cell (a hybridoma).

monohybrid cross   A cross of two individuals who are heterozygous for a single trait.

monosomy   A human cell with 45 (one missing) chromosomes.

monozygotic twins   Twins that originate as a single fertilized ovum and are thus identical.

morula   The forming body in the prenatal stage preceding the embryo and resembling a mulberry.

motif   A DNA sequence common to several genes, encoding portions of proteins having characteristic conformations.

Müllerian ducts   Unspecialized tissue in an early embryo that can develop into a female reproductive tract.

multifactorial trait   A trait or illness determined by several genes and the environment.

multiregional hypothesis   The theory that *Homo erectus* gave rise to various geographically widespread human populations.

mutagen   A substance that changes a DNA base.

mutant   An allele that differs from the wild type (normal or most common) allele, altering the phenotype.

mutant selection   Growing cells in the presence of a toxin, such as an herbicide, so that only resistant cells survive.

mutation   A change in a gene's biochemical makeup; a change in DNA.

myoblast   Immature skeletal muscle cell. This cell is used in gene therapy for muscular dystrophies.

myoblast transfer therapy   Implanting healthy or genetically altered myoblasts to correct muscular dystrophy.

n

natural selection   Differential survival and reproduction of individuals with particular phenotypes in particular environments, which may alter allele frequencies in subsequent generations.

negative eugenics   Interfering with or preventing reproduction of individuals considered genetically inferior.

neural tube   An embryonic structure that develops into the brain and spinal cord.

nondisjunction   The unequal partitioning of chromosomes into gametes during meiosis.

notochord   An embryonic structure that forms the framework of the skeleton and induces formation of the neural tube.

nuclear envelope The outer boundary of the nucleus.

nucleic acid DNA or RNA.

nuclein A substance in cell nuclei identified in 1871. It was DNA.

nucleolus A structure within the nucleus where ribosomes are assembled from ribosomal RNA and protein.

nucleotide The building block of a nucleic acid, consisting of a phosphate group, a nitrogenous base, and a 5-carbon sugar.

nucleus A large, membrane-bound region of a eukaryotic cell that houses the genetic material.

oncogene A dominant gene that promotes cell division. An oncogene normally controls the cell cycle but leads to cancer when over-expressed.

oogenesis Oocyte development.

oogonium The diploid cell that begins oogenesis.

operon Genes whose enzyme products interact in a coordinated fashion in a particular metabolic pathway in bacteria.

organelle A specialized structure in a eukaryotic cell that carries out a specific function.

organogenesis Development of organs from a three-layered embryo.

orgasm Pleasurable sensations associated with sperm release or rubbing of the clitoris.

ovaries Paired structures in the female reproductive tract where oocytes mature.

ovulation Release of a secondary oocyte from an ovary in response to hormonal stimulation.

ovum A female reproductive cell (meiotic product). "Egg."

P₁ The parental (oldest) generation in a pedigree.

p53 A tumor suppressor gene whose loss of function is implicated in a number of different types of cancer. The wild type allele enables a cell to repair damaged DNA or cease dividing.

palindrome A nucleic acid sequence that reads the same in either direction.

paracentric inversion An inverted chromosome that does not include the centromere.

parsimony analysis A statistical method used to identify the most realistic evolutionary tree possible from a given data set.

particle bombardment Shooting DNA from a gunlike device into cells.

pedigree A chart consisting of symbols for individuals connected by lines that depict blood relationships and transmission of inherited traits.

penis Male organ that delivers sperm.

pericentric inversion An inverted chromosome that includes the centromere.

peroxisome An organelle consisting of a double membrane that houses enzymes with various functions.

phenocopy An environmentally caused trait that occurs in a familial pattern mimicking inheritance.

phenotype The expression of a gene in traits or symptoms.

phenotypic ratio The ratio of phenotype classes expected in the progeny of a particular cross.

photolyases Enzymes that absorb energy from visible light, use the energy to bind to pyrimidine dimers, then break the extra covalent bonds creating the dimers.

photoreactivation Type of DNA repair that splits pyrimidine dimers.

placenta The organ joining pregnant woman to fetus. The fetus receives nutrients and excretes waste through the placenta.

plasma cells Descendants of activated B cells that produce large amounts of a single antibody type.

plasmid A small circle of double-stranded DNA found in some bacteria in addition to their DNA. Plasmids are commonly used as vectors for recombinant DNA technology.

pleiotropic A Mendelian disorder with several symptoms, different subsets of which may occur in different individuals.

point mutation A single base change in DNA.

polar body A product of female meiosis that contains little cytoplasm and does not continue development into an oocyte.

polyacrylamide gel electrophoresis (PAGE) A method to separate pieces of DNA based on size, which determines their speed of migration through a polyacrylamide gel in the presence of an electrical field.

polyclonal antibody response An immune system response in which B cells bearing different antigen receptors and secreting different antibodies bind to several portions of a bacterium in a multipronged attack.

polygenic traits Traits determined by more than one gene.

polymerase chain reaction (PCR) A technique in which a specific sequence of DNA from a gene of interest is replicated in a test tube to rapidly produce many copies.

polymorphism A DNA sequence at a certain chromosomal locus that varies among individuals.

polyploid (cell) A cell with one or more extra sets of chromosomes.

population genetics The study of gene frequencies in groups of interbreeding individuals.

population A group of interbreeding individuals.

population bottleneck Decrease in allele diversity resulting from an event that kills many members of a population.

population genetics The study of allele frequencies in different groups of individuals.

positive eugenics Providing incentives for individuals considered genetically superior to reproduce.

preimplantation embryo A prenatal human during the first two weeks following fertilization.

preimplantation genetic diagnosis Genetic or chromosomal testing of a cell removed from an 8-cell preimplantation embryo to decide whether the remaining 7 cells should be transferred to a woman's body and permitted to continue development.

primary (1°) structure The amino acid sequence of a protein.

primary germ layers The three basic layers of an embryo.

primary immune response The immune system's response to a first encounter with a foreign antigen.

primary oocyte A cell in the female that undergoes reduction division.

primary spermatocyte A cell in the male that undergoes reduction division.

primitive streak A band along the back of a 3-week human embryo that forms an axis other structures develop around and that eventually gives rise to the nervous system.

product rule The probability that two independent events will both occur equals the product of the chance that each event will occur on its own.

progeria An inherited rapid-aging disorder.

prokaryotic cell A simple cell bound by a cell membrane, and sometimes a cell wall, that contains ribosomes and sometimes membranes, but no other organelles and no nucleus. Bacteria and cyanobacteria are prokaryotes.

promoter A control sequence near the start of a gene.

pronuclei Packets of DNA in the fertilized ovum.

protein A type of macromolecule that is the direct product of genetic information.

proto-oncogene A gene that normally controls the cell cycle. When overexpressed, it functions as an oncogene, causing cancer.

protoplast A plant cell without its cell wall.

pseudogene A gene that does not encode protein, but whose sequence very closely resembles that of a coding gene.

purine A type of organic molecule with a two-ring structure, including the nitrogenous bases adenine and guanine.

pyrimidine A type of organic molecule with a single-ring structure, including the nitrogenous bases cytosine, thymine, and uracil.

q

quantitative trait loci Genes that determine polygenic traits.

quaternary (4°) structure A protein that has more than one polypeptide subunit.

r

reading frame The grouping of DNA base triplets encoding an amino acid sequence.

recessive An allele whose expression is masked by another allele.

reciprocal translocation A chromosome aberration in which two nonhomologous chromosomes exchange parts, conserving genetic balance but rearranging genes.

recombinant A series of alleles on a chromosome that differs from the series of either parent.

recombinant DNA technology Transferring genes between species.

reduction division The first meiotic division, which halves the chromosome number.

replacement hypothesis The theory that Africans replaced Eurasian descendants of *Homo erectus* 200,000 years ago.

replication fork Locally opened portion of a replicating DNA double helix.

representational difference analysis Comparing two genomes and identifying particular sequence differences between them.

restriction enzyme An enzyme, derived from bacteria, that cuts DNA at certain sequences.

restriction fragment length polymorphism (RFLP) Differences in restriction enzyme cutting sites among individuals at the same site among the chromosomes, resulting in different patterns of DNA fragment sizes.

retrovirus A virus whose genetic material is RNA. It enters a host cell and uses the viral enzyme reverse transcriptase to produce DNA from the viral RNA. This DNA then integrates into the host's genome, where it can direct reproduction of the virus.

reverse transcriptase A viral enzyme that enables a retrovirus to copy its RNA into DNA inside a host cell.

ribonucleic acid (RNA) A nucleic acid whose sequence of building blocks represents a gene's sequence (mRNA), or that assists protein synthesis (tRNA and rRNA).

ribose A 5-carbon sugar in RNA.

ribosomal RNA (rRNA) RNA that, with proteins, comprises ribosomes.

ribosome An organelle consisting of RNA and protein that is a scaffold for protein synthesis.

ribozyme RNA component of an RNA-protein complex that edits introns out of DNA.

RNA *See* **ribonucleic acid.**

RNA polymerase (RNAP) An enzyme that synthesizes short pieces of RNA that initiate DNA replication and adds RNA nucleotides to a growing RNA chain.

RNA primer A short sequence of RNA that initiates DNA replication.

Robertsonian translocation A chromosome aberration in which two short arms of nonhomologous chromosomes break and the long arms fuse, forming one unusual, large chromosome.

s

satellites Characteristic blobs on chromosome tips.

schizophrenia Loss of the ability to organize thoughts and perceptions, causing hallucinations and inappropriate behavior.

secondary (2°) structure Folds in a polypeptide caused by attractions between amino acids close together in the primary structure.

secondary immune response The immune system's response to a second or subsequent encounter with a foreign antigen.

secondary oocyte A cell resulting from meiosis I in the female.

secondary spermatocyte A cell resulting from meiosis I in the male.

self antigens Molecules on the body's cell surfaces that a healthy immune system perceives as self.

semiconservative replication The synthesis of new DNA in which half of each double helix comes from a preexisting double helix.

seminal fluid Secretions in which sperm travel.

seminal vesicles Structures that secrete fructose and prostaglandins into semen.

seminiferous tubules A network of tubes in the testes where sperm are manufactured.

sense RNA RNA complementary in sequence to a coding strand of DNA.

sequencing-by-hybridization A rapid DNA sequencing method that screens an unknown sequence against short labeled sequences immobilized in known positions on a small glass square. Identifying and overlapping the bound short sequences reveals the unknown sequence.

severe combined immune deficiency (SCID) A group of inherited disorders that impair humoral and cellular immunity.

sex chromosome A chromosome containing genes that specify sex. A human male has one X and one Y chromosome; a female has two X chromosomes.

sex-influenced trait Phenotype caused when an allele is recessive in one sex but dominant in the other.

sex-limited trait A trait that affects a structure or function present in only one sex.

sex-linked Genes on a sex chromosome.

signal transduction A series of biochemical reactions and interactions that pass incoming information from outside a cell to inside, triggering a cellular response.

site-directed mutagenesis Intentionally causing a mutation in amplified DNA.

somaclonal variant A plant variant that arises from a somatic mutation in a callus.

somatic cell A nonsex cell, with 23 pairs of chromosomes in humans.

somatic embryo An embryo that develops from a somatic cell, possible only in plants.

somatic gene therapy Genetic alterations of somatic tissue, which correct a defect in an individual's tissues but do not transmit the correction to future generations.

somatic mutation A mutation occurring only in a subset of somatic (nonsex) cells.

spermatid The product of meiosis II in the male.

spermatogenesis Sperm cell development.

spermatogonium A diploid cell that gives rise to a cell that undergoes meiosis, developing into a sperm.

spermatozoon (sperm) A mature male reproductive cell (meiotic product).

sperm typing A technique in which researchers compare alleles and allele configuration in sperm against the same individual's somatic cells to determine recombination frequency. This helps them develop linkage maps.

S phase The stage of interphase when DNA replicates.

spindle A structure composed of microtubules that pulls sets of chromosomes apart in a dividing cell.

spontaneous mutation A genetic change that is a result of mispairing when the replication machinery encounters a base in its rare tautomeric form.

SRY gene The sex-determining region of the Y, a gene that controls whether the unspecialized embryonic gonad will develop as testis or ovary. If the gene is activated, it becomes a testis; if not, an ovary forms.

submetacentric A chromosome in which the centromere establishes a long arm and a short arm.

surrogate mother A woman who carries an embryo and fetus for a couple. She may or may not donate the oocyte.

sustentacular cells Cells in the fetal testes that secrete anti-Müllerian hormone, which halts development of female reproductive structures.

synapsis The gene-by-gene alignment of homologous chromosomes during prophase I of meiosis.

synteny The correspondence of genes located on the same chromosome in several species.

tandem duplication A duplicated sequence of DNA located right next to the original sequence on a chromosome.

tautomers Two forms of a chemical, one stable and present most of the time, the other unstable and rare.

T cell A type of lymphocyte that produces cytokines and coordinates the immune response.

T cell receptors Peptides on T cells that bind foreign antigens.

telomerase An enzyme including a sequence of RNA that adds DNA to chromosome tips.

telomere A chromosome tip.

telophase The stage of mitosis or meiosis when progeny cells separate.

teratogen A substance that causes a birth defect.

tertiary structure Folds in a polypeptide caused by interactions between amino acids and water. This draws together amino acids that are far apart in the primary structure.

testcross Crossing an individual of unknown genotype to an individual who is homozygous recessive for the trait being studied.

testes Paired sacs that hang outside the male's body that contain the seminiferous tubules, in which sperm develop.

testosterone A hormone that controls the development of male internal reproductive structures in the fetus and of secondary sexual characteristics at puberty.

thymine One of the two pyrimidine bases in DNA.

Ti plasmid A virus that causes tumors in plants, often used as a vector in transgenic technology.

tissue rejection reaction The immune system's destruction of transplanted tissue.

transcription Manufacturing RNA from DNA.

transcription factor A protein that activates the transcription of other genes.

transfer RNA (tRNA) A type of RNA that connects mRNA to amino acids during protein synthesis.

transgenic organism An individual subject to genetic engineering at the stage of gamete or fertilized ovum, leading to development of an individual with the alteration in every cell.

transition A point mutation altering a purine to a purine or a pyrimidine to a pyrimidine.

translation Assembly of an amino acid chain according to the sequence of base triplets in a molecule of mRNA.

translation elongation The stage of protein synthesis in which ribosomes bind to the initiation complex and amino acids join.

translation initiation The start of protein synthesis, when mRNA, tRNA carrying an amino acid, ribosomes, energy-storing molecules, and protein factors begin to assemble.

translocation Exchange of genetic material between nonhomologous chromosomes.

translocation carrier An individual with exchanged chromosomes, but no signs or symptoms. The person has the usual amount of genetic material, but it is rearranged.

transmission genetics Study of the way genes and traits pass from one generation to the next.

transplantable The ability of a cancer cell to grow into a tumor if it is transplanted into another individual.

transposon A gene or DNA segment that moves to another chromosome.

transversion A point mutation altering a purine to a pyrimidine or vice versa.

triploid (cell) A cell with three complete sets of chromosomes.

trisomy A human cell with 47 (one extra) chromosomes.

trophoblast The outermost cells of the preimplantation embryo.

tumor necrosis factor A cytokine that attacks cancer cells.

tumor suppressor A recessive gene whose wild type function is to limit the number of divisions a cell undergoes.

uniparental disomy Inheriting two copies of the same gene from one parent.

urethra A tube leading from the bladder to the outside of the body.

uterus A saclike organ in a woman's reproductive tract where a prenatal human develops.

vagina A tube leading from the cervix and uterus to the outside of a woman's body.

variable regions The upper parts of antibodies, which differ in amino acid sequence among individuals.

variably expressive A genotype producing a phenotype that varies among individuals.

vas deferens Paired tubes leading from the epididymis to the urethra that deliver sperm.

vector A piece of DNA used to transfer DNA from a cell of one organism into that of another.

W

wild type The most common variant of a gene.

Wolffian ducts Unspecialized tissue in an early embryo that can develop into a male reproductive tract.

X

xenograft A transplant in which donor and recipient are different species.

X inactivation The inactivation of one X chromosome in each cell of a female mammal, occurring early in embryonic development.

X inactivation center A part of the X chromosome that inactivates the chromosome.

Y

yolk sac A structure external to the embryo that manufactures blood cells and nourishes the developing embryo.

Z

zona pellucida A glycoprotein coat surrounding an oocyte.

zygote A prenatal human from the fertilized ovum stage until formation of the primordial embryo, at about two weeks.

zygote intrafallopian transfer (ZIFT) Placing a fertilized ovum conceived in a laboratory dish into a woman's reproductive tract.

credits

Photo

Chapter 1
1.1: © Petit Format/Nestle/Photo Researchers; 1.3: © AP/Wide World Photos; 1.4: © Gwendolen Cates/Sygma; 1.5: © Southern Illinois University of Medicine; 1.6: © AP/Wide World; 1.7: Courtesy, March of Dimes Birth Defects Foundation.

Chapter 2
2.5: © Dr. K. S. Kim/Peter Arnold; 2.6: © SPL/Custom Medical Stock Photo; 2.7: © Philip & Karen Smith/Tony Stone Images; 2.8: © Keith R. Porter/Photo Researchers; 2.9: © K. G. Murti/Visuals Unlimited; 2.10: © Daniel Friend & Don Fawcett/Visuals Unlimited; 2.12: © CNRI/SPL/Photo Researchers; 2.15: © Neurofibromatosis, Inc., Lanham, MD; 2.19: From A. T. Sumner. 1991. "Mammalian Chromosomes from Prophase to Telophase." *Chromosoma*, 100:410–418, © Springer Verlag; 2.20a–e: © Ed Reschke; p. 34a: © Barry Dowsett/SPL/Photo Researchers; p. 35a: © Reuters/Ian Hodgson/Archive Photos; p. 35b: © The Nobel Foundation 1976.

Chapter 3
3.1: © Courtesy of Dr. Francis Collins; 3.11: © Professor P. Motta/Department of Anatomy/University of La Sapienza, Rome/SPL/Photo Researchers; 3.13: © Courtesy of Dr. Yury Verlinsky; 3.16a,c: © Petit Format/Nestle/Science Source/Photo Researchers; 3.16b: © P. M. Motta & J. Van Blerkom/SPL/Photo Researchers; 3.18: © Carolina Biological Supply Company/Phototake; 3.19: © James Stevenson/Photo Researchers; 3.21b–d: From Streissguth, A. P., Landesman-Dwyer, S., Martin, J. C., & Smith, D. W. July 1980. "Teratogenic effects of alcohol in human and laboratory animals." *Science*, 209(18):353–361. © 1980 American Association for the Advancement of Science; 3.22: © J. L. Bulcao/Gamma Liaison; 3.23: © Courtesy of Scios Nova, Inc.

Chapter 4
4.1a–b: © Archive Photos; 4.2: © Courtesy W. Dorsey Stuart, University of Hawaii; p. 72: © Courtesy James R. Poush; 4.7: © Nancy Hamilton/Photo Researchers; p. 73: © Kenneth Greer/Visuals Unlimited.

Chapter 5
5.2: © Porterfield-Chickering/Photo Researchers; 5.5: © Lester V. Bergman & Associates; 5.6: © North Wind Picture Archives; 5.11a: © The McGraw-Hill Companies, Inc./Carla D. Kipper; 5.11b: Courtesy Roxanne De Leon and Angelman Syndrome Foundation.

Chapter 6
6.2: © Biophoto Associates/Photo Researchers; 6.4: Courtesy of Ward F. Odenwald, National Institute of Neurological Disease and Stroke; 6.6: Courtesy, Dr. Mark A. Crowe; 6.7: © Historical Pictures Service/Stock Montage; p. 108, fig. 1: By permission of the British Library; p. 108, fig. 2: Courtesy, The Manchester Literary and Philosophical Society/ Photo: Manchester Museum of Science and Industry; p. 112: From J. M. Cantu, et al. 1984. *Human Genetics*, 66:66–70. © Springer-Verlag, Gmbh & Co. KG. Photo courtesy of Pragna I. Patel, Ph.D/Baylor College of Medicine; 6.8a(1–2): © From Wilson and Foster. 1985. *Williams Textbook of Endocrinol*, 7/e. © W. B. Saunders; 6.8a(3–4): Courtesy National Jewish Hospital & Research Center; 6.9a: © Horst Schafer/Peter Arnold; 6.9b: © William E. Ferguson; 6.10a–d: © Bettmann Archive.

Chapter 7
7.1: Library of Congress; 7.7: © Dr. Jeffrey Friedmann, MD, Ph.D/Rockefeller University & Associate Investigator, Howard Hughes Medical Institute; 7.10a–b: Courtesy of National Institute of Mental Health; p. 132: © Redneck/Gamma Liaison.

Chapter 8
8.1a: © Lee D. Simon/Science Source/Photo Researchers; 8.1b: © Dr. Gopal Murti/Science Photo Library/Photo Researchers; 8.1c: © Courtesy of Stuart Lindsay, Ph.D; 8.5: © Bettmann Archive; 8.9a: © 1948 M. C. Escher Foundation/Baarn-Holland, All Rights Reserved.

Chapter 9
9.1: © World Health Organization; 9.11b: Courtesy of Calgene Fresh, Inc.; p. 167: © Dr. Tony Brain/Science Photo Library/Photo Researchers.

Chapter 10
10.2: © Susan McCartney/Photo Researchers; 10.3a–b: © Bill Longcore/Photo Researchers; p. 181: From R. Simensen, R. Curtis Roger. May 1989. "Fragile X Syndrome." *American Family Physician*, 39(5):186. © American Academy of Family Physicians; 10.8: © Sovfoto/Eastfoto; 10.10: © Science Photo Library/Photo Researchers.

Chapter 11

11.1: Courtesy, Colleen Weisz; 11.3b: From L. Chong, et al. 1995. "A Human Telomeric Protein." *Science,* 270:1663–1667. © 1995 American Association for the Advancement of Science. Photo courtesy, Dr. Titia DeLange; 11.5: Courtesy of Jason C. Birnholz, M.D.; 11.6b: From P. C. Nowell and P. A. Hungerford. 1960. "Chromosome Studies Normal and Leukemic Leukocytes." *Journal of the National Cancer Institute,* 25:85–109; 11.6c: Courtesy Dr. Frederick Elder, Dept. of Pediatrics, University of Texas Medical School, Houston; 11.6d: © Courtesy David Ward, Department of Genetics; Yale University School of Medicine; 11.7a–b: Courtesy Integrated Genetics; p. 205: Courtesy of Dr. H. F. Willard, Case Western Reserve University; 11.9: Courtesy Dr. Frederick Elder, Dept. of Pediatrics, University of Texas Medical School, Houston; p. 212: Photo courtesy of Kathy Naylor. 11.13b: Courtesy of Donna Bennett/IDEAS; 11.15: Courtesy, Lawrence Livermore Labs; 11.16a, b: From N. B. Spinner, et al. 1994. *The American Journal of Human Genetics,* 55:239, fig. 1, published by the University of Chicago Press, © 1994 by The American Society of Human Genetics. All rights reserved.

Chapter 12

12.4: Dr. Victor McKusick/Johns Hopkins University School of Medicine; 12.7a: © Barkai Wolfson/AP/Wide World Photos; 12.7b: Courtesy, Dr. Bjornar Olaisen.

Chapter 13

13.4: Courtesy, Consulate General of Finland, Photo by Matti Tirri; 13.5: © Bettmann Archive.

Chapter 14

14.3: © John Reader/SPL/Photo Researchers; 14.4a: © G. Hinter Leitner/Gamma Liaison; 14.4b: © Burt Silverman/Silverman Studios; 14.5a–b: Courtesy, Dr. H. Hameister; 14.7(both): Courtesy of F. R. Turner; 14.9 (left,right): Courtesy, James H. Asher, Jr.; 14.9 (middle): © Vickie Jackson; 14.10: © Zoological Society of London; 14.13: © E. R. Degginger/Photo Researchers; p. 266, fig 1: © Scott Camazine/Photo Researchers; p. 266, fig 2: © Barb Zurawski; p. 267: Courtesy of Marie Deatherage.

Chapter 15

15.1a: © North Wind Picture Archives; 15.1b: © Yoav Levy/Phototake; 15.2a–b: © Martin Rotker/Phototake; 15.10: © The McGraw-Hill Companies, Inc./Bob Coyle; 15.12: © Science Photo Library/Photo Researchers; 15.13: © Sygma; 15.16a: © David Scharf/Peter Arnold; 15.16b: © Phil A. Harrington/Peter Arnold; 15.17b: © Schering-Plough Corporation/Photo by Phillip Harrington.

Chapter 16

16.1: © Gerha Hinterleitner/Gamma Liaison; 16.4a–b: © Custom Medical Stock Photo; 16.4c: © Nancy Kedersha/Immunogen/Photo Researchers; 16.4d: © Cecil H. Fox/Science Source/Photo Researchers; p. 300: From P. C. Nowell and P. A. Hurgerford. 1960. "Chromosome Studies Normal and Leukemia Leukocytes." *Journal of the National Cancer Institute,* 25:85–109; 16.7a–b: From

R. Lewis. June 1990. "The Genetic Plot Thickens." *The Journal of NIH Research,* 2:73, Reprinted with permission of The Journal of NIH Research. Washington, DC; p. 302: © Custom Medical Stock Photo; p. 303: © Ron Bennett/Corbis-Bettmann; 16.9 (both): Courtesy, Dr. Tom Mikkelsen; 16.10: © S. Benjamin/Custom Medical Stock Photo; 16.11 : From B. Vogelstein. Sept. 1990. "The Genes That Contribute To Cancer." *The Journal of NIH Research,* 2(8):66. Reprinted with permission of The Journal of NIH Research, Washington, DC.

Chapter 17

p. 310: Courtesy of Genencor International, Inc.; 17.1a–b: From D. W. Ow, V. Wood, M. Deluca, J. R. Dewet, D. R. Helsinki, S. H. Howell. November 1986. "Transient and Stable Expression of the Firefly Luciferase Gene in Plant Cells and Transgenic Plants." *Science,* 234. © 1986 American Association for the Advancement of Science; 17.3: © SPL/Photo Researchers; p. 315: © David Scharf; 17.6: Courtesy, Calgene Fresh; 17.9: From Jacks, Tyler et al. July 1994. *Nature Genetics,* 7:357, fig. 6.

Chapter 18

18.1a: Reprinted with permission from The Courier-Journal; 18.1b: © Jessica Boyatt; 18.1c: © Los Angeles Times Photo by Tammy Lechner; 18.5: © Ann States/SABA.

Chapter 19

19.1: © The McGraw-Hill Companies, Inc./Bob Coyle; 19.2 and 19.5: Courtesy, Monsanto; 19.6a: © Biophoto Associates/Photo Researchers; 19.6b: © Dr. Jeremy Burgess/SPL/Photo Researchers; 19.8: Courtesy of Pioneer Hi-Bred International, Inc./Photo by Curt Maas; 19.9: © Michael Greenlar/The Image Works; 19.10: © Douglas Kirkland/Sygma; 19.11: From Steven Tanksley & Susan McCouch. August 1997. "Seed Banks and Molecular Maps." *Science,* 277:1065. © 1997 American Association for the Advancement of Science; p. 354: Courtesy, A/F Protein, Inc., Waltham, MA.

Chapter 20

20.1: © Luciano Amendola/Imago 2000; 20.2a: © Bob Schuchman/Phototake; 20.2b: © Tony Brain/SPL/Photo Researchers; 20.4: © AP/Wide World Photos; 20.5: © CNRI/Phototake; 20.6: © *People Weekly* © Taro Yamasaki; 20.8: © Steve Goldstein; 20.9: Integra/photo courtesy of Ronald Carson, The Reproductive Science Center of Boston.

Chapter 21

21.1a: From Vesalius, Andreas. 1543. *De Humani Corporis Fabrica,* second book. RA21.1: © Jerry Telfer/San Francisco Chronicle; 21.7: © C. Stein and T. Glover.

Illustrators

Illustrious, Inc.:

figures: 1.1, 1.6a,c,d, 2.2a, 2.2b, 2.17, 2.21, RA3.1–2, RA3,2–1, 4.7a, 4.11, 4.12a, 4.12b, TA4.1, TA4.2, TA4.3, TA4.4, 5.1, 5.2b, 5.3b, 5.4b, 5.7, 5.8, 5.10, 6.3, 6.6b, TA6.1–3, TA6.2–2, 7.5, RA8.2–1, 8.17, 9.5,

9.7a,b, 9.7c, 9.7d, 9.14, 9.16, 9.17, 9.18, 10.1, 10.6, 10.9, 10.12, 10.13, 11.14a, 11.14b, 11.15, 11.16, 12.1, 12.2, 12.5, 12.6, 12.7, 13.6, RA13.1–1, 14.14, 15.9, 16.2, 16.3, 18.4, 18.6, RA18.1–1, 21.1b, 21.2, TA21.1, RA21.2–1, RA21.2–2, 21.3, 21.4

Observatory Group Inc.:

figures: 2.21, RA3.1 (fig. 1), 5.8, 5.9, 10.13, 11.11, 14.12, 14.14, 15.15, 18.4

Line Art/Text

Chapter 1

Figure 1.6a From David Shier, et al, *Hole's Human Anatomy and Physiology,* 7th ed. Copyright © 1996 The McGraw-Hill Companies. Reprinted by permission. All Rights Reserved.

Chapter 2

Figures 2.4, 2.11 From David Shier, et al., *Hole's Human Anatomy and Physiology,* 7th ed. Copyright © 1996 The McGraw-Hill Companies. Reprinted by permission. All Rights Reserved.

Chapter 9

Figure 9.2 from David Shier, et al., *Hole's Human Anatomy and Physiology,* 7th ed. Copyright © 1996 The McGraw-Hill Companies. Reprinted by permission. All Rights Reserved.

Chapter 10

Figure 10.13, *top,* From "Brain Briefings," February 1997. Copyright 1997 Society for Neuroscience. Used by permission. Figure 10.13 Source: Berry Kramer, et al, "A Worldwide Study of the Huntington's Disease Mutation in 995 Patients with Huntington Disease," *The New England Journal of Medicine,* vol. 330, no. 20, May 19, 1994.

Chapter 11

Figure 11.13 From: *Human Genetics* 2/E by Singer. Copyright © 1985 by W. H. Freeman and Company. Used with permission.

Chapter 15

Figure 15.4 Modified from David Shier, et al., *Hole's Human Anatomy and Physiology,* 7th ed. Copyright © 1996 The McGraw-Hill Companies. Reprinted by permission. All Rights Reserved. Figures 15.5, 15.7 From David Shier, et al., *Hole's Human Anatomy and Physiology,* 7th ed. Copyright © 1996 The McGraw-Hill Companies. Reprinted by permission. All Rights Reserved.

Chapter 17

Figure 17.7 Genzyme Corp. and Tufts University School of Veterinary Medicine. Used by permission.

Chapter 18

Figure 18.8 From David Shier, et al., *Hole's Human Anatomy and Physiology,* 7th ed. Copyright © 1996 The McGraw-Hill Companies. Reprinted by permission. All Rights Reserved.

Chapter 21

Figure 21.4 Source: The Genome Directory, Nature Supplement to *Nature,* September 18, 1995, col. 377, no. 6547S.

index

sex development of, 102–5
teratogenic effects on, 58–60
Fibrillin, 88
Fibroids, uterine, 362
Field tests, in plant biotechnology, 351
Filial generation, first (F_1), 69
Fingerprint, 4, 120, 121
Fingerprinting, DNA. *See* DNA fingerprinting
Finns, population of, 238
First filial generation (F_1), 69
First messenger molecules, 27, 28
Flow cytometry, 382
Fluorescence in situ hybridization, 202
Follicle cells, 40
Forensics, 3, 220–21
Founder effect, 237
Fragile X syndrome, 110, 180–81, 192
Frameshift mutation, 190–92, 194
Franklin, Rosalind, 140, 141
Freckles, 5
Fungal infection
phenylketonuria and, 243
transgenic protection against, 354
Fusion gene, 191
Fusion proteins, 299

g

Galactosemia, 328
Gambia, ethnic groups of, 247, 248
Gamete, 42
Gamete intrafallopian transfer, 366–67. *See also* Reproductive technology
Gap phases, of cell cycle, 30
Garrod, Archibald, 137
Gastrula, 50
Gaucher disease, 191
Gender identity, 104–5
Gender, phenotype and, 114–15
Gene(s), 2, 141. *See also* Allele(s)
alpha globin, 184–85
APC, 304, 305, 306
AT, 151, 152
Bcl-2, 304
behavior and, 234
beta globin, 181, 182
BRCA, 6, 7, 8, 304
cancer, 298–304
carrier frequency of, 223–24
coefficient of relationship of, 123
computer analysis of, 172–73
conservation of, 352–53
cystic fibrosis transmembrane conductance regulator, 14, 15
deletion of, 190–91, 194
detoxifying, 352
distribution of, 379–80
DPC4, 304
duplication of, 191, 194
dystrophin, 190
environment and, 10–11, 122
epistasis of, 87–88, 89, 90
erb-B, 304

expansion of, 191–92, 194
functions of, 379–80
fusion, 191
H, 88, 89
her-2neu, 304
heterogeneity of, 90
hMLH, 304
hPMS, 304
for human leukocyte antigens, 274–75
for Huntington disease, 380–83
I, 87, 88
identification of, 382–83
in coupling, 94, 96
incomplete dominance of, 87, 88, 90
jumping, 192
linkage disequilibrium of, 381
linkage of, 94–98
localization of, 382
mitochondrial, 90–92, 98
movable, 192
MTS1, 304
mutations in, 3, 70. *See also* Mutation(s)
myc, 304
NF1, 304
opsin, 109
p53, 301–3, 304
PDGF, 304
penetrance of, 88
pleiotropic, 88–89
PRAD1, 304
ras, 304
RB, 301, 304
in repulsion, 94, 96
RET, 304
secretor, 274
sex-determining, 103
sex-linked, 70
SRY, 56
synteny of, 257
tandem duplication of, 191
for transcription factors, 159
tumor suppressor, 296, 299, 301–2
WT1, 304
XIST, 111
Gene flow, 221
Gene frequencies, 221–22
balanced polymorphisms and, 242–44
calculation of, 222–25. *See also* Hardy-Weinberg equilibrium
changes in, 222
consanguinity and, 235–36
definition of, 221
for disease carriers, 223–24
in DNA fingerprinting, 221–22
founder effect and, 237
genetic drift and, 236–38, 244
historical study of, 245–49
migration and, 236, 244
mutation and, 238
natural selection and, 239–44

nonrandom mating and, 234–36, 244
population bottleneck and, 234, 237–38
Gene pool, 221
Gene targeting, 319–21
Gene therapy, 326–37
in cancer, 335–36
endothelial target of, 332, 337
ex vivo, 330
for glioma, 335–36
germline, 328–29
immune system in, 336
liver target for, 333, 337
lung target for, 333, 337
mechanics of, 329–30
muscle target for, 332–33, 337
myoblast target for, 333, 337
nerve tissue target for, 333–34
in severe combined immune deficiency, 326–27
sites of, 331–34, 337
in situ, 330
skin target of, 332, 337
somatic, 328, 329
stem cell target of, 331–32, 337
types of, 327–29
vectors for, 329–30
in vivo, 330
Genetic code, 164, 165, 168–70
mutation and, 187
nonoverlapping of, 165, 168
RNA triplets of, 168, 170
universality of, 169
Genetic discrimination, 384
Genetic drift, 236–38, 244
Genetic engineering, 310–21. *See also* Plant biotechnology
gene targeting for, 319–21
recombinant DNA for, 311–16
transgenic organisms for, 316–19
Genetic load, 238
Genetic marker, for Huntington disease, 381
Genetic tests, 2
for breast cancer, 6
forensic, 220–21
Genome, 2
Genomic imprinting, 93–94, 114–15, 116
Genomic mismatch scanning, 376
Genotype, 7, 70
penetrance of, 88, 89
Genotypic ratio, 70
Gilbert, Walter, 166
Gland cell, 18
Glioma, gene therapy for, 335–36
Glomerulonephritis, 284
Glucose-6-phosphate dehydrogenase deficiency, 110, 187
malaria and, 242–43
Gluten-sensitive enteropathy, 275
Golgi body, 21, 23, 25
Gout, 110
Grapes, 345
Grave's disease, 275, 284

Griffith, Frederick, 137–38, 141
Growth factors, 32–33
in signal transduction, 27–28
Growth hormone, recombinant, 314
Guanine, 140, 141, 142

h

H gene, 88, 89
Hairy elbows, 5
Haploid gamete, 42
Haplotype, 94
Hardy-Weinberg equilibrium, 222, 244
applications of, 224–25
in autosomal recessive traits, 224
demonstration of, 223
in DNA fingerprinting, 225–30
in DNA polymorphisms, 225
in rare inherited diseases, 225
in sex-linked recessive traits, 224–25
Height, 120
Helicases, 146, 147
Hemolytic anemia, 284
Hemophilia, 9
Hemophilia A, 106, 107, 110, 182, 183, 192
Hemophilia B, 110, 183
Hepatitis, 60, 275
vaccine against, 346
Hereditary nonpolyposis colon cancer, 150, 151
Heritability, of multifactorial complex traits, 122–23
her-2neu gene, 304
Herpes virus, 60
in cancer therapy, 335–36
in gene therapy, 330
Hershey, Alfred, 138–39, 141
Heterochromatin, 198, 199
Heterogametic sex, 102
Heteroplasmy, 92
Heterozygote, manifesting, 112
Heterozygous, definition of, 69, 70
Hind III restriction enzymes, 225
Histone, 142, 144
HIV (human immunodeficiency virus), 60, 184, 240–42, 281–83
hMLH1 gene, 304
hMSH2 gene, 304
Homeobox proteins, 258–59
Hominids, 255–56
Hominoids, 254–55
Homo erectus, 256
Homo habilis, 255–56
Homo sapiens, 254, 256
Homocystinuria, 328
Homogametic sex, 102
Homologous recombination, in gene targeting, 320
Homosexuality, 104–5
Homozygous, definition of, 69, 70
Hormones
cellular effects of, 32–33
in cellular secretion, 22
in signal transduction, 27–28

Menkes disease, 110
Meselson, Matthew, 142, 145
Mesoderm, 50, 55
Metabolism, inborn errors of, 110
Metaphase
    of meiosis I, 44
    of meiosis II, 45, 46
    of mitosis, 30, 31, 33
Methotrexate, 58
Mexican hairless dogs, 86, 87
Mibridization, 348
Microcosm experiments, in plant
        biotechnology, 351–52
Microevolution, 222
Microfilaments, 25, 26
Microsatellites, 150
Microtubules, 25, 26
Miescher, Friedrich, 137, 141
Migration, 236, 244
    ABO blood types and, 236
Milk, secretion of, 22
Minisatellites, in Belarus
        population, 186
Miscarriage, lethal alleles and, 86
Mitochondrial DNA, 91–92, 261–64
Mitochondrial encephalopathy lactic
        acidosis syndrome
        (MELAS), 92
Mitochondrial eve hypothesis, 261–62
Mitochondrial genes, 90–92, 98
Mitochondrion, 21, 23, 25
Mitosis, 29, 30–31, 32–33
    vs. meiosis, 43
Molecular clocks, 260–61
Molecular genetics, 6–7. *See also*
        Gene(s)
Monoamine oxidase A, 132
Monoclonal antibodies, 287–89
Monocots, gene transfer in, 345–46
Monod, Jacques, 158
Monohybrid, 70
Monohybrid cross, 68, 70, 73, 74
Monosomy, 206, 207
Morula, 50, 54
Motifs, 159
Movable genes, 192
MTS1 gene, 304
Müllerian ducts, 102, 103
Multifactorial complex traits, 10,
        120–22
    adoption studies of, 124
    alcoholism as, 130–31
    cardiovascular disease as, 126–27
    coefficient of relationship and, 123
    empiric risk for, 121, 122
    heritability of, 122–23
    intelligence as, 128
    manic-depressive illness as, 131
    measurement of, 121–23
    narcolepsy as, 129
    obesity as, 127–28
    schizophrenia as, 129–30
    twin studies of, 124–26
Multiple myeloma, 276
Multiple sclerosis, 275
Muscle cell, 18
    in muscular dystrophy, 27

Muscle, in gene therapy, 332–33
Muscular atrophy, 110
Muscular dystrophy, 27, 110, 112
Muscular tissue, 17
Mutagen, 179, 185, 295
    exposure to, 185–86
Mutagenesis, site-directed, 186
Mutagenicity, 185
Mutant, 70, 179
Mutant selection, in biotechnology,
        348, 349, 350
Mutation(s), 3, 70, 178–94
    balanced polymorphism and,
        242–44
    conditional, 187
    constitutional, 296
    definition of, 178–79
    deletion, 190–91, 194
    duplication, 191, 194
    engineered, 186
    expanding, 191–92, 193, 194
    frameshift, 190–92, 194
    fusion, 191
    gene frequencies and, 238
    germinal, 187–88
    hot spots for, 184–85
    induced, 185–86
    insertion, 194
    location of, 187
    missense, 188–89, 194
    natural protection against, 187
    nonsense, 189–90, 194
    point, 188–90
    protection against, 149–52, 187
    rate of, 183–84
    site-directed, 186
    somatic, 187–88, 190, 295–96
    spontaneous, 182–85
    transition, 188
    transversion, 188
    triplet repeat, 191–92, 193
    types of, 187–93
Myasthenia gravis, 275, 284
myc genes, 304
Myeloid leukemia, chronic, 116,
        299, 300
Myoblasts, in gene therapy, 333
Myotonic dystrophy, 116, 191

n

Nail-patella syndrome, 97
Narcolepsy, 129
Native Americans, 262–63
Natural selection, 222, 239–44
Neanderthals, 256, 262
Nerve cell, 18
Nervous tissue, 17
Neural tube, 56
Neural tube defects, 121, 122, 267
Neurofibromatosis, 27–28, 182, 183
Neurons, in gene therapy, 333
NF1 gene, 304
Nonrandom mating, 244
Norrie disease, 110
Notochord, 56
Nuclear envelope, 21

Nuclear pore, 21
Nucleic acids, 16. *See also* DNA; RNA
Nuclein, 137
Nucleolus, 21
Nucleosome, 142, 144
Nucleotide, 30, 141, 144
Nucleus, 18, 21, 25
Nutrition, biotechnology and, 346

o

Obesity, 127–28
Occupational hazards, 60
Okazaki fragments, 147
Oncogenes, 296, 298–99
Oocyte, 40, 49
Oogenesis, 49
Oogonium, 49
Operon, 158
Opsin gene, 109
Organ donation, 272, 287
Organelles, 20–21, 22–25
Organogenesis, 56
Orgasm, 40
Ornithine transcarbamoylase
        deficiency, 110
Osteoarthritis, 189
Osteogenesis imperfecta, 40, 183,
        187, 189
Osteoporosis, 189
Ovary, 40, 41
Ovulation, 49
Ovum, 49, 51

p

p53 gene, 301–3, 304
Palindromes, 184
Paper, production of, 346–47
Parental generation (P_1), 69
Parkinson disease, 333
Parsimony analysis, 261
Particle bombardment, in transgenic
        technology, 317
Pattern baldness, 114, 115
PDGF gene, 304
Peas, Mendel's experiments on, 67–69,
        70, 78–81
Pedigree, 8, 74–77
    for alopecia, 76, 77
    for autosomal dominant trait, 76
    for autosomal recessive trait, 76
    coefficient of relationship in,
        235–36
    molecular information for,
        77–78
    for sickle cell disease, 76–77
Penicillamine, 58
Penis, 40, 41
Pernicious anemia, 284
Peroxisomes, 21, 24, 25
Personality, twin studies of, 125–26
Phenocopy, 89, 90
Phenotype, 7, 70
    variable expression of, 88, 90
    wild type, 69, 70

Phenotypic ratio, 70
Phenylketonuria (PKU), 222, 243, 245,
        246, 328
Phenylthiocarbamide (PTC) taste,
        allele frequencies for, 224
Philadelphia chromosome, 203,
        299, 300
Photolyases, 149
Photoreactivation, 149
Pingelapese people, 237
Plant biotechnology, 3, 342–54
    bioremediation in, 352
    callus culture in, 348, 349
    cellular, 347–49
    in dicots, 345
    in drug production, 346
    ecological concerns of, 342–43
    economic concerns of, 342
    environmental concerns in,
        351–52
    field tests in, 351
    gene conservation for, 352–53
    microcosm experiments in,
        351–52
    in monocots, 345–46
    in nutrition, 346
    in paper production, 346–47
    protoplast fusion in, 348
    quantitative trait loci in, 353
    steps of, 344, 345
    in textile production, 346
    vs. traditional breeding, 343, 345
    transgenic, 345–47
    in vaccine production, 346
Plants, transgenic, 316–17
Plasma cells, 276
Plasmids
    in recombinant DNA
        technology, 312
    Ti, 316–17, 345–46
Pleiotropy, 88–89, 90
Polar body, 49, 51
Pollution, 352
Polyacrylamide gel electrophoresis, 226
Polyclonal antibody response, 276
Polycystic kidney disease, 183
Polydactyly, 88, 89
Polygenic complex traits, 120
Poly-hydroxybutyrate, 346
Polymerase chain reaction, 147–49, 150
Polymorphism, balanced, 242–44
Polyploidy, 205–6
Polyposis, adenomatous, 304–5
Polyps, of colon, 305
Poplars, genetic manipulation of, 347
Population, 221–22
    migration of, 236
    nonrandom mating in, 234–36
Population bottleneck, 234, 237–38
Population genetics, 8, 221–22. *See*
        also Gene frequencies
    applications of, 247–49
    in DNA fingerprinting, 220–21,
        226–28
Porphyria, 88–89
PRAD1 gene, 304
Prader-Willi syndrome, 93–94,
        115, 116